COLLEGE ALGEBRA

COLLEGE ALGEBRA

PAUL K. REES

Professor of Mathematics
Louisiana State University

FRED W. SPARKS

Professor of Mathematics
Texas Technological College

THIRD EDITION

McGRAW-HILL BOOK COMPANY, INC.
NEW YORK   TORONTO   LONDON
1954

COLLEGE ALGEBRA

Library of Congress Catalog Card Number: 53-9003

IX

51689

THE MAPLE PRESS COMPANY, YORK, PA.

PREFACE

The Third Edition of our College Algebra was prepared with the following goals in mind:

1. To achieve a more pleasing style and an increased clarity of expression.

2. To obtain an order that affords flexibility.

3. To provide clear and specific instructions for a systematic attack on the solution of problems.

4. To provide a great variety of pertinent illustrative examples.

5. To include an adequate number of well-selected and carefully graded problems.

6. To include some new material.

In the effort to attain the first of these goals, we rewrote seventeen of the twenty-two chapters and carefully revised the other five. We have employed an informal style and have avoided the use of long and complicated sentences. New ideas and definitions were not introduced until they were needed. Furthermore, we have refrained from the practice of opening a discussion "cold" with a formal definition, a rule of procedure, or a statement of principle. The way for new concepts is paved by an explanation of the need, by illustration, and by logical steps which lead to a final conclusion. The formal statement is then presented as a summary and an easily found reference.

Since it is difficult to cover the field of college algebra in the usual three-semester-hour course, there is considerable variation among colleges in the choice of topics presented and in the time allocated to each topic. Hence, flexibility is a highly desirable feature in any text in this field. We have attempted to achieve this flexibility by organizing the material in such a way that each exercise is preceded by a sufficient amount of subject matter to make it possible to cover this material and the exercise in one assignment. The exercise contains enough problems to enable the teacher to spend more than one lesson on it if he so desires. Sections most frequently omitted are placed at the end of the chapter so that deleting them from a course will not interfere with the sequence. The first three chapters are devoted to a review of high school algebra, and these chapters can be covered as rapidly as the teacher wishes. Furthermore, each of these chapters is followed by a comprehensive list of supplementary problems, so that teachers who desire to spend a minimum time on a review can devote this time entirely to the supplementary problems.

Often a student's difficulty with complicated problems occurs because he lacks a systematic attack. We have attempted to assist the student in this difficulty by providing detailed instructions for an orderly approach. An example may be found in the instructions for attacking stated problems in Art. 30.

Each difficult procedure and each type of problem appearing in the exercises are illustrated by carefully explained examples. In the presentation of these illustrative examples, we have avoided the practice of inserting long explanations between the steps in the solution. The steps in the solution are printed at the left of the page, and the explanation of each step is given in a terse statement at the right. This form can be used as a model by the student in the preparation of his papers.

An adequate number of drill problems is a necessary feature of any text in college algebra. We have included approximately 4200 problems grouped in 89 regular and 4 supplementary exercises. With very few exceptions, these problems are new, and they include problems similar to those found in analytic geometry and calculus. The problems in each exercise are organized into groups of four that are on about the same level of difficulty and that involve the same principle. Answers to three problems out of each four are provided. The order of difficulty increases gradually through the exercise. A good coverage can be obtained by assigning every fourth problem. This leaves an ample number of problems for class drill and for individual assignment and enables the book to be used several times without repetition. In so far as possible, we have avoided the selection of problems in which tedious numerical computation obscures the principle involved.

The additional material appearing in this edition consists of a discussion of systems of symmetric second-degree equations in Chap. 9, an article dealing with m linear equations in n unknowns, with m greater than n, and another dealing with systems of homogeneous linear equations.   The two latter articles appear in Chap. 21.

In addition to the acknowledgments mentioned in the two previous editions, we wish to express our gratitude to George A. Whetstone, Associate Professor of Civil Engineering at Texas Technological College, whose constructive criticism of the Second Edition was of great assistance to us in the preparation of the third.

Paul K. Rees
Fred W. Sparks

CONTENTS

CHAPTER 1

THE FOUR FUNDAMENTAL OPERATIONS

1. *Introduction.* College algebra, at least in the introductory phase, is an extension and enlargment of the topics in high school algebra. Hence, we shall introduce the subject by reviewing some of the basic definitions and processes studied in high school.

2. *The number system.* Algebra deals with numbers which are in actual numerical form or are represented by letters. In the first seven chapters, we shall deal only with integers, rational numbers, and irrational numbers. These numbers constitute the *real* number system and are defined below.

DEFINITION I. *An **integer** is a number used in counting.*

DEFINITION II. *A **rational number** is a number that can be expressed as the quotient of two integers.*

It is obvious that the rational numbers include all common fractions. Furthermore, since any integer can be expressed as the quotient of two others, the rational numbers include all integers.

DEFINITION III. *An **irrational number** is a real number that cannot be expressed as the quotient of two integers.*

Two examples of irrational numbers are $\sqrt{2}$ and π. Neither of these numbers can be expressed as the quotient of two integers, but each can be calculated to as many decimal places as desired.

Members of the real number system may be either positive or negative. The following graphical representation illustrates this aspect of real numbers and furnishes a useful interpretation of some of their other properties.

In order to obtain a graphical representation of the real numbers, we choose a point O (Fig. 1) on a straight line and the distance OA as the unit distance. Now we interpret the positive and negative numbers as distances measured to the right and to the left, respectively, from O. With this interpretation, we may associate any real number with a point on the line, and vice versa. For example, the rational numbers, 3, $4\frac{1}{2}$, -4 and the irrational number $\sqrt{2}$ are represented by the points B, C, D, and E, respectively. The real numbers thus are assigned a directional property, and a change in the sign of a number reverses the direction of the distance represented by this number. Hence $-(-a) = a$. The relations

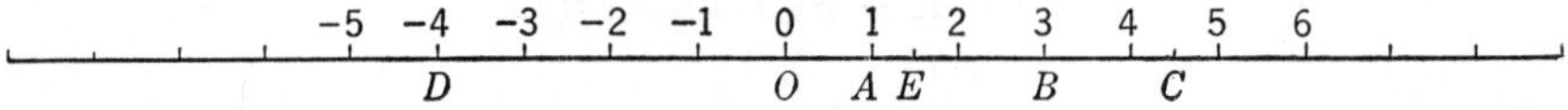

Figure 1

greater than and *less than* are designated by the signs $>$ and $<$, respectively, and may be interpreted graphically as follows: The number M is greater or less than N according as the point represented by M is to the right or left of the one represented by N. Hence $-4 < 1$, $-1 > -3$, and $4 > -4$.

We frequently have occasion to refer to the absolute or numerical value of a number, and we define it as follows:

DEFINITION IV. *The absolute or numerical value of a positive real number is the number itself. The absolute or numerical value of a negative real number is the number with the sign before it changed.*

The absolute value of n is denoted by the symbol $|n|$.

Examples

1. $|5| = 5$.   2. $|-3| = 3$.
3. $|n| = n$ if n is positive.   4. $|n| = -n$ if n is negative.

3. Essential definitions. The fundamental processes of algebra are addition, subtraction, multiplication, and division. In the discussion of these processes and throughout the remainder of this book, we shall frequently use the terminology defined below.

DEFINITION I. *A group of numbers and letters that have been combined by one or more of the fundamental processes of algebra is called an expression.*

DEFINITION II. *A number or a letter, or several numbers and letters that have been combined by multiplication or division[1] or both, are called a term.*

---

[1] It will be stated later (Art. 5) that the sum of two or more numbers that are enclosed in parentheses is considered as a single number. Hence, in the expression $a^2 - (b - c)(b + c)/(b^2 + c^2)$, $b - c$, $b + c$, and $b^2 + c^2$ are considered as three single quantities. Hence, $(b - c)(b + c)/(b^2 + c^2)$ involves multiplication and division only and is therefore a term of the expression.

Since a term does not involve either addition or subtraction, any group of letters in an expression that is separated from the remainder of the expression by plus or minus signs is a term. When thought of in this way, the sign of the term is the sign that precedes it.

Example

In the expression $3a^2 - 2ab + 4c^2$, $3a^2$, $-2ab$, and $4c^2$ are terms.

DEFINITION III. *If a term is composed of a number and one or more letters, the number is called the* **numerical coefficient** *of the letters in the term.*

For example, in $3a^2b$, 3 is the numerical coefficient of a^2b. Ordinarily, we speak of the numerical coefficient merely as the *coefficient*.

DEFINITION IV. *An expression that contains only one term is called a* **monomial.** *An expression that contains exactly two terms is called a* **binomial.** *An expression that contains exactly three terms is called a* **trinomial.** *Expressions that contain more than one term are called* **polynomials.**

It should be noted that, according to the above definition, binomials and trinomials are special cases of polynomials. However, we usually reserve the term polynomial to apply to expressions containing more than three terms.

4. *Addition and subtraction.* In algebra we use the terms *sum* and *difference* as applied to positive numbers in the same sense as in arithmetic. However, the introduction of negative numbers requires a refinement of the addition process. The extended process, known as algebraic addition, is described in the rule below.

RULE FOR ALGEBRAIC ADDITION. *The* **algebraic sum** *of two numbers with the same sign is the sum of the absolute values of the two numbers preceded by their common sign. The* **algebraic sum** *of two numbers with different signs is the difference of the absolute values of the numbers preceded by the sign of the one with the larger absolute value.*

In order to obtain the sum of several terms involving the same letters, we find the algebraic sum of the coefficients and then annex the letters.

The sum of two or more terms that contain different letters can be expressed only by placing a plus sign between them.

Examples

1. The sum of $3a^2b$ and $2a^2b$ is $5a^2b$.
2. The sum of $6xy$ and $-8xy$ (expressed this way, $6xy - 8xy$) is $-2xy$.
3. The sum of $-4ab$ and $3cd$ is $-4ab + 3cd$.

In arithmetic we may verify the fact that, for any two numbers we try, the sum is the same regardless of the order in which the addition is performed. This is known as the commutative property of addition. We shall assume that it is true for all numbers, and thus have the axiom below.

AXIOM I. *Addition is **commutative,** that is,* $a + b = b + a$.

Another property of addition that can be readily verified for any three or more given numbers is that the sum is the same regardless of the order in which the numbers are added. For example, $2 + 3 + 7 = 5 + 7 = 2 + 10 = 9 + 3 = 12$. As in the previous paragraph, we assume that this property, known as the *associative* property of addition, holds for all numbers. Thus we have the following axiom in which the parentheses are used to indicate the order in which the addition is performed.

AXIOM II. *Addition is **associative,** that is,*

$$a + (b + c) = (a + b) + c$$

These two axioms permit the usual procedure for finding the sum of two or more expressions—the procedure in which we write each successive expression below the preceding and, at the same time, rearrange the terms so that those containing the same letters form columns.

Example 4

In order to add the expressions $3x^2 + x - 1$, $2 + 2x^2 - 3x$, and $4x - 3 - x^2$, we write the expressions as shown below and then add the terms in the separate columns.

$$
\begin{array}{r}
3x^2 + x - 1 \\
2x^2 - 3x + 2 \\
-x^2 + 4x - 3 \\
\hline
4x^2 + 2x - 2
\end{array}
$$

We define algebraic subtraction as follows: In order to subtract one number (called the *subtrahend*) from another (called the *minuend*), we change the signs in the subtrahend and proceed as in addition.   The number obtained as the result of the subtraction is called the *remainder*.

Example 5

In order to subtract $3x - 5y + 7z$ from $5x + 2y - 3z$, we write the subtrahend below the minuend as shown below, then we *mentally* change the sign in each term in the subtrahend and add, obtaining the remainder indicated.

$$
\begin{array}{ll}
5x + 2y - \ 3z & \text{(minuend)} \\
\underline{3x - 5y + \ 7z} & \text{(subtrahend)} \\
2x + 7y - 10z & \text{(remainder)}
\end{array}
$$

5. *Symbols of grouping.* If a group of terms within an expression is to be treated as a single number, it is enclosed[1] in parentheses, ( ); brackets, [ ]; or braces, { }. These symbols are also used to indicate that certain algebraic operations are to be performed and the order in which the operations are to be carried out.   For example,

$$(1) \qquad (2x + 4y - z) + (3x - 2y + 3z)$$

means that the number represented by the expression in the first of the parentheses is to be added to that represented by the expression in the second.   Furthermore,

$$(2) \qquad (6a - 5b + 2c) - (2a - 3b + 2c)$$

indicates that the number represented by the last expression is to be subtracted from that represented by the first.   Finally,

$$(3) \qquad (4a^2 - b^2) - (a + b)(2a - b)$$

means that $a + b$ and $2a - b$ are to be multiplied and the product subtracted from $4a^2 - b^2$.

In order to perform the operations indicated by the use of the symbols of grouping, it is necessary to remove the symbols before the operations can be completed.   If the indicated operation is addition, we can, by the associative axiom of addition, omit the symbols of grouping and combine the terms in any order desired.   Thus in (1) we have

---

[1] The same purpose is sometimes indicated by placing the group of terms beneath the vinculum, ————.

$$(2x + 4y - z) + (3x - 2y + 3z) = 2x + 4y - z + 3x - 2y + 3z$$
$$= 2x + 3x + 4y - 2y - z + 3z$$
$$= 5x + 2y + 2z$$

If the operation indicated is subtraction, the group of terms enclosed in a pair of grouping symbols preceded by a minus sign is the subtrahend. Hence, by the definition of subtraction, we change all signs in it, omit the symbols of grouping, and then combine the terms in any order desired. Hence, in (2) we have

$$(6a - 5b + 2c) - (2a - 3b + 2c) = 6a - 5b + 2c - 2a + 3b - 2c$$
$$= 6a - 2a - 5b + 3b + 2c - 2c$$
$$= 4a - 2b$$

We thus have the following procedure for removing the symbols of grouping from an expression.

If a pair of grouping symbols preceded by a minus sign is removed from an expression, the sign of every term enclosed by the symbols must be changed. However, if the grouping symbols are preceded by a plus sign, they may be removed without further changes in the expression. Conversely, when a pair of grouping symbols is inserted in an expression, the sign of each term that is enclosed must be changed if the pair of symbols is preceded by a minus sign.

When an expression contains one or more pairs of grouping symbols enclosed in another pair, it is customary to remove the innermost pair first.

Example 1

The steps in the procedure for removing the grouping symbols from $2x - \{3x + [4x - (x - 2y) + 3y] - 4y\} + 2y$ are shown below.

$$2x - \{3x + [4x - (x - 2y) + 3y] - 4y\} + 2y$$
$$= 2x - \{3x + [4x - x + 2y + 3y] - 4y\} + 2y \qquad \text{(removing parentheses)}$$
$$= 2x - \{3x + [3x + 5y] - 4y\} + 2y \qquad \text{(collecting terms in brackets)}$$
$$= 2x - \{3x + 3x + 5y - 4y\} + 2y \qquad \text{(removing brackets)}$$
$$= 2x - \{6x + y\} + 2y \qquad \text{(collecting terms in braces)}$$
$$= 2x - 6x - y + 2y \qquad \text{(removing braces)}$$
$$= -4x + y \qquad \text{(collecting terms)}$$

In order to perform the operations indicated by (3), we first carry out the multiplication using the methods of the next article, replace the indicated product by the actual product, and enclose it in parentheses. Then we remove the parentheses and combine terms. Thus we get

$$
\begin{aligned}
4a^2 - b^2 - (a + b)(2a - b) &= 4a^2 - b^2 - (2a^2 + ab - b^2) \\
&= 4a^2 - b^2 - 2a^2 - ab + b^2 \\
&= 2a^2 - ab
\end{aligned}
$$

EXERCISE 1

Perform the operations indicated in Problems 1 to 24.

1. $3 + 4 - 5$.   **2.** $2 - 7 + 5$.   **3.** $8 - 6 + 2$.

4. $9 - 3 - 8$.   **5.** $6 - 4 - 3 + 5$.   **6.** $10 - 8 - 7 - 9$.

7. $5 - 10 + 12 - 8$.   **8.** $-14 - 7 + 9 - 3$.   **9.** $8 + (-6) - (+3)$.

10. $10 - (-7) - (+4)$.   **11.** $-(-16) + (-20) - (-4)$.

12. $7 - (-6) + (-8)$.   **13.** $(2 + 3) + (7 - 4)$.

14. $(5 - 2) - (6 + 3)$.   **15.** $6 - (4 - 2) - (7 + 1)$.

16. $-(-3) + (3 - 5) - (-3 - 4)$.   **17.** $3x - 2x + 5x$.

18. $7a - 4a - 6a$.   **19.** $4b - 7b + 10b$.

20. $-6c + 10c - 8c + 2c$.   **21.** $2a + 5b - 3a - 2b$.

22. $4x - 5y - 2x + 7y$.   **23.** $10b - 5c - 6b - 3c$.

24. $6p - 4q - 3p + 2q$.

Find the sum of the expressions in each of Problems 25 to 32.

25. $3x - 2y - 2z$
$4x + 5y + 3z$

26. $4a - 3b + 2c$
$-2a - 5b - 3c$

27. $5r - 5s + 2t$
$-7r + 3s - 4t$

28. $7h - 9j + 3k$
$4h + 3j - 8k$

29. $6a - 4b - 9c$
$-5a + 3b - 2c$
$8a - 10b + 12c$

30. $6x + 7y - 8z$
$3x - 8y + 5z$
$-9x - 4y + 7z$

31. $-4r - 6s + 8t$
$-5r - 7s - 9t$
$3r + 7s + 11t$

32. $9h - 6j - 3k$
$4h - 8j + 12k$
$-h + 6j - 11k$

Find the sum of the expressions in each of Problems 33 to 36.

33. $3a - 5b + 5c$, $2a - 5c + 2b$, $3c - 4a - 5b$.

34. $3x - 7y + 4z$, $4z - 7x - 2y$, $-2y - 6x + 4z$.

35. $5r - 6s$, $3s - 4t$, $-2r + 3t$.

36. $-6a - 4c$, $3a + 2b$, $-5b + 2c$.

In each of Problems 37 to 48, subtract the second number (or expression) from the first.

37. 20
    16

38. -7
       3

39.   8
      -4

40. -12
     $-\ 8$

41. $a - 2b$
    $a -\ b$

42. $2x - 3y$
    $x + y$

43. $-5b - 5c$
     $2b +\ c$

44. $-3h - 6k$
    $-5h - 4k$

45. $2a - 3b + 4c$
    $-5a + 5b + 6c$

46. $3x - 7y - 8z$
    $5x + 3y - 6z$

47. $-2r - 5s + 9t$
     $3r + 6s - 8t$

48. $-4h - 8i - 12k$
    $-6h + 2i +\ 4k$

Find the values of the expressions in Problems 49 to 56 if the letters have the values indicated.

49. $2x - 3y + 2z$; $x = 2$, $y = -3$, $z = -4$.
50. $3a - 2b - 4c$; $a = -3$, $b = 2$, $c = -5$.
51. $4x - 3y + 2z - 7w$; $x = -\frac{1}{2}$, $y = \frac{2}{3}$, $z = -1$, $w = -3$.
52. $6a - 12b - 5c - 8d$; $a = \frac{2}{3}$, $b = -\frac{3}{4}$, $c = -1$, $d = \frac{1}{2}$.
53. $2a + 3|a|$; $a = -2$.
54. $3a - 2b + |a + b|$; $a = 3$, $b = -4$.
55. $2x + 3|x| - |x - y|$; $x = -2$, $y = 3$.
56. $|2a| - b + |c| - |a - b + c|$; $a = 2$, $b = -1$, $c = -6$.

Remove the symbols of grouping from each of Problems 57 to 68 and combine the terms.

57. $a - (2b + c) + (a + b - c)$.
58. $(x + 2y) - (z - 2x) - (y + z)$.
59. $(h + 2i - k) - (-2h + i - 3k)$.
60. $2r - (s - 3t) + (3r - 2s) - t$.
61. $a - [3b - 4c - (2a - 3b + 4c) + 2a] - (b + c)$.
62. $x - 2y + [3x - (2y + 4x) - 3y] - 3x$.
63. $2x - (3y + 4z) - [x + 2y - (z - 2x + y) - z] - (x - y) + z$.
64. $3a - (3b + 4c) - [a - 3b - (2c - a + 3b) - 2c] - (2a - b) + 3c$.
65. $3a - \{2b - c + [6a - (4b - c)] - 2a\} + b$.
66. $\{x - [3y + (2z - x) - z] - y\} - \{x - [(z + y) - y]\}$.
67. $2r - \{3s - [4t - (2s - 4t) - 2r] - 5t\}$.
68. $4a - \{2b - [2c + (-3a - 2b) - (3b - 2c)] - 2a\} - 3b$.

6. *Multiplication.* The product of two numbers a and b is expressed as $a \times b$, $a \cdot b$, or ab. Each of the numbers that appears in a product, or the product of two or more of them, is a *factor* of the product. Since any number n is equal to $n \times 1$, then n is a factor of itself. Any number that has no factor except itself and 1 is called a *prime* number.

Example

Since $6ab = 3 \times 2 \times a \times b \times 1$, it follows that 3, 2, a, b, 6, $3a$, $3b$, $2a$, $2b$, $6a$, $6b$, $6ab$, and 1 are factors of $6ab$. However, 3, 2, a, and b are the prime factors.

We shall assume two axioms in multiplication that are similar to those of addition. That is, we shall assume that the product of two numbers is independent of the order in which the factors occur and that the product of three or more numbers is independent of the order in which they are multiplied. The formal statements of the two axioms follow.

AXIOM I. *Multiplication is* **commutative,** *that is* $a \times b = b \times a$.

AXIOM II. *Multiplication is* **associative,** *that is,* $a(bc) = (ab)c$.

In the latter axiom, the parentheses indicate the two factors that are to be multiplied first.

We shall also assume that the product obtained by multiplying a given number by the sum of two or more others is the same as the sum of the products obtained by multiplying the first number by each of the others. This is known as the *distributive* axiom of multiplication with respect to addition and is stated below.

AXIOM III. *Multiplication is* **distributive** *with respect to addition, that is,* $a(b + c) = ab + ac$.

The law of signs for multiplication is stated without proof below.

LAW OF SIGNS FOR MULTIPLICATION. *The product of two factors with the same signs is positive. The product of two factors with different signs is negative.*

7. Exponents. Laws of exponents in multiplication. The product $a \times a$ is written a^2 and is called *a-square;* the product $a \times a \times a$ is written a^3 and is called *a-cube;* and the product of n a's is written a^n and is called the *nth power* of a. This practice leads to the following definition.

DEFINITION I. *If n is a positive integer, the symbol a^n is called the* **nth power of a** *and is the product of* **n** *factors, each of which is* **a.** *The letter* **a** *is called the* **base,** *and* **n** *is called the* **exponent.**

As a result of the above definition, we have the following laws that apply to products involving powers of numbers.

$$\textbf{(1)} \qquad\qquad a^m a^n = a^{m+n}$$

Proof:

$$a^m a^n = (a \cdot a \cdot a \ldots \text{ to } m \text{ factors})(a \cdot a \cdot a \ldots \text{ to } n \text{ factors})$$
$$= a \cdot a \cdot a \ldots \text{ to } m + n \text{ factors}$$
$$= a^{m+n}$$

(2) $$a^n b^n = (ab)^n$$

Proof:

$$a^n b^n = (a \cdot a \cdot a \ldots \text{ to } n \text{ factors})(b \cdot b \cdot b \ldots \text{ to } n \text{ factors})$$
$$= ab \cdot ab \cdot ab \ldots \text{ to } n \text{ factors} \qquad \text{(by Axiom I)}$$
$$= (ab)^n \qquad\qquad\qquad\qquad\quad \text{(by Definition I)}$$

It should be noted that in (1) the bases are the same, and we *hold the base* and add the exponents. In (2) the exponents are the same and we *hold the exponent* and multiply the bases.

(3) $$(a^n)^p = a^{pn}$$

Proof:

$$(a^n)^p = a^n \cdot a^n \cdot a^n \ldots \text{ to } p \text{ factors}$$
$$= a^{n+n+n+} \ldots \text{ to } p \text{ terms} \qquad [\text{by } (1)]$$
$$= a^{pn}$$

Examples

1. $\qquad\qquad a^4 a^3 = a^7$
2. $(3a^2b^3)(2a^3b^5) = 3 \cdot 2 \cdot a^2 \cdot a^3 \cdot b^3 \cdot b^5 \qquad$ (by Axiom I)
   $\qquad\qquad\qquad = 6(a^2 a^3)(b^3 b^5) \qquad$ (by Axiom II)
   $\qquad\qquad\qquad = 6a^5 b^8 \qquad\qquad$ [by (1)]
3. $\qquad\qquad 3^2 5^2 = (3 \cdot 5)^2 = 15^2 = 225 \qquad$ [by (2)]
4. $\qquad\qquad 8a^3 b^3 = 2^3 a^3 b^3$
   $\qquad\qquad\qquad = (2ab)^3 \qquad\qquad$ [by (2)]
5. $(4a^2 b^3)^4 = 4^4 (a^2)^4 (b^3)^4 \qquad$ [by (2)]
   $\qquad\qquad = 4^4 a^8 b^{12} \qquad\qquad$ [by (3)]
   $\qquad\qquad = 256 a^8 b^{12}$

8. *Products involving polynomials.* By Axiom III, Art. 6, the product of a monomial and a polynomial is the sum of the products of the monomial and each term of the polynomial.

Example 1

$$3m(2m^2 - 4mn + 5n^2) = (3m)(2m^2) - (3m)(4mn) + (3m)(5n^2)$$
$$= 6m^3 - 12m^2 n + 15mn^2$$

Also, by use of Axiom III of Art. 6, we may show that the

product of two polynomials is equal to the sum of the products obtained by multiplying each term in one polynomial by every term of the other.   This axiom and the other two of Art. 6 permit us to use the usual method for carrying out the process as illustrated in the example below.

Example 2

$$x^3 - 2x^2y + \quad xy^2 - \quad 3y^3$$
$$3x^2 - \quad 2xy + \quad 4y^2$$

$$3x^5 - 6x^4y + 3x^3y^2 - \quad 9x^2y^3$$
$$- 2x^4y + 4x^3y^2 - 2x^2y^3 + \quad 6xy^4$$
$$+ 4x^3y^2 - 8x^2y^3 + 4xy^4 - 12y^5$$

$$3x^5 - 8x^4y + 11x^3y^2 - 19x^2y^3 + 10xy^4 - 12y^5 \quad \text{(product)}$$

EXERCISE 2

Perform the operations indicated in each of Problems 1 to 28.

1. $2a^2 \times 3a$.
2. $3b^2 \times 4b^4$.
3. $5y^3 \times 3y^5$.
4. $4c^6 \times 7y^2$.
5. $(3a^2b)(6ab^3)$.
6. $(2x^2y^3)(5x^3y)$.
7. $(6r^3s^4)(4r^2s^3)$.
8. $(7c^5d^2)(3c^2d^4)$.
9. $2a^2 \times 3ab \times b^3$.
10. $4c^3 \times c^2d^2 \times 2d^4$.
11. $3r^3s \times 2s^2 \times 3r^3$.
12. $5h^2k \times 2hk \times 3k^2$.
13. $(6ab^2c^3)(4a^3bc^2)$.
14. $(8r^3s^2t^4)(3r^2s^5t^3)$.
15. $(3x^4y^2z)(2x^3y^5z^2)$.
16. $(5a^2bc^4)(3ab^2c^3)$.
17. $(2a^2b)(3ac^2)(4b^2c)$.
18. $(3x^2y^3)(2y^2z)(xz^3)$.
19. $(4r^2st)(2rs^2)(6s^2t^2)$.
20. $(7u^2)(6uvw^2)(2u^2v^3)$.
21. $(a^2)^3$.
22. $(b^3)^2$.
23. $(x^4)^3$.
24. $(y^3)^4$.
25. $(2a^2b)^3$.
26. $(3c^3d^2)^2$.
27. $(4x^2y^3z)^3$.
28. $(5a^2b^3c^2)^2$.

Find the product of the expressions in each of Problems 29 to 48.

29. $x + 2y, 2x - y$
30. $3a - 2b, 2a + b$.
31. $2r + 3s, 3r - 4s$.
32. $5u - 2v, 3u - 4v$.
33. $x + y + z, x + y - z$.
34. $a + b + c, a - b - c$.
35. $2r - 3s + t, 3r + s - 2t$.
36. $5x - 3y - 4z, 2x + 5y - 3z$.
37. $x^2 - 2xy - y^2, x + y$.
38. $a^2 - 3ab + 2b^2, 2a - 3b$.
39. $2b^2 + 4bc - 3c^2, -3b - 2c$.
40. $3x^2 - 3xy + y^2, x - 2y$.
41. $x^2 - 3xy + y^2, 2x^2 + xy - 4y^2$.
42. $2a^2 - 4ab + 5b^2, 3a^2 - 2ab - 4b^2$.
43. $4u^2 - 3uv - 2v^2, 3u^2 + 2uv - 5v^2$.
44. $2b^2 - 3bc + 5c^2, 3b^2 + 2bc - 4c^2$.
45. $x^3 - x + 1, x^2 + x - 2$.
46. $a^3 - a^2 + a - 1, a^2 - a + 1$.
47. $2y^3 - y^2 + 2y - 1, y^2 + y - 2$.
48. $3b^4 - 2b + 3, b^3 + b^2 - 2b$.

Remove the symbols of grouping from Problems 49 to 56.

49. $a(2a + 3b) - b(a - 4b)$.
50. $2x(3x - 2y) - y(2x + 4y)$.
51. $3r(r - 2s) - s(2r - 3s) - (3r^2 - 8rs)$.

52. $2b(a - 2b + 3c) - 2c(2a + 3b) + 2a(2c - b)$.

53. $6a^2 - a[2a^2 - 3(-2a - 4b)] - 3ab$.

54. $4c[2b^2 - 3c(c - 2b) - b(6c + 2b)] + 4(b^2 + c^2)$.

55. $2[2x - 3(x + y)] - 3\{x^2 - [2y - x(x + y)]\}$.

56. $8x^3 - 3x\{y^2 - 2[3x^2 + y(x - 3y)] + 3x(2x - y)\} - 2x^2(4x + 7y)$.

9. Division. Laws of exponents in division. If a and b are two numbers, and if[1] $b \neq 0$, it is customary to indicate the division of a by b by use of the division sign, as in $a \div b$, or by writing the two numbers as the fraction $\dfrac{a}{b}$. The number a is called the *dividend*, b is the *divisor*, and the result of performing the operation is known as the *quotient*.

The law of signs for division is similar to that of multiplication, and it is stated below.

LAW OF SIGNS FOR DIVISION. *The quotient of two numbers with the same sign is positive. The quotient of two numbers with different signs is negative.*

We may verify with numerical examples the fact that the quotient of two numbers is equal to the product of the quotients of the separate factors of the two numbers taken in any order. For example,

$$\frac{168}{6} = \frac{6 \times 4 \times 7}{3 \times 2 \times 1} = \frac{6}{3} \times \frac{4}{2} \times \frac{7}{1} = 2 \times 2 \times 7 = 28$$

The above principle can be used to deal with exponents in division. For example,

$$\frac{a^5}{a^3} = \frac{a^{5-3+3}}{a^3} = (a^{5-3})\left(\frac{a^3}{a^3}\right) = (a^{5-3})(1) = a^{5-3} = a^2$$

Using the above method for the more general case, we have, if $m > n$,

$$\frac{a^m}{a^n} = \frac{a^{m-n+n}}{a^n}$$
$$= (a^{m-n})\left(\frac{a^n}{a^n}\right) \qquad \text{[by (1), Art. 7]}$$
$$= (a^{m-n})(1)$$
$$= a^{m-n}$$

[1] The symbol, $\neq$, means "is not equal to." The reason for the above restriction on b will be explained in Art. 10.

Thus we have the law of exponents for division stated below.

(1) $\dfrac{a^m}{a^n} = a^{m-n}$ (*provided m and n are integers and m > n*)

Another law of exponents that involves division is stated below. This law depends upon the method of multiplying fractions that will be discussed in Chap. 3.

(2) $$\left(\frac{a}{b}\right)^n = \frac{a^n}{b^n}$$

Examples

1. $\dfrac{12a^7b^6}{3a^2b^4} = 4a^{7-2}b^{6-4} = 4a^5b^2$

2. $\left(\dfrac{3x^2y^3}{2z}\right)^4 = \dfrac{3^4(x^2)^4(y^3)^4}{2^4z^4} = \dfrac{81x^8y^{12}}{16z^4}$

10. *Division involving polynomials.* The quotient obtained by dividing a polynomial by a monomial is the sum of the quotients of each term in the polynomial and the monomial.

Example 1

$$\frac{20c^{12} - 16c^8 - 8c^5}{4c^4} = \frac{20c^{12}}{4c^4} - \frac{16c^8}{4c^4} - \frac{8c^5}{4c^4}$$

$$= 5c^8 - 4c^4 - 2c$$

In order to divide one polynomial by another, we perform the following steps:

1. Arrange both dividend and divisor in ascending or descending powers of some letter that appears in both.

2. Divide the first term in the divisor into the first term in the dividend, thus obtaining the first term in the quotient.

3. Multiply the divisor by the first term in the quotient and subtract the product from the dividend.

4. Treat the remainder obtained in step 3 as a new divisor and repeat steps 2 and 3.

5. Continue this process until a remainder is obtained in which the largest exponent of the letter chosen as basis of arrangement in step 1 is less than the exponent of that letter in the remainder.

Example 2

The above process applied to the division of $6x^4 + 7x^3 + 6x^2 + 32x - 7$ by $3x^2 + 5x - 2$ follows.

$$
\begin{array}{r}
2x^2 - x + 5 \quad \text{(quotient)} \\
\text{(divisor)} \quad 3x^2 + 5x - 2 \overline{\smash{\big)}\, 6x^4 + 7x^3 + 6x^2 + 32x - 7} \quad \text{(dividend)} \\
\underline{6x^4 + 10x^3 - 4x^2} \\
-3x^3 + 10x^2 + 32x - 7 \\
\underline{-3x^3 - 5x^2 + 2x} \\
15x^2 + 30x - 7 \\
\underline{15x^2 + 25x - 10} \\
5x + 3 \quad \text{(remainder)}
\end{array}
$$

11. Operations involving zero. If zero is regarded as the total absence of quantity, then it is obvious that

(1) $$n + 0 = n$$
(2) $$n \times 0 = 0$$

and

(3) $$\frac{0}{n} = 0$$

However, any attempt to define a process for using zero as a divisor leads to an absurdity. For example, if we interpret the quotient $a \div b$ to mean the number of b's that must be added together in order to obtain a, then $a \div 0$ is the number of zeros that must be added to obtain a. Obviously, this is nonsense. Hence, if the divisor is zero, the operation of division is not defined, and thus division by zero is excluded.

The symbol a^n has been defined when n is a positive integer, but this definition is meaningless when $n = 0$. If, however, we require (1) of Art. 9 to hold when $m = n$, we have

$$\frac{a^n}{a^n} = a^{n-n} = a^0$$

Therefore, since a^n/a^n is equal to 1, we define the value of a^0 to be 1 and have

(4) $$a^0 = 1$$

This definition of a^0 is also consistent with (1) of Art. 7 since

$a^n \times a^0 = a^{n+0} = a^n$. This is the result we would expect if $a^0 = 1$.

EXERCISE 3

Perform the indicated division in each of Problems 1 to 16.

1. $\dfrac{a^4}{a^2}$.

2. $\dfrac{b^4}{b^3}$.

3. $\dfrac{c^{12}}{c^8}$.

4. $\dfrac{x^{10}}{x^2}$.

5. $\dfrac{12a^4}{3a^2}$.

6. $\dfrac{18x^5}{6x^2}$.

7. $\dfrac{24b^7}{8b^4}$.

8. $\dfrac{27c^9}{3c^7}$.

9. $\dfrac{a^2b^5}{ab^3}$.

10. $\dfrac{c^4d^5}{c^2d^3}$.

11. $\dfrac{x^3y^4}{x^3y^2}$.

12. $\dfrac{u^4z^5}{u^3z^5}$.

13. $\dfrac{2^4a^4b^3c^5}{2^2a^3b^3c^3}$.

14. $\dfrac{30x^5y^6c^7}{6x^3y^2c^5}$.

15. $\dfrac{15r^4s^4t^2}{3r^4s^3t^2}$.

16. $\dfrac{24u^5v^6w^3}{6u^4v^4w^3}$.

Perform the operations indicated in Problems 17 to 20.

17. $\left(\dfrac{a^2}{b^3}\right)^2$.

18. $\left(\dfrac{2x^2}{y}\right)^3$.

19. $\left(\dfrac{2c^3}{3d^2}\right)^2$.

20. $\left(\dfrac{4a^4}{3b^3}\right)^3$.

In each of Problems 21 to 36, divide the first expression by the second.

21. $2a^2 - 5a + 3$, $a - 1$.
22. $3c^2 + 4c - 4$, $c + 2$.
23. $2x^2 - 5xy - 3y^2$, $2x + y$.
24. $6a^2 - 5ab - 6b^2$, $2a - 3b$.
25. $2x^3 - 5x^2 + 5x - 6$, $x - 2$.
26. $6b^3 + 5b^2 - 4b + 3$, $2b + 3$.
27. $15y^3 + 11y^2 - 18y - 8$, $3y + 4$.
28. $6x^3 - 13x^2y + 8xy^2 - 3y^3$, $2x - 3y$.
29. $x^4 - x^3y - 2x^2y^2 - 3xy^3 - y^4$, $x^2 - 2xy - y^2$.
30. $6a^4 + a^3b + 2a^2b^2 + 5ab^3 - 2b^4$, $3a^2 + 2ab - b^2$.
31. $6u^4 + 2u^3v - 6uv^3 - 2v^4$, $3u^2 - 2uv - v^2$.
32. $2a^4 + 3a^3b - 6a^2b^2 + b^4$, $a^2 + 3ab + b^2$.
33. $y^5 - 1 - y^3 - y - y^4 - 3y^2$, $y^3 - 1 - 2y^2$.
34. $2x^2 + x^5 - 2x^3 - 1 + x$, $x^2 + x - 1$.
35. $2a + 2a^5 + 1 + 3a^4$, $1 + a^2 + 2a$.
36. $x^4 + 1 + x^5$, $1 + x^3 - x$.

In each of Problems 37 to 40, find the quotient and remainder obtained by dividing the first expression by the second.

37. $x^3 - 2x^2 + x + 1$, $x^2 - x - 1$.
38. $2a^4 - 3a^3 + 2a^2 - 12$, $a^2 - 2$.
39. $2x^3 - 3x^2y + xy^2 - y^3$, $x^2 - xy + y^2$.
40. $2a^4 - 3a^3b + 2ab^2 - b^3$, $a^3 - 3b^2$.

SUPPLEMENTARY PROBLEMS

Perform the operations indicated in Problems 1 to 20.

1. $8 - 5 + 3$.   **2.** $7 - 5 - 3 + 2$.   **3.** $9 - 6 + 3 - 4$.

4. $14 - 6 - 8 + 7$.   **5.** $5 - (-6) - 8 + (-2)$.

6. $18 - (-9) - (-6) + (-2)$.   **7.** $24 - (6 - 2) - (-3)$.

8. $17 - 6 - (8 - 3) + (-6 + 2)$.   **9.** $|-3| - |6 - 8|$.

10. $5 + |-3| - |-8 + 5|$.   **11.** $7 - |-6 - 2| + |-8|$.

12. $|7 - 9| - |5 - 3| + |1 - 3|$.   **13.** $2a - 5a + 6a$.

14. $2x - 6x + 10x$.   **15.** $3y - 8y - 4y + 6y$.

16. $5z - 8z + 9z - 6z$.   **17.** $3x - 2y - 5x + 4y$.

18. $5a - 3b + 2b - 2a$.   **19.** $7a - 4b + 5c - 2b - 3c + 3a$.

20. $8x - 7y + 4z - 2x + 3y - 5z$.

If $a = 2, b = -3, c = 5$, find the value of the expressions in Problems 21 to 32.

21. $3a - 6b - 2c$.   **22.** $5a + 7b - 3c$.   **23.** $4a - 2b - 8c$.

24. $8a + 4b - 2c$.   **25.** $2(a + b) - 3(2a - c)$.

26. $2(a - b + 2c) - 3(b - 3c)$.   **27.** $5(c - a) - 2(b + c) + 3(-a + b)$.

28. $4(a - 4c) - 5(c + a) + 5(2b + 4a)$.

29. $|2a + 5b - 3c| - |3a - 4b + c|$.

30. $|b - 3c| - 2|a - b| + 3|2a - 3b|$.

31. $|2a - 3c| - |3a - 2b| + |16c - 3a|$.

32. $|3a - b - c| - |4a + 2b - c| + |2a - 4b + 5c|$.

33. Find the sum of all prime numbers less than 10.

34. Find the product of all prime numbers less than 9.

35. Add the sum of all prime numbers less than 8 to the sum of those between 12 and 20.

36. Find the sum of the greatest prime number less than 15, the greatest prime less than 20, and the greatest prime less than 30.

Find the sum of the expressions in each of Problems 37 to 44.

37. $2a - 3b - 5c, \ -5a + 2b - 6c, \ 3a - 6b - 2c$.

38. $3x - 5y - 2z, \ -2x + 3y - 5z, \ -5x - 2y + 7z$.

39. $5r - 8s - 3t, \ 3r + 3s - 2t, \ 4r - 6s + 5t$.

40. $-2b - 3c - 5d, \ 4b - 5c + 2d, \ 3b + 2c - 4d$.

41. $3x - 4y, \ 3y - 4z, \ 2x + 5y, \ 5x - 2y - 3z$.

42. $-3a - 5b, \ -3c - 4a, \ 7b + 3c, \ 2c - 4a + 2b$.

43. $3r - 2t + 4s, \ -2r + 3s, \ 2t - 3s, \ -5t + 3r - 5s$.

44. $5c - 6d + 3e, \ 2e + 4c, \ 5d - 2e, \ 2d - 3e + 5c$.

In Problems 45 to 52, subtract the second expression from the first.

45. $2a - 3b, \ -a + 4b$.   **46.** $-4x + 3y, \ 2x - 5y$.

47. $-5c + 3d, \ -2c + 3d$.   **48.** $3r - 6s, \ 5r + 3s$.

49. $3a - 2b + 5c, \ -5a + 3b - 2c$.   **50.** $-2x + 3y - 5z, \ -3x - 2y - 3z$.

51. $3r + 2s - 4t, \ -5r - 3s - 7t$.   **52.** $6a - 2b - 3c, \ -4a + 3b - 5c$.

In Problems 53 to 56, subtract the sum of the first two expressions from the third.

53. $3a^2 + 2a - 1$, $2a^2 - 3a + 2$, $-4a^2 - 2a + 5$.

54. $2x^2 - 3x - 7$, $-3x^2 + 2x + 8$, $5x^2 - 4x + 7$.

55. $2a^2 - 3ab + 2b^2$, $-3a^2 + 2ab + 3b^2$, $5a^2 + 3ab + 2b^2$.

56. $-2x^2 - 7xy + 8y^2$, $5x^2 - 2y^2 + 4xy$, $5xy - 2y^2 + 8x^2$.

Perform the indicated operations in Problems 57 to 68 and combine the like terms.

57. $3a^2(2b) - 2a(3b^2) + 2a(ab) + 2b(ab)$.

58. $2x^2(3y) + 2x(2y^2) - 3x(xy) - 3y(xy)$.

59. $2ab(a^2b) - 3a(a^2b^2) - 3b(2a^3b)$.

60. $2x^2y(6xy) - 2xy(3xy^2) + 3xy(x^2y) - 2x^2y^2(xy)$.

61. $\dfrac{6a^4}{3a^2} - \dfrac{2a^5}{a^3} + \dfrac{12a^8}{4a^6}$.   **62.** $\dfrac{8x^6}{4x^3} - \dfrac{9x^7}{3x^4} - \dfrac{8x^8}{2x^5}$.

63. $\dfrac{12a^2b^3}{4ab} - \dfrac{5a^5b^6}{a^4b^4} - \dfrac{6a^7b^5}{2a^6b^3}$.

64. $\dfrac{27x^3y^2z^2}{3xyz} - \dfrac{24x^4y^4z^6}{6x^3y^2z^4} + \dfrac{12x^5y^4z^6}{4x^3y^3z^4} + \dfrac{18x^5y^3z^4}{9x^4yz^2}$.

65. $a^2b(ab^2 - a^2b) + [(a^5b^3 - a^6b^2) \div a^2]$.

66. $x^3y(x^2y^2 - xy^3) + [(x^8y^5 + x^7y^7) \div x^3y^3]$.

67. $2a^2bc(3ab^2c - 2abc^2) + [(6a^5b^5c^4 - a^5b^4c^5) \div a^2b^2c^2]$.

68. $3x^2y^3z^5(2x^3yz^2 - 3x^2y^3z) + [(8x^8y^6z^8 - 6x^7y^8z^7) \div 2x^3y^2z]$.

Find the products indicated in Problems 69 to 80.

69. $(a - 2b)(a - 2b)$.   **70.** $(2a - 5b)(3a + 2b)$.

71. $(4x - 3y)(3x - 2y)$.   **72.** $(5r - 7s)(6r + 3s)$.

73. $(2a - b + 3c)(3a + 4b - 2c)$.   **74.** $(3x + 5y + 6z)(2x - 4y - 7z)$.

75. $(4r^2 - 3r + 2)(5r^2 - 6r - 3)$.   **76.** $(6u^2 - 3u + 5)(4u^2 + u - 2)$.

77. $(a^4 + b^2 + a^2b)(a^4 + b^2 - a^2b)$.

78. $(2x^3y^2 + x^6 + 3y^4)(2x^3y^2 - x^6 - 3y^4)$.

79. $(a^3 + a^2 + ab^2 + b^2)(-a^3 + a^2 + ab^2 - b^2)$.

80. $(x^2 + 2xy + 2y^2 + 3)(x^2 - 2xy + 2y^2 - 3)$.

In each of Problems 81 to 96, divide the first expression by the second.

81. $6x^2 - 7xy - 3y^2$, $3x + y$.   **82.** $8a^2 - 22ab + 5b^2$, $2a - 5b$.

83. $15h^2 - 14hk - 8k^2$, $5h + 2k$.   **84.** $14b^2 - 41bc + 15c^2$, $7b - 3c$.

85. $x^3 - 2x^2y + 2xy^2 - y^3$, $x - y$.   **86.** $x^3 - y^3$, $x - y$.

87. $a^3 - 2ab^2 + 4b^3$, $a + 2b$.   **88.** $c^3 + 4cd^2 - 8d^3$, $c + 2d$.

89. $6x^2 + xy - 5xz - 2y^2 + 6yz - 4z^2$, $2x - y + z$.

90. $10b^2 + 9bc - 14bd - 9c^2 + 4d^2$, $5b - 3c - 2d$.

91. $4a^2 - 9b^2 - c^2 + 6bc$, $2a - 3b + c$.

92. $9r^2 - 25s^2 + 20st - 4t^2$, $3r - 5s + 2t$.

93. $6x^2 - xy - x - y^2 + 6y - 2$, $2x - y + 1$.

94. $12x^4 - 3 + x^2 - 17x^3 + 9x$, $3x^2 - 2x - 2$.

95. $3a^4 + 2a^2b - b^2 + 2a^2 - 7a^3 + 3ab, 3a^2 - a - b.$

96. $6x^5 + 3 - 7x^2 - 5x^4, 3x^3 - 4x^2 - x + 1.$

Remove the symbols of grouping from Problems 97 to 108.

97. $2(a - 3b - c) - 3(a - 2b + 3c).$

98. $2a(a^2 + 3b + 3c) - 3b(2a + b - 4c) - 6c(a + 2b - 2c).$

99. $3x(2x^2 - 3xy + 5y^2) - 4y(3x^2 + 2xy - 3y^2) + 7xy(3x - y).$

100. $3xy(4x^2 - 2y^2 + 8xy) - 6x^2y(2x + 4y + 3y^2) - 2xy^2(x^2 - 2xy - 3y).$

101. $[(a + b)(a - b) - a(a + 3b)] - 3[a^2 - b(a + 3b)].$

102. $[3x(x - y) - (x - 2y)(x + y)] - [2x(x + y) - 4y(x - 2y)].$

103. $3c[c - 2d(c - 4d)] - [(2c - d)(c + 2d) + c(c - 3d)].$

104. $[2a^2 - 3b(2a - b) - 2a(a - 3b)][(2a + b)(a - b) - b(3a - b)]$
$$- [2a^2(a^2 + 3b^2) - 4ab^3].$$

105. $3x^2 - \{2x[x - y(x - 2y)] - [4x^2 - 3y(x^2 - xy)]\}.$

106. $3x(x - y) - \{(x - 2y)(x + y) - [3xy - 2y(x + 4y)]\}.$

107. $(2a - 5b)(3a + b) - \{4a(a + 3b) - [b(2a + 4b) - 2a(5a + 2b)]\}.$

108. $4a\{a + [2a - 3a(a - 2b)]\} - \{a[(2b - 3a)(b + 4a)] + 2ab(9a - b)\}.$

CHAPTER 2

SPECIAL PRODUCTS AND FACTORING

12. Introduction. In this chapter, methods will be presented that enable us to perform mentally many of the steps in the procedure explained in Art. 8. Thus we can condense the multiplication process for many types of products. We shall also discuss methods for factoring certain types of polynomials. Skill in each of these procedures is essential for efficiency and speed in the computation necessary for college algebra.

13. The product of two binomials. If we use the method of Art. 8 to obtain the product of the two binomials $ax + by$ and $cx + dy$, we get

$$(1) \qquad (ax + by)(cx + dy) = acx^2 + (ad + bc)xy + bdy^2$$

By observing the product on the right, we see that

1. *The first term in the product is the product of the two first terms in the binomials.*

2. *The middle term is the algebraic sum of the two products obtained by multiplying the first term in each binomial by the second term in the other.*

3. *The third term is the product of the two second terms in the binomials.*

Example 1

If we use the above method to obtain the product of $2x - 3$ and $7x + 5$, we note that (1) the product of the two first terms is $14x^2$; (2) the algebraic sum of the first term in each binomial by the second term in the other is

$$10x - 21x = -11x$$

(3) the product of the two second terms is -15. Hence,

$$(2x - 3)(7x + 5) = 14x^2 - 11x - 15$$

19

This process may be expressed in the following easily remembered diagrammatic form, in which the arrows connect the terms that are to be multiplied.

$$14x^2 \quad -15$$
$$(2x - 3)(7x + 5) = 14x^2 - 11x - 15$$
$$21x$$
$$10x$$

We may obtain the square of the binomial $x + y$ by first writing $(x + y)^2 = (x + y)(x + y)$ and then applying the above procedure to the product on the right. Thus we get

(2) $$(x + y)^2 = x^2 + 2xy + y^2$$

If we state formula (2) in words, we get the following:

The square of a binomial is the square of the first term plus twice the product of the first by the second plus the square of the last.

It should be noted that if the sign between the terms in the binomial is minus as in $(x - y)^2$, then the product of the two terms is minus and we have

(3) $$(x - y)^2 = x^2 - 2xy + y^2$$

Examples

2.
$$(2x + 3y)^2 = (2x)^2 + 2(2x)(3y) + (3y)^2$$
$$= 4x^2 + 12xy + 9y^2$$

3.
$$(3x - 4)^2 = (3x)^2 + 2(3x)(-4) + (-4)^2$$
$$= 9x^2 - 24x + 16$$

We may also use (1) to obtain a formula for the product of the sum and difference of two numbers. If we express this product in the form $(x + y)(x - y)$ and apply (1), we get

$$x^2 - xy + xy - y^2 = x^2 - y^2$$

Hence,

(4) $$(x + y)(x - y) = x^2 - y^2$$

Thus we see that *the product of the sum and the difference of two numbers is equal to the difference of their squares.*

Examples

4. $$(x^3 + 4y)(x^3 - 4y) = (x^3)^2 - (4y)^2 = x^6 - 16y^2$$

5. $$(23)(17) = (20 + 3)(20 - 3) = 400 - 9 = 391$$

14. *The square of a polynomial.* By use of the method of Art. 8, the following statement can be verified.

The square of a polynomial is equal to the sum of the squares of the separate terms increased by the algebraic sum of twice the product of each term by every term that follows it.

Example

$$(2x + 3y - 4z - 2w)^2 = (2x)^2 + (3y)^2 + (-4z)^2 + (-2w)^2 + 2(2x)(3y)$$
$$+ 2(2x)(-4z) + 2(2x)(-2w) + 2(3y)(-4z)$$
$$+ 2(3y)(-2w) + 2(-4z)(-2w)$$
$$= 4x^2 + 9y^2 + 16z^2 + 4w^2 + 12xy - 16xz - 8xw$$
$$- 24yz - 12yw + 16zw$$

EXERCISE 4

Find the products indicated below by use of the methods of Arts. 13 and 14.

1. $(x + 1)(x + 2)$.
2. $(2x + 1)(x + 1)$.
3. $(4a + 1)(a + 2)$.
4. $(3b + 1)(b + 2)$.
5. $(2x - 1)(x + 3)$.
6. $(3b - 1)(b + 2)$.
7. $(5a - 1)(a + 2)$.
8. $(7c - 1)(c + 4)$.
9. $(3x - 2)(2x + 3)$.
10. $(5h + 3)(2h - 5)$.
11. $(7i - 5)(3i + 4)$.
12. $(4a - 7)(5a + 3)$.
13. $(2r + 3s)(3r + 2s)$.
14. $(7a + 2b)(6a + 5b)$.
15. $(4x + 5y)(2x + 3y)$.
16. $(8a + 3c)(2a + 5c)$.
17. $(2a - 5b)(4a - 3b)$.
18. $(10x - 3y)(2x - 5y)$.
19. $(8c - 3d)(2c - 7d)$.
20. $(6r - 5s)(2r - 7s)$.
21. $(5h + 7k)(3h - 8k)$.
22. $(10i - 3j)(11i + 2j)$.
23. $(12x - 5y)(3x + 2y)$.
24. $(9a + 8b)(7a - 6b)$.
25. $(a + 2b)^2$.
26. $(x + 3y)^2$.
27. $(2x + 3)^2$.
28. $(3h + 1)^2$.
29. $(2x - 1)^2$.
30. $(3i - j)^2$.
31. $(3a - 4b)^2$.
32. $(6m - 5n)^2$.
33. $(5a - 2b)^2$.
34. $(4x + 5y)^2$.
35. $(7r - 3s)^2$.
36. $(10h + 3k)^2$.
37. $(8u - 3v)^2$.
38. $(3i + 11j)^2$.
39. $(12z - 5w)^2$.
40. $(9a + 7b)^2$.
41. $(15 + 2)(15 - 2)$.
42. $(33)(27)$.
43. $(54)(46)$.
44. $(75)(65)$.
45. $(x + 5)(x - 5)$.
46. $(x + 7)(x - 7)$.
47. $(a + b)(a - b)$.
48. $(x + y)(x - y)$.
49. $(a + 2x)(a - 2x)$.
50. $(x + 3y)(x - 3y)$.
51. $(3x + b)(3x - b)$.
52. $(5c + d)(5c - d)$.
53. $(2a + 3b)(2a - 3b)$.
54. $(3x + 4z)(3x - 4z)$.
55. $(4y + 5c)(4y - 5c)$.
56. $(7x + 4w)(7x - 4w)$.
57. $(2x^3 + y)(2x^3 - y)$.
58. $(3a^2 + 2b)(3a^2 - 2b)$.
59. $(5b^2 + 6c^3)(5b^2 - 6c^3)$.
60. $(7b^4 + 3x^2)(7b^4 - 3x^2)$.
61. $\left(\dfrac{h}{3} + \dfrac{k}{9}\right)\left(\dfrac{h}{3} - \dfrac{k}{2}\right)$.
62. $\left(\dfrac{2x}{5} + \dfrac{y}{4}\right)\left(\dfrac{2x}{5} - \dfrac{y}{4}\right)$.

63. $\left(\dfrac{a^2}{2} + \dfrac{2b^3}{3}\right)\left(\dfrac{a^2}{2} - \dfrac{2b^3}{3}\right).$ **64.** $\left(\dfrac{3x^2}{4} + \dfrac{2y^4}{3}\right)\left(\dfrac{3x^2}{4} - \dfrac{2y^4}{3}\right).$

65. $\left(\dfrac{x}{3} + \dfrac{2}{x}\right)\left(\dfrac{x}{3} - \dfrac{2}{x}\right).$ **66.** $\left(\dfrac{x^2}{5} + \dfrac{2}{3x}\right)\left(\dfrac{x^2}{5} - \dfrac{2}{3x}\right).$

67. $\left(\dfrac{2a}{x} + \dfrac{y}{3b}\right)\left(\dfrac{2a}{x} - \dfrac{y}{3b}\right).$ **68.** $\left(\dfrac{3a^2}{2b} + \dfrac{5x}{4y^3}\right)\left(\dfrac{3a^2}{2b} - \dfrac{5x}{4y^3}\right).$

69. $(a + b + d)^2.$ **70.** $(w + x - y)^2.$ **71.** $(m + n - t)^2.$

72. $(s - t + u)^2.$ **73.** $(p - q + 2r)^2.$ **74.** $(p - 2d - q)^2.$

75. $(a^2 - 2a + 3)^2.$ **76.** $(2x^2 - 3x + 1)^2.$ **77.** $(a - 2b + c - 3d)^2.$

78. $(2x - y + 3z - 2)^2.$ **79.** $(a^3 + 2a^2 - a + 1)^2.$

80. $(2x^3 - x^2 + 3x - 4)^2.$ **81.** $[3(a + b) - 2][5(a + b) + 3].$

82. $[2(3x - y) + 3][5(3x - y) - 7].$ **83.** $[4(2a - c) + 5][3(2a - c) - 4].$

84. $[7(2y + 3b) + 2][3(2y + 3b) - 1].$

85. $[(a^2 - 1) + a][(a^2 - 1) - a].$ **86.** $[(x^2 + 2) - x][(x^2 + 2) + x].$

87. $[(2b^2 + c^2) - 2bc][(2b^2 + c^2) + 2bc].$

88. $[(2u^2 + 4v^2) - 4uv][(2u^2 + 4v^2) + 4uv].$

89. $[(a^3 + a) + (a^2 + 1)][(a^3 + a) - (a^2 + 1)].$

90. $[(x^3 - x) + (x^2 - 1)][(x^3 - x) - (x^2 - 1)].$

91. $[(2b^4 - b) + (b^3 - 2b^2)][(2b^4 - b) - (b^3 - 2b^2)].$

92. $[(3c^5 + 2c^3) - (4c^4 + 1)][(3c^5 + 2c^3) + (4c^4 + 1)].$

15. *The process of factoring.* In order to factor a polynomial, we must find two or more polynomials, or a monomial and one or more polynomials, whose product is the given polynomial. In this article we shall discuss the following types of polynomials that occur frequently:

1. Polynomials that have a common factor.
2. The difference of two squares.
3. Trinomials that are perfect squares.
4. Factorable trinomials that are not perfect squares.

The last three types can be factored by use of the formulas of Art. 13.

1. *Polynomials that have a common factor.* If each term of a polynomial is divisible by the same monomial, we may factor it by first dividing the polynomial by the monomial by the method of Art. 10. Then we express the polynomial as the product of the divisor and the quotient thus obtained. This procedure applied to $ax + ay - az$ yields

(1) $ax + ay - az = a(x + y - z)$

Examples

1. $$3x^3 - 15x^2 + 9x = 3x(x^2 - 5x + 3)$$
2. $(a+b)(a-b) + 3a(a+b) + (a+b)^2 = (a+b)(a-b+3a+a+b)$
$$= (a+b)5a$$

Frequently the polynomial factor can be factored by one of the methods that follow.

2. *The difference of two squares.* If we interchange the members of (4) of Art. 13, we have

(2) $$x^2 - y^2 = (x+y)(x-y)$$

Hence, we see that *the factors of the difference of the squares of two numbers are the sum of the two numbers and the difference of the two numbers.*

Examples

3. $$4x^2 - y^2 = (2x)^2 - y^2 = (2x+y)(2x-y)$$
4. $$9x^4 - 16y^2 = (3x^2)^2 - (4y)^2 = (3x^2 + 4y)(3x^2 - 4y)$$

In the following examples the above method is applied to expressions that are the difference of two squares in which at least one of the terms is not the square of a monomial.

Example 5

The expression $(4x)^2 - (3y+z)^2$ is the difference of the squares of $4x$ and $3y+z$. Hence the two factors are the sum and the difference of these two numbers. Thus we have

$$(4x)^2 - (3y+z)^2 = [4x + (3y+z)][4x - (3y+z)]$$
$$= (4x + 3y + z)(4x - 3y - z)$$

Example 6

$$(2a-3b)^2 - (c+d)^2 = [(2a-3b)+(c+d)][(2a-3b)-(c+d)]$$
$$= (2a - 3b + c + d)(2a - 3b - c - d)$$

3. *Trinomials that are perfect squares.* By formulas (2) and (3) of Art. 13, we have

(3) $$x^2 + 2xy + y^2 = (x+y)^2$$
(4) $$x^2 - 2xy + y^2 = (x-y)^2$$

The trinomial on the left in (3) and in (4) is a perfect square, and we notice in each case that two of the terms are positive and are perfect squares and the third term is twice the product of the square roots of the other two. Furthermore, if the product term is plus, the trinomial is the square of the sum of the two square roots; and if the product term is minus, the trinomial is the square of the difference of the two square roots.

Examples

7. In the trinomial

$$9x^2 - 30x + 25, \quad 9x^2 = (3x)^2, \quad 25 = 5^2, \quad \text{and} \quad -30x = -2(3x)(5)$$

Hence,

$$9x^2 - 30x + 25 = (3x - 5)^2$$

8. $\quad 4a^2 + 12ab + 9b^2 = (2a)^2 + 2(2a)(3b) + (3b^2) = (2a + 3b)^2$

9. $\quad (3x + y)^2 - 2(3x + y)(z + w) + (z + w)^2 = [(3x + y) - (z + w)]^2$
$$= (3x + y - z - w)^2$$

4. Factorable trinomials that are not perfect squares. We shall consider a trinomial of the type $px^2 + qxy + ry^2$. If

$$(5) \qquad px^2 + qxy + ry^2 = (ax + by)(cx + dy)$$

then by (1) of Art. 13

$$p = ac, \qquad r = bd, \qquad \text{and} \qquad q = ad + bc$$

Thus, if $px^2 + qxy + ry^2$ is expressed as the product of two binomials, the first terms in the binomials must be factors of px^2, the two second terms must be factors of ry^2, and the sum of the products of the first term in each binomial by the second term of the other must be qxy. We shall refer to the two latter products as the cross products.

Example 10

In factoring $6x^2 + 11x - 10$, we know that two factors of $6x^2$ are the first terms in the factors and the two factors of -10 are the second terms, but these factors must be arranged so that the algebraic sum of the cross products is $11x$. The desired arrangement is $(3x - 2)(2x + 5)$ since the sum of the cross products $15x$ and $-4x$ is $11x$.

Frequently, the first or the last term or both the first and last terms of a trinomial may be factored in several ways. In such cases, we may attempt several combinations before the correct factors are found.

Example 11

As a simple example of the above situation, we shall consider $x^2 - 5x - 6$. The factors of -6 are 3 and -2, -3 and 2, 6 and -1, -6 and 1. However a trial of the various possibilities reveals that the proper factors are $(x - 6)(x + 1)$.

EXERCISE 5

Factor each of the following expressions.

1. $ac - ad - a^2$.
2. $3x^2 - 6xy + 9xy^2$.
3. $2a^2b - 4ab^2 + 8a^3b^2$.
4. $3x^3y^2 - 9x^2y^3 - 27x^3y^3$.
5. $(a - b)2c + (a - b)4b$.
6. $(x - y)(x - y) + (x - y)y$.
7. $(3r - 2s)2t + (3r - 2s)3u - (3r - 2s)(4t - u)$.
8. $(4x - 2y)(x + 2y) + (4x - 2y)(x + y) - (4x - 2y)(2x + y)$.
9. $x^2 - a^2$.
10. $w^2 - b^2$.
11. $y^2 - 4x^2$.
12. $a^2 - 9b^2$.
13. $16w^2 - x^2$.
14. $25b^2 - y^2$.
15. $c^2 - 36d^2$.
16. $x^2 - 64y^2$.
17. $4a^2 - 9b^2$.
18. $9h^2 - 16k^2$.
19. $36r^2 - 25s^2$.
20. $25a^2 - 16y^2$.
21. $9x^4 - 16y^6$.
22. $49a^3 - 25b^2$.
23. $25x^6 - 9y^4$.
24. $64h^8 - 81k^6$.
25. $\frac{4}{9}r^4 - \frac{25}{16}s^2$.
26. $\frac{9}{16}i^6 - \frac{49}{25}j^4$.
27. $\frac{81}{100}a^{12} - \frac{64}{9}b^2$.
28. $\frac{100}{121}c^{10} - \frac{36}{49}d^4$.
29. $a^8 - b^4$.
30. $16x^4 - d^8$.
31. $81c^{12} - 16c^4$.
32. $625r^{16} - 256s^{12}$.
33. $a^2 + 4a + 4$.
34. $x^2 + 6a + 9$.
35. $y^2 + 10y + 25$.
36. $z^2 + 12z + 36$.
37. $4h^2 - 4h + 1$.
38. $9k^2 - 6k + 1$.
39. $16s^2 - 8s + 1$.
40. $36t^2 - 12t + 1$.
41. $4a^2 + 12ab + 9b^2$.
42. $9x^2 + 30xy + 25y^2$.
43. $36c^2 + 84cd + 49d^2$.
44. $25u^2 + 80uv + 64v^2$.
45. $\frac{a^2}{4} - \frac{2a}{b} + \frac{4}{b^2}$.
46. $\frac{c^2}{9} + \frac{2c}{d} + \frac{9}{d^2}$.
47. $\frac{4x^2}{9} - 3xy + \frac{81y^2}{16}$.
48. $\frac{9h^2}{16} + \frac{4hk}{3} + \frac{64k^2}{81}$.
49. $4r^6 - 12r^3s^2 + 9s^4$.
50. $16a^8 - 24a^4b^5 + 9b^{10}$.
51. $25h^4 + 60h^2k^5 + 36k^{10}$.
52. $49c^8 - 56c^4d^6 + 16d^{12}$.
53. $x^2 + 5x + 6$.
54. $3y^2 + 4y + 1$.
55. $4a^2 + 5a + 1$.
56. $3b^2 + 5b + 2$.
57. $5c^2 - 17c + 6$.
58. $7x^2 - 26x + 15$.
59. $8c^2 - 13c + 5$.
60. $6x^2 - 13x + 7$.
61. $2y^2 + 3y - 2$.
62. $3x^2 - 5x - 2$.
63. $5h^2 + 2h - 3$.
64. $7p^2 + 2p - 5$.
65. $6r^2 + 13r - 5$.
66. $8y^2 + 3y - 5$.
67. $9y^2 - 18y - 7$.
68. $9a^2 + 98a - 11$.
69. $3a^2 + 12ab + 12b^2$.
70. $5x^2 + 18xy + 16y^2$.
71. $18u^2 - 23uv + 7v^2$.
72. $24r^2 - 26rs + 5s^2$.
73. $8h^2 + 5hk - 3k^2$.
74. $2c^2 + 7cd - 9d^2$.
75. $3a^2 + 13ab - 10b^2$.
76. $5x^2 + 11xy - 12y^2$.
77. $6p^2 - 13pq + 6q^2$.
78. $12y^2 + 17yz + 6z^2$.
79. $15b^2 - 17bc + 4c^2$.
80. $16u^2 + 32uv + 15v^2$.

81. $16a^2 + 14ab - 15b^2$.

82. $16x^2 + 34xy - 15y^2$.

83. $24h^2 + 23hk - 12k^2$.

84. $18c^2 + 19cd - 12d^2$.

85. $24a^4 + 34a^3 - 45a^2$.

86. $8x^5 + 24x^4 - 54x^3$.

87. $6a^6 - 5a^3b^2 - 6b^4$.

88. $12a^4b^6 + 4a^2b^3 - 21$.

89. $24x^8y^6 + 2x^4y^3 - 35$.

90. $12c^{10}b^8 + 7c^5b^4 - 34$.

91. $12h^6 + 11h^3k^5 - 15k^{10}$.

92. $16y^{12} - 32y^6h^4 - 9h^8$.

93. $(a + b)^2 - c^2$.

94. $(x - 2y)^2 - 4z^2$.

95. $(3z + w)^2 - 9x^2$.

96. $(3h - 2j)^2 - 16i^2$.

97. $25a^2 - (b + 2)^2$.

98. $36 - (2x - y)^2$.

99. $49x^2 - (2y - 3z)^2$.

100. $100p^2 - (7q - 5r)^2$.

101. $(a + 2b)^2 - (c - 3d)^2$.

102. $(3x - 4y)^2 - (2z - 5w)^2$.

103. $(5r - 4s)^2 - (4t + 3u)^2$.

104. $(6a + 5b)^2 - (4c + 7d)^2$.

16. *Factors of binomials of the type* $a^n + b^n$. Binomials of the type $a^n + b^n$ may be divided into the four cases discussed below.

1. *The sum or difference of two cubes.* If we divide $x^3 + y^3$ by $x + y$ by the method shown in Art. 10, we obtain the quotient $x^2 - xy + y^2$. Hence,

(1) $$x^3 + y^3 = (x + y)(x^2 - xy + y^2)$$

Similarly,

(2) $$x^3 - y^3 = (x - y)(x^2 + xy + y^2)$$

Thus we see that *the first factor of the sum of the cubes of two numbers is the sum of the two numbers. The second factor is the square of the first number minus the product of the first by the second plus the square of the second number.*

Furthermore, *one factor of the difference of the cubes of two numbers is the difference of the numbers. The other factor is the square of the first number plus the product of the first number by the second plus the square of the second number.*

Examples

1. $8a^3 + b^3 = (2a)^3 + b^3 = (2a + b)[(2a)^2 - (2a)(b) + b^2]$
    $= (2a + b)(4a^2 - 2ab + b^2)$

2. $x^3 - 27y^6 = x^3 - (3y^2)^3 = (x - 3y^2)[x^2 + x(3y^2) + (3y^2)^2]$
    $= (x - 3y^2)(x^2 + 3xy^2 + 9y^4)$

3. $8a^3 + (c - d)^3 = [2a + (c - d)][(2a)^2 - (2a)(c - d) + (c - d)^2]$
    $= (2a + c - d)(4a^2 - 2ac + 2ad + c^2 - 2cd + d^2)$

2. *Binomials of the type* $x^n - y^n$ *with* n *greater than 3 and divisible by 2.* In this case, we express $x^n - y^n$ in the form $(x^{n/2})^2 -$

$(y^{n/2})^2$. The binomial in this form is the difference of two squares, and we may factor it by the use of (2) of Art. 15. If $n/2$ is divisible by 2, we apply the preceding method again; in fact, we continue to employ it as long as it is applicable.

Example 4

$$x^4 - y^4 = (x^2)^2 - (y^2)^2$$
$$= (x^2 - y^2)(x^2 + y^2)$$
$$= (x - y)(x + y)(x^2 + y^2)$$

The factor $x^2 + y^2$ is irreducible since it is the sum of two squares.

3. *Binomials of the type* $x^n \pm y^n$, *n greater than 3 and divisible by 3.* In this case, $x^n \pm y^n$ may be expressed as $(x^{n/3})^3 \pm (y^{n/3})^3$. Hence, binomials of this type may be considered as the sum or the difference of two cubes and method 1 or 2 may be applied.

Example 5

$$x^6 + y^6 = (x^2)^3 + (y^2)^3$$
$$= (x^2 + y^2)[(x^2)^2 - x^2y^2 + (y^2)^2]$$
$$= (x^2 + y^2)(x^4 - x^2y^2 + y^4)$$

4. *Binomials of the type* $x^n + y^n$, *n greater than 3 and not divisible by 2 or 3.* If n is divisible by 2 or 3, the expression should be factored by means of the first or second method above. However, if n is not a multiple of 2 or 3, the expression can be factored by means of the following formulas which are not proved here but that can be verified for any positive integral of n by long division. If n is not divisible by 2, then

$$(1) \quad x^n + y^n = (x + y)(x^{n-1} - x^{n-2}y + x^{n-3}y^2 - \cdots \\ + x^2y^{n-3} - xy^{n-2} + y^{n-1})$$

For *any* integral value of n,

$$(2) \quad x^n - y^n = (x - y)(x^{n-1} + x^{n-2}y + x^{n-3}y^2 + \cdots \\ + x^2y^{n-3} + xy^{n-2} + y^{n-1})$$

Example 6

The binomial $x^{12} - y^{12}$ may be written $(x^6)^2 - (y^6)^2$ or $(x^4)^3 - (y^4)^3$. Using the first of these, we have

$$x^{12} - y^{12} = (x^6)^2 - (y^6)^2$$
$$= (x^6 - y^6)(x^6 + y^6)$$
$$= [(x^3)^2 - (y^3)^2](x^6 + y^6)$$
$$= (x^3 - y^3)(x^3 + y^3)(x^6 + y^6)$$

Since neither of the binomials in the last expression can be expressed as the difference of two squares, we shall apply method 3 and continue factoring, thus obtaining

$$\begin{aligned}
x^{12} - y^{12} &= (x^3 - y^3)(x^3 + y^3)[(x^2)^3 + (y^2)^3] \\
&= (x - y)(x^2 + xy + y^2)(x + y)(x^2 - xy + y^2)(x^2 + y^2) \\
&\qquad\qquad\qquad\qquad\qquad\qquad\qquad\qquad (x^4 - x^2 y^2 + y^4)
\end{aligned}$$

Example 7

The binomial $x^{10} - y^{10}$ may be expressed as the difference of two squares. Thus,

$$\begin{aligned}
x^{10} - y^{10} &= (x^5)^2 - (y^5)^2 \\
&= (x^5 - y^5)(x^5 + y^5) \\
&= (x - y)(x^4 + x^3 y + x^2 y^2 + xy^3 + y^4)(x + y) \\
&\qquad\qquad\qquad\qquad (x^4 - x^3 y + x^2 y^2 - xy^3 + y^4)
\end{aligned}$$

EXERCISE 6

Factor each of the following expressions.

1. $a^3 - b^3$.	**2.** $c^3 - d^3$.	**3.** $r^3 + s^3$.
4. $p^3 + q^3$.	**5.** $x^3 - 8y^3$.	**6.** $a^3 - 27b^3$.
7. $j^3 + 64k^3$.	**8.** $c^3 + 125d^3$.	**9.** $8u^3 - 27v^3$.
10. $27p^3 - 64q^3$.	**11.** $125x^3 + 8y^3$.	**12.** $216r^3 + 125s^3$.
13. $a^6 b^3 - 8$.	**14.** $8h^9 k^6 - 27$.	**15.** $64u^{12} v^9 + 125$.
16. $343c^{15} d^9 + 216$.	**17.** $a^4 - b^4$.	**18.** $h^4 - k^4$.
19. $x^4 - 16$.	**20.** $y^4 - 81$.	**21.** $x^6 - y^6$.
22. $a^6 + 64$.	**23.** $729c^6 - 1$.	**24.** $a^8 - x^8$.
25. $x^{12} + y^{12}$.	**26.** $r^8 - s^4$.	**27.** $p^9 + q^6$.
28. $m^{16} - n^{16}$.	**29.** $a^9 - b^9$.	**30.** $64a^6 - 1$.
31. $x^5 + y^5$.	**32.** $a^7 - b^7$.	**33.** $x^{14} - y^{14}$.
34. $x^{18} - y^{18}$.	**35.** $x^{15} - y^{15}$.	**36.** $a^{20} - b^{20}$.
37. $(m - n)^3 - 1$.	**38.** $(s + t)^3 + 1$.	**39.** $(2a - b)^3 + 8$.
40. $(3x - 2y)^3 - 27$.	**41.** $1 - (2c - 3d)^3$.	**42.** $64 + (u - v)^3$.
43. $a^9 - (a^2 - 1)^3$.	**44.** $x^{12} + (x^3 - 1)^3$.	

17. *Factoring by grouping.* Frequently a polynomial containing four or more terms can be reduced to a factorable form by suitably grouping the terms and then factoring the groups. If this is possible, the polynomial can then be factored by one of the preceding methods. We shall illustrate the procedure with several examples.

Example 1

$$ax - bx - ay + by = (ax - bx) - (ay - by)$$ (grouping the first two and the last two terms)

$$= x(a - b) - y(a - b)$$ (dividing the first group by x and the second by y)

$$= (a - b)(x - y)$$ (dividing each group by the common factor $a - b$)

Example 2

$$x - y - x^2 + y^2 = (x - y) - (x^2 - y^2)$$ (grouping the first two and the last two terms)

$$= (x - y) - (x - y)(x + y)$$ (factoring $x^2 - y^2$)

$$= (x - y)[1 - (x + y)]$$ (dividing each group by the common factor $x - y$)

$$= (x - y)(1 - x - y)$$ (simplifying the last factor)

The following example is an illustration of an expression that can be reduced to the difference of two squares by suitably grouping the terms.

Example 3

$$9c^2 - 4a^2 + 4ab - b^2 = 9c^2 - (4a^2 - 4ab + b^2)$$
$$= 9c^2 - (2a - b)^2$$ [by (4), Art. 15]
$$= [3c + (2a - b)][3c - (2a - b)]$$ [by (2), Art. 15]
$$= (3c + 2a - b)(3c - 2a + b)$$

18. Trinomials that are reducible to the difference of two squares. If a trinomial can be made a perfect square by the addition of a term that is a perfect square, then the trinomial can be expressed as the difference of two squares. For example, the trinomial $4x^4 + 8x^2y^2 + 9y^4$ would be a perfect square if the middle term were $12x^2y^2$. Hence, if we add and subtract $4x^2y^2$, we get

$$4x^4 + 8x^2y^2 + 9y^4 = 4x^4 + 12x^2y^2 + 9y^4 - 4x^2y^2$$
$$= (2x^2 + 3y^2)^2 - (2xy)^2$$
$$= (2x^2 + 3y^2 + 2xy)(2x^2 + 3y^2 - 2xy)$$

It should be noted that this method is applicable only if the trinomial becomes a perfect square when a *perfect square* is *added* to it. For example, $x^4 - x^2y^2 + y^4$ becomes a perfect square when x^2y^2 is subtracted from it.   However, then we have

$$x^4 - 2x^2y^2 + y^4 + x^2y^2 = (x^2 - y^2)^2 + x^2y^2$$

and since this is the sum of two squares, it cannot be factored.

EXERCISE 7

Factor the expressions in Problems 1 to 40 by the method of Art. 17.

1. $ab + a + b + 1.$ **2.** $xy + 2x + y + 2.$

3. $uv + 3u + 2v + 6.$ **4.** $rs + 4r + 2s + 8.$

5. $a^2 - ab + a - b.$ **6.** $xy + x - 2y^2 - 2y.$

7. $2c^2 + 4cd - 3c - 6d.$ **8.** $2h^2 - 5hk + 4h - 10k.$

9. $ac + ad + bc + bd.$ **10.** $xy - y^2 + xz - yz.$

11. $6rt + 2ru - 15st - 5su.$ **12.** $6uv - 12ux - 15vw + 10vx.$

13. $6a^2 - 4ac - 15ab + 10bc.$ **14.** $4x^2 - 3xy - 24xz + 18yz.$

15. $15h^2 - 9hk + 35hj - 21kj.$ **16.** $6r^2 - 5rs + 18rt - 15st.$

17. $a^2 - ab + ac - a + b - c.$ **18.** $x^2 - xy - xz + x - y - z.$

19. $r^2 - 2rs - rt - 3ru + 6su + 3tu.$

20. $6bc - 9c^2 - 12cd - 8be + 12ce + 16de.$

21. $x^2 - y^2 - x - y.$ **22.** $a^2 - b^2 - a + b.$

23. $a^2 - 2ab + b^2 - ac + bc.$ **24.** $x^2 + 2xy + y^2 - xz - yz.$

25. $x^3 - y^3 - x^2 + 2xy - y^2.$ **26.** $a^2 + 2ab + b^2 - a^3 - b^3.$

27. $x^2 + xy - 2y^2 - x^3 + y^3.$ **28.** $2c^2 + 5cd - 3d^2 + 8c^3 - d^3.$

29. $h^2 - 4hk + 4k^2 - 16.$ **30.** $r^2 + 6rs + 9s^2 - 4t^2.$

31. $25a^2 - b^2 + 4bd - 4d^2.$ **32.** $9x^2 - 4y^2 - 12yz - 9z^2.$

33. $x^2 - 4xy + 4y^2 - 4z^2 - 12zw - 9w^2.$

34. $4a^2 - 4ab + b^2 - c^2 + 6cd - 9d^2.$

35. $4r^2 + 12rs + 9s^2 - t^2 - 8tu - 16u^2.$

36. $9h^2 - 6hi + i^2 - 16j^2 + 8jk - k^2.$

37. $a^2 - 3ab + 3ac + 2b^2 - 3bc.$ **38.** $x^2 - 3xy + 2y^2 - xz + yz.$

39. $4rs - 6s^2 + 17st - 6rt - 12t^2.$ **40.** $6ab - 12b^2 + 11bs - 4as - 2s^2.$

Factor the following problems by the method of Art. 18.

41. $a^4 + 3a^2 + 4.$ **42.** $x^4 + x^2 + 1.$ **43.** $c^4 + 2c^2 + 9.$

44. $y^4 - 13y^2 + 4.$ **45.** $x^4 + 4.$ **46.** $a^4 + 3a^2b^2 + 4b^4.$

47. $y^4 + 5y^2z^2 + 9z^4.$ **48.** $b^4 - 9b^2c^2 + 16c^4.$ **49.** $9a^4 - 16a^2b^2 + 4b^4.$

50. $16x^4 + 15x^2y^2 + 9y^4.$ **51.** $25r^4 - 36r^2s^2 + 4s^4.$

52. $64u^4 - 57u^2v^2 + 9v^4.$

SUPPLEMENTARY PROBLEMS

Find the products in Problems 1 to 60 by inspection.

1. $(3x + 1)(x + 2).$ **2.** $(5a + 1)(a + 2).$ **3.** $(3c + d)(c + 4d).$

4. $(2x + y)(x + 4y).$ **5.** $(4s - 3t)(5s - 2t).$ **6.** $(5a - 3b)(2a - 7b).$

7. $(3h - 4k)(2h - 3k).$ **8.** $(5i - 3j)(4i - j).$

9. $(4s - 3t)(5s + 2t).$ **10.** $(5a - 3b)(2a + 7b).$

11. $(7t + 2u)(4t - 3u)$.　　　　**12.** $(6u + 5v)(2u - 3v)$.

13. $(8x - 7y)(3x + 2y)$.　　　　**14.** $(9c + 7d)(5c - 4d)$.

15. $(6a + 9b)(5a - 8b)$.　　　　**16.** $(7s + 10t)(5s - 7t)$.

17. $(8h - 11k)(4h + 5k)$.　　　　**18.** $(12x + 7y)(7x - 4y)$.

19. $(9c + 11d)(5c - 6d)$.　　　　**20.** $(13t + 8u)(8t - 5u)$.

21. $(a + 3)(a - 3)$.　　**22.** $(b + 4)(b - 4)$.　　**23.** $(2c - 1)(2c + 1)$.

24. $(3s + 1)(3s - 1)$.　　**25.** $(2x + y)(2x - y)$.　　**26.** $(3t + s)(3t - s)$.

27. $(4a + 3b)(4a - 3b)$.　　　　**28.** $(5x - 3y)(5x + 3y)$.

29. $(6c - 5d)(6c + 5d)$.　　　　**30.** $(7h + 3k)(7h - 3k)$.

31. $(8h + 5k)(8h - 5k)$.　　　　**32.** $(12p + 5q)(12p - 5q)$.

33. $(a + 2b)^2$.　　**34.** $(2x - y)^2$.　　**35.** $(2r + 3s)^2$.

36. $(5h - 3k)^2$.　　**37.** $(\frac{1}{2}x + 2y)^2$.　　**38.** $(\frac{2}{3}a - \frac{3}{2}b)^2$.

39. $(\frac{3}{4}r + \frac{8}{3}s)^2$.　　**40.** $(\frac{3}{5}u - \frac{5}{9}v)^2$.　　**41.** $(5a^2 + 2b^3)^2$.

42. $(3x^3 - 5y^4)^2$.　　**43.** $(6p^5 + 7q^2)^2$.　　**44.** $(4a^2b^4 - 7c^3)^2$.

45. $[(a + b) + c][(a + b) - c]$.　　**46.** $(x + y + z)(x + y - z)$.

47. $(u + v - 2w)(u + v + 2w)$.　　**48.** $(p + 2q - 3w)(p + 2q + 3w)$.

49. $(r - 2s + 3t)(r + 2s + 3t)$.　　**50.** $(2a - 3b + 4c)(2a + 3b + 4c)$.

51. $(x - 2y - z)(x + 2y + z)$.　　**52.** $(3x - 5y - 2z)(3x + 5y + 2z)$.

53. $(a + b + c)^2$.　　**54.** $(a - b + c)^2$.　　**55.** $(x + y - 2z)^2$.

56. $(2x - y - 3z)^2$.　　　　**57.** $(a + 2b + c + 3d)^2$.

58. $(x^3 + 2x^2 - x - 3)^2$.　　　　**59.** $(a^3 - 3a^2 - 2a + 4)^2$.

60. $(2x^4 - 3x^2 + x - 4)^2$.

Factor the following expressions.

61. $2x^2 - 6xy - 10xz$.　　　　**62.** $3u^2v + 6uv^2 - 9uvw$.

63. $12rst - 8s^2t + 20st^2$.　　　　**64.** $4a^5 - 10a^4 - 14a^3$.

65. $9x^2y^3 + 6x^3y^2 + 3xy$.　　　　**66.** $16p^3q^3 - 20p^2q + 28pq^2$.

67. $10u^2v^2 - 20u^2vw - 25uv^2w$.　　**68.** $2a^2b^2 - 4a^2bc + 6ab^2c$.

69. $x^2 - 9$.　　**70.** $a^2 - 16$.　　**71.** $4u^2 - 49b^2$.

72. $64x^2 - 25y^2$.　　**73.** $45b^4 - 80c^2$.　　**74.** $8b^9 - 18b^3$.

75. $27c^3d - 12cd^3$.　　**76.** $64x^5y - 36xy^7$.　　**77.** $9a^2 + 6ab + b^2$.

78. $16x^2 - 8xy + y^2$.　　**79.** $9u^2 + 12uv + 4v^2$.　　**80.** $64r^2 - 56rs + 49s^2$.

81. $25h^6 - 20h^3t^2 + 4t^4$.　　　　**82.** $49a^4 - 28a^2b^4 + 4b^8$.

83. $9x^2 + 12xy^5 + 4y^{10}$.　　　　**84.** $16b^8 - 24b^4c^3 + 9c^6$.

85. $x^2 - 5x + 6$.　　**86.** $y^2 + 7y + 12$.　　**87.** $a^2 + a - 6$.

88. $b^2 - b - 20$.　　**89.** $6x^2 + xy - 2y^2$.　　**90.** $6r^2 + 7rs - 3t^2$.

91. $12a^2 + 13ab - 4b^2$.　　**92.** $9b^2 + 9bc - 10c^2$.

93. $c^3 + d^3$.　　**94.** $u^3 - v^3$.　　**95.** $8x^3 + y^3$.

96. $27r^3 - s^3$.　　**97.** $27a^3 + 64b^3$.　　**98.** $8a^6 + 1$.

99. $27 + x^9$.　　　　**100.** $a^6 - 8b^{12}$.

101. $bdk - 4bk + 3kd - 12k$.　　**102.** $acy + 4cy - 2ac - 8c$.

103. $ax - by + cx + bx - ay - cy$.

104. $2ax - 2by - 2cx + cy + 4bx - ay$.

105. $a^2 - b^2 + a - b$.　　**106.** $x^3 + y^3 + x + y$.　　**107.** $u^2 - v^2 + u^3 - v^3$.

108. $x^2 - y^2 + x^2y - xy^2$.　　　　**109.** $x^4 - y^4$.

110. $a^4 - 16$.　　**111.** $z^4 - 81w^4$.　　**112.** $c^8 - d^8$.

113. $a^6 - b^6$.   **114.** $x^9 + y^9$.   **115.** $r^6 - s^{12}$.

116. $a^9 - 8b^6$.   **117.** $a^5 - b^5$.   **118.** $x^7 + y^7$.

119. $u^{10} - v^{10}$.   **120.** $a^{14} - 1$.   **121.** $x^4 + x^2 + 1$.

122. $a^4 + 5a^2 + 9$.   **123.** $4b^4 + 3b^2 + 1$.   **124.** $16y^4 - 9y^2 + 1$.

125. $4x^4 - 17x^2y^2 + 4y^4$.   **126.** $a^4 + 4b^4$.

127. $9b^4 - 16b^2c^2 + 4c^4$.   **128.** $16u^4 - 25u^2v^2 + 4v^4$.

129. $x^2 - 2xy + y^2 - x + y$.   **130.** $a^3 - b^3 - a^2 + 2ab - b^2$.

131. $8 + x^6 + x^4 + 2x^2$.   **132.** $x^4 - y^4 - x^2 + y^2$.

133. $4 - a^2 + 4ab - 4b^2$.   **134.** $9x^4 - x^2 - 6xy - 9y^2$.

135. $a^2 - x^2 + b^2 - y^2 + 2ab - 2xy$.   **136.** $8x^3 + 4x^2 - y^3 - y^2$.

CHAPTER 3

FRACTIONS

19. *The fundamental principle of fractions*. In Art. 9 the fraction a/b was defined to be the indicated division of a by b. The symbol a is called the *numerator*, and b is called the *denominator* of the fraction, and each is referred to as a *member* of the fraction.

The product of the two fractions a/b and c/d is defined by the formula below.

(1)
$$\frac{a}{b} \times \frac{c}{d} = \frac{ac}{bd}$$

By use of (1), with $c = d = n$, we have

$$\frac{a}{b} \times \frac{n}{n} = \frac{an}{bn}$$

However, since $n/n = 1$,

$$\frac{a}{b} \times \frac{n}{n} = \frac{a}{b}$$

Hence, we have

(2)
$$\frac{a}{b} = \frac{an}{bn}$$

Now, if we read (2) from left to right and from right to left, we have the following fundamental principle of fractions.

FUNDAMENTAL PRINCIPLE OF FRACTIONS. *If each member of a fraction is multiplied or divided by the same nonzero quantity, the value of the fraction is not changed.*

Examples

1. $$\frac{3}{4} = \frac{3 \times 5}{4 \times 5} = \frac{15}{20}$$

2.
$$\frac{8}{10} = \frac{8 \div 2}{10 \div 2} = \frac{4}{5}$$

3.
$$\frac{a^3 b^2}{a^4 b} = \frac{a^3 b^2 \div a^3 b}{a^4 b \div a^3 b} = \frac{b}{a}.$$

As a further consequence of (2), we have

$$\frac{a}{b} = \frac{a \times (-1)}{b \times (-1)} = \frac{-a}{-b}$$

Furthermore,

$$\frac{-a}{b} = \frac{-1 \times a}{1 \times b}$$

$$= \frac{-1}{1} \times \frac{a}{b} \qquad [\text{by } (1)]$$

$$= -1 \times \frac{a}{b} \qquad \left(\text{since } \frac{-1}{1} = -1\right)$$

$$= -\frac{a}{b}$$

Similarly,

$$\frac{a}{-b} = -\frac{a}{b}$$

Hence, we have

(3)
$$\frac{a}{b} = \frac{-a}{-b}$$

and

(4)
$$\frac{-a}{b} = \frac{a}{-b} = -\frac{a}{b}$$

Thus we see that the sign of *the numerator and of the denominator of a fraction may be changed without altering the value of the fraction.* However, *if we change the sign of either the numerator or the denominator, we must change the sign before the fraction.*

Example 4

$$\frac{a-2}{a-3} = \frac{2-a}{3-a} = -\frac{a-2}{3-a} = -\frac{2-a}{a-3}$$

20. Reduction to lowest terms. A fraction is said to be in lowest terms when the numerator and the denominator have no common factors. Hence, in order to reduce a fraction to lowest terms, we first factor the numerator and the denominator and then divide each of them by every factor that occurs in both.

Example 1

$$\frac{x^3 + x^2 - 6x}{x^3 - 3x^2 + 2x} = \frac{x(x - 2)(x + 3)}{x(x - 2)(x - 1)}$$ (factoring the numerator and the denominator)

$$= \frac{x + 3}{x - 1}$$ [dividing the numerator and the denominator by $x(x - 2)$]

It is a common practice in the reduction of fractions to indicate the factor to be divided out of the numerator and the denominator by striking it out or by canceling it.

Example 2

(The cancellation indicates that $a - c$ can be divided out of *each term* of the numerator and of the denominator)

$$\frac{a^5 - a^4c - ab^4 - b^4c}{a^4 - a^3c - a^2b^2 + ab^2c} = \frac{a^4(a - c) - b^4(a - c)}{a^3(a - c) - ab^2(a - c)}$$

$$= \frac{a^4 - b^4}{a^3 - ab^2}$$

$$= \frac{(a^2 - b^2)(a^2 + b^2)}{a(a^2 - b^2)}$$ (factoring each member)

$$= \frac{a^2 + b^2}{a}$$ (dividing each member by $a^2 - b^2$)

It should be noted that the first time we used cancellation, the canceled expression $a - c$ was a factor of *each term* of the two members of the fraction and that the fraction could have been placed in the form $(a - c)(a^4 - b^4)/(a - c)(a^3 - ab^2)$. The second time cancellation was used, the numerator and denominator were in factored form and the canceled factor $a^2 - b^2$ was common to both.

The practice of cancellation leads to serious errors when it is carelessly applied or when it is not thoroughly understood. One must be sure that if the numerator or denominator is not completely factored, the canceled expression must be a factor of *every* term above and below the line. It would be an error to cancel $a - 2b$ in $\dfrac{(a - 2b)(3a + b)}{(a - 2b)3a + b}$ since the denominator is not in factored form and $a - 2b$ is a divisor of the first term, $(a - 2b)3a$, but not of the second, b. If the cancellation process is not thoroughly understood, it should not be applied before the two members of the fraction are completely factored.

EXERCISE 8

Change the fraction in each of Problems 1 to 24 into an equivalent fraction that has the second expression in the problem as a denominator.

1. $\dfrac{-2}{y - x}, \ x - y.$

2. $\dfrac{a + b}{b - a}, \ a - b.$

3. $\dfrac{2x - 3y + z}{x - z - y}, \ z + y - x.$

4. $\dfrac{a - 3b + c}{-a - b + c}, \ a + b - c.$

5. $\dfrac{a}{2b}, \ 2ab.$

6. $\dfrac{2x}{3y}, \ 9xy.$

7. $\dfrac{a + b}{a - b}, \ a^2 - b^2.$

8. $\dfrac{x - 2}{x - 3}, \ x^2 - 9.$

9. $\dfrac{3xy}{9x^2}, \ 3x.$

10. $\dfrac{12a^2b}{16ab^2}, \ 4b.$

11. $\dfrac{a^2 - b^2}{a^2 + 2ab + b^2}, \ a + b.$

12. $\dfrac{x^2 - y^2}{x^3 + y^3}, \ x^2 - xy + y^2.$

13. $\dfrac{a - 2b}{2a}, \ 6a^2.$

14. $\dfrac{2x - 3y}{3x}, \ 12xy.$

15. $\dfrac{4u - v}{-5v}, \ 20v^2.$

16. $\dfrac{5b + 3c}{4b}, \ -16b^2.$

17. $\dfrac{x - 2y}{x - y}, \ x^2 - y^2.$

18. $\dfrac{2a - b}{b - a}, \ a^2 - b^2.$

19. $\dfrac{3h + 4k}{2h - k}, \ 2h^2 + 3hk - 2k^2.$

20. $\dfrac{p^2 - pq + q^2}{p - 2q}, \ p^2 - pq - 2q^2.$

21. $\dfrac{5x + 2y}{x^2 + xy + y^2}, \ x^3 - y^3.$

22. $\dfrac{a^2 - ab + b^2}{a - b}, \ a^3 - b^3.$

23. $\dfrac{b^2 - bc - c^2}{b^2 - bc + c^2}, \ b^3 + c^3.$

24. $\dfrac{r^2 - rt - t^2}{r^2 - rt + t^2}, \ r^4 + r^2t^2 + t^4.$

Reduce the following fractions to lowest terms.

25. $\dfrac{x^2 + x - 6}{x^2 + 5x + 6}.$

26. $\dfrac{a^2 + 4a + 3}{a^2 - a - 2}.$

27. $\dfrac{2h^2 + 3h - 2}{3h^2 + 7h + 2}.$

28. $\dfrac{3w^2 - 8w + 4}{2w^2 - w - 6}.$

29. $\dfrac{(x - y)(2x^2 + xy - 6y^2)}{(x + 2y)(3x^2 - xy - 2y^2)}.$

30. $\dfrac{(2a - b)(a^2 - ab - 6b^2)}{(a + 2b)(2a^2 + 3ab - 2b^2)}.$

31. $\dfrac{(w + 2z)(6w^2 + 7wz - 3z^2)}{(3w - z)(2w^2 - wz - 6z^2)}.$

32. $\dfrac{(2c - d)(6c^2 + 11cd + 3d^2)}{(3c + 2d)(6c^2 - cd - d^2)}.$

33. $\dfrac{ms - 2mt - 2nt + ns}{2ms - mt - nt + 2ns}.$

34. $\dfrac{ax - ay - 2by + 2bx}{ax + 2bx + 2by + ay}.$

35. $\dfrac{3ah + 4bk - 2ak - 6bh}{2ah - 4bh + ak - 2bk}.$

36. $\dfrac{xy + 3xz - 2wy - 6wz}{2xy + wy + 3wz + 6xz}.$

37. $\dfrac{a^3 + b^3}{a^2 - b^2}.$

38. $\dfrac{x^3 - y^3}{x^2 - y^2}.$

39. $\dfrac{u^2 - v^2}{u^4 - v^4}.$

40. $\dfrac{m^6 - n^6}{m^9 - n^9}.$

41. $\dfrac{b^6 - c^6}{b^4 - c^4}.$

42. $\dfrac{a^4 + a^2b^2 + b^4}{a^3 - b^3}.$

43. $\dfrac{x^4 + x^2y^2 + y^4}{x^6 - y^6}.$

44. $\dfrac{r^4 + 4}{r^3 + 8}$.

45. $\dfrac{x - 3}{(2x - 5)x - 3}$.

46. $\dfrac{a - 4}{(3a - 11)a - 4}$.

47. $\dfrac{y - 3}{(5y - 14)y - 3}$.

48. $\dfrac{b - 4}{(4b - 15) - 4}$.

49. $\dfrac{x + 1}{x(x + 1) + (x + 2)x + 1}$.

50. $\dfrac{2b + 1}{3(2b + 1) + 2(3b + 2)2b + 1}$.

51. $\dfrac{(a + 1)(2a - 3)}{-4(a + 1) + (2a + 3)a + 1}$.

52. $\dfrac{(y + 3)(2y - 1)}{-2(y + 3) + (2y + 7) + 3}$.

21. Multiplication of fractions. Formula (1), Art. 19, states that *the product of two fractions is the product of the numerators divided by the product of the denominators.*

Examples

1.
$$\frac{ab}{c} \times \frac{a^2b}{2c} = \frac{a^3b^2}{2c^2}$$

2.
$$\frac{3x(x + y)}{2(x - y)} \times \frac{3(x - 2y)}{2y(2x - y)} \times \frac{5x}{4y} = \frac{(3x)(3)(5x)(x + y)(x - 2y)}{(2)(2y)(4y)(x - y)(2x - y)}$$

$$= \frac{45x^2(x^2 - xy - 2y^2)}{16y^2(2x^2 - 3xy + y^2)}$$

$$= \frac{45x^4 - 45x^3y - 90x^2y^2}{32x^2y^2 - 48xy^3 + 16y^4}$$

The process of multiplying two or more fractions and then expressing the product in lowest terms can usually be more easily performed if the members of the fractions are in factored form. It is then possible to determine in advance the factors that will be common to the numerator and denominator of the product. These factors can then be canceled and eliminated from consideration. For example, in performing the indicated multiplication in

$$\frac{(a - 2b)(a + b)}{(a - b)(a + 3b)} \times \frac{(a - b)(a + 5b)}{a - 2b} \times \frac{a + 3b}{(a + b)(a - 3b)}$$

it is obvious that the expressions $a - 2b$, $a + b$, $a - b$, and $a + 3b$ will appear as factors of both the numerator and the denominator of the product. Hence, since they would be divided out in the process of reducing the product to lowest terms, there is no need of writing them in the product at all. Hence we cancel them at the start of the multiplication process and thus simplify the procedure. Cancellation of the same factor from one of the numerators and one of the denominators in an indicated product amounts to replacing each of the canceled expressions by unity. When these operations are applied to the above product, we get

$$\frac{\cancel{(a-2b)}\cancel{(a+b)}}{\cancel{(a-b)}\cancel{(a+3b)}} \times \frac{\cancel{(a-b)}(a+5b)}{\cancel{a-2b}} \times \frac{\cancel{-a+3b}}{\cancel{(a+b)}(a-3b)} = \frac{a+5b}{a-3b}$$

As in the case of reducing to lower terms, the careless application of cancellation can lead to serious errors. We wish to emphasize the fact that cancellation should not be applied until each member of every fraction is factored. Furthermore, the canceled expressions must appear in like pairs, one occurring as a factor of a numerator and the other as a factor of a denominator. It would be an error to cancel $(2x - y)2x$ in

$$\frac{(2x - y)2x}{x - y} \times \frac{x - y}{(2x - y)2x + 3y}$$

since this expression is not a factor of the second denominator. The latter is the *sum* of $(2x - y)2x$ and $3y$.

Example 3

$$\frac{x^2 - 3x + 2}{2x^2 + 3x - 2} \times \frac{2x^2 + 5x - 3}{x^2 - 1} \times \frac{3x^2 + 6x}{2x - 4} = \frac{\cancel{(x-2)}\cancel{(x-1)}}{\cancel{(2x-1)}(x+2)}$$

$$\times \frac{\cancel{(2x-1)}(x+3)}{\cancel{(x-1)}(x+1)} \times \frac{3x\cancel{(x+2)}}{2\cancel{(x-2)}}$$

$$= \frac{3x(x+3)}{2(x+1)}$$

Frequently the factors that can be canceled are more easily seen if terms in the members of the fractions are rearranged and allowable changes are made in signs.

Example 4

In the problem

$$\frac{a + 2b}{a^2 - b^2} \times \frac{2b - a}{b - a} \times \frac{a + b}{4b^2 - a^2}$$

the terms involving a are positive in some places and negative in others. However, if we change all signs in both members of the second fraction, change the sign before the third fraction and both signs in the denominator, and at the same time rearrange the terms, we have

$$\frac{a+2b}{a^2-b^2} \times \frac{a-2b}{a-b} \times -\frac{a+b}{a^2-4b^2} = \frac{\cancel{a+2b}}{(a-b)\cancel{(a+b)}} \times \frac{\cancel{a-2b}}{a-b}$$

$$\times -\frac{\cancel{a+b}}{\cancel{(a-2b)}\cancel{(a+2b)}}$$

$$= -\frac{1}{(a-b)^2}$$

It should be noted that the cancellation replaces each numerator by one, so the numerator in the product is *one*, not zero.

22. *Division of fractions.* In arithmetic, the method given, usually without justification, for obtaining the quotient of two fractions was "invert the terms of the divisor and multiply." For example, $\frac{3}{4} \div \frac{2}{3} = \frac{3}{4} \times \frac{3}{2} = \frac{9}{8}$. This process depends upon the fact that if the dividend and divisor are multiplied by the same nonzero quantity, the quotient is not changed. Hence,

$$\frac{a}{b} \div \frac{c}{d} = \left(\frac{a}{b} \times \frac{d}{c}\right) \div \left(\frac{c}{d} \times \frac{d}{c}\right)$$

$$= \frac{a}{b} \times \frac{d}{c} = \frac{ad}{bc} \quad \left(\text{since } \frac{c}{d} \times \frac{d}{c} = 1\right)$$

We use the same procedure for dividing fractions in algebra, and thus reduce the division process to multiplication.

Example 1

$$\frac{x^2-3x+2}{2x^2-7x+3} \div \frac{x^2-x-2}{2x^2+3x-2} = \frac{x^2-3x+2}{2x^2-7x+3} \times \frac{2x^2+3x-2}{x^2-x-2}$$

$$= \frac{\cancel{(x-2)}(x-1)}{\cancel{(2x-1)}(x-3)} \times \frac{\cancel{(2x-1)}(x+2)}{\cancel{(x-2)}(x+1)}$$

$$= \frac{(x-1)(x+2)}{(x-3)(x+1)}$$

EXERCISE 9

Perform the operations indicated in the following problems.

1. $\dfrac{3a}{2b} \times \dfrac{4ab}{9c} \times \dfrac{3c^2}{4a^2}$.

2. $\dfrac{7y}{12x^2} \times \dfrac{10xy^2}{3z} \times \dfrac{6xz^2}{5y}$.

3. $\dfrac{14u^2}{5v} \times \dfrac{10v^2}{21vw} \times \dfrac{9w^2}{8u^2v}$.

4. $\dfrac{16rs}{7t^2} \times \dfrac{35t}{8r^2} \times \dfrac{4r}{15s^2}$.

5. $\dfrac{25a^2b^2}{12c^2} \times \dfrac{36bc^3}{5a^3} \div \dfrac{15b^3}{7ac}$.

6. $\dfrac{12pq}{r} \times \dfrac{35r^2p^3}{16q^2} \div \dfrac{7p^4}{24q^3}$.

7. $\dfrac{28b^3}{15c^2d^2} \times \dfrac{18d^3}{35b^5} \div \dfrac{21d^4}{25b^2c^3}$.

8. $\dfrac{24x^2y^3}{39z^2} \times \dfrac{25x^3z^3}{18y^4} \div \dfrac{15x^4}{26y^2z^2}$.

9. $\left(\dfrac{7a^2b^3c}{5x^3yz^5}\right)\left(\dfrac{15x^5y^2z^4}{28a^3b^4c}\right).$

10. $\left(\dfrac{12m^2n^3p^5}{25s^8t^2u^6}\right)\left(\dfrac{50s^6t^7u^5}{30mn^2p^3}\right).$

11. $\left(\dfrac{9a^2b^3}{4b^2c^4}\right)\left(\dfrac{20c^2d^4}{18a^3d^2}\right)\left(\dfrac{4b^3c^5}{5c^7d^3}\right).$

12. $\left(\dfrac{36a^2c^7}{5b^3d^8}\right)\left(\dfrac{15b^5d^4}{42a^3c^2}\right)\left(\dfrac{14a^4d^3}{18b^2c^3}\right).$

13. $\dfrac{5a - 5b}{3a + 6b} \times \dfrac{a + 2b}{a - b}.$

14. $\dfrac{4x - 2y}{5x + 10y} \times \dfrac{x^2 + 2xy}{2xy - y^2}.$

15. $\dfrac{8h + 20k}{h^2 - 3hk} \times \dfrac{hk - 3k^2}{12h + 30k}.$

16. $\dfrac{3wz - 7z^2}{w^2 + 5wz} \times \dfrac{3w + 15z}{12w - 28z}.$

17. $\dfrac{4a^2 - b^2}{a + 2b} \div (4a^2 - 2ab).$

18. $\dfrac{x^2 - 9y^2}{2x} \div 3y(x + 3y).$

19. $(3b^2 + bc - 2c^2) \div \dfrac{9b^2 - 4c^2}{2c}.$

20. $(20u^2 - 7uv - 6v^2) \div \dfrac{16u^2 - 9v^2}{3uv}.$

21. $\dfrac{2a(a + b)^2}{3b^3} \times \dfrac{b^2(a - b)}{8a^3(a + b)} \times \dfrac{12a^2b^2}{a^2 - b^2}.$

22. $\dfrac{3x^2y}{x + 2y} \times \dfrac{4y(x + 2y)^2}{3x(2x - y)} \times \dfrac{(2x - y)^2}{8xy^2(x + 2y)}.$

23. $\dfrac{4c^2(3c - 5d)}{5d^3} \times \dfrac{15c^3d^4}{8(3c - 5d)(3c + 5d)} \times \dfrac{(3c + 5d)^2}{12c^4d^2}.$

24. $\dfrac{24q^2(2p + 3q)^2}{5p^3} \times \dfrac{10p^5}{9q^3(4p^2 - 9q^2)} \times \dfrac{(2p - 3q)6q^4}{p^4}.$

25. $\dfrac{x - y}{x + y} \times \dfrac{x^2 + xy}{x^2y^2 - xy^3} \times \dfrac{y}{x^2}.$

26. $\dfrac{a^2b - ab^2}{a + b} \times \dfrac{a^2 - b^2}{ab^2 - b^3} \times \dfrac{b^2}{a^2}.$

27. $\dfrac{p^2 - q^2}{pq^2} \times \dfrac{p^2}{pq + q^2} \times \dfrac{q^4}{p^2 - pq}.$

28. $\dfrac{c^3 + dc^2}{c^2 + d^2} \times \dfrac{bc^2 + bd^2}{c^2 - d^2} \times \dfrac{c - d}{bc}.$

29. $\dfrac{u^2 - 2u}{v^2 - v} \times \dfrac{uv^2 - uv}{u^2 - 4} \div \dfrac{u^2}{u + 2}.$

30. $\dfrac{x^2y - xy}{y^2 - 1} \times \dfrac{y^3 + y^2}{x^3 - x^2} \div \dfrac{y^2}{y - 1}.$

31. $\dfrac{a^3 - 3a^2}{b^2 + 2b} \times \dfrac{b^2 - 4}{a^2b - 3ab} \div \dfrac{ab - 2a}{b^2}.$

32. $\dfrac{h^2 - 9}{k^2 - 9k} \times \dfrac{hk - 9h}{hk + 3k} \div \dfrac{h^3 - 3h^2}{k^3}.$

33. $\left(\dfrac{2x^2 - 5x + 2}{3x^2 - 8x - 3}\right)\left(\dfrac{3x^2 + 4x + 1}{x^2 - 3x + 2}\right).$

34. $\left(\dfrac{2y^2 - 3y - 9}{2y^2 - 5y - 3}\right)\left(\dfrac{y^2 + 4y + 4}{4y^2 + 4y - 3}\right).$

35. $\left(\dfrac{a^2 - ab - 2b^2}{2a^2 + 3ab - 2b^2}\right)\left(\dfrac{a^2 + ab - 2b^2}{2a^2 - 3ab - 2b^2}\right).$

36. $\left(\dfrac{4x^2 + xy - 3y^2}{4x^2 + 8xy - 5y^2}\right)\left(\dfrac{6x^2 + 17xy + 5y^2}{4x^2 + 5xy - 6y^2}\right).$

37. $\dfrac{a^2 + ab - 2b^2}{a^2 + 2ab + b^2} \times \dfrac{a^2 - b^2}{a^2 - 4b^2} \times \dfrac{a + b}{a - b}.$

38. $\dfrac{2u^2 + 3uv - 2v^2}{u^2 - v^2} \times \dfrac{2u^2 + uv - v^2}{u^2 + uv - 2v^2} \times \dfrac{u - v}{2u - v}.$

39. $\dfrac{r - s}{r + 2s} \times \dfrac{2r^2 + 5rs + 2s^2}{2r^2 - 5rs + 2s^2} \times \dfrac{r^2 - rs - 2s^2}{2r^2 - rs - s^2}.$

40. $\dfrac{2b^2 - bc - 3c^2}{2b^2 + bc - c^2} \times \dfrac{2b^2 - 3bc + c^2}{2b^2 - 5bc + 3c^2} \times \dfrac{b - c}{2b + c}.$

41. $\dfrac{x^3 + y^3}{x^2 + xy + y^2} \times \dfrac{x^2 + y^2}{x^2 - y^2} \div \dfrac{x^2 - xy + y^2}{x^3 - y^3}.$

42. $\dfrac{a^4 - b^4}{a^6 - b^6} \times \dfrac{a^2 + ab + b^2}{a^2 + b^2} \div \dfrac{a^2 - b^2}{a^2 - ab + b^2}.$

43. $\dfrac{u^2 - v^2}{u^2 - uv + v^2} \times \dfrac{u^3 + v^3}{u^2 - 2uv + v^2} \div \dfrac{2u^2 + uv - v^2}{u^2 + uv - 2v^2}.$

44. $\dfrac{y^6 - 1}{y^4 - 1} \times \dfrac{y^4 + 2y^2 + 1}{y^8 - 1} \div \dfrac{y^4 + y^2 + 1}{y^4 + 1}.$

45. $\dfrac{(a + 2)a + 1}{(a - 2)a + 1} \times \dfrac{a^2 - 1}{(a + 1)^2}$ **46.** $\dfrac{(x - 4)x + 4}{(x - 4)x + 3} \times \dfrac{(x - 4)(x + 3)}{x^2 + x - 6}.$

47. $\dfrac{(y - 2)y + 1}{(y - 1)(y + 1)} \times \dfrac{(y^2 - 1) - 3(y - 1)}{(y - 2)(y + 1)}.$

48. $\dfrac{(z - 1)z - 2}{z^2 - 4} \times \dfrac{z^2 + (z - 2)}{(z - 1)(z - 2)}.$

49. $\dfrac{(w - 2)w - 3}{w^2 - 9} \times \dfrac{w(w - 2) + 3(w - 2)}{(w - 2)(w - 3)} \div \dfrac{w + 1}{w - 3}.$

50. $\dfrac{(2b - 3)b - 2}{(2b - 3)(b + 1)} \times \dfrac{2b(b + 1) + (b + 1)}{2(b + 1)(b - 1) - 3b} \div \dfrac{2b + 1}{(2b + 1) - 4}.$

51. $\dfrac{(2c + 1)c - 3}{(2c - 1)c - 3} \times \dfrac{(2c - 1)c + (2c - 1)}{(2c - 1)c - 1} \div \dfrac{(2c - 1) + 4}{2(c - 1) - 1}.$

52. $\dfrac{(3d - 5)d - 2}{(3d + 4)3d - 5} \times \dfrac{(3d - 5)3d + 4}{(3d + 5)d + 2} \div \dfrac{(d - 2)(3d - 4)}{(3d - 5)d + 2}.$

23. The lowest common multiple. *The lowest common multiple (L.C.M.) of a set of polynomials is the polynomial of lowest degree[1] with the least integral coefficients which is exactly divisible by each polynomial of the set.*

Examples

1. The L.C.M. of $3x$, $4x^2y$, $8x^5y^2$, and $36x^4$ is $72x^5y^2$.
2. The L.C.M. of $2(x - y)$, $3(x + y)$, and $(x - y)^2$ is $6(x - y)^2(x + y)$.

If the given polynomials are in factored form, then from the definition we see that the factored form of the L.C.M. must satisfy the following requirements:

1. Every factor of each polynomial must appear as a factor of the L.C.M. Furthermore, each factor in the L.C.M. must be

---

[1] The degree of a polynomial is the largest of the numbers obtained by adding the exponents of the letters appearing in the separate terms. For example, the degree of $2x^3 - 3x^2 + 4x$ is 3, and the degree of $3x^2y^2 - 2xy + 3y^2$ is 4.

raised to a power *equal* to the largest power that this factor has in any one of the given factored polynomials.

2. The L.C.M. can have no factor that does not appear in one of the factored polynomials.

Hence, we have the following method for obtaining the L.C.M. of a set of polynomials:

1. *Factor each of the polynomials.*

2. *Write in the L.C.M. each of the **different** prime[1] factors of the polynomials, and then raise each factor to the highest power that it has in any one of the factored polynomials.*

Example 3

Find the L.C.M. of $x^2 - 2xy + y^2$, $x^2 + 2xy + y^2$, $x^2 - y^2$, $x^2 - 3xy + 2y^2$, and $2x^2 + 3xy + y^2$.

Solution

We first write each of these polynomials in the factored form shown below.

$$x^2 - 2xy + y^2 = (x - y)^2$$
$$x^2 + 2xy + y^2 = (x + y)^2$$
$$x^2 - y^2 = (x - y)(x + y)$$
$$x^2 - 3xy + 2y^2 = (x - 2y)(x - y)$$
$$2x^2 + 3xy + y^2 = (2x + y)(x + y)$$

The prime factors which appear above are $(x - y)$, $(x + y)$, $(x - 2y)$, and $(2x + y)$. However, $(x - y)$ and $(x + y)$ have exponents 2 in the first and second polynomials, respectively. Hence, the L.C.M. is $(x - y)^2(x + y)^2$ $(x - 2y)(2x + y)$.

24. The addition of fractions. *The sum of two or more fractions that have the same denominator is a fraction that has the common denominator as its denominator and the sum of the numerators as its numerator.*

Examples

1. $$\frac{2}{7} + \frac{6}{7} - \frac{3}{7} = \frac{2 + 6 - 3}{7} = \frac{5}{7}$$

2. $$\frac{2a}{a - b} - \frac{6b}{a - b} + \frac{a + 2b}{a - b} = \frac{2a - 6b + (a + 2b)}{a - b}$$
$$= \frac{2a - 6b + a + 2b}{a - b}$$
$$= \frac{3a - 4b}{a - b}$$

---

[1] A prime number is a number that has no factors except itself and one.

If the fractions to be added have different denominators, we first find the L.C.M. of the denominators. Then we change each fraction, by a method to be explained later, to an equivalent fraction which has this L.C.M. as a denominator. Then we proceed as in the above examples. The L.C.M. of the denominators is called the *least common denominator* (L.C.D.).

Example 1

In order to find the sum indicated by

$$\frac{x^2 - 2xy}{3(x^2 - y^2)} + \frac{y}{6x - 6y} - \frac{x}{4(x + y)}$$

we first factor the denominators and obtain

$$\frac{x^2 - 2xy}{3(x + y)(x - y)} + \frac{y}{6(x - y)} - \frac{x}{4(x + y)}$$

It is now obvious that the L.C.M. of the denominators is $12(x - y)(x + y)$. The next step is to convert each of the above fractions into an equivalent fraction that has the above L.C.M. as a denominator. This conversion is made by multiplying the first fraction by $\frac{4}{4}$, the second by $2(x + y)/2(x + y)$, and the third by $3(x - y)/3(x - y)$. Thus we obtain

$$\frac{x^2 - 2xy}{3(x + y)(x - y)} + \frac{y}{6(x - y)} - \frac{x}{4(x + y)}$$

$$= \left[\frac{x^2 - 2xy}{3(x + y)(x - y)}\right]\left(\frac{4}{4}\right) + \left[\frac{y}{6(x - y)}\right]\left[\frac{2(x + y)}{2(x + y)}\right] - \left[\frac{x}{4(x + y)}\right]\left[\frac{3(x - y)}{3(x - y)}\right]$$

$$= \frac{4(x^2 - 2xy)}{12(x + y)(x - y)} + \frac{2y(x + y)}{12(x + y)(x - y)} - \frac{3x(x - y)}{12(x + y)(x - y)}$$

$$= \frac{4(x^2 - 2xy) + 2y(x + y) - 3x(x - y)}{12(x + y)(x - y)}$$

$$= \frac{4x^2 - 8xy + 2xy + 2y^2 - 3x^2 + 3xy}{12(x + y)(x - y)}$$

$$= \frac{x^2 - 3xy + 2y^2}{12(x + y)(x - y)}$$

$$= \frac{(x - 2y)(x - y)}{12(x + y)(x - y)}$$

$$= \frac{x - 2y}{12(x + y)}$$

The process of adding fractions illustrated in the above example consists of the following steps.

1. *Factor each denominator.*

2. *Find the least common denominator.*

3. *Multiply the two members of each fraction by the quotient of the L.C.D. and the denominator of the fraction under consideration.*

4. *Combine the numerators obtained in step 3, using with each the sign before the fraction from which it was obtained. Then write the result thus obtained over the L.C.D.*

After some practice, steps 3 and 4 can be combined as in the following example.

Example 2

Combine into a single fraction

$$\frac{3x - y}{(x - y)(x + y)} - \frac{x + 3y}{(x + y)(x + 2y)} - \frac{1}{x + 2y}$$

Solution

The denominators are given in factored form, and it is evident that the L.C.D. is $(x - y)(x + y)(x + 2y)$. The quotients of the L.C.D. and the denominators are $x + 2y$, $x - y$, and $(x + y)(x - y)$ respectively. Now we multiply each numerator and denominator by the quotient required in step 3, and combine the products as required by step 4. The computation thus described follows.

$$\frac{3x - y}{(x - y)(x + y)} - \frac{x + 3y}{(x + y)(x + 2y)} - \frac{1}{x + 2y}$$
$$= \frac{(3x - y)(x + 2y) - (x + 3y)(x - y) - (x + y)(x - y)}{(x - y)(x + y)(x + 2y)}$$
$$= \frac{3x^2 + 5xy - 2y^2 - (x^2 + 2xy - 3y^2) - (x^2 - y^2)}{(x - y)(x + y)(x + 2y)}$$
$$= \frac{3x^2 + 5xy - 2y^2 - x^2 - 2xy + 3y^2 - x^2 + y^2}{(x - y)(x + y)(x + 2y)}$$
$$= \frac{x^2 + 3xy + 2y^2}{(x - y)(x + y)(x + 2y)}$$
$$= \frac{\cancel{(x + y)}\cancel{(x + 2y)}}{(x - y)\cancel{(x + y)}\cancel{(x + 2y)}}$$
$$= \frac{1}{x - y}$$

A convenient check on the above computation consists of assigning a numerical value to x and to y. The result obtained by adding the numerical fractions thus obtained must be equal to the numerical value of the sum. Care should be taken not to assign values for which any one of the denominators is zero. (Why?) If we let $x = 1$, and $y = 2$, we have

$$\frac{3(1) - 2}{(1 - 2)(1 + 2)} - \frac{1 + 3(2)}{(1 + 2)[1 + 2(2)]} - \frac{1}{1 + 2(2)} = \frac{1}{-3} - \frac{7}{15} - \frac{1}{5}$$
$$= \frac{-5 - 7 - 3}{15}$$
$$= \frac{-15}{15}$$
$$= -1$$

When $x = 1$ and $y = 2$, the value of the sum $1/(x - y)$ is $1/(1 - 2) = -1$. Since the two results are equal, the computation appears to be correct.

Since most of the work in adding fractions occurs in finding the new numerators and combining them, the student may forget to carry the denominator along and finally lose it. This is a serious error, and care should be taken to avoid it.

EXERCISE 10

In each of Problems 1 to 8, change the fraction into an equivalent fraction that has the expression at the right in the problem as a denominator.

1. $\dfrac{3x}{4y}$, $12x^2y^2$.

2. $\dfrac{5a^2}{3bc}$, $15ab^2c^2$.

3. $\dfrac{7uv}{5w^2}$, $20u^2v^3w^4$.

4. $\dfrac{4r}{9s^2t^3}$, $27r^2s^2t^5$.

5. $\dfrac{3}{x - 2}$, $(x - 2)(x + 3)$.

6. $\dfrac{2a}{3a - 1}$, $(3a - 1)(2a + 3)$.

7. $\dfrac{3x + 2y}{2x - 3y}$, $4x^2 - 9y^2$.

8. $\dfrac{3a + 4b}{5a - 2b}$, $15a^2 + 26ab + 8b^2$.

In each of Problems 9 to 16 find the L.C.M. of the denominators, then reduce the fractions to an equivalent set of fractions having the L.C.M. as a common denominator.

9. $\dfrac{2a}{36c}$, $\dfrac{4b^2}{9c^2}$, $\dfrac{5c^3}{12a^2c^3}$.

10. $\dfrac{4x}{9y^2z}$, $\dfrac{5y}{12xz^2}$, $\dfrac{8z}{15x^2y}$.

11. $\dfrac{3}{8rst}$, $\dfrac{5t^3}{12r^2s}$, $\dfrac{7r^2}{18s^3t^2}$.

12. $\dfrac{5w^2}{12u^2v}$, $\dfrac{7v^2}{24uw^2}$, $\dfrac{8u^2}{27v^2w}$.

13. $\dfrac{3}{x - 2}$, $\dfrac{2x}{x + 2}$, $\dfrac{4x^2}{x^2 - 4}$.

14. $\dfrac{a}{a^2 - b^2}$, $\dfrac{a - b}{(a + b)^2}$, $\dfrac{a + b}{(a - b)^2}$.

15. $\dfrac{x - y}{(x + y)(x - 2y)}$, $\dfrac{x - 2y}{(x + y)(x - y)}$, $\dfrac{x + y}{(x - y)(x - 2y)}$.

16. $\dfrac{2u + v}{4u^2 - 9v^2}$, $\dfrac{2u - 3v}{4u^2 + 8uv + 3v^2}$, $\dfrac{2u + 3v}{4u^2 - 4uv - 3v^2}$.

Perform the operations indicated in the following problems and simplify the result.

17. $\frac{3}{4} + \frac{5}{6} - \frac{2}{3}$.

18. $\frac{2}{3} + \frac{5}{7} - \frac{1}{2}$.

19. $\frac{3}{4} - \frac{4}{9} - \frac{5}{12}$.

20. $\frac{5}{4} - \frac{11}{12} + \frac{5}{18}$.

21. $\dfrac{5a}{12bc} + \dfrac{4b}{9ac} - \dfrac{3c}{16ab}$.

22. $\dfrac{3yz}{4x^2} - \dfrac{5}{8xyz} - \dfrac{7x}{36yz^2}$.

23. $\dfrac{2u}{9v^2} - \dfrac{5v}{18u^2} + \dfrac{u^2}{12v^3}$.

24. $\dfrac{4c}{5a^2b} + \dfrac{3b}{10ac^2} - \dfrac{5a}{6b^2c}$.

25. $\dfrac{2}{3b} + \dfrac{3}{2a} + \dfrac{2a - 3b}{2ab}.$

26. $\dfrac{1}{6y} + \dfrac{1}{3x} - \dfrac{2x + 3y}{12xy}.$

27. $\dfrac{u}{9} - \dfrac{v}{2} - \dfrac{4u - 9v}{18}.$

28. $\dfrac{h}{10k} - \dfrac{2h^2 - 5k^2}{20hk} - \dfrac{k}{12h}$

29. $\dfrac{a + b}{ab} - \dfrac{a}{b(a + b)} - \dfrac{1}{a}.$

30. $\dfrac{x}{x - y} - \dfrac{y^2}{x(x - y)} - \dfrac{y}{x}.$

31. $\dfrac{u^2}{v(u - v)} - \dfrac{v}{u - v} - 1.$

32. $\dfrac{h^2 - k^2}{hk} + \dfrac{h^2 + k^2}{h(h + k)} - \dfrac{h}{k}.$

33. $\dfrac{2a}{a^2 - b^2} - \dfrac{b}{a(a - b)} - \dfrac{1}{a + b}.$

34. $\dfrac{4x^2}{y(2x + y)} + \dfrac{y^2 + 4x^2}{4x^2 - y^2} - \dfrac{2x}{y}.$

35. $\dfrac{3u + v}{u^2 - v^2} - \dfrac{2v}{u(u - v)} - \dfrac{1}{u + v}.$

36. $\dfrac{h^2}{2k(h - 2k)} - \dfrac{4hk}{h^2 - 4k^2} - \dfrac{h}{2k}.$

37. $\dfrac{24uv}{4u^2 - 9v^2} - \dfrac{10uv}{(u + v)(2u - 3v)} + \dfrac{2u - 3v}{2u + 3v}$

38. $\dfrac{5a^2 - 2ab}{(a - b)(2a + b)} + \dfrac{6ab}{4a^2 - b^2} - \dfrac{2a - b}{a - b}.$

39. $\dfrac{3y^2 - 11xy}{(2x - y)(x + 2y)} + \dfrac{10xy}{x^2 - 4y^2} + \dfrac{4x - y}{2x - y}.$

40. $\dfrac{4rs + 4s^2}{(2r - s)(2r - 3s)} - \dfrac{15rs}{(r + 3s)(2r - 3s)} + \dfrac{4r + s}{2r - s}.$

41. $\dfrac{x^2 - 3xy}{(x - y)(x - 2y)} - \dfrac{4xy}{(x + y)(x - y)} + \dfrac{3xy}{(x + y)(x - 2y)}.$

42. $\dfrac{-3a^2}{(a - b)(2a + b)} + \dfrac{2a^2}{(a + b)(a - b)} + \dfrac{5a^2 + 3ab}{(a + b)(2a + b)}.$

43. $\dfrac{10uv}{(2u + 3v)(u - v)} + \dfrac{2uv}{(2u - 3v)(u - v)} + \dfrac{4u^2 - 18uv}{(2u + 3v)(2u - 3v)}.$

44. $\dfrac{2ab}{(2a - b)(a - b)} - \dfrac{6ab}{(a + 2b)(a - b)} + \dfrac{4a^2 + 8ab}{(2a - b)(a + 2b)}.$

45. $\dfrac{x + z}{(x - y)(y - z)} - \dfrac{y - z}{(x - y)(z - x)} + \dfrac{x - y}{(z - x)(y - z)}.$

46. $\dfrac{2}{x^3 - 1} - \dfrac{x^2 - x + 1}{x - 1} + \dfrac{x + 1}{x^2 + x + 1}.$

47. $\dfrac{4}{x^4 + x^2 + 1} + \dfrac{x^2 + x - 1}{x^2 - x + 1} - \dfrac{x^2 - x - 1}{x^2 + x + 1}.$

48. $\dfrac{a^2 + b^2}{(a + b)(2a + 3b)} - \dfrac{a^2 - 11b^2}{(a + b)(2a - 3b)} + \dfrac{10ab - 24b^2}{(2a + 3b)(2a - 3b)}.$

49. $\dfrac{x^2}{x^2 + 1} + \dfrac{1}{x - 1} - \dfrac{4x^2}{x^4 - 1} - \dfrac{x^2 - x}{(x + 1)(x^2 + 1)}.$

50. $\dfrac{2a}{a^2 - b^2} - \dfrac{4ab}{(a + b)^2(a - b)} - \dfrac{a - b}{(a + b)^2}.$

51. $\dfrac{2x^3}{x^4 + x^2y^2 + y^4} + \dfrac{2y^2}{x^3 + y^3} - \dfrac{x + y}{x^2 + xy + y^2} - \dfrac{x^2 + y^2}{x^3 - y^3}.$

52. $\dfrac{2a^2 + 2b^2}{a^2 - b^2} + \dfrac{a^2 + 5ab + 2b^2}{2a^2 + 3ab + b^2} + \dfrac{b^2 - ab - 3a^2}{2a^2 - ab - b^2}.$

25. Complex fractions. *If the numerator or the denominator of a fraction, or both, contain fractions, it is called a* **complex fraction.**

Examples

1. $\dfrac{3}{\frac{2}{5}}.$

2. $\dfrac{1 + \dfrac{x}{y}}{x + y}.$

3. $\dfrac{\dfrac{4x}{x + y} + \dfrac{2y}{x - y}}{3 - \dfrac{x^2 + y^2}{x^2 - y^2}}.$

There are two methods for reducing a complex fraction to a simple fraction. The first consists of *multiplying the numerator and denominator of the complex fraction by the L.C.M. of every denominator that appears in it.*

Example 1

In order to reduce

$$\dfrac{1 + \dfrac{x}{y}}{x + y}$$

to a simple fraction, we note that the denominators of 1 and $x + y$ are 1. Hence the L.C.M. of the denominators in the complex fraction is y. Therefore we multiply the numerator and the denominator by y and get

$$\dfrac{1 + \dfrac{x}{y}}{x + y} = \dfrac{y\left(1 + \dfrac{x}{y}\right)}{y(x + y)} = \dfrac{y + x}{xy + y^2} = \dfrac{y + x}{y(x + y)} = \dfrac{1}{y}.$$

Example 2

In the complex fraction

$$\dfrac{\dfrac{2}{x + y} - \dfrac{1}{x - y}}{\dfrac{4(x - y)}{x + y} - \dfrac{x + y}{x - y}}$$

the L.C.M. of the denominators is $x^2 - y^2$, and the steps in the simplification are those given below.

$$\frac{\dfrac{2}{x+y} - \dfrac{1}{x-y}}{\dfrac{4(x-y)}{x+y} - \dfrac{x+y}{x-y}} = \frac{\dfrac{2}{x+y} - \dfrac{1}{x-y}}{\dfrac{4(x-y)}{x+y} - \dfrac{x+y}{x-y}} \times \frac{x^2 - y^2}{x^2 - y^2}$$

$$= \frac{\dfrac{2}{x+y}(x^2 - y^2) - \dfrac{1}{x-y}(x^2 - y^2)}{\dfrac{4(x-y)}{x+y}(x^2 - y^2) - \dfrac{x+y}{x-y}(x^2 - y^2)}$$

$$= \frac{2(x-y) - (x+y)}{4(x-y)(x-y) - (x+y)(x+y)}$$

$$= \frac{2x - 2y - x - y}{4(x^2 - 2xy + y^2) - (x^2 + 2xy + y^2)}$$

$$= \frac{x - 3y}{4x^2 - 8xy + 4y^2 - x^2 - 2xy - y^2}$$

$$= \frac{x - 3y}{3x^2 - 10xy + 3y^2}$$

$$= \frac{x - 3y}{(3x - y)(x - 3y)}$$

$$= \frac{1}{3x - y}$$

If the expressions in the complex fraction are complicated, it is sometimes easier to reduce the numerator and the denominator to simple fractions and then proceed as in division.

Example 3

$$\frac{\dfrac{x-y}{x+y} - \dfrac{x+y}{x-y}}{1 - \dfrac{x^2 - xy - y^2}{x^2 - y^2}} = \frac{\dfrac{(x-y)^2 - (x+y)^2}{(x+y)(x-y)}}{\dfrac{x^2 - y^2 - (x^2 - xy - y^2)}{x^2 - y^2}}$$

$$= \frac{\dfrac{x^2 - 2xy + y^2 - x^2 - 2xy - y^2}{x^2 - y^2}}{\dfrac{x^2 - y^2 - x^2 + xy + y^2}{x^2 - y^2}}$$

$$= \frac{\dfrac{-4xy}{x^2 - y^2}}{\dfrac{xy}{x^2 - y^2}}$$

$$= \frac{-4xy}{x^2 - y^2} \times \frac{x^2 - y^2}{xy}$$

$$= -4$$

If the numerator or denominator of a complex fraction, or both, are complex fractions, each must be reduced to a simple fraction as the first step in the simplification.

Example 4

$$\frac{1 + \dfrac{1}{1 + \dfrac{1}{x-1}}}{1 - \dfrac{1}{x+1}} = \frac{1 + \dfrac{x-1}{x-1+1}}{\dfrac{x+1-1}{x+1}}$$

(multiplying both members of the complex fraction in the numerator by $x - 1$, and both members of the denominator by $x + 1$)

$$= \frac{1 + \dfrac{x-1}{x}}{\dfrac{x+1}{x}}$$

$$= \frac{x + x - 1}{x + 1}$$

(multiplying the numerator and the denominator by x)

$$= \frac{2x - 1}{x + 1}$$

EXERCISE 11

Reduce the following complex fractions to simple fractions.

1. $\dfrac{1 + \frac{1}{2}}{2 - \frac{1}{2}}.$

2. $\dfrac{2 + \frac{1}{3}}{3 - \frac{2}{3}}.$

3. $\dfrac{4 + \frac{2}{5}}{1 + \frac{2}{3} - \frac{1}{5}}.$

4. $\dfrac{6 - \frac{3}{7}}{2 + \frac{5}{7} + \frac{1}{14}}.$

5. $\dfrac{1 - \dfrac{1}{x}}{\dfrac{1}{x}}.$

6. $\dfrac{1 - \dfrac{1}{x^2}}{1 + \dfrac{1}{x}}.$

7. $\dfrac{2 + \dfrac{1}{x}}{4 - \dfrac{1}{x^2}}.$

8. $\dfrac{3 + \dfrac{5}{x} - \dfrac{2}{x^2}}{1 - \dfrac{4}{x^2}}.$

9. $\dfrac{\dfrac{3}{b} + \dfrac{2}{a}}{\dfrac{3}{2c} + \dfrac{b}{ac}}.$

10. $\dfrac{\dfrac{4}{3z} + \dfrac{8}{9y}}{1 + \dfrac{2z}{3y}}.$

11. $\dfrac{3r - \dfrac{4s^2}{3r}}{1 + \dfrac{3r}{2s}}.$

12. $\dfrac{3a - \dfrac{4}{b}}{9b^2 - \dfrac{16}{a^2}}.$

13. $\dfrac{1 + \dfrac{3b}{a - 2b}}{1 + \dfrac{b}{a - 2b}}.$

14. $\dfrac{a + 1 + \dfrac{a+1}{a-1}}{a - \dfrac{2}{a-1}}.$

15. $\dfrac{1 + \dfrac{y}{x+y}}{1 + \dfrac{3y}{x-y}}.$

16. $\dfrac{2 - \dfrac{d}{c+2d}}{2 + \dfrac{7d}{c-2d}}.$

17. $\dfrac{3 + \dfrac{4}{x-1}}{\dfrac{x}{x+1} - \dfrac{x+1}{x-1}}.$

18. $\dfrac{1 - \dfrac{x}{x+2}}{\dfrac{-2x}{x+1} + \dfrac{2x+3}{x+2}}.$

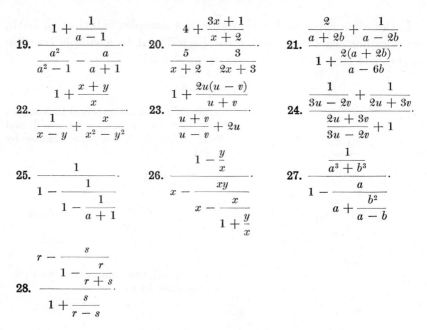

19. $\dfrac{1 + \dfrac{1}{a-1}}{\dfrac{a^2}{a^2-1} - \dfrac{a}{a+1}}.$

20. $\dfrac{4 + \dfrac{3x+1}{x+2}}{\dfrac{5}{x+2} - \dfrac{3}{2x+3}}.$

21. $\dfrac{\dfrac{2}{a+2b} + \dfrac{1}{a-2b}}{1 + \dfrac{2(a+2b)}{a-6b}}.$

22. $\dfrac{1 + \dfrac{x+y}{x}}{\dfrac{1}{x-y} + \dfrac{x}{x^2-y^2}}.$

23. $\dfrac{1 + \dfrac{2u(u-v)}{u+v}}{\dfrac{u+v}{u-v} + 2u}.$

24. $\dfrac{\dfrac{1}{3u-2v} + \dfrac{1}{2u+3v}}{\dfrac{2u+3v}{3u-2v} + 1}.$

25. $\dfrac{1}{1 - \dfrac{1}{1 - \dfrac{1}{a+1}}}.$

26. $\dfrac{1 - \dfrac{y}{x}}{x - \dfrac{xy}{x - \dfrac{x}{1 + \dfrac{y}{x}}}}.$

27. $\dfrac{\dfrac{1}{a^3+b^3}}{1 - \dfrac{a}{a + \dfrac{b^2}{a-b}}}.$

28. $\dfrac{r - \dfrac{s}{1 - \dfrac{r}{r+s}}}{1 + \dfrac{s}{r-s}}.$

SUPPLEMENTARY PROBLEMS

Reduce the fractions in Problems 1 to 24 to lowest terms.

1. $\dfrac{210a^2b^3}{140a^3b^2}.$

2. $\dfrac{216x^3y^4z^6}{120xy^7z^4}.$

3. $\dfrac{252r^3s^5t^6}{42r^4s^7t^2}.$

4. $\dfrac{480h^7d^4k^2}{420h^5j^6k^4}.$

5. $\dfrac{x^2+xy}{xy+y^2}.$

6. $\dfrac{abc+a^2b^2}{c^2+abc}.$

7. $\dfrac{rs^2t - t^2s}{rst^2 - t^3}.$

8. $\dfrac{x^4y + x^3y^2 + x^2y^3}{x^3y^2 + x^2y^3 + xy^3}.$

9. $\dfrac{x^2y - xy^2}{x^3 - xy^2}.$

10. $\dfrac{a^4 - a^2b^2}{a^4b + a^3b^2}.$

11. $\dfrac{p^3qr - pq^3r}{p^3q - p^2q^2}.$

12. $\dfrac{u^3v^2w + u^2v^3w^2}{u^3v^2w - uv^4w^3}.$

13. $\dfrac{x^2 + 3xy - 10y^2}{x^2 + 2xy - 8y^2}.$

14. $\dfrac{a^2 + 2ab - 3b^2}{a^2 + ab - 6b^2}.$

15. $\dfrac{2c^2 - cd - 3d^2}{2c^2 - 5cd + 3d^2}.$

16. $\dfrac{2r^2 + 2rs - 15s^2}{r^2 - 2rs - 3s^2}.$

17. $\dfrac{as - 6bt + 2at - 3bs}{2as - 2bt + 4at - bs}.$

18. $\dfrac{2xy - 2sx + bs - by}{-4xy - 2sx + bs + 2by}.$

19. $\dfrac{x^3y^2 - x^2y^3}{x^3 - y^3}.$

20. $\dfrac{x^3y - x^2y^2 + xy^3}{x^4y + xy^4}.$

21. $\dfrac{a^2 - b^2}{a^3 - b^3}.$

22. $\dfrac{c^2 - 4d^2}{c^3 + 8d^3}.$

23. $\dfrac{r^4 - s^4}{r^6 - s^6}.$

24. $\dfrac{a^4 + b^4}{a^8 - b^8}.$

Perform the operations indicated in Problems 25 to 48.

25. $\dfrac{3a}{4b} \times \dfrac{8b^2}{9a}.$

26. $\dfrac{6x^2}{7y^2} \times \dfrac{21y^3}{8x^3}.$

27. $\dfrac{2ab}{3c} \times \dfrac{15c^2}{8a^2}.$

28. $\dfrac{3x^2}{5y^2} \times \dfrac{10y^3}{9x^5}.$

29. $\dfrac{21c^2d}{8e^2} \div \dfrac{7cd^2}{24e^5}.$

30. $\dfrac{28x^3y}{27z^2} \div \dfrac{14x^2y^2}{3z^5}.$

31. $\dfrac{4h^2}{9k^2} \times \dfrac{27hk^3}{8j} \div \dfrac{15h^3}{16kj}.$

32. $\dfrac{2a^2}{3b^2} \times \dfrac{9b^3}{4a^3} \div \dfrac{3b^2}{8a}.$

33. $\dfrac{x^2 - y^2}{x^2y} \times \dfrac{xy}{x + y}.$

34. $\dfrac{a^2 + ab - 2b^2}{abc} \times \dfrac{a^2b^2}{a^2 - b^2}.$

35. $\dfrac{c^2 - 2cd}{d^3} \times \dfrac{c^3d}{c^2 - 4d^2}.$

36. $\dfrac{2pq^2 - 3q^3}{2p^4 + 3p^3q} \times \dfrac{2p^2 + 3pq}{2pq - 3q^2}.$

37. $\dfrac{h^4 - 5h^3k}{2hk^2 + k^3} \div \dfrac{h^3 - 5h^2k}{2hk^3 + k^4}.$

38. $\dfrac{3x^3y - 5x^2y^2}{x - 3y} \div \dfrac{3x^2y^2 - 5xy^3}{x^2 - 9y^2}.$

39. $\dfrac{a^3 + a^2b}{ab^2 + 2b^3} \times \dfrac{a^2b - 4b^3}{a^3 - ab^2}.$

40. $\dfrac{p^2q + pq + q}{pq} \times \dfrac{p^3q^2 - p^2q^2}{p^3 - 1}.$

41. $\left(\dfrac{2x^2 + 5x - 3}{x^2 - 9}\right)\left(\dfrac{2x^2 - 5x - 3}{4x^2 - 8x - 5}\right).$

42. $\left(\dfrac{2a^2 - 3ab + b^2}{2a^2 + 3ab + b^2}\right)\left(\dfrac{2a^2 - 3ab - 2b^2}{2a^2 - 5ab + 2b^2}\right).$

43. $\dfrac{b^2 + bc - 6c^2}{b^2 - bc - 2c^2} \div \dfrac{2b^2 + 7bc + 3c^2}{b^2 - c^2}.$

44. $\dfrac{2r^2 - rs - 3s^2}{r^2 - 3rs - 4s^2} \div \dfrac{4r^2 - 4rs - 3s^2}{2r^2 - 9rs + 4s^2}.$

45. $\dfrac{u^2 - uv - 2v^2}{u^2 + uv - 2v^2} \times \dfrac{2u^2 - 3uv + v^2}{2u^2 - 3uv - 2v^2} \div \dfrac{2u - v}{2u + v}.$

46. $\dfrac{9g^2 - h^2}{2g^2 + 3gh - 2h^2} \times \dfrac{g + 2h}{3g - h} \div \dfrac{3g^2 - 2gh - h^2}{2g^2 + hg - h^2}.$

47. $\dfrac{x^3 - y^3}{x^2 - y^2} \times \dfrac{x^4 - y^4}{x^2 + xy + y^2} \times \dfrac{x^2 - xy + y^2}{x^6 + y^6}.$

48. $\dfrac{a^8 - b^8}{a^6 - b^6} \times \dfrac{a^3 + b^3}{a^4 + b^4} \times \dfrac{a - b}{a^2 + b^2}.$

In each of Problems 49 to 56, change the fraction to an equivalent fraction that has the second expression in the problem as a denominator.

49. $\dfrac{a}{b - a},\ a - b.$

50. $\dfrac{x - 2y}{y - x},\ x - y.$

51. $\dfrac{y^2 - x^2}{xy - x^2 - y^2},\ x^2 + y^2 - xy.$

52. $\dfrac{-a - b}{ab - a^2 + b^2},\ a^2 - ab - b^2.$

53. $\dfrac{5}{x - 7},\ x^2 - 5x - 14.$

54. $\dfrac{4}{3x - 2},\ (2 - 3x)(x + 5).$

55. $\dfrac{a - 2}{a^2 + 2a + 4},\ a^3 - 8.$

56. $\dfrac{x^4 - x^2y^2 + y^4}{x^2 - y^2},\ x^6 - y^6.$

Combine the fractions in Problems 57 to 76 into a single fraction and simplify.

57. $\frac{2}{3} + \frac{5}{6} - \frac{1}{2}$.

58. $\frac{5}{8} + \frac{1}{3} - \frac{5}{12}$.

59. $\frac{3}{4} + \frac{5}{9} - \frac{5}{6} - \frac{1}{8}$.

60. $\frac{2}{7} + \frac{5}{14} - \frac{5}{6} + \frac{4}{21}$.

61. $\frac{x}{3} + \frac{2}{x} - \frac{x^2 - 1}{3x}$.

62. $\frac{2x}{5} + \frac{3}{x} - \frac{2x + 3}{x}$.

63. $\frac{2}{a} - \frac{4}{3b} + \frac{4a - 3b}{3ab}$.

64. $\frac{3y}{2x} - \frac{3y^2 - x^2}{2xy} - \frac{x}{3y}$.

65. $\frac{3x}{2x + y} + \frac{5y}{3x} - \frac{3}{2}$.

66. $\frac{1}{2} + \frac{3b}{4a} - \frac{a}{2a + b}$.

67. $\frac{u}{u + v} + \frac{2v}{3u} - \frac{2}{3}$.

68. $\frac{2s}{3r} + \frac{r}{2r - s} + \frac{4}{3}$.

69. $\frac{x}{x - 2y} + \frac{y}{2x + y} - 1$.

70. $\frac{2a + b}{a - 2b} - \frac{a}{3a + b} + \frac{1}{2}$.

71. $\frac{u + v}{2u + 3v} - \frac{u - v}{u + 2v} - \frac{5}{6}$.

72. $\frac{3r - 4s}{3r + 4s} + \frac{2r - 5s}{r + 4s} + \frac{9}{4}$.

73. $\frac{9}{x - 3y} - \frac{10y}{(x + 3y)(3x - y)} - \frac{24x}{(x - 3y)(3x - y)}$.

74. $\frac{2a}{(a - 3b)(a + 3b)} + \frac{9b}{(2a - 3b)(a + 3b)} - \frac{1}{a - 3b}$.

75. $\frac{10r}{(r - 6s)(2r + 3s)} + \frac{11s}{(r - 4s)(2r + 3s)} - \frac{4}{r - 6s}$.

76. $\frac{7b}{(a + 3b)(a - 4b)} - \frac{13b}{(2a + 5b)(a - 4b)} + \frac{1}{a + 3b}$.

Simplify the following complex fractions.

77. $\dfrac{1 - \frac{2}{3}}{\frac{3}{4} + 1}$.

78. $\dfrac{\frac{3}{5} + 2}{3 - \frac{5}{3}}$.

79. $\dfrac{\frac{3}{2} - \frac{2}{3}}{1 - \frac{5}{6}}$.

80. $\dfrac{5 - \frac{3}{2}}{\frac{1}{3} + 12}$.

81. $\dfrac{2 - \frac{1}{x}}{4 - \frac{1}{x^2}}$.

82. $\dfrac{1 - \frac{1}{x}}{1 - \frac{1}{x^3}}$.

83. $\dfrac{1 + \frac{b}{a}}{1 - \frac{b^2}{a^2}}$.

84. $\dfrac{1 - \frac{4v^2}{u^2}}{1 + \frac{v}{u} - \frac{2v^2}{u^2}}$.

85. $\dfrac{x - \frac{2}{x + 1}}{2x - \frac{x + 3}{x + 1}}$.

86. $\dfrac{a + 5b + \frac{12b^2}{a - 2b}}{a + 2b - \frac{3ab}{a - 2b}}$.

87. $\dfrac{4c - \frac{3d^2}{c - d}}{2c - 5d + \frac{d^2}{c - d}}$.

88. $\dfrac{r + \frac{4rs - 8s^2}{3r - 2s}}{r + \frac{10rs + 4s^2}{3r - 2s}}$.

89. $\dfrac{2 - \frac{3}{x + 2}}{\frac{1}{x - 1} + \frac{1}{x + 2}}$.

90. $\dfrac{3 - \frac{2}{2a + 1}}{\frac{2}{2a - 1} + \frac{1}{2a + 1}}$.

91. $\dfrac{\frac{12y}{2x - 3y} + 1}{\frac{3}{2x - 3y} - \frac{2}{2x + y}}$.

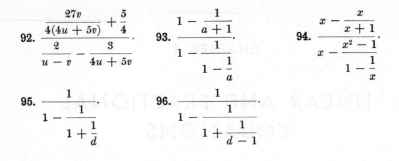

92. $\dfrac{\dfrac{27v}{4(4u+5v)}+\dfrac{5}{4}}{\dfrac{2}{u-v}-\dfrac{3}{4u+5v}}.$

93. $\dfrac{1-\dfrac{1}{a+1}}{1-\dfrac{1}{1-\dfrac{1}{a}}}.$

94. $\dfrac{x-\dfrac{x}{x+1}}{x-\dfrac{x^2-1}{1-\dfrac{1}{x}}}.$

95. $\dfrac{1}{1-\dfrac{1}{1+\dfrac{1}{d}}}.$

96. $\dfrac{1}{1-\dfrac{1}{1+\dfrac{1}{d-1}}}.$

CHAPTER 4

LINEAR AND FRACTIONAL EQUATIONS

26. *Introduction.* A statement of the type

$$(1) \qquad\qquad 3x - 6 = 2x + 1$$

is called an equation. We may readily verify that the statement (1) is true when $x = 7$, but it is not true for any other value that might be substituted for x. The equation is one of the most efficient tools of algebra, and it is widely used in all fields that involve relations between unknown or variable quantities. We shall define an equation below.

DEFINITION. *An **equation** is a statement that two expressions are equal. The two expressions are called the **members** of the equation.*

Some equations are true for all values of the letters involved in it. For example, $(x - 1)(x + 1) = x^2 - 1$ is true for all values of x, as we may readily verify by multiplying the two factors in the left member. Other equations, such as (1), are true for some values of the letters in it, but are not true for other values.

*Equations that are true for all permissible[1] values of the letters involved are called **identities**.* We shall not make use of identities to any great extent in this book except for the purpose of recording results in formulas such as those in Chap. 3.

---

[1] A permissible value of a letter in any equation is any value for which the members of the equation have a meaning. For example, in the equation

$$\frac{(x^2 + 1)}{(x + 1)} = x - 1 + \frac{2}{(x + 1)}$$

the denominators become zero when $x = -1$. Hence, the value of neither member exists. However, the equation is satisfied by any other value of x, as we may readily verify by reducing the right member to a single fraction. Hence the equation is an identity.

Equations that are true for some values of the letters in them but that are not true for other values are called **conditional equations.** Hereafter, we shall use the word *equation* to refer to conditional equations, unless otherwise stated. Such equations are used for solving problems, and our chief concern with them will be to obtain the values of the unknown for which the equation is a true statement.

Any set of numbers that, when substituted for the unknown letters in an equation, makes the members of the equation equal, is called a *solution* of the equation. If the equation contains only one unknown, each solution is called a *root*. The process of obtaining the roots is known as *solving* the equation.

Examples

1. $x = 2$, $y = -3$ is a solution of $3x + 4y = -6$, since $3(2) + 4(-3) = -6$.
2. $x = 6$ is a root of $2x + 2 = 3x - 4$, since $2(6) + 2 = 3(6) - 4$.

27. Equivalent equations. In solving equations, we make use of the concept of equivalent equations, which we define below.

DEFINITION. *Two equations are* **equivalent** *if they have the same solutions.*

Example

It may be verified by direct substitution that $x = 3$ is a solution of

$$4x - 2 = 3x + 1$$

and of $7x = 6x + 3$. Hence these equations are equivalent.

Evidently, if we add the same quantity to two expressions that are equal for some value of the unknown, or if we multiply or divide the two expressions by the same nonzero constant,[1] we obtain two new expressions that are equal for the same value of the unknown. Hence, each of the following operations on an equation yields an equivalent equation.

I. *If the same quantity is added to each member of an equation, the resulting equation is equivalent to the first.*

II. *If each member of an equation is multiplied or divided by the same nonzero constant, the resulting equation is equivalent to the first.*

---

[1] For the present, we shall define a constant as a number or an expression that does not involve the unknown. A more complete definition will be given later.

By use of I, we can derive a process that is very useful for solving equations. For example, we shall consider the equation

$$(1) \qquad ax - b = cx + d$$

If we add $b - cx$ to each member of this equation, we obtain

$$ax - b + b - cx = cx + d + b - cx$$

Now, by combining terms, we get

$$(2) \qquad ax - cx = d + b$$

and, by I, this equation is equivalent to (1). By comparing (1) and (2), we see that the latter can be obtained from the former by moving cx and $-b$ from one member of (1) to the other and at the same time changing their signs. This procedure is called *transposition*. By use of it we can transpose any term from one member of the equation to the other, provided we change the sign of the term in the process.

28. *Solution of linear equations.* If no fractions that involve the unknown in the denominator appear in an equation and if the unknown occurs to the first degree only, the equation is called a *linear equation.*

We may solve an equation of the above type by transposing the terms that involve the unknown to the left side of the equality, and the constant terms to the right. Then, after combining the terms, we get an equation of the type $ax = b$. Then we obtain the value of x by dividing both members by a.

Example

The steps in the solution of $6x - 7 = 2x + 1$ follow.

$6x - 7 = 2x + 1$	(given equation)
$6x - 2x = 1 + 7$	(transposing $2x$ to the left and -7 to the right)
$4x = 8$	(combining terms)
$x = 2$	(dividing each member by 4)

In order to check the solution, we substitute 2 for x in the equation and compute the value of each member. If the two values thus obtained are equal, the solution is correct. A convenient arrangement of the computation is given below.

Left member	Right member
$6(2) - 7 =$	$2(2) + 1 =$
$12 - 7 =$	$4 + 1 =$
5	5

Hence, $x = 2$ is correct.

29. *Fractional equations.* If an equation involves fractions, we multiply each member by the L.C.M. of the denominators and thereby obtain an equation in which no fraction appears. This process is known as *clearing the equation of fractions.* If the resulting equation is linear, we may solve it by the methods of the preceding article. We shall illustrate the process by the two examples below.

Example 1

$$\tfrac{1}{2}x - \tfrac{2}{3} = \tfrac{3}{4}x + \tfrac{1}{12}$$

$12(\tfrac{1}{2}x - \tfrac{2}{3}) = 12(\tfrac{3}{4}x + \tfrac{1}{12})$ (multiplying each member by the L.C.M., 12, of the denominators)

$\qquad 6x - 8 = 9x + 1$ (performing the indicated multiplication)

$\qquad 6x - 9x = 1 + 8$ (transposing $9x$ and -8)

$\qquad\quad -3x = 9$ (combining terms)

$\qquad\qquad x = -3$ (dividing each member by -3)

Check

Left member	*Right member*
$\tfrac{1}{2}(-3) - \tfrac{2}{3} =$	$\tfrac{3}{4}(-3) + \tfrac{1}{12} =$
$-\tfrac{3}{2} - \tfrac{2}{3} =$	$-\tfrac{9}{4} + \tfrac{1}{12} =$
$-\tfrac{9}{6} - \tfrac{4}{6} =$	$-\tfrac{27}{12} + \tfrac{1}{12} =$
$-\tfrac{13}{6}$	$-\tfrac{26}{12} = -\tfrac{13}{6}$

Example 2

$$\frac{x}{x+1} + \frac{5}{8} = \frac{5}{2(x+1)} + \frac{3}{4}$$

$8(x+1)\left(\dfrac{x}{x+1} + \dfrac{5}{8}\right) = 8(x+1)\left[\dfrac{5}{2(x+1)} + \dfrac{3}{4}\right]$ (multiplying both members by the L.C.M. of the denominators)

$\qquad 8x + 5(x+1) = 4(5) + 6(x+1)$ (performing the indicated multiplication)

$\qquad 8x + 5x + 5 = 20 + 6x + 6$

$\qquad 8x + 5x - 6x = 20 + 6 - 5$ (transposing)

$\qquad\qquad\quad 7x = 21$ (combining terms)

$\qquad\qquad\quad\ x = 3$ (dividing by 7)

Check

Left member	*Right member*
$\dfrac{3}{3+1} + \dfrac{5}{8} = \dfrac{3}{4} + \dfrac{5}{8} = \dfrac{6}{8} + \dfrac{5}{8} = \dfrac{11}{8}$	$\dfrac{5}{2(3+1)} + \dfrac{3}{4} = \dfrac{5}{8} + \dfrac{3}{4} = \dfrac{5}{8} + \dfrac{6}{8} = \dfrac{11}{8}$

If the denominators of the fractions in an equation contain the unknown, the equation obtained by clearing of fractions is not always equivalent to the first. This is illustrated in the following example.

Example 3

$$\frac{2}{x+1} - 3 = \frac{4x+6}{x+1}$$

$$(x+1)\left(\frac{2}{x+1} - 3\right) = (x+1)\left(\frac{4x+6}{x+1}\right) \quad \text{(clearing of fractions by multiplying by the L.C.M. of the denominators, } x+1)$$

$$2 - 3(x+1) = 4x+6$$
$$2 - 3x - 3 = 4x+6$$
$$-3x - 4x = 6 - 2 + 3$$
$$-7x = 7$$
$$x = -1$$

When we attempt to check this solution, we see that if $x = -1$, the two denominators in the original equation become zero and hence the fractions have no meaning. Therefore, we cannot accept $x = -1$ as a solution. If we perform the indicated division in $(4x + 6)/(x + 1)$, we obtain $4 + 2/(x + 1)$. Then the original equation becomes

$$\frac{2}{x+1} - 3 = 4 + \frac{2}{x+1}$$

and it is obvious that it has no solution.

Example 3 above illustrates the fact that if both members of an equation are multiplied by an expression containing the unknown, the resulting equation may have roots that do not satisfy the original. Such roots are called *extraneous*. For this reason, if an equation is multiplied by an expression containing the unknown in order to clear it of fractions, the solutions of the cleared equation must be checked in the original in order to see if any one of them is extraneous.

Example 4

$$\frac{a-x}{a+x} + \frac{a}{x} = -1$$

$$x(a-x) + a(a+x) = -x(a+x) \quad \text{(clearing of fractions)}$$
$$ax - x^2 + a^2 + ax = -ax - x^2 \quad \text{(performing the indicated operations)}$$

$$-x^2 + x^2 + ax + ax + ax = -a^2 \quad \text{(transposing and arranging terms)}$$
$$3ax = -a^2 \quad \text{(collecting terms)}$$

$$x = -\frac{a^2}{3a}$$

$$x = -\frac{a}{3}$$

Check

Left member

$$\frac{a + \dfrac{a}{3}}{a - \dfrac{a}{3}} + \frac{a}{-\dfrac{a}{3}} = \frac{3a + a}{3a - a} - \frac{3a}{a} = \frac{4a}{2a} - 3 = 2 - 3 = -1$$

Hence, since the right member is -1, the solution checks.

EXERCISE 12

By direct substitution, show that the number given in each of Problems 1 to 12 is a root of the equation in the problem.

1. $4x + 1 = 6x - 3$, 2.   **2.** $9x - 3 = 10x + 3$, -6.

3. $6x + 1 = 8 - 8x$, $\frac{1}{2}$.   **4.** $5x - 1 = 3x + 2$, $\frac{3}{2}$.

5. $\dfrac{x-3}{4} - \dfrac{x-1}{3} = -\dfrac{5}{6}$, 5.   **6.** $\dfrac{2x-4}{2} - \dfrac{x+1}{4} = x + 2$, **$-17$.**

7. $\dfrac{2x+1}{3} - \dfrac{x}{4} = \dfrac{x-2}{6}$, $-\dfrac{8}{3}$.   **8.** $\dfrac{x-1}{x+1} + 2 = \dfrac{3}{x+1}$, $\dfrac{2}{3}$.

9. $ax + bc - bx = ac$, c.   **10.** $a^2x - b = a - abx$, $\dfrac{1}{a}$.

11. $\dfrac{a+x}{b} + \dfrac{b}{a} = \dfrac{2b-x}{a}$, $b - a$.   **12.** $\dfrac{bx-1}{b+x} + a = \dfrac{ab+bx}{b+x}$, $\dfrac{1}{a}$.

Solve the equations in Problems 13 to 72.

13. $5x = 3x + 6$.   **14.** $9x + 1 = 2x - 13$.   **15.** $7x + 4 = 3x + 6$.

16. $5x - 1 = 2x + 1$.   **17.** $6x - 3 = 7x + 2$.   **18.** $8x - 5 = 7 + 4x$.

19. $7x - 3 = 2 - 3x$.   **20.** $9 - 8x = 7x + 3$.

21. $3(x + 2) - (x - 4) = 0$.   **22.** $3(5x - 2) + 4(1 - 3x) = 0$.

23. $7(4x + 15) - 6(8x + 4) = 1$.   **24.** $4(3x - 1) = -5(-3x + 2)$.

25. $4(\frac{1}{2}x - \frac{1}{4}) = \frac{1}{2}(8x + 6)$.   **26.** $6(\frac{2}{3}x - \frac{1}{6}) - \frac{2}{3}(12x - 6) = -5$.

27. $8(\frac{3}{2}x - \frac{1}{4}) - 3(\frac{2}{3}x - 1) = 5x - 9$.

28. $9(\frac{4}{3}x - \frac{2}{3}) - 12(\frac{3}{4}x + \frac{1}{6}) = 7x + 4$.

29. $\frac{1}{2}x - \frac{3}{4} + x - 5 = \frac{1}{4}$.   **30.** $\frac{4}{3} - \frac{1}{3}x - 3 = \frac{2}{3}x - \frac{5}{3}$.

31. $\frac{3}{4}x - \frac{2}{3} + 2x = \frac{4}{3} - \frac{1}{4}x$.   **32.** $\frac{1}{2}x - \frac{2}{3} + \frac{3}{2}x - \frac{7}{3} = 2$.

33. $\frac{1}{2}x + 5 = \frac{7}{6}x + 1$.   **34.** $\frac{3}{4}x + 5 = \frac{1}{2}x + 7$.   **35.** $\frac{2}{3}x - 1 = \frac{1}{2}x + 1$.

36. $\frac{3}{5}x - 2 = \frac{1}{3}x + \frac{2}{5}$.   **37.** $ax - \dfrac{1}{a} = \dfrac{1}{b} - bx$.

38. $ax + b(1 - x) = 2b - a$.   **39.** $a + b^2x = a^2x - b$.

40. $x - b = \dfrac{1}{a} - abx$.   **41.** $\dfrac{3x-1}{2} = 2x + 3$.

42. $x = 2 - \dfrac{2x-4}{3}$.   **43.** $x - \dfrac{1}{2} = 2 - \dfrac{x-6}{6}$.

44. $\dfrac{4x - 2}{3} - \dfrac{1}{4} = 3x + 2.$

45. $\dfrac{x - 2}{3} + \dfrac{x - 1}{2} = 3.$

46. $4 - \dfrac{3x - 4}{4} = \dfrac{4x - 5}{12}.$

47. $\dfrac{2x - 5}{5} + \dfrac{3x + 2}{3} = \dfrac{5}{6}.$

48. $\dfrac{5x - 3}{4} - \dfrac{2x - 4}{3} = \dfrac{7}{3}.$

49. $\dfrac{4x - 3}{6} - \dfrac{2x + 4}{9} = x + 1.$

50. $\dfrac{3x + 5}{5} - \dfrac{2x - 7}{4} = 3x + \dfrac{21}{5}.$

51. $\dfrac{2x - 5}{6} - \dfrac{3x + 2}{9} = 2x - \dfrac{3}{2}.$

52. $\dfrac{6x + 7}{5} - \dfrac{4x + 3}{3} + 2(6 - 2x) = 0.$

53. $\dfrac{ax + b}{a} + \dfrac{bx - a}{b} = \dfrac{b}{a}.$

54. $\dfrac{cx - d}{d} - \dfrac{dx + c}{c} = \dfrac{c^2 + d^2}{cd}.$

55. $\dfrac{a^2x - b^2}{ab} - \dfrac{bx - a}{a} = \dfrac{a - b}{b}.$

56. $\dfrac{2px - 3q}{p} = \dfrac{p - 3qx}{q} - \dfrac{3q}{p}.$

57. $\dfrac{x - 3}{x + 1} = \dfrac{x - 4}{x - 2}.$

58. $\dfrac{2x + 5}{4x + 1} = \dfrac{3x + 5}{6x - 1}.$

59. $\dfrac{4x - 3}{2x - 3} = \dfrac{8x + 5}{4x + 1}.$

60. $\dfrac{3x - 2}{2x + 1} = \dfrac{3x + 4}{2x - 5}.$

61. $\dfrac{2}{x - 1} - \dfrac{3}{x + 3} = \dfrac{6}{(x - 1)(x + 3)}.$

62. $\dfrac{5}{x + 1} - \dfrac{4}{x - 2} = \dfrac{-10}{(x + 1)(x - 2)}.$

63. $\dfrac{3}{x - 2} - \dfrac{5}{x + 4} = \dfrac{10}{x^2 + 2x - 8}.$

64. $\dfrac{1}{x + 3} + \dfrac{1}{x - 3} = \dfrac{10}{x^2 - 9}.$

65. $\dfrac{4}{x - 2} - \dfrac{3}{x + 1} = \dfrac{8}{x^2 - x - 2}.$

66. $\dfrac{1}{x + 5} + \dfrac{1}{2x + 9} = \dfrac{2}{2x^2 + 19x + 45}.$

67. $\dfrac{1}{2x + 3} - \dfrac{3}{x - 3} = \dfrac{3}{2x^2 - 3x - 9}.$

68. $\dfrac{2}{x + 2} + \dfrac{1}{2x - 1} = \dfrac{5}{2x^2 + 3x - 2}.$

69. $\dfrac{4}{2x - 3} - \dfrac{3}{x + 2} + \dfrac{5}{5x - 4} = 0.$

70. $\dfrac{4}{3x - 2} - \dfrac{1}{2x - 3} = \dfrac{5}{6x + 3}.$

71. $\dfrac{4}{3x - 1} - \dfrac{3}{2x + 3} = \dfrac{-1}{6x - 24}.$

72. $\dfrac{4}{4x + 5} - \dfrac{2}{x - 4} = \dfrac{-1}{x + 3}.$

Show that the equation in each of Problems 73 to 80 has no solution.

73. $\dfrac{4x - 7}{x - 2} = 3 + \dfrac{1}{x - 2}.$

74. $\dfrac{2}{x - 1} + 1 = \dfrac{4 - 2x}{x - 1}.$

75. $\dfrac{2}{x^2 - 1} = \dfrac{1}{x - 1} - \dfrac{1}{x + 2}.$

76. $\dfrac{1}{x - 2} + \dfrac{1}{x - 3} = \dfrac{1}{x^2 - 5x + 6}.$

77. $\dfrac{x-1}{x+2} + 1 = \dfrac{x-1}{x+1} + \dfrac{x^2+1}{(x+1)(x+2)}.$

78. $\dfrac{x+1}{x-2} + \dfrac{x}{x-1} = \dfrac{x+1}{x-1} + \dfrac{x^2}{(x-1)(x-2)}.$

79. $\dfrac{x-1}{x-2} + \dfrac{x-3}{x+1} = \dfrac{x-1}{x+1} + \dfrac{x^2-x+1}{(x-2)(x+1)}.$

80. $\dfrac{x+1}{x-3} + \dfrac{x+1}{x-1} = \dfrac{2x}{x-3} - \dfrac{x+1}{(x-3)(x-1)}.$

Solve the equation in each of Problems 81 to 92 for the letter indicated at the right.

81. $s = \dfrac{c}{1-p},\ p.$ **82.** $m = \dfrac{c(1-p)}{1-d},\ p.$

83. $l = a + (n-1)d,\ n.$ **84.** $V = \pi LT(D-T),\ D.$

85. $h = 8 + \dfrac{18-a}{2},\ a.$ **86.** $S = \dfrac{n}{2}(a+l),\ l.$

87. $S = \dfrac{a-ar^n}{1-r},\ a.$ **88.** $C = \tfrac{5}{9}(F-32),\ F.$

89. $A = P + Prt,\ P.$ **90.** $e = N\left(\dfrac{\varphi_1 - \varphi_2}{t}\right),\ \varphi_1.$

91. $V = r[1 + (B_1 - B_2)t],\ B_1.$ **92.** $T = \left(\dfrac{2m_1 m_2}{m_1 + m_2}\right)g,\ g.$

30. *Solution of problems by means of equations.* A problem that can be solved by means of an equation involves several quantities, of which some are known and others unknown. It also contains information that enables us to see that two combinations of these quantities are equal. If the problem can be solved with an equation in one variable, the unknown quantities in it must be such that they can be expressed in terms of a single letter.

The process of solving a problem by means of an equation is not always easy, and considerable practice is necessary before one becomes adept at it. The following approach is suggested.

1. Read the problem carefully and study it until the situation is thoroughly understood.

2. Identify the quantities, both known and unknown, that are involved in the problem.

3. Select one of the unknowns and represent it by a letter, usually x. Then express the other unknowns in terms of this letter.

4. Search the problem for the information that tells which quantities, or what combinations of them, are equal.

5. When the desired combinations are found, set them equal to each other, thus obtaining an equation.

6. Solve the equation thus obtained and check the solution.

We shall present below several examples of the various types of problems that can be solved by means of equations. The general procedure explained in the examples should be applied to similar problems that occur in the next exercise, and to the other exercises in this book that involve stated problems.

1. *Problems involving motion at a uniform velocity.* Problems of this type usually state a relation between the distances traveled or between the velocities (or speeds) or between the times involved. The fundamental formula for such problems is

$$(1) \qquad\qquad\qquad d = vt$$

where d represents the distance; v, the velocity (or speed); and t, the time. This formula can be solved for v and for t in order to get the following two additional formulas.

$$(2) \qquad\qquad\qquad v = \frac{d}{t}$$

and

$$(3) \qquad\qquad\qquad t = \frac{d}{v}$$

Example 1

A party of sportsmen made a trip of 380 miles to a hunting ground in 7 hr. They traveled 4 hr. on a paved highway and the remainder on a pasture road. If they averaged 25 miles per hr. less through the pasture than on the highway, find the average speed and the distance traveled on each part of the trip.

Solution

The unknown quantities in the problem are the two speeds and the distance on each part of the trip. The known quantities are 380 miles, the total distance; 7 hr., the total time; 4 hr., the time spent on the highway; and 25 miles per hr., the amount by which the speed on the highway exceeds that through the pasture. Obviously the time spent on the pasture roads was 7 hr. − 4 hr. = 3 hr., and the total distance is equal to the sum of the distances traveled on each of the two parts.

If we let
$$x = \text{the speed on the highway}$$
then
$$x - 25 = \text{the speed through the pasture}$$
Furthermore
$$4x = \text{the distance traveled on the highway}$$
$$3(x - 25) = \text{the distance through the pastures}$$
and
$$4x + 3(x - 25) = \text{the total distance}$$
Hence,
$$4x + 3(x - 25) = 380$$

This is the desired equation and we shall solve it below.

$4x + 3x - 75 = 380$	(removing parentheses)
$4x + 3x = 380 + 75$	(transposing)
$7x = 455$	(combining terms)
$x = 65$	(miles per hr. on the highway)
$x - 25 = 40$	(miles per hr. through the pasture)
$4(65) = 260$	(miles traveled on the highway)
$3(40) = 120$	(miles traveled through the pasture)

Check

$$260 + 120 = 380$$

Example 2

Three airports A, B, and C are located on a north-south line. B is 645 miles north of A, and C is 540 miles north of B. A pilot flew from A to B, delayed two hours, and continued to C. The wind was blowing from the south at 15 miles per hr. during the first part of the trip, but during the delay it changed to the north with a velocity of 20 miles per hr. If he spent the same time on each part of the trip, find the airspeed (or the speed delivered by the propeller) of the plane.

Solution

In this problem, the unknown quantities are the airspeed of the plane and the time spent on each part of the journey. We know the two latter quantities are equal. The known quantities are the two distances and the two wind velocities.
If we let
$$x = \text{the airspeed}$$
then
$$x + 15 = \text{the speed of the plane from } A \text{ to } B$$
and
$$x - 20 = \text{the speed of the plane from } B \text{ to } C$$

Furthermore,

$$\frac{645}{x + 15} = \text{time spent on the first part of the trip}$$

and

$$\frac{540}{x - 20} = \text{time spent on the second part of the journey}$$

Hence,

$$\frac{645}{x + 15} = \frac{540}{x - 20}$$

This is the required equation.   The solution follows.

$$(x - 20)(645) = (x + 15)(540) \quad \text{(clearing of fractions)}$$
$$645x - 12,900 = 540x + 8100 \quad \text{(removing parentheses)}$$
$$645x - 540x = 8100 + 12,900 \quad \text{(transposing)}$$
$$105x = 21,000$$
$$x = 200 \quad \text{(miles per hr., airspeed of the plane)}$$

Check

The speed on the first part of the trip was

$$200 \text{ miles per hr.} + 15 \text{ miles per hr.} = 215 \text{ miles per hr.}$$

and the time was $645 \div 215 = 3$ hr.   The speed on the second part of the trip was 200 miles per hr. $-$ 20 miles per hr. $=$ 180 miles per hr., and the time was $540 \div 180 = 3$ hr.   Since the time on each part was 3 hr., the solution checks.

2. Work problems.   Problems that involve the rate of doing certain things can often be solved by first finding the fractional part of the task done by each individual, or each agent, in one unit of time and then finding a relation between the fractional parts.   If this method is used, the unit "one" represents the entire job that is to be done.

Example 3

A farmer can plow a piece of land in 4 days, using a tractor.   His hired hand can plow the same piece of land, using a smaller tractor, in 6 days.   How many days will be required for the plowing if they work together?

Solution

We shall let

$x = $ the number of days required to plow the field when both work

Then

$\dfrac{1}{x} = $ the part of the field plowed in one day by the two

However,

$\frac{1}{4}$ = the part of the field plowed by the farmer in one day

and

$\frac{1}{6}$ = the part of the field plowed in one day by the hired hand

Hence,

$$\frac{1}{4} + \frac{1}{6} = \frac{1}{x}$$
$$3x + 2x = 12 \quad \text{(clearing of fractions)}$$
$$5x = 12$$
$$x = 2\frac{2}{5} \quad \text{(days)}$$

Check

If they plow the field in $2\frac{2}{5}$ days, they complete $\dfrac{1}{2\frac{2}{5}} = \dfrac{5}{12}$ of it in one day. Furthermore, one plows $\frac{1}{6}$ of it in one day, and the other, $\frac{1}{4}$, and

$$\frac{1}{6} + \frac{1}{4} = \frac{2+3}{12} = \frac{5}{12}$$

Example 4

If, in Example 3, the hired hand worked one day with the smaller machine and was then joined by his employer with the larger, how many days were required for them to finish the plowing?

Solution

The hired hand plowed $\frac{1}{6}$ of the field in one day, and hence $\frac{5}{6}$ of it remained.
Let

x = the number of days required for them to finish the job

Then

$\dfrac{x}{4}$ = the part of the field plowed by the farmer in x days

and

$\dfrac{x}{6}$ = the part plowed by the hired hand

Hence,

$$\frac{x}{4} + \frac{x}{6} = \frac{5}{6}$$
$$3x + 2x = 10 \quad \text{(clearing of fractions)}$$
$$5x = 10$$
$$x = 2 \quad \text{(days)}$$

Check

In two days the farmer plowed $\frac{2}{4} = \frac{1}{2}$ of the field, and the hired hand plowed $\frac{2}{6} = \frac{1}{3}$ of it, and

$$\frac{1}{2} + \frac{1}{3} = \frac{3+2}{6} = \frac{5}{6}$$

3. *Mixture problems.* Many problems involve the combination of certain substances of known strengths, usually expressed in percentages, into a mixture of required strength in one of the substances. Others involve the mixing of certain commodities of a given price. In such problems, it should be remembered that the total amount of any given element in a mixture is equal to the sum of the amounts of that element in the substances combined, or that the value of any mixture is the sum of the values of the substances that are put together.

Example 5

How many gallons of a liquid that is 74 per cent alcohol must be combined with 5 gal. of one that is 90 per cent alcohol in order to obtain a mixture that is 84 per cent pure?

Solution

If we let

x = the number of gallons of the 74 per cent solution used in the mixture

then

$.74x$ = the number of gallons of alcohol contributed by this solution

Furthermore,

$.90(5) = 4.5$ = the number of gallons of alcohol in the 90 per cent solution

Hence,

$.74x + 4.5$ = the number of gallons of alcohol in the mixture

Also,

$x + 5$ = the total number of gallons in the mixture

Then, since this mixture is 84 per cent pure, we have

$.84(x + 5)$ = the number of gallons of alcohol in the mixture

Therefore,

$$.74x + 4.5 = .84(x + 5)$$
$$.74x + 4.5 = .84x + 4.2$$
$$.74x - .84x = 4.2 - 4.5$$
$$-.10x = -.3$$
$$x = 3 \quad \text{(gal. added)}$$

Check

$$(.74)3 + 4.5 = 2.22 + 4.5 = 6.72$$

and

$$.84(5 + 3) = .84(8) = 6.72$$

4. *Miscellaneous problems.* In addition to the three types discussed above, there is a wide variety of problems that can be solved by means of equations. The fundamental approach to all of them is the same, that is, finding two quantities, one or both of which involve the unknown, that are equal. We shall mention three other varieties and point out the general principle or formula to be used in solving each.

Many problems in physics and mechanics involve the lever. A lever is a rigid bar supported at a point that is usually between the two ends and that is called the *fulcrum*. If two weights W_1 and W_2 at distances L_1 and L_2, respectively, from the fulcrum are balanced on a lever, then

$$W_1 L_1 = W_2 L_2$$

Furthermore, if a force F at a distance D from the fulcrum will just raise a weight R and a distance d from the fulcrum, then

$$FD = Rd$$

In solving problems dealing with investments, the formula

$$I = PRT$$

is usually employed, where P is the principal, or the amount invested; I is the interest, or the amount earned on the investment; R, expressed as a percentage, is the rate of interest or of earning per unit of time; and T is the total time the principal was invested.

Problems involving the digits in a number depend upon the place-value principle of our number system. For example, if h is the hundreds digit in a three-place number; t, the tens digit; and u, the units digit; then $100h + 10t + u$ is the number. If the hundreds digit and the units digit are interchanged, then the number is $100u + 10t + h$.

EXERCISE 13

1. Find three consecutive integers whose sum is 57.

2. Find two numbers such that one is 4 more than twice the other and their sum is 37.

3. Find two numbers such that one is 5 less than 3 times the other and their sum is 19.

4. The perimeter of a rectangle is 82 ft. Find its length and width if the former is 7 more than the latter.

5. The perimeter of a rectangle is 84 ft., and the length is twice the width. Find the dimensions.

6. Tom has $13 more than Dick. How much does each have if together they have $29?

7. John paid Tom $3 for a baseball glove, and then the two boys had the same amount of money. How much did each have before the transaction if the former had twice as much as the latter?

8. Mr. Jones, Mr. Smith, and Mr. Brown purchased a store for $25,000. Jones and Smith together contributed $17,000, and Brown's share in the purchase was $1000 more than Smith's. Find the amount of money advanced by each.

9. Three brothers, Tom, Dick, and Harry, purchased a used car. Tom's share in the cost was $\frac{1}{4}$ of the price of the car, Dick paid $50 more than Tom, and Harry paid $50 more than Dick. Find the cost of the car.

10. A man fenced a rectangular lot with a 60-ft. front and a 400-ft. perimeter at a cost of $372. If the cost of the front fence was 20 cents more per foot than that of the other three sides, find the price per foot of each type.

11. A rectangular lot that has a perimeter of 420 ft. is enclosed with a fence costing $1.20 per foot across the front and $1 per foot around the other three sides. Find the dimensions if the total cost of the front fence was one-fifth of the cost of the remainder.

12. A farmer sold 15 hogs, 20 steers, and 10 horses for $3150. The hogs sold for $\frac{4}{9}$ as much per head as the steers, and the price per head of the horses was $35 more than that of the hogs. Find the price of each.

13. A portion of $7000 was invested at 3 per cent, and the remainder at 4 per cent. If the total income was $240, how much was invested at each rate?

14. On Jan. 1, Mr. Smith invested in a certain type of stock that paid an annual dividend of 4 per cent. At the beginning of the second year, he sold $3000 worth of his stock and reinvested the proceeds in a business that paid 5 per cent per year. If the total income on these investments for two years was $430, what was the amount of the original investment?

15. The total income from two houses for one year was $1570. Find the monthly rental on each if they differ by $25 and the more expensive house was vacant for 2 months.

16. If 27 is added to a two-digit number, the units and tens digits are reversed. Find the number if the units digit is twice the tens digit.

17. Each digit after the first in a three-digit number is twice the preceding. If 297 is added to the number, the units digit and the hundreds digit are interchanged. What is the number?

18. A father and son are 30 years and 6 years of age, respectively. In how many years will the father's age be twice that of his son?

19. John is 3 times as old as Robert, and in 6 years he will be twice as old. Find the present age of each.

20. A cash drawer contains $6 in nickels, dimes, and quarters. There are twice as many dimes as quarters, and as many nickels as there are quarters and dimes combined. How many coins of each denomination are in the drawer?

21. A car left Baton Rouge at 1 P.M. for Houston, and another left Houston for Baton Rouge at 2 P.M. on the same day. They met at 4 P.M. The speed of the second car was 10 miles per hr. less than the first, and the two cities are 245 miles apart. Find the speed of each.

22. Two ships passed in mid-ocean and traveled in opposite directions. After 7 hr. they were 280 nautical miles apart. Find the speed of each if their rates differ by four knots. NOTE: A knot is a speed of one nautical mile per hour.

23. Two men left the same hotel at the same time and traveled in the same direction on the same highway. After 5 hr. their cars were 50 miles apart. Find the speed of each if one car travels $\frac{5}{6}$ as fast as the other.

24. Five minutes after an accident caused by a hit-and-run driver, a highway-patrol car reached the scene of the accident. One of the patrolmen immediately started in pursuit of the offender and overtook him in 1 hr. and 10 min. Find the speed of each car during the pursuit, if the speed of patrol car was 5 miles per hr. greater than the speed of the other car.

25. A pilot flew from his home field to another at the rate of 180 miles per hr. and returned at the rate of 150 miles per hr. If the outward trip required 1 hr. less time than the return trip, find the distance between the fields.

26. Two cars filled with tourists left the same hotel on a scenic loop and traveled in opposite directions around the loop. One car traveled at 50 miles per hr. and the other at 40 miles per hr. Find the distance around the loop if the faster car completed the round trip 54 min. ahead of the other.

27. A farmer can plow a field in 4 days. His son, using a smaller implement, can plow the field in 8 days. How long will it take them to plow the field if they work together?

28. A master painter can paint a roof in 12 hr., and his assistant can do the same job in 15 hr. How long will it take them to paint the roof if they work together?

29. The oldest of three brothers can mow a lawn in 3 hr., the second boy can mow it in 4 hr., an the youngest requires 6 hr. How long will it take them if they work together?

30. If, in Problem 29, the youngest boy works 3 hr. alone and is then joined by the other two, how long will it take them to finish the job?

31. A swimming pool is fed by two intake pipes that can fill it in 8 and 12 hr., respectively. How long will it take them to fill the pool if both are open?

32. If, in Problem 31, the smaller pipe is opened and allowed to run 3 hr. before the larger pipe is turned on, how much longer will it take to fill the tank?

33. A tank can be filled by the intake pipe in 3 hr. and drained by the outlet in 5 hr. How long will it take to fill the tank if both pipes are open?

34. A truck farmer has a storage reservoir for irrigation purposes that can be filled by the intake pipe in 6 hr. and drained by the outlet in 4 hr. At the start of a long irrigation job the reservoir is full and both pipes are opened. How long will it take to drain the reservoir?

35. How many pounds of tobacco worth $2.50 per pound should be mixed with 30 lb. worth $3 per pound in order to obtain a blend to sell at $2.80 per pound?

36. A grocer mixed coffee worth $.58 per pound with 80 pounds worth $.84 per pound in order to obtain a blend worth $.74 per pound. How many pounds of the cheaper grade were used?

37. A chemist added a certain amount of alcohol that was 86 per cent pure to 11 gal. of a grade that was 71 per cent pure, and he obtained a mixture that was 77 per cent pure. How many gallons of the first grade were used?

38. A block of metal containing 59 per cent silver is combined with 70 lb. of an alloy that was 83 per cent silver in order to obtain an alloy that contained 73 per cent silver. How many pounds of the first block were used?

39. A car radiator that holds 6 gal. is filled with a liquid containing 25 per cent alcohol. How many gallons must be drained off and replaced with a liquid containing 70 per cent alcohol in order to obtain a liquid that is 40 per cent alcohol?

40. The driver of a car with a leaking radiator found it necessary to add water twice on a trip. The radiator held 6 gal. and was filled with a 30 per cent alcohol solution at the start. At the end of the trip, the radiator was again filled and the solution tested and found to contain 25 per cent alcohol. Find the total amount of water added.

41. Airport B is due north of airport A. A pilot flew from A to B in the morning and returned in the afternoon. During the morning the wind blew from the south at the rate of 10 miles per hr., and during the afternoon it blew from the north at a speed of 30 miles per hr. If the morning trip required $4\frac{1}{2}$ hr. and the return trip 4 hr., find the airspeed of the plane.

42. A party of sportsmen traveled 160 miles on a paved highway and 120 miles on a graveled lane in order to reach their hunting camp, and found that they spent the same time on each part of the trip. Find their average speed on each road if they traveled 15 miles per hr. faster on the highway than on the lane.

43. A man can row 2 miles upstream and 6 miles downstream in the same length of time. If the stream is flowing at the rate of 2 miles per hr., find the speed of the boat in still water.

44. Airfields A and C are located 800 miles west and 600 miles north of B, respectively. A pilot flew from A to B, delayed two hours, and continued to C. The wind was blowing from the west at 20 miles per hr. during the first part of the journey and from the north at 25 miles per hr. during the second part. Find the airspeed of the plane if the two parts of the trip required the same time.

45. A rancher drove from his headquarters to an airport at 45 miles per hr., waited 10 min. and continued his journey on a plane at 120 miles per hr. If the entire trip covered 240 miles and required 3 hr., how far was his headquarters from the airport?

46. A cowboy, whose horse broke his leg, walked to the nearest camp, borrowed a horse, and rode to the ranch headquarters. If he traveled 14 miles, averaged 3 miles per hr. on foot, 6 miles per hr. on horseback, and required 3 hr. for the trip, how far was it from the scene of the accident to the camp?

47. A man can exert a force of 150 lb. on one end of a lever. Where must the fulcrum be placed on a 15-ft. lever if he can just raise a weight of 600 lb.?

48. Two girls whose weights are 50 and 60 lb., respectively, are balanced on a teeterboard that is 11 ft. long. How far is the fulcrum from the smaller girl?

CHAPTER 5

FUNCTIONS AND GRAPHS

31. Constants and variables. A formula and also an equation state relations that exist between combinations of letters and numbers. Some of these letters may represent values that never change, others may stand for quantities that do not change during a certain problem, and still others have values which vary within a certain range. For example, we shall consider the following problem:

Water is running into a cylindrical pail at the rate of 3 cubic inches per second. If the radius of the pail is 5 inches and its height is 10 inches, how fast is the water rising?

Since the water in the pail is in the form of a right circular cylinder, its volume is given by the formula

$$(1) \qquad\qquad V = \pi r^2 h$$

in which $\pi = 3.1416$ (approximately), r is the radius, and h is the depth of the water. In this problem, $r = 5$, h varies from 0 to 10, and the value of π never changes. If we let t represent the number of seconds the water has been running, then the volume of water is $V = 3t$, and we have

$$(2) \qquad\qquad 3t = \pi(5)^2 h$$

Now, since the rate at which the water rises is h/t, we solve (2) for h and get

$$(3) \qquad\qquad h = \frac{3t}{\pi(5)^2}$$

Finally, dividing by t, we obtain

$$(4) \qquad\qquad \frac{h}{t} = \frac{3}{25\pi}$$

72

Both letters on the left are constantly changing, but the values on the right are fixed. Hence, the value of the ratio h/t is always the same.

This discussion illustrates the following definitions:

DEFINITION I. *A variable is a symbol which represents a number that may vary within a given range.*

DEFINITION II. *A constant is a symbol which represents a number that does not change in any discussion or situation.*

NOTE 1: The values of some symbols, such as π, 1, 2, 3, . . . never change, and these are called *absolute constants*.

NOTE 2: We frequently use a letter whose value is temporarily unknown, but which is fixed by the conditions of the problem. For example, in the equation

$$2x - 1 = 4x - 3$$

the value of x is unknown until the solution reveals that its value is 1. Hence, in this problem, x is not a variable, but it is a constant whose value is to be determined.

32. *Functions and functional notation.* If in (3) of Art. 31 we assign a value to t, the value of h is automatically fixed and can be calculated to as many decimal places as desired. This situation is described mathematically by the statement "*h is a function of t*," and it illustrates the following definition:

DEFINITION. *One variable is a **function** of a second if at least one value of the first is determined whenever a value is assigned to the second.*

The variable to which values are assigned is called the *independent variable*, and the other is called the *dependent variable*.

Frequently functions are written without the dependent variable being explicitly shown. For example, the expression $x^2 - 2x - 2$ is a variable since its value varies with x. Furthermore, its value is determined whenever a definite number is assigned to x. Hence, it is a function of x. The statement "function of x" is often denoted by the symbol $f(x)$, which is read "f of x." The letter enclosed in the parentheses is the independent variable in the function. Thus, if in a particular discussion, $f(x) = x^2 - 2x - 2$, then $f(z) = z^2 - 2z - 2$, $f(3) = 3^2 - 2(3) - 2$ and

$$f\left(\frac{1}{x}\right) = \left(\frac{1}{x}\right)^2 - 2\left(\frac{1}{x}\right) - 2$$

If another function, such as $3x^2 - 1$, enters the same discussion, we may designate it by $F(x)$, $h(x)$, or by any letter other than f preceding (x).

Examples

1. If $f(x) = (x-1)(x+1)$, then $f(4) = (4-1)(4+1) = (3)(5) = 15$.
2. If $g(t) = 10t + 16t^2$, then $g(2) = 10(2) + 16(2^2) = 84$, and

$$g(-1) = 10(-1) + 16(-1)^2 = 6$$

3. If $h(s) = s^3 - 3s - 2$, then $h(2) = 2^3 - 3(2) - 2 = 0$, and

$$h(3) = 3^3 - 3(3) - 2 = 16$$

33. Functions of several variables. In plane geometry we have a theorem which states that the area A of a triangle is equal to one-half the product of the base b and the altitude h, or, $A = \frac{1}{2}bh$. This is an illustration of the definition that follows:

DEFINITION. *If a given variable, **w**, is so related to several others. **x, y, z**, . . . , that a value of **w** is determined when definite values are assigned to **x, y, z**, . . . , then **w** is said to be a **function of x, y, z**, ...*

We express this relation symbolically in the statement

$$w = w(x,y,z, \ldots)$$

Example

If $z(x,y) = x^2 + 3x - xy + y^2$, evaluate $z(1,2)$ and $z(\frac{1}{2}, -\frac{1}{3})$.

Solution

In order to find the value of $z(1,2)$, we replace x by 1 and y by 2 in $z(x,y)$. Hence,

$$z(1,2) = 1^2 + 3(1) - (1)(2) + 2^2$$
$$= 1 + 3 - 2 + 4$$
$$= 6$$

Similarly,

$$z(\tfrac{1}{2}, -\tfrac{1}{3}) = (\tfrac{1}{2})^2 + 3(\tfrac{1}{2}) - (\tfrac{1}{2})(-\tfrac{1}{3}) + (-\tfrac{1}{3})^2$$
$$= \tfrac{1}{4} + \tfrac{3}{2} + \tfrac{1}{6} + \tfrac{1}{9}$$
$$= \frac{9 + 54 + 6 + 4}{36}$$
$$= \tfrac{73}{36}$$

EXERCISE 14

1. If $y(x) = 3x + 5$, find $y(1)$, $y(2)$, $y(-1)$, $y(-\frac{5}{3})$.
2. If $y(x) = 2x - 3$, find $y(2)$, $y(3)$, $y(\frac{3}{2})$, $y(-2)$.

3. If $F(y) = 5y - 2$, find $F(3)$, $F(\frac{2}{5})$, $F(0)$, $F(-2)$.

4. If $F(y) = 4y + 3$, find $F(3)$, $F(1)$, $F(0)$, $(F-\frac{3}{4})$.

5. If $h(x) = x^2 - x + 1$, find $h(2)$, $h(0)$, $h(-1)$.

6. If $f(t) = 16t^2 - 5t - 3$, find $f(0)$, $f(2)$, $f(3)$.

7. If $g(y) = 5y^2 - 12y + 4$, find $g(3)$, $g(2)$, $g(-3)$.

8. If $k(x) = 3x^2 - 5x + 2$, find $k(4)$, $k(1)$, $k(-\frac{1}{2})$.

9. If $G(y) = \dfrac{2y - 1}{y^2 - y + 3}$, find $G(2)$, $G(\frac{1}{2})$, $G(-3)$.

10. If $k(t) = \dfrac{t - 3}{t^2 - t + 4}$, find $k(5)$, $k(3)$, $k(-\frac{1}{3})$.

11. If $Q(p) = \dfrac{p^2 + 2p - 3}{2p + 1}$, find $Q(1)$, $Q(0)$, $Q(-2)$.

12. If $S(m) = \dfrac{2m^2 - 3m + 1}{3m - 2}$, find $S(4)$, $S(1)$, $S(-\frac{1}{2})$.

13. If $F(t) = \dfrac{t^2 - 3t + 5}{t + 2}$, find $\dfrac{F(3)}{F(2)}$, $\dfrac{F(5)}{F(1)}$.

14. If $f(x) = \dfrac{x^2 - x + 4}{2x - 3}$, find $\dfrac{f(2)}{f(1)}$, $\dfrac{f(-3)}{f(-1)}$.

15. If $g(y) = \dfrac{y^2 - 2y + 3}{3y - 1}$, find $\dfrac{g(3)}{g(-1)}$, $\dfrac{g(-3)}{g(1)}$.

16. If $Z(w) = \dfrac{w^2 + 3w - 1}{w - 5}$, find $\dfrac{Z(-2)}{Z(3)}$, $\dfrac{Z(4)}{Z(-1)}$.

17. If $F(x) = x^2 - 1$, find $F(y)$, $F(y - 1)$, $F(2y)$.

18. If $G(z) = z^2 - 3z + 5$, find $G(t)$, $G(t + 2)$, $G(3y)$.

19. If $H(r) = 2r^2 + 4r + 3$, find $H(t - 1)$, $H(1/t)$, $H(t/2)$.

20. If $S(x) = x^2 + 3x - 1$, find $S(t - 2)$, $S\left(\dfrac{2}{t}\right)$, $S\left(\dfrac{1}{t + 1}\right)$.

21. If $y(x) = 3x - 2$, find $y(4) \div y(2)$.

22. If $h(t) = t^2 - 1$, find $h(1/x) \div h(x)$.

23. If $y(t) = 4t - 1$ and $s(t) = 2t - 3$, find $y\left(\dfrac{x - 1}{4}\right) \times s\left(\dfrac{x + 1}{2}\right)$.

24. If $g(y) = 2y + 1$ and $h(y) = 3y - 2$, find $g\left(\dfrac{s - 1}{2}\right) \times h\left(\dfrac{s + 2}{3}\right)$.

25. If $h(x,y) = x^2 + xy - y^2$, find $h(2,1)$, $h(1,-1)$.

26. If $g(s,t) = s^2 - 2st + t$, find $g(3,2)$, $g(-2,5)$.

27. If $V(r,h) = \pi r^2 h$, find $V(3,2)$, $V(2,5)$.

28. If $y(r,s) = \dfrac{r^2 + s^2}{r - s}$, find $y(4,3)$, $y(\frac{1}{3},\frac{1}{4})$, $y(\frac{1}{3},\frac{1}{9})$.

29. If $V(L,w,t) = Lwt$, find $V(5,3,1)$, $V(2,1,\frac{1}{2})$.

30. If $S(v,a,t) = vt + \frac{1}{2}at^2$, find $S(16,32,1)$, $S(2,32,5)$.

31. If $S(n,t_1,t_n) = \dfrac{n}{2}(t_1 + t_n)$, find $S(10,1,-3)$, $S(7,3,9)$.

32. If $F(x,y,z) = \dfrac{x - y + z}{x + y - z}$, find $F\left(\dfrac{1}{w}, \dfrac{1}{w + 1}, 1\right)$, $F\left(\dfrac{1}{w + 1}, \dfrac{1}{w - 1}, \dfrac{1}{w^2 - 1}\right)$.

34. *Graphical representation of functions.* The manner in which a function varies as the independent variable changes is an important subject in algebra. Its behavior can be studied by a graph or a pictorial representation of the corresponding values of the variable and the function.

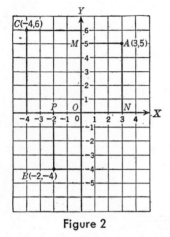

Figure 2

The graphical representation of functions depends upon a device known as the *rectangular coordinate system.* In order to set up such a system in a plane, we first select a horizontal and a vertical line in the plane and then choose a suitable scale on each. The horizontal line is called the X *axis,* the vertical line is known as the Y *axis,* and their intersection is called the *origin* (see Fig. 2). Next we shall agree that all horizontal distances measured to the right are positive, and all horizontal distances measured to the left are negative. Furthermore, all vertical distances directed upward are positive, and those directed downward are negative. Now we can see that every point in the plane determines two directed distances: from the Y axis to the point and from the X axis to the point. This brings us to the following definition:

DEFINITION. *The **abscissa,** or **x coordinate,** of a point in a plane is the directed distance from the Y axis to the point. It is positive or negative according as the point is to the right or to the left of the Y axis. The **ordinate,** or **y coordinate,** of a point is the directed distance from the X axis to the point, and it is positive or negative according as the point is above or below the X axis.*

The abscissa and ordinate are called the *coordinates* of a point and are written as a pair of numbers enclosed in parentheses and separated by a comma. The abscissa is written first.

Examples

In Fig. 2, the abscissa of A is $MA = 3$ and the ordinate is $NA = 5$. Hence, we write the coordinates as $(3,5)$. Both coordinates are positive since A is to the right of the Y axis and above the X axis. Similarly, the coordinates of B are $(-2,-4)$.

We may locate the point C, whose coordinates are $(-4,6)$, by starting at O and counting 4 units to the left on the X axis (why?) and then 6 units upward.

When a point has been located by means of its coordinates, we say that the point has been *plotted*.

We are now in position to discuss the graphical representation of functions, and we shall illustrate the procedure by explaining the steps in the construction of the graph of $x^2 - 2x - 2$. We first let the function be represented by y and thus obtain

(1) $$y = x^2 - 2x - 2$$

The next step is to assign several values to x and calculate each corresponding value of y. Before doing this, however, it is advisable to make a table like the one below in which the corresponding values of x and y can be recorded.

The values selected for x, in most cases, should be small, usually integers less than ten. In this case, we shall start with $x = 0$. Then let x equal 1, 2, 3, and 4. Finally, let $x = -1$, and $x = -2$.

When $x = 0$ $y = (0)^2 - 2(0) - 2 = -2$
$x = 1$ $y = (1)^2 - 2(1) - 2 = -3$
$x = 2$ $y = (2)^2 - 2(2) - 2 = -2$

This process is continued until the values of x mentioned above have been used. When a value is assigned to x, it should be recorded in the table and the corresponding value of y entered below it. The values of x should be entered in order of magnitude from left to right. When the value of y for each of the above values of x has been calculated and the results have been entered in the table, we have

x	-2	-1	0	1	2	3	4
y	6	1	-2	-3	-2	1	6

Now we take each pair of corresponding values of x and y as coordinates of a point and plot the points determined by the pairs of values in the above table. Finally, we connect the points thus

determined by a smooth curve. Thus, we obtain the curve in
Fig. 3. This curve is the graph of $x^2 - 2x - 2$, and it indicates
the following facts about the behavior of the function:

1. The value of the function is least, -3, when $x = 1$.

2. The value of the function increases rapidly both as x increases
and decreases from 1.

3. The value of the function is zero when x is equal to the
abscissas of the points where the graph crosses the X axis or at
$x = 2.7$ (approximately) and at
$x = -.7$ (approximately).

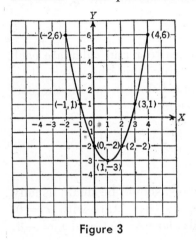

Figure 3

A *zero* of a function is a value of
the variable for which the function
is zero. For example, the zero of
$2x - 5$ is $x = 2\frac{1}{2}$. The zeros of
many classes of functions can be
obtained algebraically, but we must
depend upon graphical methods for
others. In the latter method, we
construct the graph of the function
and estimate the x coordinate of
each point where the graph crosses
the X axis. This estimate can be
made as accurate as necessary by choosing a sufficiently large scale.

For the present, we shall be concerned with functions whose
graphs are curves of unlimited length. Hence, only a portion
of the graph can be constructed, and we can usually obtain this
portion by using comparatively small values of x. It is usually
advisable to start with $x = 0$, assign several consecutive positive
integral values to x, using a sufficient number of values to determine the general trend of the curve, and then proceed in a similar
way by assigning consecutive negative values to x.

Some functions are such that the points obtained by assigning
consecutive integral values to x are so far apart in the plane that
we cannot tell how to draw the curve which connects them. For
example, if we assign the values -1, 0, and 1 to x in the function
$y = 9x^2 - 1$, we obtain the values 8, -1, and 8, respectively, for y
and thus determine the points A, B, and C in Fig. 4. These
points are not sufficient to determine the shape of the curve.

However, by using $x = -\frac{2}{3}$, $x = -\frac{1}{3}$, $x = \frac{1}{3}$, and $x = \frac{2}{3}$, we obtain the additional points D, E, F, and G. Using these, together with A, B, and C, we can easily draw the curve.

On the other hand, we have functions that, for consecutive values of x, yield points that are clustered so closely together in the plane that only a small portion of the curve is determined. In such cases, instead of using consecutive integral values for x, we assign values that are more widely separated, probably numbers that differ by 2, 3, or 5. The idea is to use values for x that will yield a sufficient number of points in the plane to determine a curve. In the function $y = x/5$, the curve can be clearly defined by letting $x = -30$, -20, -10, 0, 10, 20, and 30.

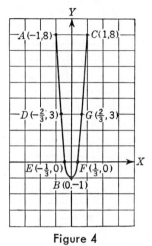

Figure 4

35. Linear functions. A *linear function* of x is a function of the type $ax + b$ in which a and b are constants and a is not zero. It is proved in analytic geometry that the graph of a linear function is a straight line. Hence, the graph of a linear function is completely determined by two points. It is advisable, however, in obtaining the graph of such a function, to determine a third point as a check on the accuracy of the other two. It is also advisable to assign values to x that will determine points that are sufficiently far apart to determine accurately the direction of the graph.

Example

In order to construct the graph of $3x - 5$, we first set the function equal to y and obtain

(1) $$y = 3x - 5$$

Now we assign the values -1, 0, and 3 to x and obtain the following table of corresponding values of x and y:

x	-1	0	3
y	-8	-5	4

When these points are plotted and connected by a straight line, we obtain the graph in Fig. 5.

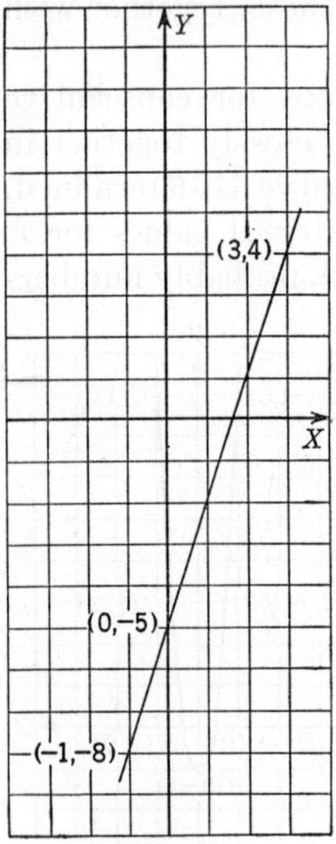

If the three points obtained for the graph of a linear function do not lie along a straight line, one must check one's computation, for certainly at least one error has been made.

Figure 5

EXERCISE 15

1. Plot the points represented by $(3,4)$; $(5,6)$; $(0,3)$; $(-3,0)$; $(0,4)$, $(5,-3)$; $(4,-1)$, $(-2,3)$; $(-4,2)$; $(-3,-2)$; $(-5,-6)$.

2. Where are all points located whose abscissas are zero? Whose ordinates are zero? Whose coordinates are equal numbers? Whose coordinates have the same numerical value but are opposite in sign?

3. Where are all points located whose abscissas are 3? Whose abscissas are -4? Whose ordinates are 5? Whose ordinates are -6?

4. In what quadrant is each of the following points located if k is positive: $(2,k)$; $(-2,k)$; $(-k,3)$; $(-k,-3)$; (k,k); $(k,-k)$; (k^2,k); $(k^2,-k)$; $(-k,k^2)$?

5. In what quadrant is each of the points in Problem 4 located if k is negative?

Plot the graphs of the functions in Problems 6 to 17.

6. $x - 2$.

7. $x + 2$.

8. $2x - 3$.

9. $3x + 2$.

10. $2x + 3$.

11. $3x - 1$.

12. $5x - 7$.

13. $4x + 5$.

14. $\frac{2}{3}x - 5$.

15. $\frac{1}{2}x + 9$.

16. $4 - \frac{3}{5}x$.

17. $5 - \frac{3}{4}x$.

Plot the graph of the function in each of Problems 18 to 25. Estimate the zeros of each function from the graph.

18. $x^2 + x - 3$.

19. $x^2 + 3x - 3$.

20. $x^2 + 5x + 5$.

21. $x^2 + 6x + 6$.

22. $2x^2 + 3x - 6$.

23. $3x^2 - 6x - 5$.

24. $-2x^2 + x + 9$.

25. $-3x^2 + 7x + 3$.

36. *Graphical representation of statistics.* Many tables of statistics or tables of scientific data set forth a set of related numbers. The information is usually written in two columns with corresponding quantities on the same horizontal line. For example, the following table shows the postal receipts for a small town for a period of 20 years:

Year	Postal receipts	Year	Postal receipts
1928	$5500	1938	$4800
1929	6000	1939	4600
1930	5700	1940	4600
1931	4800	1941	5000
1932	4400	1942	6300
1933	4000	1943	7900
1934	4400	1944	8600
1935	4400	1945	9000
1936	4400	1946	7300
1937	4800	1947	8400

This table establishes a functional relationship between two variables, the year and the postal receipts, since if any year between

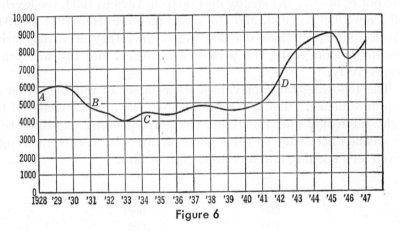

Figure 6

1927 and 1948 is specified, the amount of the postal receipts is definitely determined and can be ascertained by looking at the table. This functional relationship is in no sense mathematical, and no mathematical formula exists that connects the two quantities. We can, however, use an adaptation of the previously discussed graphing method to obtain a graphical representation of these data. For this purpose, we choose a horizontal line in the plane and lay off 19 equal intervals on it (see Fig. 6), and let the successive left ends of each interval represent the years taken in order from 1928 to 1946, and the right end of the last interval represent 1947. Through the left end of the first interval, we draw a vertical line and lay off on it intervals of equal length whose upper extremities, taken in order, represent successive multiples of $1000. If graph paper is used, it is advisable to choose 10 of the shortest units on the paper as the length of each of the above intervals. Then the upper extremities of the short units represent multiples of $100. Now, with respect to these two lines as axes, we may plot a point representing each year and the corresponding amount of the postal receipts listed in the table. For example, the point A represents the $5500 for 1928, and the points B, C, and D represent the amounts for 1931, 1934, and 1942, respectively. When the plotted points are joined by a curve, we obtain the graph in Fig. 6. While this curve is in no sense algebraic, it is a decided visual aid in interpreting the data. We notice at once the steady decline from 1929 to 1933, the leveling off from 1933 to 1940, and the sharp increase from 1941 to 1945. We would expect these decided trends since they occurred during the depression years, the period of recovery, and the war years, respectively.

The following table of values shows a set of readings from an exposure meter. The left column shows the measurements of the light intensity, and the right, the corresponding exposure time in seconds necessary to get a good picture with a camera using a given lens opening and a certain type of film.

Light intensity	Exposure in seconds
600	.0025
400	.004
300	.0057
200	.0087
150	.011
100	.017
75	.022
50	.033
25	.067

Figure 7 shows the graph of these data. In this case, we obtain a smooth and regular curve, and this suggests that the length of the exposure might be a mathematical function of the light intensity. In fact, it is, but the method of obtaining this relationship will not be discussed here. We can use the curve, however, to obtain the exposure corresponding to light intensities not shown in the table. For example, the exposure corresponding to the light intensity of 175 is .009.

The graphs of scientific data frequently lead to the discovery of laws. When the curve is regular, advanced methods enable

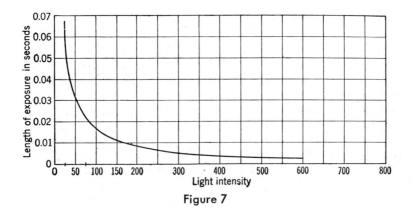

Figure 7

us to find an equation that fits the curve, or at least a portion of it. When we obtain the equation, we have the law governing the situation.

EXERCISE 16

Construct a graph representing the data given in each of the following problems.

1. The table below shows the pressure of saturated water vapor at various temperatures (centigrade).

Temperature in degrees (C.)	Pressure in centimeters of mercury	Temperature in degrees (C.)	Pressure in centimeters of mercury
0	0.46	60	14.9
10	0.92	80	35.5
20	1.75	100	76.0
30	3.17	120	148.9
40	5.51	140	270.9

2. The osmotic pressure for sucrose solution at various concentrations at 0°C. is given in the table below. The concentration is expressed in moles per 1000 g., and the pressure is expressed in atmospheres.

Concentration	Pressure	Concentration	Pressure
0.1	2.462	0.6	14.381
0.2	4.723	0.8	19.476
0.4	9.443	1.0	24.826

3. The following table shows the distance that a car, traveling at the indicated speed, will move after the application of the brakes. The speed is given in miles per hour and the distance in feet.

Speed	Distance	Speed	Distance
0	0	60	230
10	29	70	300
20	39	80	380
30	70	90	470
40	110	100	560
50	160		

4. In the table below, the left column indicates the measurement of light intensity and the right the corresponding exposure time in seconds necessary to get a good picture using a camera with a given lens opening and a certain type of film.

Light intensity	Exposure time	Light intensity	Exposure time
25	.05	200	.007
50	.025	300	.004
75	.018	400	.003
100	.013	600	.002
150	.01		

5. In the table below, the left column represents the temperature in degrees Fahrenheit, and the right the corresponding development time in minutes required to obtain a negative of required density using a certain type of film.

Temperature	Time	Temperature	Time
55	15	75	7.4
60	12.8	80	6
65	10.9	85	4.5
70	9	90	3.6

6. The following table gives the value of urban building in the United States for the indicated year. The average of the values from 1935 to 1939 is taken as 100.

Year	Value	Year	Value
1930	162	1942	129
1933	35	1945	94
1936	96	1948	332
1939	128		

7. The public school attendance in millions of students is given in the table below.

Year	Attendance	Year	Attendance
1880	6.1	1920	16.2
1890	8.2	1930	21.3
1900	10.6	1940	22.0
1910	12.8	1947	20.5

8. The table below gives the number of teachers in the United States in units of 10,000.

Year	Teachers	Year	Teachers
1880	28.7	1920	67.9
1890	36.4	1930	85.4
1900	42.3	1940	87.5
1910	52.3	1947	83.3

9. The following table shows the total amount of teachers' salaries, in units of 10 million dollars, paid during the indicated year in the United States.

Year	Amount paid in salaries	Year	Amount paid in salaries
1880	5.6	1920	61.3
1890	9.1	1930	129.5
1900	13.8	1940	137.0
1910	25.4	1947	198.0

10. The number of millions of express shipments for the indicated year is given in the table below.

Year	Shipments	Year	Shipments
1940	1.1	1945	2.1
1941	1.3	1946	3.2
1942	1.4	1947	3.8
1943	1.5	1948	4.1
1944	1.8		

11. The following table gives the number of millions of motor vehicles in the United States at intervals of 2 years from 1936 to 1948.

Year	Vehicles	Year	Vehicles
1936	26.4	1944	30.5
1938	30.0	1946	34.4
1940	31.1	1948	41.2
1942	30.0		

12. The average hourly income for workers in the industrial trades for the years 1941 to 1949 is given in the table below.

Year	Income	Year	Income
1941	$.70	1946	$1.05
1942	.80	1947	1.18
1943	.89	1948	1.29
1944	.95	1949	1.34
1945	.96		

13. The table below shows the number of automobiles, in units of 100,000, manufactured in the United States during the indicated year.

Year	Automobiles	Year	Automobiles
1900	.04	1940	37.2
1910	1.8	1945	.69
1920	19.1	1947	35.6
1930	27.8	1948	39.1
1935	32.5		

14. The electric energy in units of 10^9 kilowatt hours produced in the United States for the indicated year is given in the following table.

Year	Electric energy	Year	Electric energy
1925	61	1942	186
1930	91	1944	228
1935	95	1946	223
1940	142	1948	283

15. For the indicated year, the cigar production in the United States in units of 10^9 cigars is given below.

Year	Cigars	Year	Cigars
1920	8.1	1940	5.2
1925	6.5	1942	5.8
1930	5.9	1944	5.2
1935	4.7	1946	5.6

16. The value of the minerals produced in the United States in units of 10^9 dollars is shown in the table below.

Year	Minerals	Year	Minerals
1910	2.0	1942	7.6
1920	7.0	1944	8.4
1930	4.7	1946	8.9
1940	5.6	1948	15.6

17. The amount, in units of one billion dollars, of the Federal, state, and local public debt in the United States for the indicated year is given in the table below.

Year	Debt	Year	Debt
1917	12	1937	55
1921	30	1941	73
1925	30	1945	266
1929	30	1948	233
1933	41		

18. The following table shows the amount, in units of 10^9 dollars, of life insurance in force in the United States for the indicated year.

Year	Insurance	Year	Insurance
1925	72	1942	130
1930	108	1944	149
1935	101	1946	175
1940	118	1948	207

19. The number of soldiers, in units of 10,000, in the United States Army for the indicated year is given in the table below.

Year	Soldiers	Year	Soldiers
1920	20.2	1942	307.4
1925	13.6	1944	799.3
1930	13.8	1946	189.0
1935	13.9	1948	55.2
1940	26.8		

20. The number of persons, in units of 10,000, receiving pensions in the United States for the indicated year is given in the table below.

Year	Persons	Year	Persons
1890	538	1935	839
1900	994	1940	849
1910	921	1943	860
1920	770	1946	2632
1930	841	1949	2949

21. The snowfall in inches in New York City for the indicated year is given in the following table.

Year	Snowfall	Year	Snowfall
1888	47	1932	5
1899	58	1937	12
1915	29	1942	10
1922	30	1947	33
1927	22	1948	62

CHAPTER 6

SIMULTANEOUS LINEAR EQUATIONS

37. Linear equations in two unknowns. If the dependent variable appears explicitly in a functional relationship, we have an equation in two unknowns. For example, the statement

$$(1) \qquad\qquad y = \tfrac{3}{4}x - 5$$

not only exhibits y as a linear function of x, but it also asserts that two quantities are equal, and hence it is an equation. Any pair of numbers, one for x and the other for y, for which the two members of (1) are equal is a *solution* of the equation. We can obtain as many solutions of (1) as we please by simply assigning values to x and then computing each corresponding value of y. Obviously, the coordinates of any point on the graph of (1) constitute a solution.

By Axioms I and II of Art. 27,[1] we know that any solution of (1) is also a solution of

$$(2) \quad 4y = 3x - 20 \qquad \text{[obtained by multiplying each member of (1) by 4]}$$

and also of

$$(3) \quad 3x - 4y = 20 \qquad \text{(obtained by transposing } 3x \text{ and dividing by } -1)$$

If two equations have the same solution, we say that they are *equivalent*.

In the next three articles, we shall discuss equations described in the following definition:

[1] The content of Art. 27 applies to equations containing any number of unknowns, and in this article, and in the following articles that deal with equations, we shall use the ideas presented there.

DEFINITION. *An equation that is equivalent to one of the type* $ax + by = c$, *where* a, b, *and* c *are constants, is called a* **linear equation in two unknowns.**

38. Solution of two linear equations in two unknowns—graphical method. We stated in the previous article that a linear equation in two unknowns has infinitely many solutions. Usually, however, only one pair of values will satisfy two such equations simultaneously. This pair of values is called the *solution* of the two equations.

Since the coordinates of any point on the graph of a linear equation in two unknowns satisfy the equation, the coordinates of the point of intersection of the graphs of two such equations form the solution of the two. In order to obtain the graph, we solve the equation for y and then apply the method of Art. 35.

Example

Solve the equations

(1) $$3x + 2y = 14$$
(2) $$2x - y = 2$$

graphically.

Solution

First, we solve (1) and (2) for y and obtain

(3) $$y = -\tfrac{3}{2}x + 7$$

and

(4) $$y = 2x - 2$$

Now, using the method of Art. 35, we assign the values -2, 0, and 4 to x in (3) and -3, 0, and 3 to x in (4), and obtain the following tables of corresponding values of x and y:

x	-2	0	4
y	10	7	1

from (3) and

x	-3	0	3
y	-8	-2	4

from (4)

When we plot the points determined by these two tables and draw the graphs, we obtain Fig. 8. These graphs intersect at the point whose coordinates are approximately $(2.6, 3.2)$. Hence, we say that, according to our graph, the solution of Eqs. (1) and (2) is $x = 2.6$ and $y = 3.2$. This is as accurate as we can get the solution without using a larger scale. If we substitute these values in the left member of (1), we get

$$3(2.6) + 2(3.2) = 7.8 + 6.4 = 14.2$$

Similarly, for the same values of x and y, the left member of (2) becomes

$$2(2.6) - 3.2 = 5.2 - 3.2 = 2$$

Since the right members of (1) and (2) are 14 and 2, respectively, we see that the pair of values $x = 2.6$, $y = 3.2$, is not the exact solution of the two equations, but to one decimal place these values are probably correct.

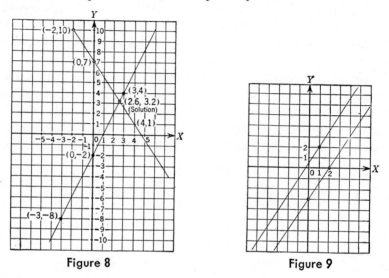

Figure 8   Figure 9

It may happen that the graphs of two linear equations are parallel lines. For example, the graphs of the equations

$$(5) \qquad\qquad 3x - 2y = 6$$

and

$$(6) \qquad\qquad 9x - 6y = -3$$

shown in Fig. 9 are parallel lines. Hence, the equations have no solution. This fact can be seen algebraically if one observes that the left member of (6) is exactly 3 times the left member of (5). Hence, any pair of values which makes the left member of (5) equal to 6 makes the left member of (6) equal to 18, and not -3.

Again, we might have two equations whose graphs coincide. Then every pair of values which satisfies the first equation satisfies the second also, and the pair of equations has an infinite number of solutions.

If two equations in two unknowns have one and only one solution, they are called *consistent equations*. If they have no solution, they are called *inconsistent equations*, and if they have an infinite number of solutions, they are called *dependent equations*.

Although the graphical approach helps us to understand the above three types of linear equation pairs, it is not an efficient method for obtaining the solution, when one exists. In the first place, it is too cumbersome. In the second, the accuracy of the method depends upon the solver's skill in constructing the two graphs and in estimating the coordinates of their point of intersection. The two algebraic methods which we shall next present can be performed more easily, and they yield the solution, when it exists, with absolute accuracy.

EXERCISE 17

Find the solutions of the following pairs of equations to one decimal place, using the graphical method. Identify the pairs that are inconsistent and those that are dependent.

1. $3x + y = 7$
$2x - 3y = 12.$

2. $x + 3y = 2$
$3x + 4y = -4.$

3. $x - 7y = 11$
$x + 3y = 1.$

4. $2x + y = 3$
$x - 2y = 9.$

5. $x + 2y = 4$
$5x - 2y = 2.$

6. $4x + y = -1$
$2x + y = 0.$

7. $2x + 3y = 1$
$4x + 3y = -4.$

8. $x + 2y = -1$
$x - 2y = 5.$

9. $3x + 4y = 12$
$x - y = 1.$

10. $3x - 2y = 6$
$3x - 2y = -6.$

11. $x - 2y = 1$
$2x - 4y = 3.$

12. $3x - 5y = 15$
$2x + 3y = 6.$

13. $x + 3y = 4$
$2x + 6y = 8.$

14. $2x - 4y = 6$
$3x - 6y = 9.$

15. $2x - 5y = 10$
$x + 2y = -2.$

16. $2x + 4y = 3$
$x - 2y = 1.$

17. $2x - 4y = 3$
$3x - 6y = 1.$

18. $3x - 6y = 4$
$2x - 4y = 3.$

19. $5x - 3y = 6$
$4x + 5y = 3.$

20. $4x + 5y = 0$
$2x - 4y = 3.$

21. $7x - 5y = 3$
$5x + 7y = 2.$

22. $7x + 4y = 2$
$5x - 3y = -7.$

23. $3x - 9y = 6$
$2x - 6y = 4.$

24. $x - 2y = 4$
$2x + y = 2.$

39. *Elimination of a variable by addition or subtraction.* In order to solve two linear equations in two unknowns, we first *eliminate* one of the variables. That is, we obtain from the two given equations a third equation in one unknown whose solution is one of the values sought. We then substitute this value in one of the given equations and solve for the other unknown. Probably the method most often used is the one known as *elimination by* *addition or subtraction*, and we shall explain the process by applying it to the equations

(1) $\qquad\qquad\qquad\qquad 2x - 3y = 6$
(2) $\qquad\qquad\qquad\qquad 3x + 2y = 12$

We assume at the start that there is a value of x and an associated value of y that will satisfy each of these equations. Then by Axiom II of Art. 27, the same pair of values will satisfy

(3) $4x - 6y = 12$ [obtained by multiplying each member of (1) by 2]

(4) $9x + 6y = 36$ [obtained by multiplying each member of (2) by 3]

Furthermore, by I of Art. 27, the equation obtained by adding the corresponding members of (3) and (4) will also be satisfied by the same pair of values. However, this addition yields

(5) $\qquad\qquad\qquad\qquad 13x = 48$

which contains only one variable x, and the solution is

(6) $\qquad\qquad\qquad\qquad x = \frac{48}{13}$

This is the value of x sought. We can complete the process by substituting $\frac{48}{13}$ for x in either of the given equations and then solving for y. If we use Eq. (1), we get

$$2\left(\frac{48}{13}\right) - 3y = 6$$

or

$$\frac{96}{13} - 3y = 6$$

Transposing $\frac{96}{13}$, we get

$$-3y = 6 - \frac{96}{13}$$
$$= \frac{78 - 96}{13}$$
$$= -\frac{18}{13}$$

Hence,

$$y = -\frac{18}{13} \div -3$$
$$= \frac{6}{13}$$

Therefore, the solution is $x = \frac{48}{13}$, $y = \frac{6}{13}$.

Since we used Eq. (1) to obtain the value of y, the above solution will satisfy (1) unless an error was made in computation. However, if the solution satisfies (2), we can be reasonably certain that it is correct. For the above values of x and y, the left member of (2) becomes

$$3\left(\tfrac{48}{13}\right) + 2\left(\tfrac{6}{13}\right) = \tfrac{144}{13} + \tfrac{12}{13} = \tfrac{156}{13} = 12$$

Hence, since the right member of (2) is 12, the solution checks.

We could have solved this problem with about the same amount of computation if we had started by eliminating x instead of y. Often, however, the process of elimination will be slightly longer for one variable than for the other. Hence, it is advisable to study the problem before starting, so as to select the method that will involve the least amount of computation.

The steps in the solution of two linear equations in two unknowns may be summarized as follows:

1. *Select the unknown that will be easier to eliminate.*

2. *Find the L.C.M. of the two coefficients of this unknown.*

3. *Multiply both members of each equation by the quotient of the above L.C.M. and the coefficient of the selected variable in that equation.*

4. *Add or subtract the corresponding members of the equations obtained in step 3 according as the terms containing the selected unknown have unlike or like signs.*

5. *Solve the resulting equation for the variable that remains.*

6. *Substitute the value obtained in step 5 in one of the given equations and solve for the other unknown.*

7. *Write as the solution,* $x =$ _____, $y =$ _____, *filling the blanks with the values obtained in steps 5 and 6.*

8. *Check by substituting the values in step 7 in the original equation not used in step 6.*

Example

Solve the equations

(7) $\qquad\qquad\qquad 4x - 11y = -3$
(8) $\qquad\qquad\qquad 6x + 7y = 19$

Solution

The lowest common multiples of the coefficients of x and of y are 12 and 77, respectively. Hence, we shall introduce smaller numbers if we eliminate x instead of y.

If we divide 12 by 4 and then by 6, we get 3 and 2, respectively. Hence, we multiply both members of (7) by 3, and both members of (8) by 2 and get

(9) $$12x - 33y = -9$$
(10) $$12x + 14y = 38$$

Since the terms involving x have the same sign, we subtract (10) from (9) and get

(11) $$-47y = -47$$

Hence,

$$y = 1$$

Substituting $y = 1$ in (7), we get

(12) $$4x - 11 = -3$$

Therefore,

$$4x = 11 - 3 = 8$$

and

$$x = 2$$

Hence, the solution is $x = 2$, $y = 1$.

Since Eq. (7) was used in the process of obtaining the value of x, we must check our solution by the use of (8). When $x = 2$ and $y = 1$, the left member of (8) becomes

$$6(2) + 7(1) = 12 + 7 = 19$$

Hence, since the right member of (8) is 19, the solution checks.

40. Elimination of a variable by substitution. We shall list below the steps in the method of elimination by substitution, and then we shall illustrate the application of these steps by means of two examples. For the sake of definiteness, we shall assume that y is the variable to be eliminated. However, the directions below can be used for the elimination of x by interchanging x and y in each of the following steps:

1. *Solve one of the equations for* **y** *in terms of* **x**.

2. *Substitute this linear function of* **x** *for* **y** *in the other equation, thus obtaining an equation that contains only the unknown* **x**.

3. *Solve the latter equation for* **x**.

4. *Substitute this value of* **x** *in the function obtained in step 1, and then calculate the value of* **y**.

5. *State the solution as* **x** = ____, **y** = ____, *filling the blanks with the values obtained in steps 3 and 4.*

6. *Check by substituting the solution in the equation not used in step 1.*

Example 1

Solve the equations

$$(1) \qquad\qquad 5x + 3y = 13$$
$$(2) \qquad\qquad 3x - y = 5$$

simultaneously.

Solution

1. We note here that if we solve Eq. (2) for y, we do not obtain fractions. If this is done, we get

$$(3) \qquad\qquad y = 3x - 5$$

2. Next we substitute $3x - 5$ for y in Eq. (1) and get

$$5x + 3(3x - 5) = 13$$

3. Solving this equation, we have

$$5x + 9x - 15 = 13$$
$$14x = 28$$
$$x = 2$$

4. Now we substitute 2 for x in Eq. (3) and obtain

$$y = 3(2) - 5$$

and

$$y = 1$$

5. Hence, the solution is $x = 2$, $y = 1$.

6. Since we used Eq. (2) in step 1, we shall check by substituting the above solution in the left member of Eq. (1). Thus, we get

$$5(2) + 3(1) = 10 + 3 = 13$$

Hence, since the right member of (2) is 13, the solution checks.

Example 2

Solve the equations

$$(4) \qquad\qquad 6x + 5y = 13$$
$$(5) \qquad\qquad 7x - 4y = 25$$

simultaneously.

Solution

1. Since we cannot avoid fractions in the first step in the solution of these two equations, it makes little difference which equation we start with or which

unknown we solve for. Hence, we shall arbitrarily start with (4) and solve it for x and obtain

(6) $$x = \frac{13 - 5y}{6}$$

2. When the right member of (6) is substituted for x in (5), we have

(7) $$7\left(\frac{13 - 5y}{6}\right) - 4y = 25$$

3. Clearing (7) of fractions by multiplying each of its members by 6, we have

$$7(13 - 5y) - 24y = 150$$

or

$$91 - 35y - 24y = 150$$

Combining and transposing, we have

$$-59y = 150 - 91$$
$$= 59$$

Hence,

$$y = -1$$

4. Substituting -1 for y in (6), we have

$$x = \frac{13 - 5(-1)}{6}$$
$$= \frac{13 + 5}{6}$$
$$= 3$$

5. Hence, the solution is $x = 3$, $y = -1$.

6. Now we check by substituting this solution in the left member of (5) and get

$$7(3) - 4(-1) = 25$$

Hence, since the right member of (5) is 25, the solution checks.

EXERCISE 18

Solve the pair of equations in each of Problems 1 to 16 by the method of addition or subtraction.

1. $x + 2y = 5$
$3x - y = 1.$

2. $3x - 4y = -2$
$x + 2y = -4.$

3. $4x + 3y = -1$
$2x - y = 7.$

4. $6x - 5y = -4$
$3x + y = 5.$

5. $2x + 3y = 3$
$3x + 5y = 4.$

6. $5x - 4y = 1$
$2x - 3y = 6.$

7. $3x + 8y = 1$
$2x + 7y = 4.$

8. $4x + 5y = 1$
$3x + 2y = -8.$

9. $2x + 4y = 11$
$4x - 3y = 0.$

10. $3x - 2y = 1$
$12x - 18y = -11.$

11. $24x + 12y = 49$
$3x + 8y = -2.$

12. $20x - 30y = -27$
$8x + 15y = 0.$

13. $\frac{2}{3}x - \frac{1}{4}y = 1$
$\frac{1}{3}x + \frac{3}{4}y = 4.$

14. $\frac{1}{2}x - \frac{3}{5}y = 3$
$\frac{3}{2}x - \frac{2}{5}y = 2.$

15. $\frac{3}{4}x - 2y = \frac{1}{4}$
$\frac{2}{3}x - y = -\frac{3}{4}.$

16. $\frac{3}{2}x - \frac{1}{3}y = 2$
$\frac{1}{4}x + \frac{1}{6}y = 1.$

Solve the pair of equations in each of Problems 17 to 32 by substitution.

17. $2x + 7y = 3$
$x - 5y = -7.$

18. $4x + 9y = -1$
$5x - y = 11.$

19. $5x - 7y = 1$
$x + 3y = 9.$

20. $8x + 3y = 12$
$6x - y = 22.$

21. $7x - 3y = -1$
$3x - 2y = -4.$

22. $4x + 5y = -14$
$2x - 3y = 26.$

23. $6x + 5y = 5$
$4x + 3y = 1.$

24. $3x - 5y = -10$
$4x - 3y = 16.$

25. $x + 2y = 3$
$12x - 18y = 1.$

26. $2x - 4y = -5$
$4x + 2y = 5.$

27. $3x + 4y = 5$
$24x - 36y = -11.$

28. $5x + 2y = 3$
$30x - 50y = -13.$

29. $\frac{1}{2}x + \frac{1}{3}y = \frac{3}{2}$
$x - 2y = -5.$

30. $\frac{3}{2}x + \frac{2}{3}y = 1$
$3x + 2y = 0.$

31. $\frac{2}{3}x + \frac{3}{4}y = \frac{5}{6}$
$4x + 3y = 4.$

32. $\frac{5}{3}x + \frac{2}{5}y = \frac{1}{4}$
$2x + y = -1.$

Solve the equations in Problems 33 to 48 by either method.

33. $\dfrac{x+y}{2} + \dfrac{y}{3} = \dfrac{1}{6}$
$x - y = 3.$

34. $\dfrac{x}{4} - \dfrac{x-y}{6} = -\dfrac{1}{4}$
$3x - y = 5.$

35. $\dfrac{x+2y}{2} + \dfrac{2x-y}{4} = \dfrac{15}{4}$
$x + 3y = 6.$

36. $\dfrac{2x-y}{3} - \dfrac{3x-2y}{4} = \dfrac{5}{12}$
$2x - 3y = -6.$

37. $\dfrac{2x-2y+1}{x-y+2} = 3$
$x + 2y = 1.$

38. $\dfrac{3x-y+2}{x+3y-1} = 2$
$2x - 3y = 14.$

39. $\dfrac{2x+y-1}{3x-y+1} = \dfrac{3}{2}$
$3x - 4y = 1.$

40. $\dfrac{3x+y-2}{2x-3y+2} = \dfrac{3}{4}$
$3x + 2y = -2.$

41. $\dfrac{2x-y}{3} + \dfrac{x+2y}{2} = 1$
$\dfrac{x-y}{2} - \dfrac{2x+y}{3} = \dfrac{4}{3}.$

42. $\dfrac{4x-y}{3} - \dfrac{2x+y}{2} = -\dfrac{13}{6}$
$\dfrac{x+2y}{4} + \dfrac{3x-4y}{3} = -\dfrac{5}{4}$

43. $\dfrac{3x-4y}{5} - \dfrac{2x-3y}{3} = \dfrac{1}{3}$
$\dfrac{2x+5y}{3} - \dfrac{2x-y}{6} = \dfrac{7}{6}.$

44. $\dfrac{4x-y}{6} - \dfrac{2x+5y}{4} = \dfrac{10}{3}$
$\dfrac{5x-2y}{3} - \dfrac{3x-y}{9} = \dfrac{46}{9}.$

45. $ax + b^2y = m$
$a^2x + by = am.$

46. $ax + (a - b)y = b$
$bx + (a + b)y = -a.$

47. $ax + b^2y = a$
$bx + a^2y = b.$

48. $abx + b^2y = 1$
$a^3x + b^3y = a.$

In Problems 49 to 56, solve for $1/x$ and $1/y$ and then for x and for y.

49. $\dfrac{2}{x} - \dfrac{1}{y} = 1$

$\dfrac{3}{x} + \dfrac{2}{y} = -1.$

50. $\dfrac{3}{x} + \dfrac{2}{y} = 3$

$\dfrac{4}{x} + \dfrac{3}{y} = 2.$

51. $\dfrac{5}{x} + \dfrac{3}{y} = 7$

$\dfrac{3}{x} + \dfrac{4}{y} = 2.$

52. $\dfrac{4}{x} + \dfrac{5}{y} = 7$

$\dfrac{5}{x} - \dfrac{2}{y} = 12.$

53. $\dfrac{9}{x} - \dfrac{3}{y} = 1$

$\dfrac{5}{x} + \dfrac{2}{y} = 3.$

54. $\dfrac{11}{x} + \dfrac{3}{y} = 28$

$\dfrac{9}{x} - \dfrac{5}{y} = 8.$

55. $\dfrac{8}{x} - \dfrac{3}{y} = 27$

$\dfrac{7}{x} + \dfrac{6}{y} = 15.$

56. $\dfrac{10}{x} + \dfrac{7}{y} = 6$

$\dfrac{8}{x} + \dfrac{5}{y} = 3.$

57. If $I_a = \dfrac{E}{R + R_a}$ and $E = RI$, show that $R = \dfrac{R_a I_a}{I - I_a}$.

41. *Three linear equations in three unknowns.* The solution of three linear equations in three unknowns, when it exists, consists of three numbers, one for each of the unknowns, which satisfy all the given equations. In order to determine this solution, we first eliminate one of the variables. That is, we obtain from the given equations two linear equations in two unknowns, whose solution is two of the numbers sought. The value of the third unknown can then be determined by substitution.

The method most often used for eliminating the first unknown is that of addition or subtraction, and we shall illustrate it by means of the following examples:

Example 1

Solve the equations

(1) $\qquad\qquad 3x - 2y + 3z = 16$
(2) $\qquad\qquad x + 3y - 6z = -23$
(3) $\qquad\qquad 5x + 4y - 2z = -9$

simultaneously.

Solution

Since the coefficient of z in (2) is divisible by the coefficients of z in (1) and (3), we shall start by eliminating z. We accomplish this by first multiplying (1) by 2 and then adding (2); thus,

(4) $\qquad\qquad 6x - 4y + 6z = 32 \qquad$ [Eq. (1) $\times$ 2]
(2) $\qquad\qquad \underline{x + 3y - 6z = -23}$
(5) $\qquad\qquad 7x - y = 9 \qquad$ [Eq. (4) + Eq. (2)]

Next we multiply Eq. (3) by 3 and subtract the result from Eq. (2) and get

$$(2) \qquad x + 3y - 6z = -23$$
$$(6) \qquad \underline{15x + 12y - 6z = -27} \qquad [\text{Eq. (3)} \times 3]$$
$$(7) \qquad -14x - 9y \qquad\quad = 4 \qquad [\text{Eq. (2)} - \text{Eq. (6)}]$$

Now we have Eqs. (5) and (7) which contain x and y only, and we can solve them by the method of Art. 39, as indicated below.

$$(8) \qquad 14x - 2y = 18 \qquad [\text{Eq. (5)} \times 2]$$
$$(7) \qquad \underline{-14x - 9y = 4}$$
$$\qquad\qquad - 11y = 22 \qquad [\text{Eq. (8)} + \text{Eq. (7)}]$$
$$\qquad\qquad\qquad y = -2$$

Substituting $y = -2$ in (5), we get

$$7x - (-2) = 9$$
$$7x + 2 = 9$$
$$7x = 7$$
$$x = 1$$

Hence, $x = 1$, $y = -2$, are two of the values sought. We may obtain z by substituting these values in any one of the three original equations. We shall choose (1), and after substituting we have

$$3(1) - 2(-2) + 3z = 16$$

or

$$3 + 4 + 3z = 16$$

Combining, transposing, and solving for z, we get

$$3z = 16 - 7$$
$$3z = 9$$
$$z = 3$$

Hence, the solution is $x = 1$, $y = -2$, $z = 3$. This solution may be checked by substituting in either (2) or (3).

Example 2

Solve the equations

$$(9) \qquad 3x + 4y - 5z = 37$$
$$(10) \qquad 2x - 3y + 2z = -8$$
$$(11) \qquad x \qquad\quad - 2z = 11$$

simultaneously.

Solution

Since Eq. (11) contains x and z only, we shall eliminate y from (9) and (10) and solve the resulting equation with (11). The steps in this process follow.

(12) $9x + 12y - 15z = 111$ [Eq. (9) × 3]
(13) $8x - 12y + 8z = -32$ [Eq. (10) × 4]
(14) $17x \quad\quad - 7z = 79$ [Eq. (12) + Eq. (13)]

We shall next eliminate x from (11) and (14) and solve for z.

(15) $17x - 34z = 187$ [Eq. (11) × 17]
(14) $17x - 7z = 79$

$$-27z = 108 \quad\quad \text{[Eq. (15) − Eq. (14)]}$$
$$z = -4$$

Substituting $z = -4$ in (11), we have

$$x - 2(-4) = 11$$
$$x + 8 = 11$$
$$x = 3$$

Finally, we substitute $x = 3$, $z = -4$ in (9) and get

$$3(3) + 4y - 5(-4) = 37$$
$$9 + 4y + 20 = 37$$
$$4y = 37 - 29 = 8$$
$$y = 2$$

Thus, the solution is $x = 3$, $y = 2$, $z = -4$.

This solution may be checked by substituting these values in Eq. (10).

The method of elimination by substitution may also be employed in the solution of three linear equations in three unknowns. In fact, it is advisable to use this method when two of the equations contain only two variables.

Example 3

Solve the equations

(16) $2x - y \quad\quad = 11$
(17) $3x \quad\quad + 5z = 17$
(18) $2x + 5y + 4z = -3$

simultaneously.

Solution

We shall solve (16) for y in terms of x, and (17) for z in terms of x. Then we shall substitute the resulting expressions for y and z in (18) and thus get one equation in one unknown. Solving (16) for y, we have

(19) $y = 2x - 11$

Similarly, solving (17) for z, we get

(20)
$$z = \frac{17 - 3x}{5}$$

Now we substitute the right members of (19) and (20) for y and z, respectively, in (18) and solve the resulting equation as indicated below.

(21)
$$2x + 5(2x - 11) + 4\left(\frac{17 - 3x}{5}\right) = -3$$

$$2x + 10x - 55 + \frac{68 - 12x}{5} = -3$$

$$10x + 50x - 275 + 68 - 12x = -15$$
$$10x + 50x - 12x = -15 + 275 - 68$$
$$48x = 192$$
$$x = 4$$

Now we substitute $x = 4$ in (19) and (20) and obtain the complete solution $x = 4$, $y = -3$, $z = 1$.

EXERCISE 19

Solve the following equations for x, y, and z.

1. $2x - y + z = 7$
  $x - 2y - z = 2$
  $3x + 2y + z = 2.$

2. $3x + y + 2z = 1$
  $2x - y + 3z = -6$
  $x + y + 2z = -3.$

3. $x + y + 2z = 3$
  $x + 2y + 4z = 3$
  $x - 3y - 5z = 5.$

4. $2x + 3y + z = 8$
  $3x - 2y + z = -5$
  $x + 3y + z = 6.$

5. $3x - 2y + z = -1$
  $2x + 3y + 2z = 17$
  $4x - 4y - z = -1.$

6. $5x + 2y + 2z = -9$
  $3x - y + 3z = 8$
  $7x + y + 4z = -3.$

7. $x + 2y + 3z = 6$
  $x + 3y + 2z = -2$
  $2x + 5y + 7z = 10.$

8. $2x - 3y + 3z = -9$
  $5x - 7y + z = -1$
  $3x - 2y + z = 7.$

9. $3x + 5y + 2z = -7$
  $2x + 4y + 3z = -2$
  $5x + 7y + 5z = 3.$

10. $2x - 3y + 2z = 13$
  $3x + 5y - 3z = 31$
  $5x + 2y - 5z = 20.$

11. $4x + 2y - 6z = 10$
  $3x - 5y + 7z = -7$
  $5x + 3y - 5z = 17.$

12. $4x + 2y - 3z = 10$
  $5x - 3y + 2z = 8$
  $3x + 5y - 7z = 6.$

13. $2x + 3y + 4z = 6$
  $3x - 6y + 2z = -1$
  $4x + 9y - 8z = 2.$

14. $6x - 5y - 3z = 3$
  $4x - 10y + 6z = 10$
  $2x + 15y - 9z = -3.$

15. $8x - 6y + 4z = 5$
  $4x + 9y - 8z = 5$
  $6x + 3y + 3z = 10.$

16. $3x - 4y + 6z = -2$
    $6x + 2y + 3z = 7$
    $2x + 8y + 4z = 12.$

17. $4x + 3y + 2z = 6$
    $2x - 6y + z = -7$
    $6x + 9y - 3z = 0.$

18. $10x + 5y - 4z = 6$
    $x + y + 4z = 2$
    $6x + y - 8z = 1.$

19. $6x - 3y - 4z = -4$
    $2x - y + 4z = 8$
    $3x - 6y + 2z = 2.$

20. $8x - 6y - 3z = 4$
    $16x - 2y + z = 9$
    $4x + 3y + 6z = 7.$

21. $x + 2z = 5$
    $y + 3z = 14$
    $3x + 2y - 3z = -17.$

22. $3x + y = 9$
    $2x + z = 17$
    $2x + 3y - 5z = -43.$

23. $x + 2y = 3$
    $y + 2z = 2$
    $3x - 5y + 6z = 8.$

24. $4y + z = 4$
    $3x + z = 5$
    $3x - 4y + 5z = 16.$

25. $x + 2z = -3$
    $2y + z = 3$
    $2x - 3y = 2.$

26. $x - 3y = 1$
    $y + 2z = 14$
    $3x + 2z = 1.$

27. $3x + z = 1$
    $3y + 2z = -1$
    $4x - 3y = -1.$

28. $2x + 3y = -12$
    $4x - 7z = 3$
    $3y + 9z = 3.$

29. If $E = I_x(R_x + R)$, $E = I_a(R_a + R)$, and $E = IR$, show that

$$R_x = \left(\frac{\dfrac{I - I_x}{I_x}}{\dfrac{I - I_a}{I_a}} \right) R_a$$

42. Problems leading to systems of linear equations. Many stated problems involve more than one unknown quantity, and often the symbolic statement for solving such a problem can be more easily obtained if more than one unknown letter is introduced. However, before the problem can be completely solved, the number of equations formed must be equal to the number of unknown letters used. The general procedure for obtaining the equations is the same as that in Art. 30, and the student is advised to reread that article before he studies the following examples or attempts the problems in Exercise 20.

Example 1

A real-estate dealer received \$1200 in rents on two dwellings in 1948, and one of them brought \$10 per month more than the other. How much did he receive per month for each if the more expensive house was vacant for 2 months?

Solution

If we let

$x =$ the monthly rental on the more expensive house

and

$y =$ the monthly rental on the other

then

(1) $$x - y = 10$$

Furthermore, since the first of the above houses was rented for 10 months and the other was rented for 12 months, we know that $10x + 12y$ is the total amount received in rentals. Hence,

(2) $$10x + 12y = 1200$$

We now have the two equations (1) and (2) in the unknowns x and y, and we shall solve them simultaneously by eliminating y. The solution follows.

(3) $\qquad 12x - 12y = 120 \qquad$ [Eq. (1) $\times$ 12]
(2) $\qquad \underline{10x + 12y = 1200}$
$\qquad\qquad 22x = 1320 \qquad$ [Eq. (3) + Eq. (2)]

Hence,

$$x = 60$$

Substituting 60 for x in (1), we get

$$60 - y = 10$$

Hence,

$$-y = 10 - 60 = -50$$

and

$$y = 50$$

Therefore, the monthly rentals were \$60 and \$50, respectively.

Example 2

A tobacco dealer mixed one grade of tobacco worth \$1.40 per pound with another worth \$1.80 per pound in order to obtain 50 lb. of a blend that sold for \$1.56 per pound. How much of each grade did he use?

Solution

We shall let

$x =$ the number of pounds of the \$1.40 grade used

and

$y =$ the number of pounds of the \$1.80 grade

Then

(4) $$x + y = 50$$

since there were 50 lb. in the mixture. Furthermore, $1.40x$ is the value in dollars of the first grade, $1.80y$ is the value in dollars of the second, and $(1.56)50 = 78$ is the value in dollars of the mixture. Therefore,

$$(5) \qquad 1.40x + 1.80y = 78$$

Hence, (4) and (5) are the two required equations, and we shall solve them by eliminating x.

$$(6) \qquad 1.40x + 1.40y = 70 \qquad \text{[Eq. (4)} \times 1.40]$$
$$(5) \qquad \underline{1.40x + 1.80y = 78}$$
$$ - .40y = -8 \qquad \text{[Eq. (6)} - \text{Eq. (5)]}$$

Therefore,

$$y = \frac{-8}{-.40} = 20$$

Substituting 20 for y in (4), we have

$$x + 20 = 50$$
$$x = 30$$

Hence, the dealer used 30 lb. of the \$1.40 grade and 20 lb. of the \$1.80 grade in the mixture.

Example 3

Two airfields A and B are 400 miles apart and B is due east of A. A plane flew from A to B in 2 hr. and then returned to A in $2\frac{1}{2}$ hr. If the wind blew with a constant velocity from the west during the entire trip, find the speed of the plane in still air and the speed of the wind.

Solution

Let

$$x = \text{the speed of the plane in still air}$$

and

$$y = \text{the speed of the wind}$$

Then, since the wind was blowing from the west

$$x + y = \text{the speed of the plane from } A \text{ to } B$$

and

$$x - y = \text{the speed of the plane on the return trip}$$

Hence,

$$\frac{400}{x + y} = \text{the time required for the first half of the trip}$$

and

$$\frac{400}{x - y} = \text{the time required to return}$$

Therefore,

(7)
$$\frac{400}{x+y} = 2$$

(8)
$$\frac{400}{x-y} = 2\frac{1}{2}$$

Now we clear of fractions by multiplying both members of (7) by $x + y$ and of (8) by $2(x - y)$ and get

(9)
$$400 = 2x + 2y$$

and

(10)
$$800 = 5x - 5y$$

We shall solve (9) and (10) simultaneously by first eliminating y.

(11) $2000 = 10x + 10y$ [Eq. (9) × 5]
(12) $\underline{1600 = 10x - 10y}$ [Eq. (10) × 2]
   $3600 = 20x$ [Eq. (11) + Eq. (12)]

Hence,

$$x = 180$$

Substituting 180 for x in (9), we have

$$400 = 2(180) + 2y$$
$$400 = 360 + 2y$$
$$2y = 40$$
$$y = 20$$

Hence, the speed of the plane in still air was 180 miles per hr., and the speed of the wind was 20 miles per hr.

Example 4

A cash drawer contains $50 in nickels, dimes, and quarters. There are 802 coins in all, and 10 times as many nickels as dimes. How many coins of each denomination are in the drawer?

Solution

Let

$$q = \text{the number of quarters}$$
$$d = \text{the number of dimes}$$

and

$$n = \text{the number of nickels}$$

We now form the following three linear equations in q, d, and n:

(13)
$$25q + 10d + 5n = 5000$$

since $50 = 5000 cents;

(14)
$$q + d + n = 802$$

since there were 802 coins in all;

(15) $$n = 10d$$

since there were 10 times as many nickels as dimes.

If we substitute $10d$ for n [given by Eq. (15)] in Eqs. (13) and (14), we obtain two linear equations in q and d. From (13), we get

$$25q + 10d + 5(10d) = 5000$$

which reduces to

(16) $$25q + 60d = 5000$$

Furthermore, from (14) we have

$$q + d + 10d = 802$$

or

(17) $$q + 11d = 802$$

We may eliminate q from (16) and (17) as shown below.

$$
\begin{aligned}
(16) \quad 25q + 60d &= 5{,}000 \\
(18) \quad 25q + 275d &= 20{,}050 \qquad \text{[Eq. (17)} \times 25] \\
\hline
-215d &= -15{,}050 \qquad \text{[Eq. (16)} - \text{Eq. (18)]} \\
d &= 70
\end{aligned}
$$

Now, substituting 70 for d in (15), we get

$$n = 10(70) = 700$$

Finally, substituting $d = 70$ in (17), we have

$$q + 11(70) = 802$$

Hence,

$$q = 802 - 770 = 32$$

Consequently, there were 32 quarters, 70 dimes, and 700 nickels in the cash drawer.

EXERCISE 20

Solve the following problems by introducing more than one variable.

1. Two brothers bought a jalopy for $300. Find the amount paid by each if one of them paid $12 more than the other.

2. A fisherman drove to a lake and returned by another route that was 15 miles longer. If he traveled 265 miles all together, find the distance traveled on each route.

3. After James paid Frank $5 for a fishing rod, he had half as much money as the latter. If the boys had $21 together, how much did each have before the transaction?

4. A farmer sold 30 chickens, comprising both hens and roosters, for $50. If he received $1 each for the roosters and $2 each for the hens, how many of each were sold?

5. The collection in the junior department of a Sunday school amounted to $4.50. If there were 65 children present and each contributed either a nickel or a dime, how many coins of each denomination were in the collection?

6. The sum of the digits in a two-digit number is 11. If the digits are interchanged, the number is increased by 45. Find the number.

7. The sum of the digits in a two-digit number is 8. If the number is subtracted from the one obtained by interchanging the digits, the result is 18. What is the number?

8. A husband and wife each made out a mail order and found that the sum of the two was $85. The wife then eliminated an article whose price was $\frac{1}{9}$ of her original order, and the husband left off one that was $\frac{1}{8}$ of his. If the sum thus saved was $10, what was the amount of each original order?

9. During 1950 a real-estate owner received $1810 in rentals from two apartments, and one of them was vacant 2 months. Find the monthly rental on each if the sum of the two was $165.

10. A contractor has 40 men on his payroll and pays a part of them $8 per day and the remainder $10 per day. If the total daily wage is $350, how many are hired at each rate?

11. In 10 months the owner of a tenant house received an amount in rent that was $50 less than 10 per cent of the cost of the house. During the next 12 months, at a rate that was $5 per month less, he received an amount that was $10 more than 10 per cent of the cost. Find the cost and the first monthly rent.

12. A high school football squad of 40 members made a trip to a neighboring town, using a chartered bus and private cars. The bus fare was $1.50, and each car owner received $1.25 for each passenger. If the total transportation charge was $57.50, how many traveled by each method?

13. Two boys whose weights total 156 lb. are balanced on a teeterboard. If the fulcrum is 7 ft. from one and 6 ft. from the other, find the weight of each.

14. The amounts that a man has invested in two different companies differ by $250. The larger sum earns 4 per cent, and the other, 3 per cent. If the annual income from the two sources is $272.50, find the amount invested in each.

15. A pilot flew to a field 700 miles due north and returned to his starting point. The wind was blowing from the north at a constant velocity during the entire trip. Find the airspeed of the plane and the velocity of the wind if the trip north required 7 hr. and the return trip required 5 hr.

16. A college student made a trip to his home on a bus and returned by a more direct route in a car. The average speeds of the bus and car were 50 miles per hr. and 60 miles per hr. respectively. Find the length of each route if he spent one hour longer on the bus than in the car and traveled a total of 9 hr.

17. Two cars of tourists left the same hotel at the same time and traveled in opposite directions on a highway around a lake. When they met on the opposite side, the faster car had traveled 150 miles, and the other, 120 miles. Find the speed of each car if the faster car completed the round trip 1 hr. and 21 min. ahead of the other.

18. Two towns A and B are 324 miles apart. At 6 A.M. a car left A for a round trip to B, and at 8:15 A.M. a truck left B for a round trip to A. They met at 10 A.M. Seven hours later they met on their return trips. If each lost one hour before starting the return trip, find the speed of each.

19. Two blocks of metal containing 10 per cent and 25 per cent copper, respectively, were melted together in order to obtain 60 lb. of an alloy that contained 20 per cent copper. Find the weight of each block.

20. Two grades of milk, containing 4 per cent and 3 per cent butterfat, respectively, were combined in order to obtain 80 gal. that contained $3\frac{1}{4}$ per cent butterfat. How many gallons of each grade were used?

21. Two acid solutions that were 90 and 97 per cent pure were mixed together in order to obtain 21 gal. of a solution that was 95 per cent pure. How many gallons of each grade were used?

22. A painter and his helper applied the first coat of paint to a house in $3\frac{3}{5}$ days. If the application of the second coat required 4 days with the helper working only 3 days of that time, how long does it take each man to apply one coat when working alone? Assume that the application of each of the two coats requires the same length of time.

23. Airfield B is 700 miles east of A. A pilot left A for B at the same time that another left B for A, and their planes passed each other at the end of 2 hr. The eastward plane completed the trip $1\frac{1}{2}$ hr. later, and the westward, $2\frac{2}{3}$ hr. later. If the wind was blowing from the west at 20 miles per hr., find the airspeed of the two planes.

24. A man fenced a rectangular plot with one of the shorter sides bordering on a highway, and at the same time divided it into two parts with a fence parallel to the longer sides. Along the highway, the cost of the fencing was 50 cents per foot, and elsewhere it was 40 cents per foot. The total cost of the fencing was $540, and the fence along the highway cost $340 less than the remainder. Find the dimensions of the plot.

25. A boy bought a bat, a ball, and a fielder's glove for $8. The cost of the glove was $1 more than the combined cost of the bat and the ball, and the price of the ball was $4 less than the combined prices of the bat and the glove. How much was paid for each?

26. A football squad composed of 45 members is made up of seniors, juniors, and sophomores. The number of seniors and juniors combined is 5 more than the number of sophomores, and the number of seniors and sophomores combined is twice the number of juniors. How many members of each class are on the squad?

27. A collection plate contained \$32 in dimes, quarters, and half dollars. How many coins of each kind were in the plate if there were 150 coins in all and there was \$22 in dimes and quarters?

28. The sum of the three digits in a number is 11. If 396 is added to the number, the hundreds and units digits are interchanged, and if 27 is added to the number, the tens and units digits are interchanged. Find the number.

29. The combined ages of a father, son, and daughter is 65 years. In 10 years the father will be twice as old as his son, and 5 years ago the boy's age was twice his sister's. Find the age of each.

30. A cattleman rode a horse at 6 miles per hr. to his ranch headquarters, then drove his car at 40 miles per hr. to the railroad station and took a train that averaged 50 miles per hr. at the nearest city. The total distance traveled was 382 miles, and the journey required $9\frac{1}{2}$ hr. If he was 5 hr. longer on the train than on horseback, find the distance traveled by each method.

31. Tom, Dick, and Harry can mow a lawn in $1\frac{1}{3}$ hr., working together. When only Tom and Harry worked, $2\frac{2}{5}$ hr. were required for the job, and Dick and Harry mowed the lawn in 2 hr. How long would it take each boy to mow the lawn alone?

32. A grocer had three grades of coffee priced at 70 cents, 72 cents, and 80 cents per pound, respectively. He mixed half of the 72-cent grade with the 70-cent coffee and sold the mixture at 71 cents per pound, and combined the remainder of the 72-cent grade with the 80-cent coffee and priced the blend at 77 cents per pound. How many pounds of each grade were there if he had 140 lb. in all?

43. *Solution of two linear equations in two unknowns by means of determinants.* If we solve the equations

$$(1) \qquad ax + by = m$$
$$(2) \qquad cx + dy = n$$

by the method of Art. 39, we have the following.

$$(3) \qquad adx + bdy = dm \qquad [\text{Eq. (1)} \times d]$$
$$(4) \qquad \underline{bcx + bdy = bn} \qquad [\text{Eq. (2)} \times b]$$
$$adx - bcx = dm - bn \qquad [\text{Eq. (3)} - \text{Eq. (4)}]$$
$$x(ad - bc) = dm - bn$$
$$(5) \qquad x = \frac{dm - bn}{ad - bc}$$

Similarly, we obtain

$$(6) \qquad y = \frac{an - cm}{ad - bc}$$

If, in (5) and (6), $ad - bc = 0$, unique values of x and y do not exist, and the system of equations is either inconsistent or dependent.

The statements (5) and (6) can be used as formulas for obtaining the solution of any pair of consistent equations. However, their use in this form is somewhat difficult on account of the memory work involved. The latter is made considerably easier by the introduction of a notation that is discussed below.

We shall define the square array of numbers

$$\begin{vmatrix} a & b \\ c & d \end{vmatrix}$$

to be equal to $ad - bc$. This relationship may be more easily remembered by means of the following diagram

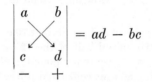

$$= ad - bc$$

Each arrow indicates that we are to take the product of the letters connected by it. The minus sign at the end of the arrow from the upper right to the lower left indicates that we are to subtract this product from the other.

Examples

1.
$$\begin{vmatrix} 3 & 4 \\ 2 & 5 \end{vmatrix} = (3)(5) - (4)(2) = 15 - 8 = 7$$

2.
$$\begin{vmatrix} -2 & 7 \\ -3 & 5 \end{vmatrix} = (-2)(5) - (7)(-3) = -10 + 21 = 11$$

The above discussion is summarized in the following definition.

DEFINITION. *The square array*

$$\begin{vmatrix} a & b \\ c & d \end{vmatrix}$$

is called **a determinant of the second order,** *and its* **value** *or* **expansion** *is* **ad − bc.**   *The letters* **a, b, c,** *and* **d** *are called the* **elements** *of the determinant.*

In terms of the above notation, we may now write the solutions (5) and (6) of Eqs. (1) and (2) in the form

$$x = \frac{\begin{vmatrix} m & b \\ n & d \end{vmatrix}}{\begin{vmatrix} a & b \\ c & d \end{vmatrix}} \qquad y = \frac{\begin{vmatrix} a & m \\ c & n \end{vmatrix}}{\begin{vmatrix} a & b \\ c & d \end{vmatrix}}$$

The determinant

$$\begin{vmatrix} a & b \\ c & d \end{vmatrix}$$

is known as the *determinant of the coefficients.*

Determinants of the second order may be used to solve any pair of consistent linear equations, and the solution consists of the following steps.

1. *Transpose and arrange terms in the equations so that the constant terms appear in the right and the terms involving the variables occur in the same order on the left.*

2. *Express each solution (or the value of each unknown) as the quotient of two determinants.   The divisor (or denominator) in each case is the determinant of the coefficients.*

3. *The dividend (or numerator) in the value of each unknown is the determinant formed by replacing the coefficients of this unknown in the determinant of the coefficients by the constant terms.*

Example 3

In order to solve
$$2x + 3y = 8$$
$$3x - y = 1$$

by determinants, we first notice that the determinant of the coefficients is

$$\begin{vmatrix} 2 & 3 \\ 3 & -1 \end{vmatrix}$$

Then, by step 3 above, we replace the coefficients 2 and 3 of x in the above determinant by the constant terms 8 and 1 in order to obtain the numerator of the value of x.   Thus we have

$$x = \frac{\begin{vmatrix} 8 & 3 \\ 1 & -1 \end{vmatrix}}{\begin{vmatrix} 2 & 3 \\ 3 & -1 \end{vmatrix}} = \frac{8(-1) - (3)(1)}{2(-1) - (3)(3)} = \frac{-8 - 3}{-2 - 9} = \frac{-11}{-11} = 1$$

Similarly,

$$y = \frac{\begin{vmatrix} 2 & 8 \\ 3 & 1 \end{vmatrix}}{\begin{vmatrix} 2 & 3 \\ 3 & -1 \end{vmatrix}} = \frac{2 - 24}{-11} = \frac{-22}{-11} = 2$$

44. Determinants of order 3.   The definition in the previous article can be extended to include square arrays of any number of rows.   We shall define a determinant of order 3 below and then shall show how the expansion is obtained.

DEFINITION.   *The square array*

$$\begin{vmatrix} a_1 & b_1 & c_1 \\ a_2 & b_2 & c_2 \\ a_3 & b_3 & c_3 \end{vmatrix}$$

*is called a **determinant of the third order,** and its value or expansion is*

$$a_1 b_2 c_3 + a_3 b_1 c_2 + a_2 b_3 c_1 - a_3 b_2 c_1 - a_1 b_3 c_2 - a_2 b_1 c_3$$

NOTE: The reader should notice that in each product in the expansion there is exactly one term from each row and one from each column.   Furthermore, a plus or minus is attached to each product according as the number of times a larger subscript precedes a smaller is even or odd after the letters have been arranged in alphabetical order.

Such a symbol can be expanded by rewriting the first two columns, multiplying as indicated by the arrows, and giving each product obtained the sign determined by the product or the opposite sign according as the arrow is pointing down to the right or to the left, and then taking the algebraic sum of these products. Thus

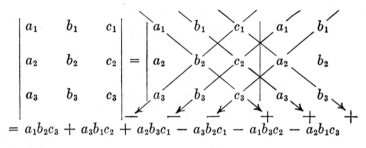

$$= a_1b_2c_3 + a_3b_1c_2 + a_2b_3c_1 - a_3b_2c_1 - a_1b_3c_2 - a_2b_1c_3$$

45. Solution of a system of three linear equations.   If we solve the system

(1) $$\qquad\qquad a_1x + b_1y + c_1z = d_1$$
(2) $$\qquad\qquad a_2x + b_2y + c_2z = d_2$$
(3) $$\qquad\qquad a_3x + b_3y + c_3z = d_3$$

simultaneously, by the method of Art. 41, we get

$$x = \frac{b_3c_2d_1 - b_2c_3d_1 - b_3c_1d_2 - b_1c_2d_3 + b_1c_3d_2 + b_2c_1d_3}{b_3c_2a_1 - b_2c_3a_1 - b_3c_1a_2 - b_1c_2a_3 + b_1c_3a_2 + b_2c_1a_3}$$

provided the denominator is not zero.

This result may be expressed as the quotient of two determinants in the form

$$x = \frac{N_x}{D} = \frac{\begin{vmatrix} d_1 & b_1 & c_1 \\ d_2 & b_2 & c_2 \\ d_3 & b_3 & c_3 \end{vmatrix}}{\begin{vmatrix} a_1 & b_1 & c_1 \\ a_2 & b_2 & c_2 \\ a_3 & b_3 & c_3 \end{vmatrix}} \qquad D \neq 0$$

Note that in the above the symbol N_x represents the determinant in the numerator of the value of x.   We shall use a similar notation in the values of y and z below.   It should be noticed that N_x can be obtained from D by replacing each a by the corresponding d.

Similarly, if we solve for y and z, we get

$$y = \frac{N_y}{D} = \frac{\begin{vmatrix} a_1 & d_1 & c_1 \\ a_2 & d_2 & c_2 \\ a_3 & d_3 & c_3 \end{vmatrix}}{D}$$

and

$$z = \frac{N_z}{D} = \frac{\begin{vmatrix} a_1 & b_1 & d_1 \\ a_2 & b_2 & d_2 \\ a_3 & b_3 & d_3 \end{vmatrix}}{D}$$

Regardless of the unknown for which we are solving, its numerator is obtained by replacing its coefficients in D by the constant terms.

Example

Solve

$$3x + 2y - z = 12$$
$$x + y + z = 6$$

and

$$x - 2y - z = -2$$

simultaneously by use of determinants.

Solution

The determinant of the coefficients is the denominator of each of the unknowns; hence, we shall calculate its value.

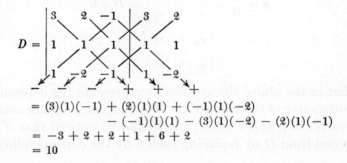

$$= (3)(1)(-1) + (2)(1)(1) + (-1)(1)(-2)$$
$$- (-1)(1)(1) - (3)(1)(-2) - (2)(1)(-1)$$
$$= -3 + 2 + 2 + 1 + 6 + 2$$
$$= 10$$

Replacing the coefficients of x in D by the constant terms, we get

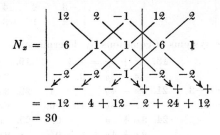

$$N_z = \begin{vmatrix} 12 & 2 & -1 \\ 6 & 1 & 1 \\ -2 & -2 & -1 \end{vmatrix} \begin{matrix} 12 & 2 \\ 6 & 1 \\ -2 & -2 \end{matrix}$$

$$= -12 - 4 + 12 - 2 + 24 + 12$$
$$= 30$$

Similarly,

$$N_y = \begin{vmatrix} 3 & 12 & -1 \\ 1 & 6 & 1 \\ 1 & -2 & -1 \end{vmatrix} \begin{matrix} 3 & 12 \\ 1 & 6 \\ 1 & -2 \end{matrix}$$

$$= -18 + 12 + 2 + 6 + 6 + 12$$
$$= 20$$

Therefore,

$$x = \frac{N_x}{D} = \frac{30}{10} = 3 \quad \text{and} \quad y = \frac{N_y}{D} = \frac{20}{10} = 2$$

The value of z can be determined by substituting the value of x and of y in either of the original equations. Using the second, we get

$$3 + 2 + z = 6$$

or

$$z = 1$$

Consequently, the solution is $x = 3$, $y = 2$, $z = 1$

EXERCISE 21

Expand the determinants in Problems 1 to 16.

1. $\begin{vmatrix} 2 & 3 \\ 1 & 4 \end{vmatrix}$.

2. $\begin{vmatrix} 3 & 5 \\ 2 & 4 \end{vmatrix}$.

3. $\begin{vmatrix} 5 & -1 \\ 2 & 3 \end{vmatrix}$.

4. $\begin{vmatrix} -3 & 4 \\ -2 & 5 \end{vmatrix}$.

5. $\begin{vmatrix} 6 & 3 \\ -2 & -1 \end{vmatrix}$.

6. $\begin{vmatrix} 4 & -5 \\ -2 & 7 \end{vmatrix}$.

7. $\begin{vmatrix} 8 & 12 \\ 6 & 9 \end{vmatrix}$.

8. $\begin{vmatrix} -9 & -4 \\ 7 & -3 \end{vmatrix}$.

9. $\begin{vmatrix} 1 & 3 & 5 \\ 2 & 2 & 3 \\ 4 & 1 & 2 \end{vmatrix}$.

10. $\begin{vmatrix} 2 & 5 & 2 \\ 1 & 0 & 4 \\ 3 & 2 & 3 \end{vmatrix}$.

11. $\begin{vmatrix} -1 & 2 & -2 \\ 2 & -3 & 3 \\ 4 & 1 & 5 \end{vmatrix}$.

12. $\begin{vmatrix} 3 & 5 & 4 \\ 0 & -3 & 1 \\ 2 & 1 & -2 \end{vmatrix}$.

13. $\begin{vmatrix} 2 & -6 & 9 \\ 3 & 2 & -1 \\ 4 & 2 & -2 \end{vmatrix}$.

14. $\begin{vmatrix} 3 & 6 & 9 \\ 2 & 4 & 6 \\ 3 & 1 & 2 \end{vmatrix}$.

15. $\begin{vmatrix} 4 & 2 & 3 \\ 8 & -3 & 6 \\ 16 & 1 & 12 \end{vmatrix}$.

16. $\begin{vmatrix} 5 & -4 & -2 \\ -3 & 2 & 4 \\ -2 & 1 & -3 \end{vmatrix}$.

Solve the following systems of equations by determinants.

17. $3x - y = 5$
$2x + 3y = 7$.

18. $2x + 5y = -4$
$x - 3y = 9$.

19. $x + 2y = 4$
$3x + y + 3 = 0$.

20. $4x - 5y = -3$
$3x + 2y + 8 = 0$.

21. $3x - 4y = 4$
$7x - 8y - 10 = 0$.

22. $3x + 2y = 3$
$6x - y = 1$.

23. $4x + 3y = 2$
$8x + 9y = 6$.

24. $3x + y = 0$
$2x + 4y + 5 = 0$.

25. $x - y = b$
$2x - y = a + b$.

26. $5ax - 2by = 3ab$
$2a^2x + 3aby = 5a^2b$.

27. $ax - by = a^2 - b^2$
$bx + ay = 2ab$.

28. $x + ay = 2ab$
$2x - ay = ab$.

29. $2x + 3y - 2z = 2$
$3x + 4y - 3z = 2$
$5x - 3y + 2z = 5$.

30. $x + y - z = 3$
$2x + 3y + z = 10$
$3x - y - 7z = 1$.

31. $2x - 3y + 2z = 3$
$3x + 2y + 5z + 6 = 0$
$x + 5y - 2z = 1$.

32. $x + y + z = 0$
$2x - 3y - z + 5 = 0$
$3x + 2y - 3z = 2$.

33. $2x + 4y + 3z = 2$
$3x + 2y - 2z = 2$
$5x - 2y + 5z - 2 = 0$.

34. $x - y - 2z = 0$
$2x - 3y + 4z = -2$
$2x + y + 2z = 1$.

35. $3x + y = 7$
$x + z = 4$
$y - z + 1 = 0$.

36. $2x - z = 4$
$x - y = 4$
$2y + z = 0$.

37. $x + z = 1$
$2x - y = 8$
$3y + 2z + 6 = 0$.

38. $x - y = -1$
$y + 2z = 3$
$2x + 3z = 4$.

39. $2x + 2y - z = a$
$3x + y - 3z + 2b = 0$
$x + y - z = 0$.

40. $x + y + z = 2b$
$2x + 2y - z = b$
$3x + y - 3z = 2a$.

41. $3x + y + 3z = 4b$
$2x + y - z = 3a$
$x - 2y + 2z = -a$.

42. $5x + 5y - 3z = 7a$
$2x - 3y + z + 5b = 0$
$x + y + z = 3a$.

CHAPTER 7

EXPONENTS AND RADICALS

46. *Introduction.* In this chapter we shall extend the interpretation of exponents and develop several laws for their use. For the convenience of the reader we shall list below the definition and several laws previously presented.

(1) $\qquad a^n = a \times a \times a \ldots$ (to n factors) $\qquad$ (Def. I, Art. 7)

In (1), the letter a is called the *base* and n is the exponent.

(2)	$a^m a^n = a^{m+n}$	[(1), Art. 7]
(3)	$(ab)^n = a^n b^n$	[(2), Art. 7]
(4)	$(a^m)^n = a^{mn}$	[(3), Art. 7]
(5)	$\dfrac{a^m}{a^n} = a^{m-n} \qquad m > n$	[(1), Art. 9]
(6)	$\left(\dfrac{a}{b}\right)^n = \dfrac{a^n}{b^n}$	[(2), Art. 9]
(7)	$a^0 = 1 \qquad a \neq 0$	[(4), Art. 11]

The proofs of Laws (2) to (5) were given in Arts. 7 and 9, and we shall present the proof of (6) below.

$$\left(\frac{a}{b}\right)^n = \frac{a}{b} \times \frac{a}{b} \times \frac{a}{b} \cdots \text{ (to } n \text{ factors)} \qquad \text{[by (1)]}$$

$$= \frac{a \times a \times a \ldots \text{ (to } n \text{ factors)}}{b \times b \times b \ldots \text{ (to } n \text{ factors)}} \qquad \text{[by (1), Art. 19]}$$

$$= \frac{a^n}{b^n} \qquad \text{[by (1)]}$$

It should be noted that, in (7), $a = 0$ is excluded. This is due to the fact that if we use the method just above (4), Art. 11, in attempting to arrive at an interpretation of 0^0, we get $0/0$ and this has no meaning. Hence we attach no meaning to 0^0.

At this point the reader should review the examples at the ends of Arts. 7 and 9.

47. *Simplification of exponential expressions involving positive integral and zero exponents.* In order to simplify an expression involving positive integral and zero exponents, we perform all possible operations by means of Laws (2) to (7). If the result is a fraction, we reduce it to lowest terms.

Example 1

In order to simplify

$$\left(\frac{2x^3y^4}{z^3}\right)^4 \left(\frac{3y^2z^3}{2x^2}\right)^2$$

we perform the following steps.

1. Apply (3) and (6) to the expressions in the parentheses.

2. Apply (4) to all expressions thus obtained that are in the form "power of a power."

3. Perform the indicated multiplication in the result thus obtained.

4. Reduce the result obtained in step 3 to lowest terms by dividing the numerator and denominator by the highest common factor of the two.

If we carry out these operations, we get

$$\left(\frac{2x^3y^4}{z^3}\right)^4 \left(\frac{3y^2z^3}{2x^2}\right)^2 = \left[\frac{2^4(x^3)^4(y^4)^4}{(z^3)^4}\right] \left[\frac{3^2(y^2)^2(z^3)^2}{2^2(x^2)^2}\right] \quad \text{[by (3) and (6)]}$$

$$= \left(\frac{16x^{12}y^{16}}{z^{12}}\right) \left(\frac{9y^4z^6}{4x^4}\right) \quad \text{[by (4)]}$$

$$= \frac{144x^{12}y^{20}z^6}{4x^4z^{12}}$$

$$= \frac{36x^8y^{20}}{z^6} \quad \text{(dividing numerator and denominator by } 4x^4z^6\text{)}$$

Example 2

The simplification of

$$\left(\frac{12x^{2a-2}}{6x^{a-2}}\right)^4 \left(\frac{1}{2x^{2a}}\right)^2$$

is easier if we first apply (5) to the expression in the first parentheses, then use (3), (4), and (6), and finally simplify the result thus obtained. These operations yield

$$\left(\frac{12x^{2a-2}}{6x^{a-2}}\right)^4 \left(\frac{1}{2x^{2a}}\right)^2 = [2x^{2a-2-(a-2)}]^4 \left(\frac{1}{2x^{2a}}\right)^2 \qquad \text{[by (5)]}$$

$$= (2x^{2a-2-a+2})^4 \left(\frac{1}{2x^{2a}}\right)^2$$

$$= (2x^a)^4 \left(\frac{1}{2x^{2a}}\right)^2$$

$$= (16x^{4a}) \left(\frac{1}{4x^{4a}}\right) \qquad \text{[by (3), (4), and (6)]}$$

$$= \frac{16x^{4a}}{4x^{4a}}$$

$$= 4x^0 \qquad \text{[by (5)]}$$

$$= 4(1) = 4 \qquad \text{[by (7)]}$$

NOTE: The above solution shows every step in the simplification process. After some practice, many of these steps can be performed mentally and simultaneously, and the result be thus achieved more quickly.

Law (3), read from right to left, may be used to obtain the product of two equal powers. For example, $(2a^3)^4(3a^2)^4 = (6a^5)^4$. When multiplying equal powers of two or more expressions it is frequently more efficient to apply (3) in this way and then proceed with the multiplication. Law (6) may be used in a similar way when dealing with the quotients of equal powers.

Example 3

If we apply the above procedure to

$$\left(\frac{2a^2c^3}{15b^4}\right)^3 \left(\frac{30b^6}{4a^2c^2}\right)^3$$

we have

$$\left(\frac{2a^2c^3}{15b^4}\right)^3 \left(\frac{30b^6}{4a^2c^2}\right)^3 = \left[\left(\frac{2a^2c^3}{15b^4}\right)\left(\frac{30b^6}{4a^2c^2}\right)\right]^3 \qquad \text{[by (3)]}$$

$$= \left(\frac{60a^2b^6c^3}{60a^2b^4c^2}\right)^3$$

$$= (a^0b^2c)^3 \qquad \text{[by (5)]}$$

$$= (b^2c)^3 \qquad \text{[by (7)]}$$

$$= b^6c^3 \qquad \text{[by (3)]}$$

NOTE 1: In the application of (4), it should be noted that the exponent inside the parentheses is multiplied by the one on the outside. It is not raised to the power indicated by the outside exponent. For example,

$$(2a^2)^3 = 8a^{2(3)} = 8a^6, \quad not \ 8a^{2^3} = 8a^8$$

NOTE 2: When we multiply two powers of the same base, we *hold that base* and add the exponents. For example,

$$(2a^2)^3(2a^2)^2 = (2a^2)^5, \quad not \ (4a^4)^5$$

NOTE 3: When we multiply two equal powers of different bases, we *hold the exponent* and multiply the bases. For example,

$$(3a^2)^3(2a^4)^3 = (6a^6)^3, \quad not \ (6a^6)^6$$

EXERCISE 22

Perform the operations indicated in each of Problems 1 to 32.

1. $2^3 2^2$. 2. $3^4 3^2$. 3. $5^2 5^2$. 4. $4^2 4^4$. 5. $\dfrac{3^6}{3^4}$.

6. $\dfrac{2^5}{2^3}$. 7. $\dfrac{4^5}{4^2}$. 8. $\dfrac{5^7}{5^5}$. 9. $5^2 2^2$. 10. $3^4 4^3$.

11. $\dfrac{10^2}{5^2}$. 12. $\dfrac{25^3}{5^3}$. 13. $(\tfrac{4}{5})^2$. 14. $(\tfrac{3}{4})^2$. 15. $(\tfrac{2}{3})^3$.

16. $(\tfrac{1}{5})^4$. 17. $(4^2)^3$. 18. $(2^3 3^2)^2$. 19. $(2^4 3)^2$. 20. $(4^2 2)^3$.

21. $(3a^6)(2a^4)$. 22. $(4x^4)(3x^3)$. 23. $(2a^2)(3a^4)(a^5)$. 24. $(-3a^2)(-5a^5)$.

25. $\dfrac{a^7}{a^3}$. 26. $\dfrac{b^9}{b^5}$. 27. $\dfrac{20c^4d^2}{5c^2d}$. 28. $\dfrac{18x^5y^7}{3x^2y^3}$.

29. $(3x^3)^2$. 30. $(5a^4)^2$. 31. $(-4b^2)^3$. 32. $(-4a^3b^2c^4)^2$.

Simplify the following exponential expressions.

33. $\dfrac{24x^4y^5z^2}{3x^2y^3z^2}$. 34. $\dfrac{27c^5d^4e^5}{3c^4d^2e^3}$. 35. $\dfrac{28a^7b^8d^3}{4a^2b^4d^3}$. 36. $\dfrac{42h^9j^7k^4}{6h^5j^4k^3}$.

37. $\left(\dfrac{4x^2y^3}{2y^2}\right)^3$. 38. $\left(\dfrac{9a^4b^6c^8}{3a^3b^4c^5}\right)^3$. 39. $\left(\dfrac{18a^4b^2}{6a^3b^2}\right)^4$. 40. $\left(\dfrac{36x^5y^6z^3}{18a^4y^3z}\right)^5$.

41. $\dfrac{24h^3k^5}{16h^5k^3}$. 42. $\dfrac{27r^4s^2t^2}{12r^2s^2t^5}$. 43. $\dfrac{48a^7b^3c^5}{32a^5b^4c}$. 44. $\dfrac{81x^8y^6z^4}{36x^4y^7z^5}$.

45. $\left(\dfrac{3a^2b^3}{2c^4}\right)\left(\dfrac{4a^3c^2}{9b^2}\right)$. 46. $\left(\dfrac{6x^4y^3z^5}{5w^2}\right)\left(\dfrac{10w^5x^2}{9y^5z^7}\right)$. 47. $\left(\dfrac{12h^3j^4}{5k^5}\right)\left(\dfrac{15h^4k^3}{8j^6}\right)$.

48. $\left(\dfrac{7c^3d^4}{6e^5}\right)\left(\dfrac{18c^4e^7}{21d^6}\right)$. 49. $\left(\dfrac{2r^3s^5}{3r^5s^3}\right)^2$. 50. $\left(\dfrac{6h^4k^7}{9h^3k^9}\right)^3$.

51. $\left(\dfrac{12a^7b^3c^6}{18a^5b^6c^{10}}\right)^4$. 52. $\left(\dfrac{14x^5y^4z^9}{7x^2y^7z^8}\right)^5$. 53. $(3a^3)^2(4a^4)^2$.

54. $(2c^2)^3(3c^5)^3$. 55. $(2a^2bc^3)^2(4a^3b^2c)^2$. 56. $(5h^4j^3k^2)^4(h^2j^4k)^4$.

57. $\left(\dfrac{3r^3}{2r^2}\right)^2 \left(\dfrac{4r}{3r^3}\right)^2.$ **58.** $\left(\dfrac{3a^2b}{2c^3}\right)^3 \left(\dfrac{c^4}{3a^2b^2}\right)^3.$ **59.** $\left(\dfrac{2x^3y^2}{3z^4}\right)^4 \left(\dfrac{6z^5}{2x^4y}\right)^4.$

60. $\left(\dfrac{4c^3d^2}{3e^4}\right)^5 \left(\dfrac{3e^5}{8c^2d^2}\right)^5.$ **61.** $\left(\dfrac{2a^2}{b^3}\right)^2 \left(\dfrac{3b}{a^3}\right)^2 \left(\dfrac{a^2}{6b}\right)^2.$

62. $\left(\dfrac{3c^2}{d^3}\right)^3 \left(\dfrac{2d^5}{3c^3}\right)^3 \left(\dfrac{c}{d^6}\right)^3.$ **63.** $\left(\dfrac{3x^3}{2y^2}\right)^4 \left(\dfrac{4y}{3x^3}\right)^4 \left(\dfrac{2x}{y}\right)^4.$

64. $\left(\dfrac{4h^2}{3k^3}\right)^3 \left(\dfrac{9h^4}{2k^2}\right)^3 \left(\dfrac{6k^6}{18k^7}\right)^3.$ **65.** $\dfrac{(a^2b^3)^2(ab^2)^2}{(a^2b)^3}.$

66. $\dfrac{(a^2x^3)^4}{(ax^2)^2(a^2x^3)^2}.$ **67.** $\dfrac{(h^3k^2)^3(h^3k^2)^4}{(h^3k^2)^5}.$ **68.** $\dfrac{(2a^3x^4)^2(4a^2b)^3}{(2a^2x^3)^3}.$

69. $\dfrac{(4c^2de^2)^3(2c^3d^2e^4)^3}{(6c^3d^3e^7)^3}.$ **70.** $\dfrac{(2x^3y^2z^3)^2(6x^4yz^2)^2}{(12x^5y^4z^5)^2}.$ **71.** $\dfrac{(5a^4b^2c^3)^4(4a^3b^4c^2)^4}{(10a^8b^5c^5)^4}.$

72. $\dfrac{(8h^4j^3k^2)^5(2h^3j^2k^3)^5}{(16h^6j^6k^6)^5}.$ **73.** $a^{3n+5}a^{2n-5}.$ **74.** $b^{2x+3}b^{x-1}b^{x-2}.$

75. $a^{3y+2}a^{2y-4}a^{2-5y}.$ **76.** $c^{2z-1}c^{z+2}c^{1-3z}.$ **77.** $\dfrac{a^{n+2}x^{2n+1}}{a^{n-2}x^{1-2n}}.$

78. $\dfrac{a^{3n-4}b^{2n-1}}{a^{n+2}b^{2+n}}.$ **79.** $\dfrac{a^{n-2}x^{3n+1}}{a^{n-4}x^{1-n}}.$ **80.** $\dfrac{a^{5n-4}b^{3n-6}}{a^{2n+1}}.$

81. $\dfrac{(a^{n+1}b^{n+2})^2}{a^{2n}b^4}.$ **82.** $\dfrac{(a^{2n-1}b^{n+1})^3}{a^{n-3}b^3}.$

83. $\dfrac{(a^{x+2}b^{2x-3})^3}{a^{3x}b^{x-9}}.$ **84.** $\dfrac{(a^{2y-2}b^{y-3})^4}{a^{8y}b^{4y-12}}.$

48. Negative integral exponents. In this article we shall extend our interpretation of exponents so as to include exponents that are negative integers.

We shall assume that a^{-n}, $a \neq 0$, represents a number and that (2), Art. 46, holds for exponents of this type. Now we multiply a^{-n} by a^n/a^n and obtain

$$a^{-n} = a^{-n}\left(\frac{a^n}{a^n}\right) = \frac{a^{-n+n}}{a^n} \qquad \text{[by (2), Art. 46]}$$

$$= \frac{a^0}{a^n}$$

$$= \frac{1}{a^n} \qquad \text{[by (7), Art. 46]}$$

Hence we shall define a^{-n} as follows.

DEFINITION. *If* $a \neq 0$ *and* n *is a positive integer, then*

(1) $$a^{-n} = \frac{1}{a^n}$$

Since this definition gives us an interpretation of negative exponents, we may now remove the restriction $m > n$ in (5), Art. 46. Furthermore, Laws (3) to (6), Art. 46, hold for this interpretation. We shall illustrate the general method for proving this statement by applying it below to (5), Art. 46.

$$\frac{a^{-m}}{a^{-n}} = \frac{\dfrac{1}{a^m}}{\dfrac{1}{a^n}} \qquad \text{[by (1)]}$$

$$= \frac{a^n}{a^m} \qquad \text{(multiplying the numerator and denominator by } a^m a^n)$$

$$= a^{n-m} \qquad \text{[by (5), Art. 46]}$$

$$= a^{-m-(-n)}$$

By use of (1) of this article and Laws (3) to (7), Art. 46, we can change any expression that involves negative exponents into an equal expression in which all exponents are positive.

Examples

1. $$4^{-2} = \frac{1}{4^2} = \frac{1}{16}$$

2. $$2^{-4} \times 2^{-2} = 2^{-6} = \frac{1}{2^6} = \frac{1}{64}$$

3. $$\frac{3^{-5}}{3^{-3}} = 3^{-5-(-3)} = 3^{-5+3} = 3^{-2} = \frac{1}{3^2} = \frac{1}{9}$$

4. $$\frac{4x^a y^{-b}}{z^{-c}} = \frac{4x^a \left(\dfrac{1}{y^b}\right)}{\dfrac{1}{z^c}} = \frac{\dfrac{4x^a}{y^b}}{\dfrac{1}{z^c}} = \frac{\dfrac{4x^a}{y^b}(y^b z^c)}{\dfrac{1}{z^c}(y^b z^c)} = \frac{4x^a z^c}{y^b}$$

If, in Example 4, we compare the original fraction with the result, we see that each letter with a negative exponent which occurs in either member of the original fraction appears, with the sign of the exponent changed, in the other member of the fraction in the result. This is an illustration of the following rule for negative exponents.

*Any **factor** in one member of a fraction can be transferred to the other member, provided the sign of the exponent in that factor is changed.*

Example 5

$$\frac{2a^{-2}bc^{-3}}{x^{-4}y^{-2}z^3} = \frac{2bx^4y^2}{a^2c^3z^3}$$

It should be noted that the statement above Example 5 applies to *factors*, not to *terms*. Any attempt to apply it to a fraction in which the members are not in factored form leads to serious errors, as the following example will show.

Example 6

If we apply (1) to $(2^{-2} + 2^{-3})/2^{-4}$, we get

$$\frac{2^{-2} + 2^{-3}}{2^{-4}} = \frac{\dfrac{1}{2^2} + \dfrac{1}{2^3}}{\dfrac{1}{2^4}} = \frac{\dfrac{1}{4} + \dfrac{1}{8}}{\dfrac{1}{16}} = \frac{\dfrac{2+1}{8}}{\dfrac{1}{16}} = \frac{\dfrac{3}{8}}{\dfrac{1}{16}} = 6$$

This result is *not* equal to $2^4/(2^2 + 2^3) = \frac{16}{12} = \frac{4}{3}$, a result one would get if one tried to use the statement above Example 5 on this problem.

We shall agree that an expression involving negative exponents is simplified when all combinations by use of Laws (2) to (6), Art. 46, have been made and the result has been expressed without zero or negative exponents. If the final result is a fraction, it should be reduced to lowest terms.

Example 7

Simplify

$$\left(\frac{3a^{-2}b^2}{a^3c^{-3}}\right)^{-2}$$

Solution

$$\left(\frac{3a^{-2}b^2}{a^3c^{-3}}\right)^{-2} = \frac{3^{-2}(a^{-2})^{-2}(b^2)^{-2}}{(a^3)^{-2}(c^{-3})^{-2}} \qquad \text{[by (6) Art. 46]}$$

$$= \frac{3^{-2}a^4b^{-4}}{a^{-6}c^6} \qquad \text{[by (4), Art. 46]}$$

$$= \frac{a^6a^4}{3^2b^4c^6} \qquad \text{(by the statement above Example 5)}$$

$$= \frac{a^{10}}{9b^4c^6} \qquad \text{[by (2), Art. 46]}$$

Each step in the solution is shown in detail in the above example. After some practice, many of them can be performed mentally. It is sometimes shorter to eliminate all negative exponents as the first step and then proceed with the simplification. If we use this procedure for the above problem, we get

$$\left(\frac{3a^{-2}b^2}{a^3c^{-3}}\right)^{-2} = \frac{1}{\left(\frac{3b^2c^3}{a^2a^3}\right)^2} \qquad \text{[by the statement above Example 5 and (1)]}$$

$$= \frac{1}{\left(\frac{3b^2c^3}{a^5}\right)^2} = \frac{(a^5)^2}{(3b^2c^3)^2} = \frac{a^{10}}{9b^4c^6}$$

Example 8

Simplify

$$\frac{x^{-3} - y^{-3}}{x^{-2} - y^{-2}}$$

Solution

$$\frac{x^{-3} - y^{-3}}{x^{-2} - y^{-2}} = \frac{\dfrac{1}{x^3} - \dfrac{1}{y^3}}{\dfrac{1}{x^2} - \dfrac{1}{y^2}} \qquad \text{[by (1) of this article]}$$

$$= \frac{y^3 - x^3}{xy^3 - x^3y} \qquad \text{(multiplying the numerator and the denominator by } x^3y^3\text{)}$$

$$= \frac{(y - x)(y^2 + xy + x^2)}{xy(y - x)(y + x)} \qquad \text{(factoring)}$$

$$= \frac{y^2 + xy + x^2}{xy(y + x)}$$

EXERCISE 23

Find the value of the expressions in each of Problems 1 to 24.

1. 4^{-1}.
2. 5^{-2}.
3. $(-2)^0$.
4. $(\frac{2}{3})^0$.
5. $(-\frac{3}{4})^0$.
6. $[(3)(5)]^0$.
7. 2^{-3}.
8. 3^{-4}.
9. $(3^{-1})(3^{-2})$.
10. $(2^{-4})(2^{-2})$.
11. $(4^{-5})(4^2)$.
12. $(3^{-6})(3^5)$.
13. $(3^{-2})^{-1}$.
14. $(5^{-1})^2$.
15. $(4^{-2})^2$.
16. $(2^{-3})^{-3}$.
17. $(3^2)^{-1}(2^2)^{-1}$.
18. $(3^{-2})^{-1}(2^2)^{-1}$.
19. $(3^2)^{-1}(2^{-2})^{-1}$.
20. $(3^{-2})^{-1}(2^{-2})^{-1}$.
21. $(3^{-1}2^2)^{-3}$.
22. $(4^23^{-3})^{-2}$.
23. $(5^{-2}3^3)^{-2}$.
24. $(2^{-2}4^3)^{-3}$.

By use of negative exponents, write the expressions in each of Problems 25 to 36 without denominators.

25. $\dfrac{4x^2}{y^3}$.
26. $\dfrac{2a^2}{b}$.
27. $\dfrac{3h^2k}{k^2j^3}$.
28. $\dfrac{4a^2b^3}{2cd^2}$.

29. $\dfrac{z^3}{3x^2z^5}.$ 30. $\dfrac{4x^2y}{3y^3z^2}.$ 31. $\dfrac{3a^2b^4}{4^0a^3b^5}.$ 32. $\dfrac{7x^3y^2}{3x^5y^3}.$

33. $\dfrac{3a^2b^3c}{2^{-1}a^{-1}b^4c^{-2}}.$ 34. $\dfrac{2h^3j^2k^4}{3^{-2}h^4jk^{-2}}.$ 35. $\dfrac{4r^3s^{-1}t^2}{2^{-1}r^4s^{-2}t^{-1}}.$ 36. $\dfrac{8x^3y^{-3}z}{4^{-1}x^4y^{-2}z^3}.$

Simplify the following.

37. $x^0y^{-2}.$ 38. $by^{-4}.$ 39. $c^0z^{-3}.$ 40. $\dfrac{e^0f^{-1}}{g^{-3}}.$

41. $x^{-3}x.$ 42. $x^{-2}x^{-3}.$ 43. $a^{-1}x^{-1}.$ 44. $a^{-1}b^{-2}.$

45. $\dfrac{a^2c^{-2}}{a^{-1}}.$ 46. $\dfrac{x^{-1}y^{-3}}{x^{-4}w^2}.$ 47. $\dfrac{2r^{-2}s^{-3}}{4^{-1}r^3s^{-2}}.$ 48. $\dfrac{3^{-2}a^2b^2}{2^{-1}a^2b^{-1}}.$

49. $\left(\dfrac{a^2}{b^{-3}}\right)^2.$ 50. $\left(\dfrac{x^{-3}}{y^2}\right)^3.$ 51. $\left(\dfrac{a^{-2}}{b^{-3}}\right)^{-2}.$ 52. $\left(\dfrac{c^{-3}}{d^2}\right)^{-2}.$

53. $\dfrac{24p^{-4}q^{-2}r^4}{15p^{-3}q^{-4}r^5}.$ 54. $\dfrac{18x^3y^{-2}z^0}{12x^{-1}yz^{-2}}$ 55. $\dfrac{4^{-2}a^{-1}b^2c^{-3}}{2^{-3}a^2b^{-3}c^{-2}}.$

56. $\dfrac{6^2x^{-2}y^{-3}z^{-1}}{2^3xy^{-2}z^{-3}}.$ 57. $\dfrac{5^0h^2k^{-1}}{2^{-2}j^{-1}k^2}.$ 58. $\dfrac{12x^3y^{-2}z^0}{8x^{-1}yz^{-2}}.$

59. $\dfrac{9c^{-1}d^{-3}e^2}{12bc^2d^{-1}e^0}.$ 60. $\dfrac{2^{-2}a^{-3}b^2c^{-1}}{3^{-2}ab^{-2}c^{-3}}.$ 61. $\left(\dfrac{a^{-2}b^3c^{-2}}{a^{-1}b^{-2}}\right)^3.$

62. $\left(\dfrac{x^{-1}y^2z^{-3}}{y^{-1}z^{-2}}\right)^5.$ 63. $\left(\dfrac{a^{-2}x^{-3}y^{-1}}{b^{-3}x^{-2}y^3}\right)^2.$ 64. $\left(\dfrac{c^{-2}d^{-4}e^5}{c^{-3}d^{-3}e^3}\right)^3.$

65. $\left(\dfrac{4^2x^{-3}y^{-4}}{16x^{-5}y^{-2}}\right)^{-4}.$ 66. $\left(\dfrac{5^{-3}c^{-4}d^{-2}}{25^{-2}c^3d^{-5}}\right)^{-3}.$ 67. $\left(\dfrac{8^{-2}a^0b^{-3}}{4^{-3}a^{-2}b^2}\right)^{-3}.$

68. $\left(\dfrac{2^{-6}c^{-3}y^0}{64^{-1}c^2y^{-3}}\right)^{-2}.$ 69. $x^a + \dfrac{2}{x^{-a}}.$ 70. $3x^{-a} + \dfrac{2}{x^a}.$

71. $\dfrac{a}{b} + \dfrac{b^{-1}}{a^{-1}}.$ 72. $\dfrac{a}{b^{-1}} + \dfrac{b}{a^{-1}}.$ 73. $a^{-1} + b^{-1}.$

74. $2x^{-1} + 3b^{-1}.$ 75. $3x^{-1}y + 2xy^{-1}.$ 76. $a^{-1}b^{-1}c - abc^{-1}.$

77. $\dfrac{a^{-3} + b^{-2}}{a^{-1}}.$ 78. $\dfrac{x^{-1} + y^{-2}}{y^{-1}}.$ 79. $\dfrac{x^{-2} - y^{-1}}{x^{-3}}.$

80. $\dfrac{z^{-3} - z^{-2}}{z^{-4}}.$ 81. $\dfrac{x^{-1} + y^{-1}}{x^{-2} - y^{-2}}.$ 82. $\dfrac{x^{-1} - y^{-1}}{x^{-2} - y^{-2}}.$

83. $\dfrac{y^{-2} + x^{-1}y^{-1}}{y^{-2} - x^{-1}y^{-1}}.$ 84. $\dfrac{y^{-1} + x^{-2}}{x^{-1}y^{-1} - x^{-2}y}.$

85. $\dfrac{y^{-2} + 2x^{-1}y^{-1} + x^{-2}}{x^{-1}y^{-2} + x^{-2}y^{-1}}.$ 86. $\dfrac{y^{-3} - x^{-3}}{x^{-2}y^{-3} - x^{-3}y^{-2}}.$

87. $\dfrac{y^{-2} + 3x^{-1}y^{-1} + 2x^{-2}}{x^{-1}y^{-2} + x^{-2}y^{-1}}.$ 88. $\dfrac{xy^{-2} - x^{-1}}{y^{-2} + x^{-1}y^{-1}}.$

89. $-3(x + 1)(x - 1)^{-4} + (x - 1)^{-3}.$
90. $-2(2x + 5)^2(x + 1)^{-3} + 4(2x + 5)(x + 1)^{-2}.$
91. $-2(2x - 1)^2(x - 3)^{-3} + 4(2x - 1)(x - 3)^{-2}.$
92. $2(3x + 1)^{-1}(x + 2)^{-3} + 3(3x + 1)^{-2}(x + 2)^{-2}.$

49. *Roots of numbers.* In the statement $3^2 = 9$, we say that 9 is the second power, or the square, of 3, and that 3 is the *square root* of 9. Similarly, since $4^3 = 64$, 4 is the *cube root* of 64, and since $2^5 = 32$, 2 is the *fifth root* of 32. In general, we have the following definition.

DEFINITION. *A number **a** is an **nth** root of **b** if $a^n = b$.*

Since $(-a)^2 = a^2$, it is true that any positive number has two square roots, one positive and the other negative, with their numerical values equal. Furthermore, since the square of any real[1] number is positive, there is no *real* square root of $-a$, no *real* fourth root of $-a$, and, in general, no real *n*th root of $-a$, if *n* is an even integer and *a* is positive. We call such roots *imaginary numbers* and shall discuss them more fully in later articles. We shall prove in Chap. 11 that every number has *n* *n*th roots. However, except when $n = 2$, and $n = 4$, most of the roots are imaginary.[2]

If there is a *positive real n*th root of a number, it is called the *principal n*th root. If there is no positive real *n*th root of a number, but there is a *negative* real *n*th root, the negative root is called the principal *n*th root.

In Chap. 11 we define the principal *n*th root of a number if all *n* roots are imaginary.

Examples

1. The principal square root of 9 is 3.
2. The principal cube root of -27 is -3.

*The customary notation for **the principal nth root of a is** $\sqrt[n]{a}$. This symbol is called a **radical of order n**. The letter **a** is the **radicand**, and **n** is the **index** of the radical.*

By the above definition,

$$(1) \qquad (\sqrt[n]{a})^n = a$$

If *a* is not the *n*th power of a rational number, the value of $\sqrt[n]{a}$ cannot be expressed *exactly* as an integer or a fraction. Often, it can be expressed in other forms, but never exactly without the

---

[1] At this point the reader should review Art. 2.

[2] If *a* is positive, the square roots of *a* are $\sqrt{a}$ and $-\sqrt{a}$, both of which are real. If $n = 4$, and *a* is positive, we have two real and two imaginary fourth roots of *a*. For example, the four fourth roots of 16 are 2, -2, $\sqrt{-4}$, and $-\sqrt{-4}$.

use of a radical. However, if $\sqrt[n]{a}$ is real, its value can be expressed *approximately* as a decimal fraction.

50. Fractional exponents. We are now in position to extend further the definition of exponents so as to obtain an interpretation of fractional exponents.

We shall assume that Law (4), Art. 46, holds when $m = 1/n$. Then we have

$$(a^{1/n})^n = a^{n/n} = a$$

Hence, $a^{1/n}$ is a number whose nth power is a, and, consequently, by the definition in Art. 49, it is an nth root of a. Hence, we have

(1) $$a^{1/n} = \sqrt[n]{a}$$

Consequently, we accept (1) as the interpretation of a fractional exponent when the numerator is one. Furthermore, if we interpret $a^{q/p}$ as below,

(2) $$a^{q/p} = (\sqrt[p]{a})^q$$

the

$$a^{q/p} = (a^{1/p})^q$$

and thus Law (4), Art. 46, holds with $m = 1/p$, and $n = q$.

Therefore, *we define a number with a fractional exponent as a power of a radical. The denominator of the exponent is the index of the radical and the numerator denotes the power to which the radical is raised.*

If $\sqrt[p]{a}$ is a real number,[1] then

(3) $$a^{q/p} = (a^{1/p})^q = (a^q)^{1/p}$$

[1] This excludes only the case in which a is negative and p is even. Relation (4) states that, except for the excluded case, the successive processes of extracting a root and then raising the result to a power are commutative. To prove (4), we place $(\sqrt[p]{a^q})$ in the exponential form and then raise the expression to the pth power. Thus we get

$$[(a^{1/p})^q]^p = (a^{1/p})^{pq} \qquad \text{[by (4), Art. 46]}$$
$$= a^{pq/p} \qquad \text{[by (4), Art. 46, with } n = pq \text{ and } m = 1/p]$$
$$= a^q$$

Hence, $(a^{1/p})^q$ is a pth root of a^q. If a is positive, then $(a^{1/p})^q$ is positive. If a is negative, then p is odd and therefore both $(a^{1/p})^q$ and a^q are positive or negative according as q is even or odd. Hence, except for the excluded case, $(a^{1/p})^q$ is the *principal pth root* of a^q. Hence, $(\sqrt[p]{a})^q = \sqrt[p]{a^q}$.

and Law (4), Art. 46, holds when $m = q$ and $n = 1/p$. If we use the radical form for the second and third expressions in (3), we get

$$(4) \qquad a^{q/p} = (\sqrt[p]{a})^q = \sqrt[p]{a^q}$$

If $\sqrt[p]{a}$ is rational it is more convenient to use the first radical form in (4). Otherwise, the second radical form is better.

Examples

1. $64^{\frac{2}{3}} = (\sqrt[3]{64})^2 = 4^2 = 16.$

2. If we use the first radical form in (4) in connection with $25^{\frac{2}{3}}$, we have $(\sqrt[3]{25})^2$. Since there is no rational cube root of 25, we cannot express $(\sqrt[3]{25})^2$ without the use of a radical. However, we can express in another form by using the last radical expression in (4) as below.

$$(\sqrt[3]{25})^2 = \sqrt[3]{25^2} = \sqrt[3]{625}$$

In a later article, we shall show how to simplify $\sqrt[3]{625}$.

It can be proved that Laws (2) to (6), Art. 46, hold for the interpretation (4) of fractional exponents. As a sample proof, we shall show that (4), Art. 46, holds with both m and n fractions. As the first step, we have

$$\begin{aligned}
[(a^{1/u})^{1/v}]^{uv} &= (a^{1/u})^{uv/v} \\
&= (a^{1/u})^u \\
&= a^{u/u} = a \qquad \text{[all by the application of (3)]}
\end{aligned}$$

Hence, $(a^{1/u})^{1/v}$ is a uvth root of a, and except for the excluded cases (*i.e.*, a negative and either u or v even) it is the principal root. Hence

$$(5) \qquad (a^{1/u})^{1/v} = a^{1/uv}$$

Now, we consider

$$\begin{aligned}
(a^{u/v})^{r/s} &= \{[(a^u)^{1/v}]^{1/s}\}^r & \text{[by (3)]} \\
&= [(a^u)^{1/vs}]^r & \text{[by (5)]} \\
&= [(a^{1/vs})^u[^r & \text{[by (3)]} \\
&= (a^{1/vs})^{ur} & \text{[by (4) Art. 46]} \\
&= a^{ur/vs} & \text{[by (3)]}
\end{aligned}$$

Since

$$a^{-r/s} = (a^{-r})^{1/s} = \left(\frac{1}{a^r}\right)^{1/s} = \frac{1}{a^{r/s}}$$

it follows that (1) of Art. 48 applies when n is a fraction.

Example 3

Write $\sqrt{5x^6y^3}/\sqrt[3]{z^4w^9}$ without radicals.

Solution

$$\frac{\sqrt{5x^6y^3}}{\sqrt[3]{z^4w^9}} = \frac{(5x^6y^3)^{\frac{1}{2}}}{(z^4w^9)^{\frac{1}{3}}} = \frac{5^{\frac{1}{2}}x^3y^{\frac{3}{2}}}{z^{\frac{4}{3}}w^3} = \frac{5^{\frac{1}{2}}x^3y^{\frac{3}{2}}}{z^{\frac{4}{3}}w^3}$$

Example 4

Express $3a^{\frac{1}{2}}b^{\frac{3}{2}}/c^{\frac{2}{3}}d^{\frac{4}{3}}$ without fractional exponents.

Solution

$$\frac{3a^{\frac{1}{2}}b^{\frac{3}{2}}}{c^{\frac{2}{3}}d^{\frac{4}{3}}} = \frac{3(ab^3)^{\frac{1}{2}}}{(c^2d^4)^{\frac{1}{3}}} = \frac{3\sqrt{ab^3}}{\sqrt[3]{c^2d^4}}$$

Example 5

Write $3x^{\frac{3}{4}}y^{-\frac{2}{3}}$ without fractional or negative exponents.

Solution

$$3x^{\frac{3}{4}}y^{-\frac{2}{3}} = \frac{3x^{\frac{3}{4}}}{y^{\frac{2}{3}}} = \frac{3\sqrt[4]{x^3}}{\sqrt[3]{y^2}}$$

51. Simplification of exponential expressions. We shall agree that an exponential expression is simplified if the following steps are performed.

1. *Make all possible combinations by means of* (2) *to* (6), *Art.* 46.
2. *Express the result without zero or negative exponents.*

In many problems, it is more efficient to perform step 2 first. However, after some practice, it is often possible to perform the two steps simultaneously.

In order to simplify an exponential expression that also contains radicals, we first convert the radicals to fractional exponents and then apply steps 1 and 2.

Example 1

Simplify

$$\frac{6a^2b^{-3}c^{-\frac{1}{2}}}{18a^{\frac{3}{2}}b^{\frac{1}{4}}}$$

Solution

We first apply (5), Art. 46, to the powers of a and also move the factors b^{-3} and $c^{-\frac{1}{2}}$ into the denominator by changing the signs of the exponents. Thus we get

$$\frac{6a^2b^{-3}c^{-\frac{1}{2}}}{18a^{\frac{2}{3}}b^{\frac{1}{4}}} = \frac{6a^{2-\frac{2}{3}}}{18b^{\frac{1}{4}+3}c^{\frac{1}{2}}}$$

$$= \frac{6a^{\frac{4}{3}}}{18b^{\frac{13}{4}}c^{\frac{1}{2}}}$$

$$= \frac{a^{\frac{4}{3}}}{3b^{\frac{13}{4}}c^{\frac{1}{2}}}$$

Example 2

Simplify

$$\left(\frac{2x^3y^{\frac{1}{2}}z^2}{3x^{\frac{3}{4}}z^4}\right)\left(\frac{x^{-\frac{1}{2}}y^{\frac{3}{2}}}{z^{-1}}\right)^2$$

Solution

We shall first square the expression in the second parentheses, then multiply the result by the expression in the first, and finally simplify the product.

$$\left(\frac{2x^3y^{\frac{1}{2}}z^2}{3x^{\frac{3}{4}}z^4}\right)\left(\frac{x^{-\frac{1}{2}}y^{\frac{3}{2}}}{z^{-1}}\right)^2 = \left(\frac{2x^3y^{\frac{1}{2}}z^2}{3x^{\frac{3}{4}}z^4}\right)\left(\frac{x^{(-\frac{1}{2})2}y^{(\frac{3}{2})2}}{z^{(-1)2}}\right)$$

$$= \left(\frac{2x^3y^{\frac{1}{2}}z^2}{3x^{\frac{3}{4}}z^4}\right)\left(\frac{x^{-1}y^3}{z^{-2}}\right)$$

$$= \frac{2x^{3-1}y^{\frac{1}{2}+3}z^2}{3x^{\frac{3}{4}}z^{4-2}}$$

$$= \frac{2x^2y^{\frac{7}{2}}z^2}{3x^{\frac{3}{4}}z^2}$$

$$= \frac{2}{3}x^{\frac{5}{4}}y^{\frac{7}{2}}z^0$$

$$= \frac{2}{3}x^{\frac{5}{4}}y^{\frac{7}{2}}$$

Example 3

Simplify

$$\left(\frac{x^{-\frac{1}{2}}y^{-\frac{1}{2}}}{x^{-\frac{1}{2}} - y^{-\frac{1}{2}}}\right)^{-2}$$

Solution

Since the denominator is not in factored form, we must replace each term having a negative exponent with an equal term in which the exponent is positive, and then proceed with the simplification. When this is done, we have

$$\left(\frac{x^{-\frac{1}{2}}y^{-\frac{1}{2}}}{x^{-\frac{1}{2}} - y^{-\frac{1}{2}}}\right)^{-2} = \left[\frac{\left(\frac{1}{x^{\frac{1}{2}}}\right)\left(\frac{1}{y^{\frac{1}{2}}}\right)}{\frac{1}{x^{\frac{1}{2}}} - \frac{1}{y^{\frac{1}{2}}}}\right]^{-2}$$

$$= \left[\frac{(x^{\frac{1}{2}}y^{\frac{1}{2}})\left(\frac{1}{x^{\frac{1}{2}}}\right)\left(\frac{1}{y^{\frac{1}{2}}}\right)}{(x^{\frac{1}{2}}y^{\frac{1}{2}})\left(\frac{1}{x^{\frac{1}{2}}} - \frac{1}{y^{\frac{1}{2}}}\right)}\right]^{-2}$$

(multiplying the numerator and denominator by $x^{\frac{1}{2}}y^{\frac{1}{2}}$)

$$= \left(\frac{1}{y^{\frac{1}{2}} - x^{\frac{1}{2}}}\right)^{-2}$$

$$= \frac{1^{-2}}{(y^{\frac{1}{2}} - x^{\frac{1}{2}})^{-2}}$$

$$= (y^{\frac{1}{2}} - x^{\frac{1}{2}})^2$$

$$= (y^{\frac{1}{2}})^2 - 2(y^{\frac{1}{2}}x^{\frac{1}{2}}) + (x^{\frac{1}{2}})^2$$

$$= y - 2x^{\frac{1}{2}}y^{\frac{1}{2}} + x$$

Example 4

Simplify

$$(2x + 1)^{\frac{1}{2}} - (x + 1)(2x + 1)^{-\frac{1}{2}}$$

Solution

$$(2x + 1)^{\frac{1}{2}} - (x + 1)(2x + 1)^{-\frac{1}{2}} = (2x + 1)^{\frac{1}{2}} - \frac{x + 1}{(2x + 1)^{\frac{1}{2}}}$$

$$= \frac{(2x + 1)^{\frac{1}{2}}(2x + 1)^{\frac{1}{2}} - (x + 1)}{(2x + 1)^{\frac{1}{2}}}$$

$$= \frac{2x + 1 - x - 1}{(2x + 1)^{\frac{1}{2}}}$$

$$= \frac{x}{(2x + 1)^{\frac{1}{2}}}$$

EXERCISE 24

Write the value of the expression in each of Problems 1 to 24 without exponents or radicals.

1. $9^{\frac{1}{2}}$.

2. $27^{\frac{1}{3}}$.

3. $.01^{\frac{1}{2}}$.

4. $64^{\frac{2}{3}}$.

5. $64^{\frac{1}{3}}$.

6. $32^{\frac{2}{3}}$.

7. $8^{\frac{4}{3}}$.

8. $25^{\frac{3}{2}}$.

9. $(.001)^{\frac{2}{3}}$.

10. $(100)^{\frac{3}{2}}$.

11. $81^{\frac{1}{4}}$.

12. $16^{\frac{3}{4}}$.

13. $(\frac{8}{27})^{\frac{2}{3}}$.

14. $(\frac{4}{9})^{\frac{3}{2}}$.

15. $(\frac{81}{16})^{\frac{1}{4}}$.

16. $(\frac{4}{25})^{\frac{3}{2}}$.

17. $8^{-\frac{1}{3}}$.

18. $25^{-\frac{1}{2}}$.

19. $64^{-\frac{1}{3}}$.

20. $32^{-\frac{2}{5}}$.

21. $(\frac{27}{125})^{-\frac{1}{3}}$.

22. $(\frac{4}{25})^{-\frac{3}{2}}$.

23. $(.001)^{-\frac{1}{3}}$.

24. $(\frac{125}{27})^{-\frac{2}{3}}$.

Write the value of the expression in each of Problems 25 to 44 without radicals.

25. $\sqrt{25}$.   **26.** $\sqrt[3]{64}$.   **27.** $\sqrt[5]{5^5}$.   **28.** $\sqrt[n]{3^n}$.

29. $\sqrt{4^3}$.   **30.** $\sqrt[3]{8^2}$.   **31.** $\sqrt[4]{4}$.   **32.** $\sqrt[6]{32}$.

33. $\sqrt{64x^4y^6}$.   **34.** $\sqrt[3]{27a^6b^9}$.   **35.** $\sqrt[5]{32h^{10}k^5}$.   **36.** $\sqrt[4]{256r^8s^{12}}$.

37. $\sqrt[3]{25a^3b^2}$.   **38.** $\sqrt{8x^3y^4}$.   **39.** $\sqrt[3]{16a^5b^0c^3}$.   **40.** $\sqrt[4]{4a^2b^3}$.

41. $\sqrt[6]{\dfrac{16x^3y^4}{9z^2}}$.   **42.** $\sqrt[12]{\dfrac{27a^4x^8}{64b^9y^{18}}}$.   **43.** $\sqrt[8]{\dfrac{9p^3q^4}{16r^6s^0}}$.   **44.** $\sqrt{\dfrac{9x^3y^4}{25z^{\frac{1}{2}}}}$.

Write the expression in each of Problems 45 to 60 in simplest form without the use of fractional or negative exponents.

45. $x^{\frac{3}{2}}$.   **46.** $b^{\frac{3}{2}}$.   **47.** $c^{\frac{3}{4}}$.   **48.** $a^{\frac{3}{2}}$.

49. $x^{\frac{3}{4}}y^{\frac{1}{4}}$.   **50.** $4^{\frac{1}{2}}a^{\frac{3}{2}}b^{\frac{3}{2}}$.   **51.** $8^{\frac{1}{2}}x^{\frac{3}{2}}y^2$.   **52.** $32^{\frac{2}{5}}a^{\frac{3}{5}}b^{\frac{4}{5}}$.

53. $8^{\frac{2}{3}}x^{\frac{1}{2}}y^{-\frac{3}{2}}$.   **54.** $9^{\frac{3}{2}}x^{\frac{1}{2}}y^{-\frac{1}{2}}$.   **55.** $\dfrac{a^{\frac{5}{6}}y^{-\frac{3}{4}}}{x^{\frac{5}{8}}}$.   **56.** $\dfrac{x^{\frac{1}{2}}b^{-\frac{2}{3}}}{c^{-\frac{3}{4}}}$.

57. $\dfrac{a^{-\frac{3}{4}}b^{-\frac{5}{6}}}{c^{-\frac{7}{8}}}$.   **58.** $\dfrac{3a^{\frac{1}{2}}b^{-\frac{1}{4}}}{a^{\frac{1}{4}}}$.   **59.** $\dfrac{4^{\frac{1}{2}}x^{\frac{3}{2}}y^{-\frac{1}{3}}}{8^{\frac{2}{3}}x^{\frac{3}{4}}}$.   **60.** $\dfrac{32^{\frac{3}{5}}h^{\frac{1}{3}}k^{-\frac{2}{3}}}{8^{\frac{2}{3}}h^{-\frac{3}{4}}k^{-\frac{3}{4}}}$.

Simplify the following.

61. $a^{\frac{2}{3}}a^{\frac{3}{2}}$.   **62.** $b^{\frac{1}{3}}b^{\frac{1}{4}}$.   **63.** $c^{\frac{2}{3}}c^{-\frac{4}{5}}$.   **64.** $x^{\frac{5}{3}}x^{-\frac{1}{4}}$.

65. $\dfrac{y^{\frac{3}{4}}}{y^{\frac{1}{2}}}$.   **66.** $\dfrac{h^{\frac{5}{3}}}{h^{\frac{1}{3}}}$.   **67.** $\dfrac{r^{\frac{8}{5}}}{r^{\frac{2}{3}}}$.   **68.** $\dfrac{a^{\frac{1}{6}}}{a^{\frac{1}{4}}}$.

69. $(9x^2y^4)^{\frac{1}{2}}$.   **70.** $(64a^{-6}y^3)^{\frac{1}{3}}$.   **71.** $(16h^{\frac{1}{2}}k^{-6})^{\frac{1}{4}}$.   **72.** $(32r^{10}s^{-5})^{\frac{1}{5}}$.

73. $(5^{-\frac{1}{2}}a^{-\frac{2}{5}}b^{\frac{3}{2}})^2$.   **74.** $(9^{\frac{1}{6}}c^{-\frac{2}{3}}q^{\frac{1}{2}})^3$.   **75.** $(16^{-\frac{1}{4}}x^{\frac{2}{3}}y^{-\frac{3}{2}})^6$.   **76.** $(8^{-\frac{1}{3}}a^{\frac{2}{3}}b^{-\frac{5}{6}})^9$.

77. $(32h^{\frac{3}{8}}k^{-5})^{-\frac{2}{5}}$.   **78.** $(27^{\frac{1}{4}}a^{-\frac{3}{4}}b^{\frac{1}{2}})^{-\frac{2}{3}}$.   **79.** $(5^{\frac{3}{2}}r^{-\frac{2}{3}}y^{-4})^{-\frac{3}{4}}$.   **80.** $(4x^{\frac{3}{5}}s^{-\frac{3}{4}}t^{-\frac{2}{3}})^{-\frac{1}{2}}$.

81. $\left(\dfrac{16p^{-2}q^{\frac{2}{3}}}{4^{-1}r^4d^{-4}}\right)^{\frac{1}{2}}$.   **82.** $\left(\dfrac{81^{\frac{1}{4}}a^{\frac{1}{2}}b^{-\frac{2}{3}}}{9^{-\frac{1}{2}}c^{-\frac{1}{6}}}\right)^2$.   **83.** $\left(\dfrac{27c^{-3}d^{-\frac{3}{2}}}{9^{-\frac{3}{4}}e^{\frac{2}{3}}}\right)^{-\frac{2}{3}}$.

84. $\left(\dfrac{3^{\frac{1}{3}}x^{-\frac{1}{2}}y^{\frac{3}{4}}}{z^{\frac{3}{2}}b^{\frac{1}{3}}}\right)^{-6}$.   **85.** $(3u^{-2}v^{\frac{1}{2}})(u^2v^{\frac{3}{2}})$.   **86.** $(5h^2k^{\frac{1}{3}})(2h^{-3}k^{\frac{3}{4}})$.

87. $(6r^{\frac{3}{5}}s^{\frac{3}{4}})(\frac{2}{3}r^{-\frac{1}{2}}s^{-\frac{3}{4}})$.   **88.** $(\frac{3}{8}a^{\frac{3}{4}}b^{\frac{1}{2}}c^{\frac{2}{3}})(\frac{2}{3}a^{-\frac{1}{4}}b^{\frac{3}{4}}c^{-1})$.

89. $\dfrac{8^{\frac{1}{3}}x^{\frac{3}{4}}yz^0}{4x^{\frac{1}{2}}y^{-1}z^{-\frac{1}{2}}}$.   **90.** $\dfrac{8a^{\frac{3}{4}}b^{-\frac{1}{2}}c^{\frac{1}{4}}}{4^{\frac{1}{2}}a^{\frac{1}{2}}b^{\frac{3}{4}}c^{-\frac{1}{4}}}$.   **91.** $\dfrac{27^{\frac{1}{3}}r^{\frac{1}{4}}s^{-\frac{2}{3}}}{9^{\frac{1}{2}}r^{-\frac{1}{4}}s^{-\frac{3}{5}}}$.

92. $\dfrac{4^{\frac{1}{2}}p^{-\frac{3}{4}}q^{\frac{3}{4}}r^{-1}}{6p^{\frac{1}{4}}r^{-2}}$.   **93.** $(9u^4v^6)^{\frac{1}{2}}(8u^6v^3)^{\frac{1}{3}}$.   **94.** $(81h^{-2}k^3)^{\frac{1}{4}}(8h^{\frac{1}{4}}k^{-\frac{2}{3}})^{\frac{2}{3}}$.

95. $(5^{\frac{1}{2}}x^{-2}y^{\frac{3}{2}}z^4)^{\frac{3}{2}}(5^{\frac{1}{2}}x^4y^2z^{-3})^{-\frac{1}{2}}$.   **96.** $(2a^{-\frac{1}{2}}b^{\frac{3}{2}})^2(4u^{-2}v^{-\frac{3}{4}})^{-\frac{1}{2}}$.

97. $\left(\dfrac{25x^{-6}y^{-\frac{3}{4}}}{16x^{-2}y^{\frac{1}{4}}}\right)^{-\frac{1}{2}}$.   **98.** $\left(\dfrac{27a^{-\frac{3}{2}}b^{\frac{1}{2}}}{64a^0b^{-\frac{7}{2}}}\right)^{\frac{1}{3}}$.   **99.** $\dfrac{(4^{\frac{3}{4}}h^{\frac{1}{4}}k^4)^{-\frac{1}{2}}}{(2^{\frac{3}{4}}h^{-\frac{3}{8}}k^3)^{-\frac{1}{3}}}$.

100. $\dfrac{(9^{\frac{3}{4}}x^3y^{-\frac{1}{2}})^{\frac{2}{3}}}{(3^{-2}x^{\frac{1}{4}}y^{-1})^{\frac{1}{2}}}$.   **101.** $(x^{\frac{1}{2}}+y^{\frac{1}{2}})(x^{\frac{1}{2}}-y^{\frac{1}{2}})$.   **102.** $(a^{\frac{1}{4}}-a^{\frac{1}{2}})(a^{\frac{1}{2}}+a^{\frac{1}{4}})$.

103. $(x^{\frac{1}{3}}+y^{\frac{1}{3}})(x^{\frac{2}{3}}-x^{\frac{1}{3}}y^{\frac{1}{3}}+y^{\frac{2}{3}})$.   **104.** $(a^{\frac{2}{3}}-b^{\frac{2}{3}})(a^{\frac{4}{3}}+a^{\frac{2}{3}}b^{\frac{2}{3}}+b^{\frac{4}{3}})$.

105. $(r^{\frac{2}{3}}-r^{-\frac{2}{3}})(r^{\frac{2}{3}}+r^{-\frac{2}{3}})$.   **106.** $(2w^{\frac{2}{3}}-w^{\frac{1}{3}})^2$.

107. $(3u^{\frac{4}{3}}-2u^{\frac{1}{3}})(u^{\frac{2}{3}}+u^{\frac{1}{3}})$.   **108.** $(2b^{\frac{3}{4}}+b^{\frac{1}{4}})(b^{\frac{1}{4}}-b^{\frac{3}{4}})$.

109. $(3x+1)^{\frac{1}{3}}+(3x+1)^{-\frac{2}{3}}(x+3)$.

110. $(2x+3)^{\frac{3}{2}}+2(2x+3)^{-\frac{1}{2}}(3x+1)$.

111. $(2x - 3)^{\frac{1}{2}} + (x + 1)(2x - 3)^{-\frac{1}{2}}$.

112. $(3x - 1)^{\frac{1}{2}} + (2x - 3)(3x - 1)^{-\frac{1}{2}}$.

113. $(2x + 1)^{\frac{1}{2}}(3x - 1)^{-\frac{2}{3}} + (2x + 1)^{-\frac{1}{2}}(3x - 1)^{\frac{1}{3}}$.

114. $(2x - 1)^{\frac{1}{2}}(5x - 2)^{-\frac{1}{2}} + (5x - 2)^{\frac{1}{2}}(2x - 1)^{-\frac{1}{2}}$.

115. $3(x - 1)^{\frac{1}{3}}(x + 1)^{-\frac{2}{3}} + 4(x + 1)^{\frac{1}{3}}(x - 1)^{-\frac{2}{3}}$.

116. $5(x - 3)^{\frac{1}{3}}(x + 3)^{-\frac{2}{3}} + 4(x + 3)^{\frac{1}{3}}(x - 3)^{-\frac{2}{3}}$.

117. $\left(\dfrac{w^{a+2b}}{w^b}\right)^{a-b}$.

118. $\left(\dfrac{z^{a-2b}}{z^{-b}}\right)^{a/(a-b)}$.

119. $\left(\dfrac{x^{3a-2}}{x^a}\right)^{(a+1)/2}$.

120. $\left(\dfrac{y^{m+n}}{y^n}\right)^m \left(\dfrac{y^{n-m}}{y^n}\right)^{(m-n)}$.

52. Laws of radicals. Since Laws (3), (4), and (6) of Art. 46 are valid for fractional exponents, we may use them to derive three useful laws of radicals.

If in Law (3), Art. 46, n is replaced by $1/n$, we get

$$(ab)^{1/n} = a^{1/n}b^{1/n}$$

and if this is expressed in radical form, we have

$$(1) \qquad \sqrt[n]{ab} = \sqrt[n]{a}\,\sqrt[n]{b}$$

Similarly, we obtain from (6), Art. 46,

$$\left(\frac{a}{b}\right)^{1/n} = \frac{a^{1/n}}{b^{1/n}}$$

or

$$(2) \qquad \sqrt[n]{\frac{a}{b}} = \frac{\sqrt[n]{a}}{\sqrt[n]{b}}$$

The same procedure applied to (4), Art. 46, yields

$$(a^{1/n})^{1/m} = (a^{1/m})^{1/n} = a^{1/mn}$$

and this is equal to

$$(3) \qquad \sqrt[m]{\sqrt[n]{a}} = \sqrt[n]{\sqrt[m]{a}} = \sqrt[mn]{a}$$

53. Reduction of monomial integral radicals. By a monomial integral radical, we mean a radical in which the radicand consists of a single term that involves no fractions.

The reduction of a radical of this type consists of the following operations.

1. *Removing rational factors from the radical.* Law (1) of the

previous article enables us to remove one or more factors from a radical of order n if the radicand has factors that are nth powers.

Examples

1. If, in $\sqrt{72}$, we write $72 = (36)2 = (6^2)2$, we get

$$
\begin{aligned}
\sqrt{72} &= \sqrt{(6^2)(2)} \\
&= \sqrt{6^2}\sqrt{2} && \text{[by (1), Art. 52]} \\
&= 6\sqrt{2} && \text{(by the definition of Art. 49)}
\end{aligned}
$$

2. $\quad \begin{aligned}[t]
\sqrt[3]{54a^3b^5} &= \sqrt[3]{(27a^3b^3)2b^2} \\
&= \sqrt[3]{(3ab)^3 2b^2} \\
&= \sqrt[3]{(3ab)^3} \cdot \sqrt[3]{2b^2} && \text{[by (1), Art. 52]} \\
&= 3ab\sqrt[3]{2b^2}
\end{aligned}$

2. *Reducing the order of a radical.* The simplest method for reducing the order of a radical, when a reduction is possible, is to express it in terms of fractional exponents, then reduce the fractional exponents to lowest terms, and, finally, rewrite the result in radical form.

Examples

3. $\quad \begin{aligned}[t]
\sqrt[4]{9a^2} &= \sqrt[4]{(3a)^2} \\
&= (3a)^{\frac{2}{4}} \\
&= (3a)^{\frac{1}{2}} \\
&= \sqrt{3a}
\end{aligned}$

4. $\quad \begin{aligned}[t]
\sqrt[9]{64a^6b^{12}} &= \sqrt[9]{4^3a^6b^{12}} \\
&= 4^{\frac{3}{9}}a^{\frac{6}{9}}b^{\frac{12}{9}} \\
&= 4^{\frac{1}{3}}a^{\frac{2}{3}}b^{\frac{4}{3}} \\
&= (4a^2b^4)^{\frac{1}{3}} && \text{[by (2), Art. 46]} \\
&= \sqrt[3]{4a^2b^4} && \text{[by (1), Art. 50]}
\end{aligned}$

It is obvious from the above examples that the order of a radical can be reduced if the index of the radical and all exponents of the factors have a common factor. In order to reduce the order of a radical of this type without first changing to fractional exponents, we divide the index of the radical and each exponent in the radicand by their highest common factor.

Example 5

In the radical

$$\sqrt[12]{64x^3y^9} = \sqrt[12]{2^6x^3y^9}$$

the highest common factor of the index of the radical and the exponents of the factors of the radicand is 3. Hence, if we divide each of them by 3 we get

$$\sqrt[12]{64x^3y^9} = \sqrt[12]{2^6x^3y^9} = \sqrt[4]{2^2xy^3} = \sqrt[4]{4xy^3}$$

3. *Reducing a radical of the type* $\sqrt[m]{\sqrt[n]{a}}$. By use of (3), Art. 52, we may reduce a radical of the type $\sqrt[m]{\sqrt[n]{a}}$ to a single radical.

Example 6

$$\sqrt[3]{\sqrt[2]{6a^5}} = \sqrt[(3)(2)]{6a^5}$$
$$= \sqrt[6]{6a^5}$$

Frequently, after a reduction of this type has been made, the radical obtained can be reduced to a lower order.

Example 7

$$\sqrt[4]{\sqrt[3]{9x^2y^4}} = \sqrt[12]{9x^2y^4}$$
$$= \sqrt[12]{(3xy^2)^2}$$
$$= (3xy^2)^{\frac{2}{12}} = (3xy^2)^{\frac{1}{6}}$$
$$= \sqrt[6]{3xy^2}$$

EXERCISE 25

Remove all rational factors from the radicals in Problems 1 to 68.

1. $\sqrt{32}$.   2. $\sqrt{96}$.   3. $\sqrt{128}$.   4. $\sqrt{162}$.   5. $\sqrt{150}$.

6. $\sqrt{320}$.   7. $\sqrt{450}$.   8. $\sqrt{588}$.   9. $\sqrt[3]{16}$.   10. $\sqrt[3]{81}$.

11. $\sqrt[3]{250}$.   12. $\sqrt[3]{108}$.   13. $\sqrt[4]{32}$.   14. $\sqrt[4]{162}$.   15. $\sqrt[4]{384}$.

16. $\sqrt[4]{324}$.   17. $\sqrt{2x^2}$.   18. $\sqrt{5x^2y^4}$.   19. $\sqrt{7a^6b^2}$.   20. $\sqrt{3h^4k^6}$.

21. $\sqrt[3]{4r^3s^6}$.   22. $\sqrt[3]{6u^9v^6}$.   23. $\sqrt[3]{2p^9q^{12}}$.   24. $\sqrt[3]{16a^{12}b^{15}}$.

25. $\sqrt{8x^3}$.   26. $\sqrt{12y^5}$.   27. $\sqrt{27a^2b^5}$.   28. $\sqrt{45x^5y^4}$.

29. $\sqrt[3]{54a^4b^7}$.   30. $\sqrt[3]{192x^5y^8}$.   31. $\sqrt[3]{48u^7v^{10}}$.   32. $\sqrt[3]{725r^{11}s^{10}}$.

33. $\sqrt[4]{80a^5b^8c^6}$.   34. $\sqrt[5]{64x^7y^{15}z^{11}}$.   35. $\sqrt[5]{243p^{20}q^7r^{12}}$.

36. $\sqrt[4]{625r^{16}s^{12}t^7}$.   37. $\sqrt{294a^9b^{10}c^{13}}$.   38. $\sqrt{396x^8y^{12}z^{15}}$.

39. $\sqrt{768h^{17}j^8k^5}$.   40. $\sqrt{960u^9v^{11}w^{10}}$.   41. $\sqrt{\dfrac{9x}{4y^2}}$.

42. $\sqrt{\dfrac{20a^5}{b^6}}$.   43. $\sqrt[3]{\dfrac{16b^3}{c^6}}$.   44. $\sqrt[3]{\dfrac{48a^7}{b^9}}$.   45. $\sqrt{\dfrac{16x^3}{y^5}}$.

46. $\sqrt[3]{\dfrac{27a^4}{b^7}}$.   47. $\sqrt[4]{\dfrac{81b^9}{c^{12}}}$.   48. $\sqrt[3]{\dfrac{8a^7}{b^9}}$.   49. $\sqrt{\dfrac{18a^2b^3}{25c^4}}$.

50. $\sqrt{\dfrac{50e^5f^4}{64g^8}}$.   51. $\sqrt{\dfrac{72x^6y^7}{49z^{10}}}$.   52. $\sqrt{\dfrac{98r^9s^8}{25t^{12}}}$.   53. $\sqrt[3]{\dfrac{40a^5b^6}{54c^7}}$.

54. $\sqrt[4]{\dfrac{128x^7y^{12}}{162z^8}}.$ **55.** $\sqrt[5]{\dfrac{128u^9v^6}{486w^{20}}}.$ **56.** $\sqrt[4]{\dfrac{256c^6d^{12}}{625e^8}}.$

57. $\sqrt{(a-b)(a^2-b^2)}.$ **58.** $\sqrt{(2a+b)(4a^2-b^2)}.$

59. $\sqrt{(x^2-3x+2)(x^2+x-6)}.$ **60.** $\sqrt[3]{(a-b)(a^2-b^2)(a^3-b^3)}.$

61. $\sqrt{9x^{\frac{3}{2}}y^{\frac{3}{2}}}.$ **62.** $\sqrt[3]{8x^{\frac{3}{4}}}.$ **63.** $\sqrt{8x^{\frac{3}{2}}}.$ **64.** $\sqrt[3]{16a^{\frac{3}{4}}}.$

65. $\sqrt{a^{2n}b^{3n}}.$ **66.** $\sqrt[3]{a^{2n}b^{3n}}.$ **67.** $\sqrt[n]{a^{2n}b^{3n}}.$ **68.** $\sqrt[4]{a^{4n}b^{8n}}.$

Reduce the order of the radicals in Problems 69 to 84 and remove all possible factors from the reduced radical.

69. $\sqrt[6]{8}.$ **70.** $\sqrt[4]{25}.$ **71.** $\sqrt[9]{27}.$ **72.** $\sqrt[6]{4}.$ **73.** $\sqrt[12]{x^6}.$

74. $\sqrt[10]{x^2}.$ **75.** $\sqrt[6]{8x^3}.$ **76.** $\sqrt[4]{64x^6}.$ **77.** $\sqrt[4]{16a^6b^2}.$ **78.** $\sqrt[6]{27x^3y^6}.$

79. $\sqrt[4]{81u^8v^{10}}.$ **80.** $\sqrt[9]{64a^3b^{12}}.$ **81.** $\sqrt[8]{16r^2s^4}.$

82. $\sqrt[12]{27h^6k^9}.$ **83.** $\sqrt[6]{x^2+2x+1}.$ **84.** $\sqrt[4]{a^2-4a+4}.$

Reduce each of the following radicals to an expression containing only one radical sign. Reduce the order of the radical in the result if possible.

85. $\sqrt[3]{\sqrt{a^3}}.$ **86.** $\sqrt[4]{\sqrt[3]{x^2}}.$ **87.** $\sqrt{\sqrt[4]{8a^3}}.$ **88.** $\sqrt[3]{\sqrt{9a^3}}.$

89. $\sqrt[5]{\sqrt[3]{32a^{15}}}.$ **90.** $\sqrt[4]{\sqrt[6]{25a^2b^{12}}}.$ **91.** $\sqrt[3]{\sqrt[6]{27a^6b^9}}.$ **92.** $\sqrt[4]{\sqrt[8]{81x^6y^{12}}}.$

54. *Multiplication of radicals of the same order.* Law (1), Art. 52, read from right to left, enables us to obtain the product of two or more radicals of the same order.

Examples

1. $\qquad\qquad\sqrt{3}\,\sqrt{7} = \sqrt{(3)(7)} = \sqrt{21}$

2. $\qquad\sqrt[5]{2ab}\,\sqrt[5]{5a^2b^3} = \sqrt[5]{(2ab)(5a^2b^3)} = \sqrt[5]{10a^3b^4}$

Frequently the radicand in the product of two radicals of the nth order has factors that are nth powers. In such cases, all possible rational factors should be removed from the radical.

Examples

3. $\qquad\sqrt{5ab^2}\,\sqrt{15ab^3} = \sqrt{(5ab^2)(15ab^3)}$

$\qquad\qquad\qquad\qquad = \sqrt{75a^2b^5}$

$\qquad\qquad\qquad\qquad = \sqrt{(25a^2b^4)3b}$

$\qquad\qquad\qquad\qquad = 5ab^2\sqrt{3b}$

4. $\quad\sqrt[3]{6x^4y^5}\,\sqrt[3]{4xy^2}\,\sqrt[3]{9x^2y^3} = \sqrt[3]{(6x^4y^5)(4xy^2)(9x^2y^3)}$

$\qquad\qquad\qquad\qquad = \sqrt[3]{216x^7y^{10}}$

$\qquad\qquad\qquad\qquad = \sqrt[3]{(6x^2y^3)^3(xy)}$

$\qquad\qquad\qquad\qquad = 6x^2y^3\sqrt[3]{xy}$

55. *Division of radicals of the same order.* We employ Law (2), Art. 52, read from right to left, to obtain the quotient of two radicals of the nth order. The following examples illustrate the procedure.

Examples

1.
$$\frac{\sqrt{24a^3b^4c^5}}{\sqrt{3ab^2c^2}} = \sqrt{\frac{24a^3b^4c^5}{3ab^2c^2}} \qquad \text{[by (2), Art. 52]}$$
$$= \sqrt{8a^2b^2c^3}$$
$$= \sqrt{(2^2a^2b^2c^2)2c}$$
$$= 2abc\sqrt{2c}$$

2.
$$\frac{\sqrt[5]{384a^7b^2c^{11}}}{\sqrt[5]{9a^2b^9c^5}} = \sqrt[5]{\frac{384a^7b^2c^{11}}{9a^2b^9c^5}} \qquad \text{[by (2), Art. 52]}$$
$$= \sqrt[5]{\frac{128a^5c^6}{3b^7}}$$
$$= \sqrt[5]{\frac{(2^5a^5c^5)(4c)}{b^5(3b^2)}}$$
$$= \frac{2ac}{b}\sqrt[5]{\frac{4c}{3b^2}}$$

56. *Rationalizing monomial denominators.* It is always possible to express a fraction that has a radical in the denominator as an equal fraction in which the denominator contains no radicals. This process is called *rationalizing the denominator.* Many computations that involve radicals become easier if all denominators are rationalized at the start.

If the radicand is a fraction that has a monomial denominator, or if the denominator of a fraction has a radical factor, we eliminate the radical from the denominator by the method illustrated in the examples below.

Example 1

To rationalize the denominator in $2/\sqrt{3}$, we multiply each member of the fraction by $\sqrt{3}$, and get

$$\frac{2}{\sqrt{3}} = \frac{2}{\sqrt{3}}\frac{\sqrt{3}}{\sqrt{3}} = \frac{2\sqrt{3}}{\sqrt{3^2}} = \frac{2\sqrt{3}}{3}$$

One advantage that the rationalized form has over the original appears in the process of obtaining a decimal approximation for the expression. Since

$\sqrt{3} = 1.732$, the decimal approximation of $2/\sqrt{3} = 2/1.732$ requires trouble-some division. In the rationalized form, $2\sqrt{3}/3 = 2(1.732)/3$, the computation requires two simple steps that can be performed mentally.

Example 2

In order to rationalize the denominator of $\sqrt[3]{3a/2b^2c}$, we convert the fraction into an equal one in which the denominator is a perfect cube. This is accomplished by multiplying the radical by $\sqrt[3]{4bc^2/4bc^2} = 1$. Thus we get

$$\sqrt[3]{\frac{3a}{2b^2c}} = \sqrt[3]{\frac{3a}{2b^2c}}\,\sqrt[3]{\frac{4bc^2}{4bc^2}}$$

$$= \sqrt[3]{\frac{12abc^2}{8b^3c^3}} \qquad \text{[by (1), Art. 52]}$$

$$= \frac{\sqrt[3]{12abc^2}}{2bc}$$

Example 3

We rationalize the denominator of $(x^2 - y^2)/(2x\sqrt{x+y})$ by multiplying each member of the fraction by $\sqrt{x+y}/\sqrt{x+y}$ and obtain

$$\frac{x^2 - y^2}{2x\sqrt{x+y}} = \frac{(x^2 - y^2)\sqrt{x+y}}{2x\sqrt{x+y}\,\sqrt{x+y}}$$

$$= \frac{(x^2 - y^2)\sqrt{x+y}}{2x\sqrt{(x+y)^2}}$$

$$= \frac{(x+y)(x-y)\sqrt{x+y}}{2x(x+y)}$$

$$= \frac{(x-y)\sqrt{x+y}}{2x}$$

57. Simplification of radical expressions. In order to simplify a radical expression, we perform the following steps.

1. Perform all possible operations by use of the laws of Art. 52.
2. Remove all possible rational factors from the radicals.
3. Rationalize the denominator.
4. If the final result contains a radical, reduce it to the lowest order.

Example 1

Simplify

$$\frac{\sqrt{3x^3y}\,\sqrt{15xy^5}}{\sqrt{80x^7y}}$$

Solution

$$\frac{\sqrt{3x^3y}\,\sqrt{15xy^5}}{\sqrt{80x^7y}} = \sqrt{\frac{(3x^3y)(15xy^5)}{80x^7y}} \qquad \text{[by (1) and (2), Art. 52]}$$

$$= \sqrt{\frac{45x^4y^6}{80x^7y}} \qquad \text{(performing the indicated operations)}$$

$$= \sqrt{\frac{9y^5}{16x^3}} \qquad \text{(reducing the radicand to lowest terms)}$$

$$= \frac{3y^2}{4x}\sqrt{\frac{y}{x}} \qquad \text{(removing a rational factor)}$$

$$= \frac{3y^2}{4x}\sqrt{\frac{xy}{x^2}} \qquad \text{(rationalizing the denominator)}$$

$$= \frac{3y^2\sqrt{xy}}{4x^2}$$

NOTE: The computation can be abbreviated somewhat by noticing in the third step that the denominator can be made a perfect square by multiplying each member of the fraction by x. Thus we get

$$\sqrt{\frac{9y^5}{16x^3}} = \sqrt{\frac{9xy^5}{16x^4}} = \frac{3y^2\sqrt{xy}}{4x^2}$$

Example 2

Simplify

$$\frac{\sqrt[4]{24a^3b^2c^2}}{\sqrt[4]{8a^5b^6c^3}\,\sqrt[4]{48a^2b^2c^9}}$$

Solution

$$\frac{\sqrt[4]{24a^3b^2c^2}}{\sqrt[4]{8a^5b^6c^3}\,\sqrt[4]{48a^2b^2c^9}} = \sqrt[4]{\frac{24a^3b^2c^2}{(8a^5b^6c^3)(48a^2b^2c^9)}} \qquad \text{[by (2) and (3), Art. 52]}$$

$$= \sqrt[4]{\frac{24a^3b^2c^2}{384a^7b^8c^{12}}}$$

$$= \sqrt[4]{\frac{1}{16a^4b^6c^{10}}} \qquad \text{(reducing the radicand to lowest terms)}$$

$$= \sqrt[4]{\frac{1}{(16a^4b^4c^8)(b^2c^2)}}$$

$$= \frac{1}{2abc^2}\sqrt[4]{\frac{1}{b^2c^2}} \qquad$$

$$= \frac{1}{2abc^2}\sqrt[4]{\frac{b^2c^2}{b^4c^4}} \qquad \text{(rationalizing the denominator)}$$

$$= \frac{1}{(2abc^2)(bc)}\sqrt[4]{b^2c^2} \qquad$$

$$= \frac{1}{2ab^2c^3}\sqrt{bc} \qquad \text{(reducing the order of the radical)}$$

After some practice, it will be possible to combine some of the above steps by performing the operations mentally.

Example 3

$$\frac{(\sqrt{6x^3yz})^2(\sqrt{2xy^5z^3})^3}{\sqrt{8x^7y^3z^5}} = \sqrt{\frac{(6x^3yz)^2(2xy^5z^3)^3}{8x^7y^3z^5}}$$

$$= 6x^3yz\sqrt{\frac{(2xy^5z^3)^3}{8x^7y^3z^5}}$$

$$= 6x^3yz\sqrt{\frac{8x^3y^{15}z^9}{8x^7y^3z^5}}$$

$$= 6x^3yz\sqrt{\frac{y^{12}z^4}{x^4}}$$

$$= (6x^3yz)\left(\frac{y^6z^2}{x^2}\right)$$

$$= \frac{6x^3y^7z^3}{x^2}$$

$$= 6xy^7z^3$$

EXERCISE 26

Simplify the following radical expressions.

1. $\sqrt{2}\,\sqrt{8}$.
2. $\sqrt{3}\,\sqrt{27}$.
3. $\sqrt{3}\,\sqrt{75}$.
4. $\sqrt{8}\,\sqrt{32}$.

5. $\sqrt[3]{4}\,\sqrt[3]{16}$.
6. $\sqrt[3]{3}\,\sqrt[3]{9}$.
7. $\sqrt[3]{4}\,\sqrt[3]{54}$.
8. $\sqrt[3]{9}\,\sqrt[3]{81}$.

9. $\sqrt{\frac{1}{2}}\,\sqrt{\frac{128}{9}}$.
10. $\sqrt{\frac{2}{3}}\,\sqrt{\frac{27}{32}}$.
11. $\sqrt[3]{\frac{1}{2}}\,\sqrt[3]{\frac{16}{27}}$.
12. $\sqrt[3]{\frac{3}{4}}\,\sqrt[3]{\frac{1}{6}}$.

13. $\dfrac{\sqrt{243}}{\sqrt{3}}$.
14. $\dfrac{\sqrt[4]{80}}{\sqrt[4]{5}}$.
15. $\dfrac{\sqrt[3]{500}}{\sqrt[3]{4}}$.
16. $\dfrac{\sqrt[5]{288}}{\sqrt[5]{9}}$.

17. $\sqrt{\frac{2}{3}}$.
18. $\sqrt{\frac{5}{8}}$.
19. $\sqrt{\frac{7}{12}}$.
20. $\sqrt{\frac{4}{5}}$.

21. $\sqrt{2a^3b}\,\sqrt{6ab^2}$.
22. $\sqrt{10xy^5}\,\sqrt{6x^3y^2}$.
23. $\sqrt{8u^3vw^5}\,\sqrt{12uv^7}$.

24. $\sqrt{15r^4s^3}\,\sqrt{10rs^2}$.
25. $\sqrt{8h^3k}\,\sqrt{6h^5k}$.
26. $\sqrt{6c^5d^7}\,\sqrt{12cd^3}$.

27. $\sqrt[3]{5a^5b^3}\,\sqrt[3]{15a^2b}$.
28. $\sqrt[3]{8x^5y}\,\sqrt[3]{4xy^3}$.
29. $\sqrt[3]{16u^2v^4}\,\sqrt[3]{4uv^4}$.

30. $\sqrt[3]{6c^5d^7}\,\sqrt[3]{9cd^4}$.
31. $\sqrt[3]{4p^4q^2}\,\sqrt[3]{2p^7q^5}$.
32. $\sqrt[3]{9x^2y^4z}\,\sqrt[3]{12xy^4z}$.

33. $\sqrt{\frac{3x}{4y}}\,\sqrt{\frac{2}{3xy}}$.
34. $\sqrt{\frac{2a^3}{3b}}\,\sqrt{\frac{9b^5}{8a^5}}$.
35. $\sqrt{\frac{6c^5}{5d^8}}\,\sqrt{\frac{10d^2}{5c^7}}$.

36. $\sqrt{\frac{12u^3}{5v^5}}\,\sqrt{\frac{20v^7}{27u^4}}$.
37. $\dfrac{\sqrt{12r^5s^2}}{\sqrt{24rs^7}}$.
38. $\dfrac{\sqrt{28x^3y}}{\sqrt{35x^5y^3}}$.

39. $\dfrac{\sqrt{125a^7b^2}}{\sqrt{75a^5b^5}}$.
40. $\dfrac{\sqrt{216h^4k^7}}{\sqrt{42h^7k^5}}$.
41. $\dfrac{\sqrt[3]{32c^4d^2}}{\sqrt[3]{48c^2d^7}}$.

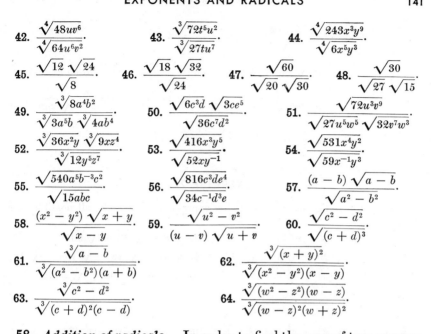

42. $\dfrac{\sqrt[4]{48uv^6}}{\sqrt[4]{64u^6v^2}}.$

43. $\dfrac{\sqrt[3]{72t^5u^2}}{\sqrt[3]{27tu^7}}.$

44. $\dfrac{\sqrt[4]{243x^3y^9}}{\sqrt[4]{6x^5y^3}}.$

45. $\dfrac{\sqrt{12}\,\sqrt{24}}{\sqrt{8}}.$

46. $\dfrac{\sqrt{18}\,\sqrt{32}}{\sqrt{24}}.$

47. $\dfrac{\sqrt{60}}{\sqrt{20}\,\sqrt{30}}.$

48. $\dfrac{\sqrt{30}}{\sqrt{27}\,\sqrt{15}}.$

49. $\dfrac{\sqrt[3]{8a^4b^2}}{\sqrt[3]{3a^5b}\,\sqrt[3]{4ab^4}}.$

50. $\dfrac{\sqrt{6c^3d}\,\sqrt{3ce^5}}{\sqrt{36c^7d^2}}.$

51. $\dfrac{\sqrt{72u^3v^9}}{\sqrt{27u^5w^5}\,\sqrt{32v^7w^3}}.$

52. $\dfrac{\sqrt[3]{36x^2y}\,\sqrt[3]{9xz^4}}{\sqrt[3]{12y^5z^7}}.$

53. $\dfrac{\sqrt{416x^3y^5}}{\sqrt{52xy^{-1}}}.$

54. $\dfrac{\sqrt{531x^4y^2}}{\sqrt{59x^{-1}y^3}}.$

55. $\dfrac{\sqrt{540a^5b^{-3}c^2}}{\sqrt{15abc}}.$

56. $\dfrac{\sqrt{816c^3de^4}}{\sqrt{34c^{-1}d^3e}}.$

57. $\dfrac{(a-b)\,\sqrt{a-b}}{\sqrt{a^2-b^2}}.$

58. $\dfrac{(x^2-y^2)\,\sqrt{x+y}}{\sqrt{x-y}}.$

59. $\dfrac{\sqrt{u^2-v^2}}{(u-v)\,\sqrt{u+v}}.$

60. $\dfrac{\sqrt{c^2-d^2}}{\sqrt{(c+d)^3}}.$

61. $\dfrac{\sqrt[3]{a-b}}{\sqrt[3]{(a^2-b^2)(a+b)}}.$

62. $\dfrac{\sqrt[3]{(x+y)^2}}{\sqrt[3]{(x^2-y^2)(x-y)}}.$

63. $\dfrac{\sqrt[3]{c^2-d^2}}{\sqrt[3]{(c+d)^2(c-d)}}.$

64. $\dfrac{\sqrt[3]{(w^2-z^2)(w-z)}}{\sqrt[3]{(w-z)^2(w+z)^2}}.$

58. Addition of radicals. In order to find the sum of two or more radicals that are of the same order and that have the same radicand, we add the coefficients of the radicals and multiply this sum by the radical.

Example 1

$$2\sqrt{a} + 5\sqrt{a} - 3\sqrt{a} = (2 + 5 - 3)\sqrt{a}$$
$$= 4\sqrt{a}$$

Two radicals in which either the radicands or the orders are different cannot be combined by the addition process. For example, neither $\sqrt{a} + \sqrt{b}$ nor $\sqrt{a} + \sqrt[3]{a}$ can be expressed as a single term.

If the radicals to be added are not in simplest form, we simplify them by the methods of Art. 57 and then combine the radicals that have the same index and the same radicand.

Examples

2.
$$\sqrt{108} + \sqrt{48} - \sqrt{3} = \sqrt{(36)3} + \sqrt{(16)3} - \sqrt{3}$$
$$= 6\sqrt{3} + 4\sqrt{3} - \sqrt{3}$$
$$= (6 + 4 - 1)\sqrt{3}$$
$$= 9\sqrt{3}$$

3. $\sqrt{8a^3b^3} + \sqrt[3]{ab} - \sqrt{\dfrac{2}{ab}} - \sqrt[3]{8a^4b^4} - \sqrt[4]{4a^2b^2}$

$$= \sqrt{(4a^2b^2)2ab} + \sqrt[3]{ab} - \sqrt{\dfrac{2ab}{a^2b^2}} - \sqrt[3]{(2ab)^3ab} - \sqrt[4]{(2ab)^2}$$

$$= 2ab\sqrt{2ab} + \sqrt[3]{ab} - \dfrac{\sqrt{2ab}}{ab} - 2ab\sqrt[3]{ab} - \sqrt{2ab}$$

$$= \left(2ab - \dfrac{1}{ab} - 1\right)\sqrt{2ab} + (1 - 2ab)\sqrt[3]{ab}$$

EXERCISE 27

Simplify the radicals in the following expressions and make all possible combinations.

1. $\sqrt{3} - \sqrt{12} + \sqrt{48}$.

2. $\sqrt{8} - \sqrt{18} + \sqrt{50}$.

3. $\sqrt{45} + \sqrt{20} - \sqrt{5} - \sqrt{125}$.

4. $\sqrt{75} + \sqrt{48} - \sqrt{108} - \sqrt{12}$.

5. $\sqrt[3]{16} - \sqrt[3]{54} + \sqrt[3]{250}$.

6. $\sqrt[3]{32} - \sqrt[3]{108} + \sqrt[3]{256}$.

7. $\sqrt[3]{24} + \sqrt[3]{192} - \sqrt[3]{375} - \sqrt[3]{81}$.

8. $\sqrt[3]{432} - \sqrt[3]{343} + \sqrt[3]{128} - \sqrt[3]{54}$.

9. $\sqrt{50} + \sqrt[3]{24} - \sqrt[3]{192} - \sqrt{8}$.

10. $\sqrt[4]{32} + \sqrt{18} + \sqrt[4]{1250} - \sqrt{72}$.

11. $\sqrt{32} - \sqrt{45} + \sqrt{72} - \sqrt{20}$.

12. $\sqrt[3]{54} + \sqrt[3]{32} - \sqrt[3]{16} - \sqrt[3]{256}$.

13. $x\sqrt{8x^2y} - \sqrt{18x^4y} + x^2\sqrt{32y}$.

14. $\sqrt{12a^4b} + a^2\sqrt{27b} - 2a\sqrt{12a^2b}$.

15. $6\sqrt{5u^6v} - u\sqrt{20u^4v} - u^2\sqrt{45u^2v}$.

16. $\sqrt{48x^7y} - x\sqrt{27x^5y} + x^2\sqrt{12x^3y}$.

17. $\dfrac{\sqrt{4a}}{a} + \dfrac{\sqrt{9a^3}}{a^2} - \dfrac{4}{\sqrt{a}}$.

18. $\dfrac{\sqrt{18x}}{x} - \dfrac{\sqrt{32x^3}}{x^2} + \dfrac{4}{\sqrt{2x}}$.

19. $\dfrac{a\sqrt{27a}}{b} + \sqrt{\dfrac{3a^3}{b^2}} - \dfrac{6a^2}{b\sqrt{3a}}$.

20. $\dfrac{2\sqrt{5u^2}}{v} - \sqrt{\dfrac{80u^3}{v}} + \dfrac{25u^2}{v\sqrt{5u}}$.

21. $\sqrt{9a^2b} + \sqrt{25ab^2} - \sqrt{16ab^2} - \sqrt{4a^2b}$.

22. $\sqrt{8rs^2} - \sqrt{27r^2s} + \sqrt{2rs^2} + \sqrt{3r^2s}$.

23. $\sqrt[3]{8u^2v^7} + \sqrt[3]{27u^{10}v^2} - u\sqrt[3]{8u^7v^2} - v\sqrt[3]{u^2v^4}$.

24. $\sqrt[3]{54x^2y^{10}} - \sqrt[3]{24x^5y^4} - y\sqrt[3]{2x^2y^7} + 2x\sqrt[3]{24x^2y^4}$.

25. $\sqrt{\dfrac{cd^2}{2}} + \sqrt{\dfrac{16c^2d}{3}} - \sqrt{\dfrac{9cd^2}{2}} - \sqrt{\dfrac{c^2d}{3}}$.

26. $\sqrt{\dfrac{25p}{2q}} + \dfrac{4}{3}\sqrt{\dfrac{2q}{p}} - 3\sqrt{\dfrac{p}{2q}} - \sqrt{\dfrac{2q}{9p}}$.

27. $\dfrac{3h}{2}\sqrt{\dfrac{3h}{k}} + 5k^2\sqrt{\dfrac{3k}{4h}} - \sqrt{\dfrac{3h^3}{k}} - \dfrac{3}{2k}\sqrt{\dfrac{3k^7}{h}}$.

28. $\sqrt{\dfrac{3a}{2b^3}} + 3\sqrt{\dfrac{3b}{8a^3}} - \dfrac{1}{b}\sqrt{\dfrac{2a}{3b}} - \dfrac{1}{2a}\sqrt{\dfrac{3b}{2a}}.$

29. $\sqrt{2ab} + \sqrt[4]{4a^2b^2} + \sqrt[6]{8a^3b^3}.$ **30.** $\sqrt[3]{8x^4y} + x\sqrt[6]{x^2y^2} - 2\sqrt[9]{x^{12}y^3}.$

31. $\sqrt[8]{\dfrac{81a^4}{16b^4}} - \sqrt[4]{\dfrac{729a^2}{4b^2}} + \sqrt{\dfrac{75a}{2b}}.$ **32.** $\sqrt[6]{\dfrac{64x^2y^2}{4z^2}} - 2\sqrt[9]{\dfrac{512x^3y^3}{8z^3}} + \sqrt[12]{\dfrac{x^4y^4}{16z^4}}.$

33. $\sqrt{\dfrac{a+b}{a-b}} + \sqrt{\dfrac{a-b}{a+b}}.$

34. $x\sqrt{\dfrac{x+y}{x-y}} - y\sqrt{\dfrac{x-y}{x+y}} + \dfrac{x^2 - 3y^2}{\sqrt{x^2 - y^2}}.$

35. $\sqrt{x - 18 + 81x^{-1}} + \sqrt{x^2y^{-1} - 18xy^{-1} + 81y^{-1}}.$

36. $\sqrt{x^2y^{-2} - 2x + y^2} + \sqrt{x^2y^{-1} - 2xy + y^3}.$

37. $\dfrac{x+1}{2\sqrt{x+1}} + \sqrt{x+1}.$ **38.** $\dfrac{x}{\sqrt{x+3}} + 2\sqrt{x+3}.$

39. $\dfrac{(x+1)^2}{2\sqrt{x+1}} + 2(x+1)\sqrt{x+1}.$ **40.** $\dfrac{(x-2)^2}{2\sqrt{x+1}} + 2(x-2)\sqrt{x+1}.$

59. Additional operations on radicals

1. *Multiplication of polynomials with radical terms.* In order to obtain the product of two polynomials in which the terms involve radicals, we employ the methods of Arts. 8 and 54.

Example 1

Find the product of $\sqrt{x} - 2\sqrt{xy} + \sqrt{y}$ and $\sqrt{x} + 2\sqrt{xy} - \sqrt{y}$.

Solution

$\sqrt{x} - 2\sqrt{xy} + \sqrt{y}$

$\sqrt{x} + 2\sqrt{xy} - \sqrt{y}$

$x - 2x\sqrt{y} + \sqrt{xy}$ (multiplying $\sqrt{x} - 2\sqrt{xy}$ $+ \sqrt{y}$ by $\sqrt{x}$)

$2x\sqrt{y} \qquad - 4xy + 2y\sqrt{x}$ (multiplying $\sqrt{x} - 2\sqrt{xy}$ $+ \sqrt{y}$ by $2\sqrt{xy}$)

$\qquad - \sqrt{xy} \qquad + 2y\sqrt{x} - y$ (multiplying $\sqrt{x} - 2\sqrt{xy}$ $+ \sqrt{y}$ by $- \sqrt{y}$)

$x \qquad\qquad - 4xy + 4y\sqrt{x} - y$

Therefore the product is $x - 4xy + 4y\sqrt{x} - y$.

2. *Introducing a factor under the radical sign.* In an expression of the type $a\sqrt[n]{b}$, the factor a may be placed under the radical sign if it is raised to the nth power, thus, $a\sqrt[n]{b} = \sqrt[n]{a^n b}$.

Examples

2. $$a^2b \sqrt[3]{ab} = \sqrt[3]{(a^2)^3 b^3 (ab)}$$
$$= \sqrt[3]{a^7 b^4}$$

3. $$2x^3y^2 \sqrt[4]{3xy^3} = \sqrt[4]{(2x^3y^2)^4 3xy^3}$$
$$= \sqrt[4]{48x^{13}y^{11}}$$

Example 4

In each of the following radical expressions, place the factor under the radical sign, then arrange the radicals in order of magnitude: $3\sqrt{3}$, $2\sqrt{6}$, $4\sqrt{2}$.

Solution

$$3\sqrt{3} = \sqrt{(9)(3)} = \sqrt{27}; \; 2\sqrt{6} = \sqrt{(4)(6)} = \sqrt{24};$$
$$4\sqrt{2} = \sqrt{(16)(2)} = \sqrt{32}$$

Then, since $24 < 27 < 32$, the desired arrangement is $2\sqrt{6}$, $3\sqrt{3}$, $4\sqrt{2}$.

3. Changing two or more radicals to radicals of the same order. Two or more radicals may be changed to the same order by, first, expressing each in the exponential form; second, reducing the fractional exponents to a common denominator; third, rewriting the results in radical form.

Example 5

Change $\sqrt{2xy^3}$, $\sqrt[3]{3x^2y}$, $\sqrt[4]{x^3y^2}$ to the same order.

Solution

$$\sqrt{2xy^3} = 2^{\frac{1}{2}}x^{\frac{1}{2}}y^{\frac{3}{2}}; \; \sqrt[3]{3x^2y} = 3^{\frac{1}{3}}x^{\frac{2}{3}}y^{\frac{1}{3}}; \; \sqrt[4]{x^3y^2} = x^{\frac{3}{4}}y^{\frac{1}{2}}$$

The lowest common multiple of the denominators 2, 3, and 4 is 12. Hence, if we reduce each of the fractional exponents to fractions with 12 as a denominator, we get

$$2^{\frac{6}{12}}x^{\frac{6}{12}}y^{\frac{18}{12}}; \; 3^{\frac{4}{12}}x^{\frac{8}{12}}y^{\frac{4}{12}}; \; x^{\frac{9}{12}}y^{\frac{6}{12}}$$

When the above expressions are placed in radical form, we get

$$\sqrt[12]{2^6 x^6 y^{18}}; \; \sqrt[12]{3^4 x^8 y^4}; \; \sqrt[12]{x^9 y^6}$$

Example 6

Find the product of $\sqrt{2a^3b}$ and $\sqrt[3]{4ab^4}$ by reducing the radicals to the same order and then multiplying.

Solution

$$(\sqrt{2a^3b})(\sqrt[3]{4ab^4}) = (2^{\frac{1}{2}}a^{\frac{3}{2}}b^{\frac{1}{2}})(4^{\frac{1}{3}}a^{\frac{1}{3}}b^{\frac{4}{3}})$$
$$= (2^{\frac{3}{6}}a^{\frac{9}{6}}b^{\frac{3}{6}})(4^{\frac{2}{6}}a^{\frac{2}{6}}b^{\frac{8}{6}})$$
$$= \sqrt[6]{2^3a^9b^3}\ \sqrt[6]{4^2a^2b^8}$$
$$= \sqrt[6]{(2^3)(4^2)a^{11}b^{11}}$$
$$= \sqrt[6]{2^7a^{11}b^{11}} \quad (\text{since } 4^2 = 2^4)$$
$$= \sqrt[6]{(2ab)^6 2a^5b^5}$$
$$= 2ab\ \sqrt[6]{2a^5b^5}$$

Two or more radicals may be reduced to the same order without first changing to fractional exponents by use of the following method.

1. Find the L.C.M. of the indices of the radicals. This will be the index of the radicals to be obtained.

2. Multiply each exponent in each radicand by the quotient of the above L.C.M. and the index of the radicand.

Example 7

In order to reduce

$$\sqrt[3]{2a^2b}, \ \sqrt{3ab}, \ \sqrt[4]{4a^3b^2}$$

to the same order, we note that the L.C.M. of the indices is 12. Hence, we multiply each exponent in the first radical by 4; in the second, by 6; and in the third, by 3. Thus, we get

$$\sqrt[3]{2a^2b} = \sqrt[12]{2^4a^8b^4} = \sqrt[12]{16a^8b^4}$$
$$\sqrt{3ab} = \sqrt[12]{3^6a^6b^6} = \sqrt[12]{729a^6b^6}$$
$$\sqrt[4]{4a^3b^2} = \sqrt[12]{4^3a^9b^6} = \sqrt[12]{64a^9b^6}$$

4. *Rationalizing binomial denominators.* If the denominator of a fraction is the sum or the difference of two terms at least one of which contains a radical of the second order, we rationalize the denominator by the method illustrated below.

Example 8

Rationalize the denominator of $4/(\sqrt{5} - 1)$.

Solution

Since the product of the sum and the difference of two numbers is the difference of their squares, we multiply each member of the above fraction by $\sqrt{5} + 1$

and get

$$\frac{4}{\sqrt{5}-1} = \frac{4(\sqrt{5}+1)}{(\sqrt{5}-1)(\sqrt{5}+1)} = \frac{4(\sqrt{5}+1)}{(\sqrt{5})^2-1} = \frac{4(\sqrt{5}+1)}{5-1} = \frac{4(\sqrt{5}+1)}{4}$$
$$= \sqrt{5}+1$$

Example 9

$$\frac{a+b+2\sqrt{ab}}{\sqrt{a}+\sqrt{b}} = \frac{(a+b+2\sqrt{ab})(\sqrt{a}-\sqrt{b})}{(\sqrt{a}+\sqrt{b})(\sqrt{a}-\sqrt{b})}$$

$$= \frac{a\sqrt{a} - a\sqrt{b} + b\sqrt{a} - b\sqrt{b} + 2a\sqrt{b} - 2b\sqrt{a}}{a-b}$$

$$= \frac{\sqrt{a}\,(a+b-2b) + \sqrt{b}\,(-a-b+2a)}{a-b}$$

$$= \frac{\sqrt{a}\,(a-b) + \sqrt{b}\,(a-b)}{a-b}$$

$$= \frac{(a-b)(\sqrt{a}+\sqrt{b})}{a-b}$$

$$= \sqrt{a}+\sqrt{b}$$

In the above examples, the desired rationalization was accomplished by multiplying both members of the fraction by a binomial containing the same terms as the denominator but with the sign between them changed. If we apply this procedure to any fraction having a binomial denominator that contains a radical of the second order, we obtain an equivalent fraction whose denominator is the difference of the squares of the terms in the original binomial. Hence, it contains no radicals.

EXERCISE 28

Find the products indicated in Problems 1 to 16.

1. $(\sqrt{3}+\sqrt{2})(\sqrt{3}-\sqrt{2})$.

2. $(\sqrt{2}-\sqrt{3}+\sqrt{5})(\sqrt{2}-\sqrt{3}-\sqrt{5})$.

3. $(2+2\sqrt{3})(7-2\sqrt{3})$.   4. $(5+\sqrt{6})(\sqrt{2}-\sqrt{3})$.

5. $(2\sqrt{3}-3\sqrt{5})(3\sqrt{3}+4\sqrt{5})$.

6. $\left(\frac{1}{2}-\frac{\sqrt{3}}{2}\right)\left(\frac{1}{2}+\frac{\sqrt{3}}{2}\right)$.   7. $\left(\frac{3}{4}-\frac{\sqrt{5}}{4}\right)\left(\frac{3}{4}+\frac{\sqrt{5}}{4}\right)$.

8. $\left(\frac{3}{8}-\frac{\sqrt{5}}{8}\right)\left(\frac{3}{8}+\frac{\sqrt{5}}{8}\right)$.   9. $(\sqrt{a}+\sqrt{b})(\sqrt{a}-\sqrt{b})$.

10. $(\sqrt{x}+\sqrt{y})^2$.   11. $(\sqrt{h}-\sqrt{k})^3$.

12. $(u + \sqrt{uv} + v)(\sqrt{u} - \sqrt{v})$.

13. $(\sqrt{r} + \sqrt{s} - \sqrt{rs})(\sqrt{r} - \sqrt{s} + \sqrt{rs})$.

14. $(\sqrt{a} - \sqrt{2b} + \sqrt{c})(\sqrt{a} - \sqrt{2b} - \sqrt{c})$.

15. $(\sqrt{xy} - \sqrt{xz} + \sqrt{yz})(\sqrt{xy} - \sqrt{xz} - \sqrt{yz})$.

16. $(2x - 3x\sqrt{x} + \sqrt{2x})(x - 2x\sqrt{x} - \sqrt{2x})$.

In each of Problems 17 to 28, introduce the factors under the radical sign and then arrange the radicals in order of magnitude.

17. $4\sqrt{3}, 3\sqrt{6}, 2\sqrt{10}$.

18. $3\sqrt[3]{4}, 2\sqrt[3]{6}, 4\sqrt[3]{2}$.

19. $2\sqrt[4]{33}, 3\sqrt[4]{6}, 4\sqrt[4]{2}$.

20. $2\sqrt{70}, 3\sqrt{30}, 5\sqrt{10}$.

21. $a\sqrt{2}, a\sqrt{2a}, a\sqrt{2a^3}, a < 1$.

22. $2ab\sqrt{6b}, 3a\sqrt{3b^3}, 2b\sqrt{7a^2b}$.

23. $6\sqrt{17}, 10\sqrt{6}, 7\sqrt{13}$.

24. $6\sqrt{\frac{1}{3}}, 3\sqrt{\frac{2}{3}}, 4\sqrt{\frac{1}{2}}$.

25. $3\sqrt[3]{5}, 5\sqrt[3]{\frac{6}{5}}, 7\sqrt[3]{\frac{3}{7}}$.

26. $a\sqrt{\frac{1}{a}}, a^5\sqrt{\frac{1}{a^5}}, a^3\sqrt{\frac{1}{a^3}}, a < 1$.

27. $5\sqrt{13}, 12\sqrt{2}, 7\sqrt{6}, 8\sqrt{5}$.

28. $6\sqrt[3]{5}, 4\sqrt[3]{17}, 7\sqrt[3]{3}, 8\sqrt[3]{2}$.

Reduce the radicals in Problems 29 to 36 to the same order.

29. $\sqrt{3x}, \sqrt[3]{4x^2}$.

30. $\sqrt[3]{4ab^2}, \sqrt[4]{2a^3b}$.

31. $\sqrt{2xy}, \sqrt[3]{3x^2y}, \sqrt[4]{x^3y^2}$.

32. $\sqrt[3]{ab^2c}, \sqrt[4]{2a^3bc}, \sqrt[6]{3a^5b^4c^2}$.

33. $\sqrt[4]{2a^2b^3}, \sqrt[6]{3a^5b}, \sqrt[8]{4a^5b^7}$.

34. $\sqrt{a^\frac{1}{2}}, \sqrt[3]{3a^\frac{1}{2}}, \sqrt[4]{2a^\frac{3}{2}}$.

35. $\sqrt[4]{x^\frac{3}{2}y^\frac{1}{2}}, \sqrt[4]{x^\frac{1}{2}y^\frac{3}{2}}, \sqrt[6]{x^\frac{1}{2}y}$.

36. $\sqrt[3]{r^2s}, \sqrt[6]{3r^5s^2}, \sqrt[9]{2r^7s^5}$.

Reduce the radicals in Problems 37 to 44 to the same order and then perform the indicated operations.

37. $\sqrt{2}\sqrt[3]{4}$.

38. $\sqrt[3]{4}\sqrt[4]{8}$.

39. $\sqrt[3]{4a^2}\sqrt{8a^3}$.

40. $\sqrt{3b^3}\sqrt[4]{27b^2}$.

41. $\dfrac{\sqrt{2x}\sqrt[3]{2x^2}}{\sqrt[4]{4x^3}}$.

42. $\dfrac{\sqrt{2ab}\sqrt[4]{8a^3b^5}}{\sqrt[3]{4a^2b}}$.

43. $\dfrac{\sqrt[3]{3x^2y}\sqrt[4]{27xy^3}}{\sqrt[6]{243xy^5}}$.

44. $\dfrac{\sqrt{2ab}\sqrt[3]{4a^5b^4}}{\sqrt[6]{2ac^5}}$.

Rationalize the denominators in Problems 45 to 64.

45. $\dfrac{2}{\sqrt{3} - 1}$.

46. $\dfrac{1}{\sqrt{5} + 2}$.

47. $\dfrac{2}{\sqrt{6} + 2}$.

48. $\dfrac{3}{\sqrt{7} + 2}$.

49. $\dfrac{5 + \sqrt{5}}{1 + \sqrt{5}}$.

50. $\dfrac{\sqrt{3} + 3}{\sqrt{3} + 1}$.

51. $\dfrac{\sqrt{6} + 2}{\sqrt{3} + \sqrt{2}}$.

52. $\dfrac{\sqrt{14} + \sqrt{7}}{\sqrt{2} + 1}$.

53. $\dfrac{\sqrt{6} - 4}{\sqrt{2} - \sqrt{3}}$.

54. $\dfrac{14 - 4\sqrt{15}}{\sqrt{5} - \sqrt{3}}$.

55. $\dfrac{\sqrt{14} - 8}{\sqrt{2} + \sqrt{7}}$.

56. $\dfrac{-14 - \sqrt{10}}{\sqrt{2} + \sqrt{5}}$.

57. $\dfrac{x + y - 2\sqrt{xy}}{\sqrt{x} - \sqrt{y}}$.

58. $\dfrac{\sqrt{3} - \sqrt{2}}{\sqrt{3} + \sqrt{2}}$.

59. $\dfrac{2a - b + \sqrt{ab}}{2\sqrt{a} - \sqrt{b}}.$ **60.** $\dfrac{x^3 + x\sqrt{x}}{x + \sqrt{x}}.$ **61.**[1] $\dfrac{2\sqrt{2}}{1 + \sqrt{2} + \sqrt{3}}.$

62. $\dfrac{2\sqrt{6}}{\sqrt{3} + \sqrt{2} - \sqrt{5}}.$ **63.** $\dfrac{\sqrt{6} + \sqrt{3} - 1}{1 - \sqrt{2} + \sqrt{3}}.$ **64.** $\dfrac{\sqrt{3} - \sqrt{6} - 1}{1 + \sqrt{2} - \sqrt{3}}.$

By use of Table III find the value of the following to three decimal places.

65. $\dfrac{1}{\sqrt{3}}.$ **66.** $\dfrac{1}{\sqrt{5}}.$ **67.** $\dfrac{1}{1 - \sqrt{2}}.$ **68.** $\dfrac{2}{\sqrt{3} - 1}.$

69. $\dfrac{1 - \sqrt{3}}{1 + \sqrt{3}}.$ **70.** $\dfrac{\sqrt{5} - \sqrt{3}}{\sqrt{5} + \sqrt{3}}.$ **71.** $\dfrac{\sqrt{5}}{\sqrt{3} + 1}.$ **72.** $\dfrac{\sqrt{7} - \sqrt{2}}{\sqrt{7} + \sqrt{2}}.$

[1] HINT: As the first step, multiply the numerator and the denominator by $1 + \sqrt{2} - \sqrt{3}.$

CHAPTER 8

QUADRATIC EQUATIONS

60. *Introduction.* An equation in one unknown that involves the second but no higher power of the unknown is called a *quadratic equation*. Equations that involve both the first and second powers of the unknown are called *affected quadratic equations*, and those that contain only the second power are called *pure quadratic equations*.

Examples

Affected quadratic equations:

$$2x^2 - 3x + 2 = 0$$
$$4x^2 = 2x - 1$$

Pure quadratic equations:

$$3x^2 = 4$$
$$2x^2 - 9 = 0$$

61. *Solution of pure quadratic equations.* We obtain the roots of a pure quadratic equation by first solving it for the second power of the unknown. Then the roots will be the *two* square roots of the solution thus obtained.

Example 1

Solve the equation $3x^2 - 27 = 0$.

Solution

We first transpose 27 and then solve for x^2; thus,

$$3x^2 = 27$$
$$x^2 = 9$$

Hence,

$$x = + \sqrt{9} = 3$$

and also

$$x = - \sqrt{9} = -3$$

NOTE: The last two statements are usually written in a shorter form by use of the double sign $\pm$. Using this notation, the two statements become

$$x = \pm \sqrt{9} = \pm 3$$

Example 2

Solve the equation $4x^2 + 16 = 0$.

Solution

$$4x^2 + 16 = 0$$
$$4x^2 = -16 \qquad \text{(transposing 16)}$$
$$x^2 = -4 \qquad \text{(dividing by 4)}$$
$$x = \pm \sqrt{-4}$$
$$x = \pm \sqrt{(4)(-1)}$$
$$x = \pm 2 \sqrt{-1} \qquad \text{[by (1), Art. 52]}$$

NOTE: In mathematics, the letter i is used to denote $\sqrt{-1}$. Hence, $i^2 = -1$. In terms of this notation, the solutions of Example 2 are $x = \pm 2i$.

62. Solution of quadratic equations by factoring. The use of factoring in solving a quadratic equation depends upon the following principle:

The product of two or more factors is zero if any one of the factors is zero.

Thus, the equation $(x - 2)(x + 1) = 0$ is satisfied if either $x - 2 = 0$ or $x + 1 = 0$. Hence, the roots of the equation are $x = 2$ and $x = -1$.

This principle furnishes us with a very efficient method for solving quadratic equations and also for solving equations of higher order. However, we cannot use it unless the equation is equivalent to one in which the left member is a product of two or more factors and the right member is zero.

We solve a quadratic equation by use of the factoring method by performing the following steps:

1. *Transpose all terms in the equation to the left of the equality sign, thus making the right member zero.*

2. *Factor the left member into linear factors.*

3. *Set each factor equal to zero and solve the resulting two linear equations for x.*

Obviously, the process cannot be completed if, after step 1 has been performed, the left member of the resulting equation is not factorable.

Example

Solve the equation $2x^2 = x + 6$ by use of factoring.

Solution

We show below steps 1, 2, and 3 applied to this problem.

$$2x^2 = x + 6 \qquad \text{(given equation)}$$

1. $\quad 2x^2 - x - 6 = 0 \qquad$ (transposing $x + 6$)
2. $(2x + 3)(x - 2) = 0 \qquad$ (factoring $2x^2 - x - 6$)
3. $\qquad 2x + 3 = 0 \qquad$ (setting the first factor equal to zero and solving)

$$2x = -3$$
$$x = -\tfrac{3}{2}$$

$$x - 2 = 0 \qquad \text{(setting the second factor equal to zero and solving)}$$

$$x = 2$$

Hence, the two solutions are $x = -\frac{3}{2}$ and $x = 2$.

NOTE: We wish to impress the reader with the fact that this method is applicable *only when the right member of the equation is zero*. If one of the factors of the left member is zero, their product is zero, regardless of the value of the other factor. However, if the right member of the equation is not zero, as in $(x - 1)(x - 2) = 6$, we cannot arbitrarily assign a value to either factor without at the same time fixing the value of the other. For example, if in the above example we let $x - 1 = 3$, then surely $x + 2 = 2$, if their product is 6. Obviously, these two conditions cannot be satisfied by the same value of x.

EXERCISE 29

Solve the pure quadratic equation in each of Problems 1 to 20.

1. $9x^2 - 4 = 0$.
2. $16x^2 - 1 = 0$.
3. $25x^2 - 36 = 0$.
4. $49x^2 - 9 = 0$.
5. $7x^2 - 28 = 0$.
6. $8x^2 - 32 = 0$.
7. $3x^2 - 27 = 0$.
8. $2x^2 - 18 = 0$.
9. $3x^2 - 4 = 0$.
10. $2x^2 - 9 = 0$.
11. $4x^2 - 12 = 0$.
12. $10x^2 - 45 = 0$.
13. $x^2 + 4 = 0$.
14. $3x^2 + 27 = 0$.
15. $5x^2 + 45 = 0$.
16. $6x^2 + 24 = 0$.
17. $4x^2 + 9 = 0$.
18. $8x^2 + 50 = 0$.
19. $x^2 + 5 = 0$.
20. $3x^2 + 21 = 0$.

Solving the following equations by the factoring method.

21. $x^2 - x - 2 = 0$.   **22.** $x^2 - x - 6 = 0$.   **23.** $x^2 + x = 12$.

24. $x^2 + x = 20$.   **25.** $x^2 + 4x + 3 = 0$.   **26.** $x^2 + 2 = 3x$.

27. $x^2 + 12 = 7x$.   **28.** $x^2 - 6x + 5 = 0$.   **29.** $2x^2 + 1 = 3x$.

30. $3x^2 - 2x = 1$.   **31.** $4x^2 = 1 - 3x$.   **32.** $2x^2 + 3x + 1 = 0$.

33. $2x^2 + 7x + 3 = 0$.   **34.** $3x^2 + 2 = 7x$.   **35.** $4x^2 + 7x = 2$.

36. $4x^2 = 11x + 3$.   **37.** $6x^2 = 1 - x$.   **38.** $6x^2 = 3 - 7x$.

39. $14x = 8x^2 + 3$.   **40.** $6x^2 + 17x + 5 = 0$.   **41.** $6 = 6x^2 + 5x$.

42. $6x^2 - 6 = 5x$.   **43.** $10x^2 = 3 - 13x$.   **44.** $12x^2 = 3x + 2$.

45. $10x^2 - 11x = 6$.   **46.** $20x^2 + 6 = 23x$.   **47.** $16x^2 = 2x + 5$.

48. $15x^2 + 14x = 8$.   **49.** $40x^2 + 6 = 31x$.   **50.** $21x^2 = 5x + 6$.

51. $52x = 12 + 35x^2$.   **52.** $33x = 40x^2 - 18$.   **53.** $14 = 54x^2 - 51x$.

54. $7x = 15 - 36x^2$.   **55.** $35x^2 + 94x + 24 = 0$.

56. $16x^2 = 54x - 35$.   **57.** $15 = 64x^2 + 68x$.   **58.** $45x^2 = 69x + 10$.

59. $36x^2 + 69x + 28 = 0$.   **60.** $34x + 15 = 72x^2$.

61. $x^2 + 2ax = 3a^2$.   **62.** $6x^2 + bx - 2b^2 = 0$.

63. $2a^2x^2 - abx - 3b^2 = 0$.   **64.** $3d^2x^2 + 2dcx - 8c^2 = 0$.

65. $x^2 - ax - bx + ab = 0$.   **66.** $abx^2 + a^2x + b^2x + ab = 0$.

67. $2x^2 - ax + 2bx - ab = 0$.   **68.** $3ax^2 + 9ax + 2x + 6 = 0$.

63. *Solution of quadratic equations by completing the square.* If we square the binomial $x + a$, we get $x^2 + 2ax + a^2$. Thus, we see that a trinomial with x^2 as the first term is a perfect square provided that (1) the second term contains the first power of x and (2) the last term is positive and equal to the square of one-half the coefficient of x. Furthermore, the square root of such a trinomial is the square roots of the first and last terms connected by the sign of the second term.

Examples

1. The trinomial $x^2 - 6x + 9$ is a perfect square since the first term is x^2, the second term contains only the first power of x, and the third term, 9, is equal to the square of one-half the coefficient of x. Furthermore, the square root of the trinomial is $x - 3$.

2. In the trinomial $x^2 + 5x + \frac{25}{4}$, the last term $\frac{25}{4}$ is equal to $(\frac{1}{2}$ of $5)^2$. Hence,

$$x^2 + 5x + \frac{25}{4} = (x + \frac{5}{2})^2$$

The above facts constitute the basis for the process of solving an affected quadratic equation by the method of completing the square. We shall illustrate the method by means of the following examples:

Example 3

In order to solve

(1) $x + 3 = 2x^2$

we first transpose and arrange our terms so that the first and second terms of the left member involve x^2 and x, respectively, and the constant term (or the term that does not involve x) appears in the right member; thus

$$-2x^2 + x = -3$$

Now we divide both members by the coefficient of x^2 and get

(2) $$x^2 - \tfrac{1}{2}x = \tfrac{3}{2}$$

Next we add to both members of (2) the square of one-half the coefficient of x, or $(\tfrac{1}{2}$ of $-\tfrac{1}{2})^2 = (-\tfrac{1}{4})^2 = \tfrac{1}{16}$, and obtain

(3) $$x^2 - \tfrac{1}{2}x + \tfrac{1}{16} = \tfrac{3}{2} + \tfrac{1}{16}$$

We now express the left member of (3) as the square of the binomial $x - \tfrac{1}{4}$ and simplify the right member and get

$$(x - \tfrac{1}{4})^2 = \frac{24 + 1}{16}$$

or

(4) $$(x - \tfrac{1}{4})^2 = \tfrac{25}{16}$$

Now, since corresponding square roots of equal numbers are equal and also since the square roots of $\tfrac{25}{16}$ are $\tfrac{5}{4}$ and $-\tfrac{5}{4}$, we have

(5) $$x - \tfrac{1}{4} = \tfrac{5}{4}$$

and

(6) $$x - \tfrac{1}{4} = -\tfrac{5}{4}$$

Hence, from (5)

$$x = \tfrac{1}{4} + \tfrac{5}{4}$$
$$= \tfrac{6}{4}$$
$$= \tfrac{3}{2}$$

and from (6)

$$x = \tfrac{1}{4} - \tfrac{5}{4}$$
$$= -\tfrac{4}{4}$$
$$= -1$$

Hence, the solutions of (1) are $x = \tfrac{3}{2}$ and $x = -1$.

NOTE 1: Usually Eqs. (5) and (6) are combined in the form

(7) $$x - \tfrac{1}{4} = \pm\tfrac{5}{4}$$

and the solution completed thus:

$$x = \tfrac{1}{4} \pm \tfrac{5}{4}$$
$$= \tfrac{6}{4} \text{ and } -\tfrac{4}{4}$$
$$= \tfrac{3}{2} \text{ and } -1$$

NOTE 2: Frequently a student asks, "Why not use both the plus and minus signs on the left member also?" The answer is that so doing leads to no new solutions. If we use the double sign on the left member of (7) we have

$$\pm (x - \tfrac{1}{4}) = \pm \tfrac{5}{4}$$

then the use of the plus sign on the left leads to the above roots, and the use of the minus sign yields

$$-(x - \tfrac{1}{4}) = \pm \tfrac{5}{4}$$

Then, dividing by -1, we have

$$x - \tfrac{1}{4} = \mp \tfrac{5}{4}$$

and when this is solved, we get the roots already obtained.

The process of solving a quadratic equation by completing the square consists of five formal steps which we shall list below.

1. *Transpose and arrange the terms in the equation so that the terms involving x^2 and x appear as the first and second terms, respectively, in the left member, and the constant term appears as the right member.*

2. *Divide both members by the coefficient of x^2.*

3. *Add to both members the square of one-half the coefficient of x.*

4. *Equate the square roots of the two members of the equation obtained in step 3, giving the square root of the constant term both the plus and minus signs. This step yields two linear equations.*

5. *Solve the two linear equations obtained in step 4 for x.*

Example 4

Solve the equation $4x^2 = 4x + 11$ by completing the square.

Solution

The numbers at the left in the discussion below indicate the steps in the solution that we are performing.

$$4x^2 = 4x + 11 \qquad \text{(given equation)}$$

1. $\qquad 4x^2 - 4x = 11 \qquad \text{(transposing } 4x)$

2. $\qquad x^2 - x = \tfrac{11}{4} \qquad \text{(dividing both members by 4)}$

3. $x^2 - x + (-\tfrac{1}{2})^2 = \tfrac{11}{4} + (-\tfrac{1}{2})^2 \qquad$ [adding $(\tfrac{1}{2}$ of $-1)^2$ to both sides]

$$= \tfrac{11}{4} + \tfrac{1}{4}$$

$$= \tfrac{12}{4}$$

$$(x - \tfrac{1}{2})^2 = 3$$

4. $\qquad x - \tfrac{1}{2} = \pm \sqrt{3}$

5. $\qquad x = \tfrac{1}{2} \pm \sqrt{3} \qquad \text{(solving for } x)$

Since $\sqrt{3}$ is an irrational number, we can simplify the solution no further.

We may check the solution by substituting $\frac{1}{2} \pm \sqrt{3}$ for x in each member of the given equation. Thus, we get

$$4(\tfrac{1}{2} \pm \sqrt{3})^2 = 4[\tfrac{1}{4} \pm 2(\tfrac{1}{2} \sqrt{3}) + (\sqrt{3})^2] = 4(\tfrac{1}{4} \pm \sqrt{3} + 3)$$
$$= 13 \pm 4 \sqrt{3}$$

for the left member and

$$4(\tfrac{1}{2} \pm \sqrt{3}) + 11 = 2 \pm 4 \sqrt{3} + 11 = 13 \pm 4 \sqrt{3}$$

for the right member. Since the two above values are equal, the solution checks.

If an approximate numerical value of x is desired, we may obtain the value of $\sqrt{3}$ to as many decimal places as we need and complete the solution. To three decimal places, $\sqrt{3} = 1.732$. Then $x = \frac{1}{2} \pm 1.732 = .5 \pm 1.732 = 2.232$ and -1.232, correct to three decimal places.

Example 5

Solve the equation $x^2 + 8 = 4x$ by completing the square.

Solution

	$x^2 + 8 = 4x$	(given equation)
1.	$x^2 - 4x = -8$	(transposing and arranging terms. Note that step 2 is unnecessary)
3.	$x^2 - 4x + (-2)^2 = -8 + (-2)^2$	[adding ($\frac{1}{2}$ of -4)^2 to both sides]
	$(x - 2)^2 = -4$	(simplifying)
4.	$x - 2 = \pm \sqrt{-4}$	
	$= \pm \sqrt{4(-1)}$	
	$= \pm 2 \sqrt{-1}$	
	$= \pm 2i$	(See Note 2, Art. 61)
5.	$x = 2 \pm 2i$	

In order to check, we substitute $2 \pm 2i$ in each member of the given equation and obtain from the left member

$$(2 \pm 2i)^2 + 8 = 4 \pm 8i + (2i)^2 + 8$$
$$= 4 \pm 8i + 4i^2 + 8$$
$$= 4 \pm 8i - 4 + 8 \qquad \text{(since } i^2 = -1)$$
$$= 8 \pm 8i$$

and from the right member we have

$$4(2 \pm 2i) = 8 \pm 8i$$

Hence, the solution checks.

64. *Complex numbers*. The solution of Example 5 of the previous article introduces a type of number which we have not previously met. We shall describe such numbers in the following definition:

DEFINITION. *A number of the type $a + bi$ where a and b are real and $i = \sqrt{-1}$ is called a **complex number**.*

If neither a nor b is zero, then $a + bi$ is called an *imaginary number*. If $a = 0$ and $b \neq 0$, then $a + bi$ is called a *pure imaginary number*. If $a \neq 0$ and $b = 0$, then $a + bi$ is a real number. Hence, the field of complex numbers includes all the real numbers as special cases.

The imaginary numbers $2 + 3i$, $\frac{3}{4} - \frac{1}{4}i$, the pure imaginary number $2i$, and the real number 3 are examples of complex numbers.

EXERCISE 30

Solve the quadratic equations in Problems 1 to 60 by completing the square.

1. $x^2 + 4x + 3 = 0$.	2. $x^2 + 2x - 8 = 0$.	3. $x^2 + 2x - 24 = 0$.
4. $x^2 = 4x + 21$.	5. $x^2 = 2 - x$.	6. $x^2 + x - 6 = 0$.
7. $x^2 = 5x - 6$.	8. $x^2 - 4 = 3x$.	9. $4x^2 + 15 = 16x$.
10. $4x^2 = 8x + 5$.	11. $9x^2 + 5 = 18x$.	12. $3x^2 - 2x = 5$.
13. $2x^2 + 3x = 2$.	14. $3x^2 + 7x - 6 = 0$.	15. $2x^2 - x = 3$.
16. $3x^2 - 5x = 2$.	17. $3x^2 + 10x = 8$.	18. $6x^2 = x + 15$.
19. $6x^2 + 2 = -7x$.	20. $10x^2 + 3 = -17x$.	21. $8x^2 - 22x - 21 = 0$.
22. $12x^2 = -11x - 2$.	23. $10x^2 - 7x = 12$.	24. $x^2 + 6x = 5$.
25. $x^2 - 2x = 1$.	26. $x^2 + 1 = 4x$.	27. $x^2 + 7 = 6x$.
28. $x^2 = 2x + 2$.	29. $4x^2 = 4x + 1$.	30. $9x^2 + 1 = 12x$.
31. $4x^2 + 1 = 12x$.	32. $4x^2 - 2x = 1$.	33. $3x^2 + 6x + 2 = 0$.
34. $9x^2 + 9x + 1 = 0$.	35. $4x^2 + 9 = 16x$.	36. $9x^2 + 23 = 30x$.
37. $x^2 + 2x + 2 = 0$.	38. $x^2 + 5 = 4x$.	39. $x^2 + 2x + 10 = 0$.
40. $x^2 + 13 = 6x$.	41. $2x^2 + 1 = 2x$.	42. $2x^2 + 5 = 6x$.
43. $9x^2 - 6x + 5 = 0$.	44. $9x^2 - 12x + 5 = 0$.	45. $4x^2 + 7 = 8x$.
46. $4x^2 + 8x + 7 = 0$.	47. $x^2 + 5x + 7 = 0$.	48. $9x^2 + 18x + 14 = 0$.
49. $x^2 + ax = 2a^2$.	50. $x^2 - 3b^2 = 2bx$.	51. $x^2 - ab = (a - b)x$.
52. $x^2 - 2ab = (b - 2a)x$.		53. $x^2 - 2ax + a^2 - b^2 = 0$.
54. $b^2x^2 - b^3x = a^2 - ab^2$.		55. $a^2x^2 - a^3x + a^2b - b^2 = 0$.
56. $abx^2 - (a^2 - b^2)x - ab = 0$.		57. $6x^2 + (2b - 3a)x = ab$.
58. $(a + b)x^2 - 2ax = b - a$.		59. $a^2x^2 - a^2x = ab + b^2$.
60. $(a^2 - b^2)x^2 + 4abx + 1 = 0$.		

Find the value of the roots of the following equations to three decimal places. Use Table III.

61. $x^2 - 3x + 1 = 0$.	62. $2x^2 - 4x + 1 = 0$.	63. $3x^2 - 6x + 2 = 0$.
64. $5x^2 = 8x - 2$.	65. $4x^2 - 7x + 1 = 0$.	66. $7x^2 + 1 = 6x$.
67. $6x^2 - 10x + 3 = 0$.	68. $8x^2 + 9x + 2 = 0$.	
69. $4x^2 + 7x + 2 = 0$.	70. $5x^2 - 4x - 3 = 0$.	

65. *The quadratic formula.* By transposing and arranging the terms, any quadratic equation can be placed in the form

(1) $$ax^2 + bx + c = 0 \qquad a \neq 0$$

For example, if we transpose and arrange the terms in

$$3 = 4x - 2x^2$$

we get

(2) $$2x^2 - 4x + 3 = 0$$

Hence, (2) is in form (1) with $a = 2$, $b = -4$, and $c = 3$.

If we solve (1) by completing the square, we obtain a formula which is useful and efficient for obtaining the roots of any quadratic equation. We shall first derive the formula by solving (1) and then we shall explain its use. The solution of (1) follows:

$$ax^2 + bx + c = 0 \qquad \text{(given equation)}$$

$$ax^2 + bx = -c \qquad \text{(transposing } c)$$

$$x^2 + \frac{b}{a}x = \frac{-c}{a} \qquad \text{(dividing both members by } a)$$

$$x^2 + \frac{b}{a}x + \left(\frac{b}{2a}\right)^2 = \frac{-c}{a} + \frac{b^2}{4a^2} \qquad \left[\text{adding } \left(\frac{1}{2}\text{ of }\frac{b}{a}\right)^2 \text{ to both members}\right]$$

$$\left(x + \frac{b}{2a}\right)^2 = \frac{b^2 - 4ac}{4a^2} \qquad \text{(simplifying)}$$

$$x + \frac{b}{2a} = \pm \frac{\sqrt{b^2 - 4ac}}{2a} \qquad \text{(equating the square roots of the two members)}$$

$$x = -\frac{b}{2a} \pm \frac{\sqrt{b^2 - 4ac}}{2a} \qquad \text{(solving for } x)$$

Now, since the two denominators in the right member of the last equation are the same, we have

(3) $$x = \frac{-b \pm \sqrt{b^2 - 4ac}}{2a}$$

The formula (3) is known as the *quadratic formula*, and we shall illustrate its use in the following examples:

Example 1

In order to solve the equation $6x^2 = 12 + x$ by the use of (3), we first transpose and arrange the terms so that the term involving x^2 is first, the term involving x is second, the constant term is third, and the right member is zero. Thus, we obtain

$$6x^2 - x - 12 = 0$$

Now, if we compare the coefficients in this equation with those in (1), we see that $a = 6$, $b = -1$, and $c = -12$. Then, if we substitute these values in (3), we get

$$x = \frac{-(-1) \pm \sqrt{(-1)^2 - 4(6)(-12)}}{2(6)}$$

$$= \frac{1 \pm \sqrt{1 + 288}}{12}$$

$$= \frac{1 \pm 17}{12}$$

$$= \tfrac{18}{12} \text{ and } -\tfrac{16}{12}$$

$$= \tfrac{3}{2} \text{ and } -\tfrac{4}{3}$$

Example 2

Solve $8x - 13 = 4x^2$ by use of the quadratic formula.

Solution

If we transpose and arrange terms, we get

$$-4x^2 + 8x - 13 = 0$$

Hence, comparing with (1), we have $a = -4$, $b = 8$, and $c = -13$. Substituting these values in (3) we get

$$x = \frac{-8 \pm \sqrt{8^2 - 4(-4)(-13)}}{2(-4)}$$

$$= \frac{-8 \pm \sqrt{64 - 208}}{-8}$$

$$= \frac{-8 \pm \sqrt{-144}}{-8}$$

$$= \frac{-8 \pm 12\sqrt{-1}}{-8}$$

$$= \frac{-8 \pm 12i}{-8}$$

$$= \frac{2 - 3i}{2} \text{ and } \frac{2 + 3i}{2}$$

EXERCISE 31

Solve the equations in Problems 1 to 60 by use of the quadratic formula.

1. $x^2 - 5x + 6 = 0.$
2. $x^2 - 5x + 4 = 0.$
3. $x^2 + x - 6 = 0.$
4. $x^2 - 2x - 8 = 0.$
5. $2x^2 + 3 = 7x.$
6. $3x^2 + x = 2.$
7. $4x^2 + 7x - 2 = 0.$
8. $5x^2 + 3x - 2 = 0.$
9. $6x^2 + 5x = 6.$
10. $15x^2 = 14x + 8.$
11. $12x^2 + 6 = 17x.$
12. $40x^2 = 7x + 20.$
13. $16x^2 + 18x + 5 = 0.$
14. $8x^2 + 18x + 9 = 0.$
15. $27x^2 = 12x + 7.$
16. $56x^2 + 17x - 28 = 0.$
17. $x^2 - 2x = 1.$
18. $x^2 + 4x = -1.$
19. $x^2 - 6x + 7 = 0.$
20. $x^2 + 6x + 4 = 0.$
21. $4x^2 = 4x + 1.$
22. $9x^2 + 12x + 1 = 0.$
23. $4x^2 + 7 = 12x.$
24. $9x^2 - 6x = 4.$
25. $3x^2 + 2 = 6x.$
26. $5x^2 = 3x + 9.$
27. $6x^2 - 1 = 2x.$
28. $7x^2 + 8x = 4.$
29. $2x^2 = 9 - 6x.$
30. $4x^2 - 3 = 2x.$
31. $9x^2 - 12x + 2 = 0.$
32. $8x^2 + 9x - 18 = 0.$
33. $x^2 + 2x + 2 = 0.$
34. $x^2 + 5 = 4x.$
35. $x^2 + 13 = 6x.$
36. $x^2 = 4x - 13.$
37. $2x^2 = 2x - 1.$
38. $2x^2 - 6x = -5.$
39. $9x^2 = 6x - 5.$
40. $9x^2 + 12x + 5 = 0.$
41. $3x^2 + 2x + 2 = 0.$
42. $4x^2 + 9 = 3x.$
43. $7x^2 + 6x + 18 = 0.$
44. $5x^2 + 10x + 24 = 0.$
45. $6x^2 + 3 = 8x.$
46. $12x^2 = 2x - 3.$
47. $10x^2 + 4x + 5 = 0.$
48. $8x^2 + 9 = 6x.$
49. $x^2 + (q - p)x = pq.$
50. $x^2 - (s - r)x = rs.$
51. $ax^2 - x(a^2 + 1) + a = 0.$
52. $2b^2x^2 - 3abx + a^2 = 0.$
53. $d^2x^2 + cdx - 2c^2 = 0.$
54. $x^2 + 4m^2 - n^2 = 4mx.$
55. $2pqx^2 - (4p^2 + q^2)x + 2pq = 0.$
56. $cx^2 - 2ax + 2a - c = 0.$
57. $(h^2 - 1)x^2 - 2h^2x + h^2 = 0.$
58. $a^2x^2 - 2a^2x + a^2 - 1 = 0.$
59. $bx^2 - ax = a + b.$
60. $(c^2 - 1)x^2 - 2c^2x + c^2 = 0.$

Use the quadratic formula to perform the operation required in Problems 61 to 68.

61. Solve $y^2 - x^2 - 3x + y - 2 = 0$ for y in terms of x.
62. Solve $y^2 - x^2 + 5x + y - 6 = 0$ for y in terms of x.
63. Solve $y^2 - 4x^2 + 8x - 2y - 3 = 0$ for x in terms of y.
64. Solve $9x^2 - y^2 - 3x + 3y - 2 = 0$ for x in terms of y.
65. Solve $y^2 - 9x^2 + 12x - 4 = 0$ for x in terms of y.
66. Solve $x^2 - 16y^2 + 24y - 9 = 0$ for y in terms of x.
67. Solve $4x^2 - 9y^2 - 2x + 9y - 2 = 0$ for y in terms of x.
68. Solve $9y^2 - 16x^2 + 6y + 16x - 3 = 0$ for x in terms of y.

Solve the equations in Problems 69 to 80 by use of the quadratic formula and find the value of the roots to three decimal places. Use Table III.

69. $3x^2 - 2x - 2 = 0.$
70. $2x^2 = 3x + 18.$
71. $4x^2 + 6x = 9.$
72. $6x^2 + 8x = 9.$
73. $5x^2 - 5x + 1 = 0.$
74. $2x^2 - 9 = 4x.$
75. $7x^2 = 2x + 1.$
76. $8x^2 + 6x = 3.$
77. $10x^2 - 3 = 4x.$
78. $3x^2 = 12x - 1.$
79. $12x^2 - 4x = 3.$
80. $9x^2 - 3x - 4 = 0.$

66. Equations in quadratic form. An equation of the type

(1) $$a[f(x)]^2 + b[f(x)] + c = 0$$

is said to be in *quadratic form*. The symbol $f(x)$ stands for an expression in x, and it should be noted that this expression appears in both brackets. For example, the equation

$$(2) \qquad 4(x^2 - x)^2 - 11(x^2 - x) + 6 = 0$$

is in quadratic form since $x^2 - x$ appears in both parentheses.

If the expression $f(x)$ in (1) is of degree one or two, we may solve the equation by the methods of this chapter. We shall illustrate the procedure in the following example:

Example 1

In order to solve the Eq. (2) for x, we first let $z = x^2 - x$. Then (2) becomes

$$(3) \qquad 4z^2 - 11z + 6 = 0$$

which is a quadratic equation in the variable z, and, by use of the quadratic formula, we get the following values for z:

$$z = \frac{-(-11) \pm \sqrt{(-11)^2 - 4(4)(6)}}{2(4)}$$

$$= \frac{11 \pm \sqrt{121 - 96}}{8}$$

$$= \frac{11 \pm \sqrt{25}}{8}$$

$$= \frac{11 \pm 5}{8}$$

$$= 2 \text{ and } \tfrac{3}{4}$$

Hence, we have

$$(4) \qquad z = 2$$

and

$$(5) \qquad z = \tfrac{3}{4}$$

We now replace z by $x^2 - x$ in each of these equations and solve for x. Thus, we obtain from (4)

$$
\begin{aligned}
x^2 - x &= 2 \\
x^2 - x - 2 &= 0 \qquad &&\text{(transposing)} \\
(x - 2)(x + 1) &= 0 \qquad &&\text{(factoring the left member)} \\
x - 2 &= 0 \qquad &&\text{(setting each factor equal to zero and solving for } x) \\
x &= 2 \\
x + 1 &= 0 \\
x &= -1
\end{aligned}
$$

Similarly, we get from (5)

$$x^2 - x = \tfrac{3}{4}$$

the solutions of which are $x = \tfrac{3}{2}$ and $x = -\tfrac{1}{2}$. Hence, the solutions of (2) are $x = 2, \tfrac{3}{2}, -\tfrac{1}{2}$, and -1.

Example 2

In order to solve $3x^4 = 2x^2 + 1$, we let $z = x^2$, and get

$$3z^2 = 2z + 1$$

The solutions of this equation by use of any one of the three methods for solving quadratics are $z = 1$ and $z = -\tfrac{1}{3}$. Now, since $z = x^2$, we have

$$x^2 = 1$$
$$x = \pm 1$$

and

$$x^2 = -\tfrac{1}{3}$$
$$x = \pm \sqrt{-\tfrac{1}{3}}$$
$$= \pm \frac{1}{\sqrt{3}} i$$

Hence, the solutions of the original equation are $x = 1$, -1, $(1/\sqrt{3})i$, and $-(1/\sqrt{3})i$.

EXERCISE 32

Reduce the following equations to the quadratic form and solve for x.

1. $x^4 + 36 = 13x^2$.
2. $x^4 = 25x^2 - 144$.
3. $4x^4 - 5x^2 + 1 = 0$.
4. $4x^4 - 17x^2 + 4 = 0$.
5. $x^4 + 27 = 12x^2$.
6. $x^4 = 9x^2 - 20$.
7. $x^4 - 11x^2 = -18$.
8. $4x^4 + 2 = 9x^2$.
9. $x^4 + x^2 = 12$.
10. $x^4 = 45 - 4x^2$.
11. $x^4 + 5x^2 + 4 = 0$.
12. $x^4 + 2x^2 = 15$.
13. $8x^4 = 2x^2 + 1$.
14. $8x^4 + 6x^2 = 27$.
15. $80x^4 = 6x^2 + 2$.
16. $6x^4 - x^2 - 2 = 0$.
17. $2x^{-2} = 3x^{-1} - 1$.
18. $2x^{-2} - x^{-1} = 6$.
19. $3x^{-2} - 6 = 7x^{-1}$.
20. $5x^{-2} + 12x^{-1} = 9$.
21. $x^6 + 7x^3 = 8$.
22. $x^8 - 17x^4 + 16 = 0$.
23. $8x^6 + 7x^3 - 1 = 0$.
24. $x^6 + 26x^3 - 27 = 0$.
25. $(x^2 + 1)^2 + 10 = 7(x^2 + 1)$.
26. $(2x^2 + 1)^2 = 12(2x^2 + 1) - 27$.
27. $2(2x^2 - 1)^2 = (2x^2 - 1) + 1$.
28. $3(3x^2 - 2)^2 - (3x^2 - 2) = 2$.
29. $(x^2 + 3x)^2 - 2(x^2 + 3x) = 8$.
30. $(x^2 - 3x)^2 = 8(x^2 - 3x) + 20$.
31. $(2x^2 - x)^2 = 4(2x^2 - x) - 3$.
32. $(3x^2 + 5x)^2 + 24 = 14(3x^2 + 5x)$.
33. $(x^2 + x)^2 - 5(x^2 + x) + 6 = 0$.
34. $(x^2 + 2x)^2 - 4(x^2 + 2x) + 3 = 0$.
35. $(2x^2 + x)^2 + 2 = 3(2x^2 + x)$.
36. $(3x^2 + 2x)^2 + 3x^2 + 2x = 2$.

37. $\left(\dfrac{x}{x+1}\right)^2 - 3\left(\dfrac{x}{x+1}\right) - 18 = 0$.

38. $2\left(\dfrac{x+1}{x-1}\right)^2 + \left(\dfrac{x+1}{x-1}\right) = 1$.

39. $\left(\dfrac{2x-1}{x}\right)^2 + 3 = 4\left(\dfrac{2x-1}{x}\right)$.

40. $3\left(\dfrac{2x-1}{1-3x}\right)^2 = 2\left(\dfrac{2x-1}{1-3x}\right) + 1$.

41. $4\left(\dfrac{x-3}{2x+1}\right) - \left(\dfrac{2x+1}{x-3}\right) = 3.$ HINT: Let $z = \dfrac{x-3}{2x+1}$, then $\dfrac{1}{z} = \dfrac{2x+1}{x-3}$.

42. $2\left(\dfrac{2x}{x-1}\right) - 5\left(\dfrac{x-1}{2x}\right) - 3 = 0.$

43. $2\left(\dfrac{2x-1}{x}\right) - 10\left(\dfrac{x}{2x-1}\right) - 1 = 0.$

44. $2\left(\dfrac{2x-1}{2x+1}\right) - 3\left(\dfrac{2x+1}{2x-1}\right) - 1 = 0.$

45. $3 - 4\sqrt{2x-1} + (2x-1) = 0.$

46. $3x + 8 = 5\sqrt{3x+2}.$ HINT: Add -6 to each member of the equation, then let $z = \sqrt{3x+2}.$

47. $7\sqrt{4x-3} = 24x - 16.$ **48.** $6\left(\dfrac{x-2}{x+1}\right) + 1 = 5\sqrt{\dfrac{x-2}{x+1}}.$

67. *Equations that involve radicals of the second order.* Since the squares of two equal quantities are equal, we have the following principle:

Any root of a given equation will also be a root of an equation obtained by equating the squares of the two members of the given equation.

The converse of this statement is not true. For example, if we equate the squares of the two members of

(1) $$\sqrt{2x^2 - 1} = x$$

we get

(2) $$2x^2 - 1 = x^2$$

Hence,

$$2x^2 - x^2 = 1 \qquad \text{(transposing)}$$
$$x^2 = 1$$
$$x = \pm 1$$

The value $x = 1$ satisfies Eq. (1). However, when $x = -1$, the left member of (1) becomes $\sqrt{2(-1)^2 - 1} = \sqrt{1} = 1$, while the right member is -1. Hence, -1 is a root of (2) but not of (1). The value $x = -1$ is called an *extraneous* root.

In order to solve an equation that involves radicals of the second order, we perform the following steps:

1. *Isolate one radical on one side of the equality sign by transposing all other terms.*

2. *Square both members of the resulting equation and equate the two squares.*

3. *If the equation thus obtained contains no radical, solve it for* **x**. *If the equation contains one or more radicals, we repeat steps 1 and 2 until we obtain an equation which is free of radicals.   We then solve the latter equation for* **x**.

4. *Substitute the values of* **x** *obtained in step 3 in the original equation in order to determine those values of* **x** *that are and are not roots.*

The process of applying steps 1 and 2 until an equation free of radicals is obtained is called *rationalizing the equation*.

Example 1

Solve the equation

$$(3) \qquad \sqrt{2x^2 - 2x + 1} - 2x + 3 = 0$$

Solution

In the following discussion, the number at the left denotes the step in the solving process that is being applied.

1. We first isolate the radical by transposing $-2x + 3$ and get

$$\sqrt{2x^2 - 2x + 1} = 2x - 3$$

2. Next we equate the squares of both members of the above equation and get

$$2x^2 - 2x + 1 = 4x^2 - 12x + 9$$

3. This equation does not involve a radical; so we solve it for x.

$2x^2 - 4x^2 - 2x + 12x + 1 - 9 = 0$	(transposing and arranging terms)
$-2x^2 + 10x - 8 = 0$	(collecting terms)
$x^2 - 5x + 4 = 0$	(dividing by -2)
$(x - 4)(x - 1) = 0$	(factoring the left member)
$x - 4 = 0$	(setting each factor equal to zero and solving)
$x = 4$	
$x - 1 = 0$	
$x = 1$	

Hence, the roots of the rationalized equation are $x = 4$ and $x = 1$.

4. Now we substitute $x = 4$ in the left member of (3) and get

$$\sqrt{2(4)^2 - 2(4) + 1} - 2(4) + 3 = \sqrt{32 - 8 + 1} - 8 + 3$$
$$= \sqrt{25} - 8 + 3$$
$$= 5 - 8 + 3$$
$$= 0$$

Hence, $x = 4$ is a solution of (3).

However, when $x = 1$ is substituted in the left member of (3), we get

$$\sqrt{2(1)^2 - 2(1) + 1} - 2(1) + 3 = \sqrt{2 - 2 + 1} - 2 + 3$$
$$= 1 - 2 + 3$$
$$= 2$$

Hence, $x = 1$ is not a solution of (3) since the right member is zero. Consequently, the only solution of (3) is $x = 4$.

Example 2

Solve the equation

(4) $$\sqrt{11x - 6} = \sqrt{4x + 5} - \sqrt{x - 1}$$

Solution

1. Since we have one radical isolated on the left of the equality sign, we proceed at once to step 2.

2. $$11x - 6 = 4x + 5 - 2\sqrt{(4x + 5)(x - 1)} + x - 1$$
[equating the squares of the members of (4)]

$$2\sqrt{(4x + 5)(x - 1)} = -11x + 4x + x + 6 + 5 - 1$$
(transposing terms so as to isolate the radical)

$$2\sqrt{4x^2 + x - 5} = -6x + 10$$
(collecting terms)

$$\sqrt{4x^2 + x - 5} = -3x + 5$$
(dividing by 2)

$$4x^2 + x - 5 = 9x^2 - 30x + 25$$
(equating the squares of the two members)

$$-5x^2 + 31x - 30 = 0$$
(transposing and collecting)

3. $$x = \frac{-31 \pm \sqrt{(31)^2 - 4(-5)(-30)}}{2(-5)}$$
(solving by the quadratic formula)

$$= \frac{-31 \pm \sqrt{961 - 600}}{-10}$$

$$= \frac{-31 \pm \sqrt{361}}{-10}$$

$$= \frac{-31 \pm 19}{-10}$$

$$= \tfrac{6}{5} \text{ and } 5$$

4. Now we substitute $x = \tfrac{6}{5}$ in both members of (4) and get for the left member

$$\sqrt{11(\tfrac{6}{5}) - 6} = \sqrt{\frac{66}{5} - 6} = \sqrt{\frac{66 - 30}{5}} = \sqrt{\frac{36}{5}} = \frac{6}{\sqrt{5}}$$

and for the right member

$$\sqrt{4(\tfrac{6}{5}) + 5} - \sqrt{\frac{6}{5} - 1} = \sqrt{\frac{49}{5}} - \sqrt{\frac{1}{5}} = \frac{7}{\sqrt{5}} - \frac{1}{\sqrt{5}} = \frac{6}{\sqrt{5}}$$

Hence, $x = \frac{6}{5}$ is a solution of (4). When we substitute $x = 5$ in (4) we get

$$\sqrt{11(5) - 6} = \sqrt{55 - 6} = \sqrt{49} = 7$$

for the left member and

$$\sqrt{4(5) + 5} - \sqrt{5 - 1} = \sqrt{25} - \sqrt{4} = 5 - 2 = 3$$

for the right member. Hence, since the right and left members of (4) are not equal when $x = 5$, this value of x is not a solution.

EXERCISE 33

Solve the following equations.

1. $\sqrt{x + 3} = \sqrt{5x - 1}$.

2. $\sqrt{2x + 1} = \sqrt{x + 5}$.

3. $\sqrt{5x + 1} = \sqrt{14x + 2}$.

4. $\sqrt{4x + 9} = \sqrt{8x + 2}$.

5. $\sqrt{3x - 1} = \sqrt{2x + 1}$.

6. $\sqrt{2x + 2} = \sqrt{3x - 1}$.

7. $\sqrt{5 - x} + \sqrt{x + 3} = 0$.

8. $\sqrt{x - 5} - \sqrt{4x - 7} = 0$.

9. $\sqrt{x^2 + 2x + 1} - \sqrt{4x + 1} = 0$.

10. $\sqrt{x^2 - 5x + 1} - \sqrt{1 - 8x} = 0$.

11. $\sqrt{2x^2 + x + 2} = \sqrt{2x + 3}$.

12. $\sqrt{3x^2 + x - 3} = \sqrt{3x - 2}$.

13. $x - \sqrt{x - 1} = 1$.

14. $2x = \sqrt{-2x + 5} - 1$.

15. $3x = \sqrt{3x + 7} - 1$.

16. $6x - \sqrt{18x - 8} = 2$.

17. $\sqrt{5x^2 - 4x + 3} - x = 1$.

18. $2x = 1 + \sqrt{2x^2 - 3x + 7}$.

19. $3x - \sqrt{6x^2 - x + 13} = 1$.

20. $3x - \sqrt{1 + 5x - x^2} = 2$.

21. $\sqrt{x + 2} - \sqrt{x - 1} = 1$.

22. $\sqrt{2x + 1} - \sqrt{x - 3} = 2$.

23. $\sqrt{5x + 1} - \sqrt{2x + 2} = 2$.

24. $\sqrt{2x + 3} + \sqrt{x - 2} = 4$.

25. $\sqrt{x + 3} + \sqrt{2x - 1} = \sqrt{7x + 2}$.

26. $\sqrt{2 - x} - \sqrt{3 + x} = \sqrt{5 + 2x}$.

27. $\sqrt{x + 1} + \sqrt{3x - 5} = \sqrt{5x + 1}$.

28. $\sqrt{x - 1} - \sqrt{2x - 9} = \sqrt{x - 4}$.

29. $\sqrt{3x + 3} - \sqrt{x - 1} = \sqrt{x + 2}$.

30. $\sqrt{5x + 1} - \sqrt{x - 2} = \sqrt{x + 6}$.

31. $\sqrt{3x + 4} - \sqrt{x + 5} = \sqrt{x - 3}$.

32. $\sqrt{x + 3} + \sqrt{x + 4} = \sqrt{2x + 7}$.

33. $\sqrt{x^2 + 3x} + \sqrt{x^2 - 1} = 2$.

34. $\sqrt{x^2 + 3x - 1} - \sqrt{x^2 + x - 2} = 1$.

35. $\sqrt{x^2 + x + 3} - \sqrt{x^2 + 3x + 4} = 1$.

36. $\sqrt{x^2 + 3x + 2} + \sqrt{x^2 + x + 2} = 2$.

37. $\dfrac{\sqrt{x + 5} - 4}{\sqrt{2x + 1} - 2} = -1$.

38. $\dfrac{\sqrt{3x - 2} + 1}{\sqrt{x + 2} - 1} = 3$.

39. $\dfrac{\sqrt{x+1}+1}{\sqrt{2x-2}+4} = \dfrac{1}{2}.$ **40.** $\dfrac{\sqrt{3x+10}+1}{2-\sqrt{x+3}} = 3.$

41. $\sqrt{bx+b^2} = \sqrt{bx-2b^2} + b.$ **42.** $\sqrt{5ax-a^2} = \sqrt{ax} + a.$

43. $\sqrt{x-a^2} - \sqrt{2x-a^2} = -a.$

44. $\sqrt{5b^2x-a^2} - \sqrt{2b^2x-3a^2} = 2a.$

68. *Problems that lead to quadratic equations.* Many stated problems, especially those which deal with products or quotients involving the unknown, lead to quadratic equations. The method of obtaining the equation for solving such problems is the same as that in Art. 30, and the reader should review that article at this point. It should be noted here that often a problem which can be solved by the use of a quadratic equation has only one solution, while the equation has two solutions. In such cases, the root which does not satisfy the conditions of the problem is discarded.

Example 1

A rectangular building whose depth is twice its frontage is divided into two parts by a partition that is 30 ft. from and parallel to the front wall. If the rear portion of the building contains 3500 sq. ft., find the dimensions of the building.

Solution

Let

$$x = \text{the frontage of the building in feet}$$

Then

$$2x = \text{the depth}$$

Also,

$$2x - 30 = \text{the length of the rear portion}$$

and

$$x = \text{the width of the rear portion}$$

Hence,

$$x(2x - 30) = \text{the area of the rear portion}$$

Therefore,

$$x(2x - 30) = 3500$$

Performing the indicated multiplication and transposing 3500, we have

$$2x^2 - 30x - 3500 = 0$$

or

$$(x - 50)(2x + 70) = 0$$

Therefore, $x = 50$ and $x = -35$. However, since the dimensions cannot be negative, we have

$$x = 50 \text{ ft. (frontage)}$$
$$2x = 100 \text{ ft. (depth)}$$

Example 2

The periods of time required by two painters to paint a square yard of floor differ by 1 min. Together, they can paint 27 sq. yd. in 1 hr. How long does it take each to paint 1 sq. yd.?

Solution

Let

x = the number of minutes required by the faster painter to paint 1 sq. yd.

Then

$x + 1$ = the number of minutes required by the other

Consequently,

$\dfrac{1}{x}$ = the fraction of a square yard the first man paints in 1 min.

and

$\dfrac{1}{x + 1}$ = the fraction of a square yard the other paints in 1 min.

Hence,

$\dfrac{1}{x} + \dfrac{1}{x + 1}$ = the fraction of a square yard painted by both men in 1 min.

However, since together they painted 27 sq. yd. in 60 min., they covered

$$\tfrac{27}{60} = \tfrac{9}{20} \text{ sq. yd. in 1 min.}$$

Therefore,

$$\frac{1}{x} + \frac{1}{x + 1} = \frac{9}{20}$$

Solving this equation, we have

$$20(x + 1) + 20x = 9x(x + 1) \quad \text{(clearing of fractions)}$$
$$20x + 20 + 20x = 9x^2 + 9x \quad \text{(performing the indicated multiplication)}$$
$$-9x^2 + 31x + 20 = 0 \quad \text{(transposing)}$$

$$x = \frac{-31 \pm \sqrt{(31)^2 - 4(-9)(20)}}{2(-9)}$$

$$= \frac{-31 \pm \sqrt{961 + 720}}{-18}$$

$$= \frac{-31 \pm \sqrt{1681}}{-18}$$

$$= \frac{-31 \pm 41}{-18}$$

$$= -\tfrac{5}{9} \text{ and } 4$$

We discard $-\frac{5}{9}$, since a negative time has no meaning in this problem. Hence,

$$x = 4$$

and

$$x + 1 = 5$$

Thus, the painters require 4 and 5 min., respectively, to paint 1 sq. yd.

EXERCISE 34

1. Find two consecutive positive integers if the sum of their squares is 85.

2. Find two consecutive integers whose product exceeds their sum by 41.

3. Find a positive number such that its square decreased by 5 times the number is 14.

4. Find a negative number such that its square increased by 3 times the number is 40.

5. Find two numbers that differ by 18 and whose product is 144.

6. Find two numbers that differ by 2 and whose product is 288.

7. Divide 40 into two parts whose product is 256.

8. Divide 33 into two parts whose product is 216.

9. If the length of each side of a square is increased by 2 units, the area is multiplied by 4. Find the original length of each side.

10. The sum of a number and its reciprocal is $\frac{13}{6}$. Find the number.

11. Find the number that is 4 greater than 12 times its reciprocal.

12. The sum of an integer and the reciprocal of the next larger integer is $\frac{13}{4}$. Find the number.

13. The area of a rectangle is 36 sq. ft., and its length exceeds its width by 5 ft. Find the dimensions.

14. A rectangular lot has an area of 9800 sq. ft., and the length exceeds the width by 70 ft. Find the dimensions.

15. A rectangular room has a floor space of 240 sq. ft. Find the dimensions if the length is 4 ft. less than twice the width.

16. The length of a rectangle exceeds the width by 7 in., and the diagonal is 13 in. in length. Find the dimensions.

17. The perimeter of a rectangle is 40 ft., and the area is 96 sq. ft. Find the dimensions.

18. A farmer built a rectangular chicken pen containing 200 sq. ft. along one side of his barn. If the other three sides contained 40 ft. of fencing, find the dimensions.

19. Find the legs of a right triangle if they differ by 7 ft. and if the area of the triangle is 30 sq. ft.

20. The area of a right triangle is 84 sq. in. Find its dimensions if the legs differ by 17 in.

21. The side of a square is 3 ft. less than the length of a rectangle and 4 ft. longer than the width. Find the dimensions if the area of the square is twice that of the rectangle.

22. The outside dimensions of a framed picture are 20 by 18 in. Find the width of the frame if its area is $\frac{1}{4}$ of the area enclosed by it.

23. Two boys paddle a canoe 6 miles downstream and back in 4 hr. If the rate of the current is 2 miles per hr., find the rate of the canoe in still water.

24. A pilot flew 400 miles against the wind and back in $4\frac{1}{2}$ hr. Find the speed of the plane in still air if the velocity of the wind was 20 miles per hr.

25. A plane travels 1000 miles at a uniform rate. If it had gone 50 miles per hr. faster, the trip would have required 1 hr. less. Find the rate traveled.

26. One car traveled 140 miles at a uniform rate. Another went 180 miles at a rate that was 5 miles per hr. faster and required 30 min. more for its trip. Find the rate of each car.

27. A message had to be taken a distance of 35 miles by a carrier. One person took it 20 miles at a uniform rate, and another carried it the remainder of the distance at a rate that was $2\frac{1}{2}$ miles per hr. slower. Find each rate if the total time for the trip was 4 hr.

28. A carpenter can do a piece of work in 2 days less than his helper. The two together can do the job in $2\frac{2}{5}$ days. How many days will it take each of them to do the job alone?

29. A man and his son working together can paint a barn in 2 days. How long will it take each of them to do it alone if the boy requires 3 more days than his father?

30. A man bought two farms and paid $45,000 for each. If he paid $50 more per acre for one than for the other and there were 750 acres in all, find the price per acre of each.

31. A grocer sold 2 lots of eggs for $22 and $15, respectively, and there were 10 doz. more in the first lot than in the second. If the price per dozen of the first lot was 5 cents more than that of the second, how many dozen were in each lot?

32. The boys in a certain family bought a used car for $300 and shared equally in the cost. After 6 months one of the boys left and sold his share to the others for $45. When this additional cost was divided equally among the remaining brothers, each found that his share was $60 less than his part of the original cost. How many boys were in the family?

69. *Nature of the roots of a quadratic equation.* Formula (3), Art. 65, enables us to ascertain important information about the roots of a quadratic equation without solving the equation. If we let r represent the value of the right member of (3), Art. 65, when the plus sign is used before the radical, and s represent the value when the minus sign is used, then the two solutions of

(1) $$ax^2 + bx + c = 0$$

are

(2) $$r = \frac{-b + \sqrt{b^2 - 4ac}}{2a}$$

and

(3) $$s = \frac{-b - \sqrt{b^2 - 4ac}}{2a}$$

The expression under the radical in (2) and (3) is called the *discriminant*, and it is usually denoted by the letter D.

We shall first assume that the coefficients a, b, and c in (1) are rational. Under this assumption we have the following possibilities.

1. If $D = 0$, then $r = s = -b/2a$. Hence the roots of (1) are rational and equal.

2. If $D < 0$ (that is, if D is negative), then $\sqrt{D}$ is a pure imaginary, and consequently r and s are imaginary.

3. If $D > 0$, two situations may exist. First, if D is a perfect square, then $\sqrt{D}$ is a rational number, and hence r and s are rational. Second, if D is not a perfect square, $\sqrt{D}$ is an irrational number, and r and s are therefore irrational. In either case, r and s are unequal, since

$$r = \frac{-b + \sqrt{D}}{2a} \quad \text{and} \quad s = \frac{-b - \sqrt{D}}{2a}$$

We may summarize the above information in the following table.

Discriminant	Roots
$D = 0$	Rational and equal
$D > 0$ and a perfect square	Rational and unequal
$D > 0$ and not a perfect square	Irrational and unequal
$D < 0$	Imaginary

Examples

Equation	Discriminant	Nature of the roots
1. $9x^2 - 24x + 16 = 0$	$D = (-24)^2 - (4)(9)(16)$ $= 576 - 576 = 0$	Rational and equal
2. $2x^2 + 3x - 20 = 0$	$D = 3^2 - (4)(2)(-20)$ $= 9 + 160 = 169 = 13^2$	Rational and unequal
3. $3x^2 - 2x - 7 = 0$	$D = (-2)^2 - (4)(3)(-7)$ $= 4 + 84 = 88$	Irrational and unequal
4. $5x^2 - 6x + 8 = 0$	$D = (-6)^2 - (4)(5)(8)$ $= 36 - 160 = -124$	Imaginary

If we assume that a, b, and c are real but not necessarily rational, then the information we gain about r and s is less specific. If

$D = 0$, the roots are real and equal (since $r = s = -b/2a$, and we only know that a and b are real)

$D > 0$, the roots are real and unequal

$D < 0$, the roots are imaginary

Examples

Equation	Discriminant	Roots
5. $2x^2 - 2\sqrt{10}\,x + 5 = 0$	$D = (-2\sqrt{10})^2 - (4)(2)(5)$ $= 40 - 40 = 0$	Real and equal
6. $\sqrt{3}\,x^2 - 5x + \sqrt{12} = 0$	$D = (-5)^2 - (4)(\sqrt{3})(\sqrt{12})$ $= 25 - 24 = 1$	Real[1] and unequal
7. $\sqrt{5}\,x^2 - \sqrt{3}\,x + \sqrt{2}$ $= 0$	$D = (-\sqrt{3})^2 - (4)(\sqrt{5})(\sqrt{2})$ $= 3 - 4\sqrt{10} < 0$	Imaginary

[1] In this case, D is a perfect square. However,

$$r = \frac{5+1}{2\sqrt{3}} = \frac{6}{2\sqrt{3}} = \sqrt{3}$$

and $s = (5 - 1)/2\sqrt{3} = 2/\sqrt{3} = 2\sqrt{3}/3$, and hence they are not rational.

70. The sum and product of the roots of a quadratic equation.
By use of (2) and (3) of Art. 69, we can see that the sum and product of the roots of a quadratic equation are simple combinations of the coefficients of the equation. For example, the sum of the two roots is

$$\left(\frac{-b}{2a} + \frac{\sqrt{b^2 - 4ac}}{2a}\right) + \left(\frac{-b}{2a} - \frac{\sqrt{b^2 - 4ac}}{2a}\right) = \frac{-2b}{2a} = -\frac{b}{a}$$

Hence,

$$(1) \qquad\qquad r + s = -\frac{b}{a}$$

Furthermore, the product is

$$\left(\frac{-b}{2a} + \frac{\sqrt{b^2 - 4ac}}{2a}\right)\left(\frac{-b}{2a} - \frac{\sqrt{b^2 - 4ac}}{2a}\right)$$
$$= \left(\frac{-b}{2a}\right)^2 - \left(\frac{\sqrt{b^2 - 4ac}}{2a}\right)^2$$
$$= \frac{b^2}{4a^2} - \frac{b^2 - 4ac}{4a^2}$$
$$= \frac{b^2 - b^2 + 4ac}{4a^2}$$
$$= \frac{4ac}{4a^2} = \frac{c}{a}$$

Consequently,

$$(2) \qquad\qquad rs = \frac{c}{a}$$

Hence, since r and s are the two roots of $ax^2 + bx + c = 0$, we see that *the sum of the two roots of a quadratic equation is equal to the negative of the quotient of the coefficients of x and x^2, and the product of the two roots is the quotient of the constant term and the coefficient of x^2.*

The two formulas (1) and (2) are useful as a rapid check on the roots of a quadratic equation. In Example 1, Art. 65, we found that the two roots of $6x^2 - x - 12 = 0$ were $\frac{3}{2}$ and $-\frac{4}{3}$. By (1) and (2), we see that the sum and product of the two roots should be $\frac{1}{6}$ and $-\frac{12}{6} = -2$, respectively.

In order to check the solution, we first add and then multiply the two roots and get $\frac{3}{2} + (-\frac{4}{3}) = \frac{9}{6} - \frac{8}{6} = \frac{1}{6}$ for the sum, and

$\left(\frac{3}{2}\right)\left(-\frac{4}{3}\right) = -\frac{12}{6} = -2$ for the product. Hence, the solution checks.

We shall now present some examples that illustrate methods for using the principles of this and the previous article to obtain information about the coefficients in equations whose roots satisfy certain predetermined conditions.

Example 1

In the equation $2x^2 + (k - 3)x + 3k - 5 = 0$, determine k so that the sum and product of the roots are equal.

Solution

In this problem $a = 2$, $b = k - 3$, and $c = 3k - 5$. Hence, by (1), the sum of the roots is

$$-\frac{b}{a} = -\frac{k - 3}{2}$$

and, by (2), the product is

$$\frac{c}{a} = \frac{3k - 5}{2}$$

Hence, if the sum is equal to the product, we have

$$-\frac{k - 3}{2} = \frac{3k - 5}{2}$$

If we solve this equation for k, we get

$$-k + 3 = 3k - 5$$
$$4k = 8$$
$$k = 2$$

Example 2

Given the equation $ax^2 + bx + c = 0$. (a) Show that if one root is the negative of the other, then $b = 0$; (b) show that if one root is zero, then $c = 0$.

Solution

(a) If one root is the negative of the other, then

$$\frac{-b + \sqrt{b^2 - 4ac}}{2a} = -\frac{-b - \sqrt{b^2 - 4ac}}{2a}$$

Hence,

$$-b + \sqrt{b^2 - 4ac} = b + \sqrt{b^2 - 4ac}$$
$$-b - b = \sqrt{b^2 - 4ac} - \sqrt{b^2 - 4ac}$$
$$-2b = 0$$
$$b = 0$$

(b) If one root is zero, then

$$\frac{-b \pm \sqrt{b^2 - 4ac}}{2a} = 0$$

where the double sign $\pm$ means either plus or minus but not both. If we multiply both members of the above equation by $2a$, we get

$$-b \pm \sqrt{b^2 - 4ac} = 0$$
$$-b = \pm \sqrt{b^2 - 4ac}$$
$$b^2 = b^2 - 4ac \qquad \text{(squaring both members)}$$
$$4ac = 0$$

Hence, since $a \neq 0$, we have $c = 0$.

71. Factors of a quadratic trinomial in one variable. We shall now prove that *if r and s are roots of the equation*

(1) $$ax^2 + bx + c = 0$$

then x − r and x − s are factors of

(2) $$ax^2 + bx + c$$

By (1) and (2) of Art. 70,

(3) $$-\frac{b}{a} = r + s$$

and

(4) $$\frac{c}{a} = rs$$

Hence, $b = -a(r + s)$ and $c = ars$. Thus, if we substitute these values in (2), we have

(5) $$ax^2 + bx + c = ax^2 - a(r + s)x + ars$$
$$= a[x^2 - (r + s)x + rs]$$
$$= a(x - r)(x - s)$$

If a, b, and c are rational and $b^2 - 4ac$ is a perfect square, then the above factors are rational. Hence, *the quadratic trinomial $ax^2 + bx + c$, with a, b, and c rational, can be expressed as the product of two rational linear factors if $b^2 - 4ac$ is a perfect square.*

If a quadratic trinomial satisfies the above conditions, its factors can be obtained by the method of Art. 15. However, if the coefficients are large, it may require considerable time to find the proper combinations. In such cases it is easier to use the method illustrated in the following example.

Example

In order to factor

(6) $$72x^2 + 95x - 1000$$

we first set (6) equal to zero and solve the equation thus obtained and get

$$x = \frac{-95 \pm \sqrt{9025 + 288{,}000}}{144} = \frac{-95 \pm \sqrt{297{,}025}}{144}$$

$$= \frac{-95 \pm 545}{144}$$

$$= \frac{450}{144} \text{ and } -\frac{640}{144}$$

$$= \frac{25}{8} \text{ and } -\frac{40}{9}$$

Hence,

$$72x^2 + 95x - 1000 = 72(x - \tfrac{25}{8})(x + \tfrac{40}{9}) \quad \text{[by (5), since } a = 72]$$
$$= 8(x - \tfrac{25}{8})9(x + \tfrac{40}{9}) \quad \text{(since } 72 = 8 \times 9)$$
$$= (8x - 25)(9x + 40)$$

Obviously,

(7) $$a(x - r)(x - s) = 0$$

where a is any number other than zero, is an equation that has r and s as roots.

If r and s are integers, we usually let $a = 1$. However, if r and s are rational and either or both are fractions, we let a be the denominator or the product of the denominators. Then the resulting equations will have integral coefficients.

Examples

We shall obtain equations whose roots are (1) 3 and -2, (2) -4 and $\tfrac{2}{3}$, (3) $-\tfrac{3}{4}$ and $\tfrac{5}{6}$. In each case we shall indicate the steps in the simplification of the equation.

(1) Roots: 3, -2

Equation: $(x - 3)(x + 2) = 0$ [by (7) with $a = 1$]
$x^2 - x - 6 = 0$ (performing the indicated multiplication)

(2) Roots: -4, $\tfrac{2}{3}$

Equation: $3(x + 4)(x - \tfrac{2}{3}) = 0$ [by (7) with $a = 3$]
$(x + 4)(3x - 2) = 0$ (multiplying second factor by 3)
$3x^2 + 10x - 8 = 0$ (performing the indicated multiplication)

(3) Roots: $-\frac{3}{4}, \frac{5}{6}$

Equation: $24(x + \frac{3}{4})(x - \frac{5}{6}) = 0$ [by (7) with $a = 4 \times 6 = 24$]

$$4(x + \frac{3}{4})6(x - \frac{5}{6}) = 0$$
$$(4x + 3)(6x - 5) = 0$$
$$24x^2 - 2x - 15 = 0$$

EXERCISE 35

By use of the discriminant, determine the nature of the roots of the equations in Problems 1 to 20.

1. $3x^2 - 5x + 2 = 0$.   2. $5x^2 - 3x + 2 = 0$.   3. $4x^2 + 4x + 1 = 0$.

4. $5x^2 - 3x - 2 = 0$.   5. $6x^2 - 5x - 2 = 0$.   6. $9x^2 - 12x + 4 = 0$.

7. $2x^2 - 3x + 7 = 0$.   8. $7x^2 - 2x - 3 = 0$.   9. $3x^2 = 2x + 1$.

10. $16x^2 = 24x - 9$.   11. $7x^2 = 3x - 4$.   12. $2x^2 = 3x + 4$.

13. $\sqrt{3}\, x^2 + \sqrt{2}\, x - \sqrt{3} = 0$.   14. $x^2 - 2\sqrt{2}\, x + 2 = 0$.

15. $\sqrt{3}\, x^2 - 3x + \sqrt{12} = 0$.   16. $3x^2 - 5x + \sqrt{10} = 0$.

17. $(1 - \sqrt{2})x^2 + 2x - (1 + \sqrt{2}) = 0$.

18. $(\sqrt{3} - 1)x^2 + 3x + \sqrt{3} - 1 = 0$.

19. $(\sqrt{5} - \sqrt{3})x^2 + \sqrt{5}\, x + \sqrt{5} + \sqrt{3} = 0$.

20. $(\sqrt{2} - \sqrt{7})x^2 - 2\sqrt{5}\, x + (\sqrt{2} + \sqrt{7}) = 0$.

Without solving, find the sum and the product of the roots in Problems 21 to 32.

21. $2x^2 + 5x + 1 = 0$.   22. $3x^2 - 4x + 5 = 0$.   23. $5x^2 - 7x - 8 = 0$.

24. $2x^2 + 9x - 3 = 0$.   25. $x^2 + 3x = -4$.   26. $3x^2 + 2 = 5x$.

27. $2x = 3x^2 - 5$.   28. $7 - x = 2x^2$.

29. $\sqrt{5}\, x^2 - \sqrt{10}\, x + 5 = 0$.   30. $\sqrt{3}\, x^2 + 9x + \sqrt{6} = 0$.

31. $(2 - \sqrt{3})x^2 - x + 7 - 2\sqrt{3} = 0$.

32. $(\sqrt{5} + 2)x^2 + x + \sqrt{5} - 2 = 0$.

Determine k so that the two roots of the quadratic equations in Problems 33 to 36 are equal.

33. $x^2 + 2kx + k = 0$.   34. $x^2 + 2(k - 1)x - 4k = 0$.

35. $(2k + 2)x^2 - 4x + k = 0$.   36. $(k + 2)x^2 - 3(k + 1)x + 3 = 0$.

Find the value of k so that the sum of the roots of the equation in each of Problems 37 to 40 is equal to the product.

37. $2x^2 + (k + 1)x + 3k - 5 = 0$.   38. $x^2 - (2k - 3)x + k = 0$.

39. $3x^2 + (2k + 1)x - k - 5 = 0$.   40. $2x^2 - (3k + 4)x + k - 2 = 0$.

Find the value of k so that one root of the equation in each of Problems 41 to 44 is zero.

41. $2x^2 - 3x + k - 2 = 0$.   42. $3x^2 - 5kx + 4k - 1 = 0$.

43. $2x^2 + 5x + k^2 - 4k + 3 = 0$.   44. $5x^2 - 3x + 2k^2 + 5k - 3 = 0$.

Form a quadratic equation that has the pair of numbers listed in each of Problems 45 to 56 as roots.

45. 3, -2.   **46.** 3, 1.   **47.** -5, -3.   **48.** -7, 2.

49. $\frac{3}{2}$, $-\frac{2}{3}$.   **50.** $\frac{3}{4}$, $\frac{1}{3}$.   **51.** $-\frac{5}{8}$, $\frac{5}{2}$.   **52.** $-\frac{3}{7}$, $-\frac{5}{4}$.

53. $3 - \sqrt{2}$, $3 + \sqrt{2}$.   **54.** $-\frac{1}{2} + \frac{\sqrt{5}}{2}$, $-\frac{1}{2} - \frac{\sqrt{5}}{2}$.

55. $\frac{1}{4} - \frac{\sqrt{3}}{4} i$, $\frac{1}{4} + \frac{\sqrt{3}}{4} i$.   **56.** $\frac{1}{2} - \frac{\sqrt{7}}{2} i$, $\frac{1}{2} + \frac{\sqrt{7}}{2} i$.

Find the factors of the quadratic function in each of Problems 57 to 64.

57. $24x^2 + 23x - 50$.   **58.** $32x^2 - 38x - 27$.   **59.** $28x^2 + 12x - 81$.

60. $96x^2 - 2x - 25$.   **61.** $12x^2 + 88x - 15$.   **62.** $24x^2 + 89x + 27$.

63. $35x^2 - 54x - 32$.   **64.** $16x^2 - 61x - 12$.

72. *Graph of a quadratic function.* The left member $ax^2 + bx + c$ of Eq. (1), Art. 69, is a quadratic function of x. We discussed the methods for constructing the graphs of such functions in Art. 34 and in Figs. 3 and 4 we show the graphs of $x^2 - 2x - 2$ and $9x^2 - 1$, respectively.

In the following examples we shall use the same method for constructing the graphs of the functions $\frac{1}{2}x^2 - 2x - 3$, $-x^2 - 6x - 5$, and $x^2 - 6x + 9$. As in Art. 34, we set each function equal to y and then assign values to x and compute each corresponding value of y. In this way we obtain the tables of values in the examples shown on page 178.

A curve of the type shown in Figs. 10, 11, and 12 is known as a *parabola*. It is proved in analytic geometry that the graph of the quadratic function $ax^2 + bx + c$ is always a *parabola* and that the curve opens upward if a is positive and downward if a is negative. The *vertex* of a parabola is the lowest point on the curve if it opens upward and the highest point if it opens downward. We shall explain how to obtain the coordinates of the vertex in the next article.

The zeros of a quadratic function are the abscissas of the points where the graph crosses the X axis. In the above examples the zeros of the first function are slightly more than 5 and slightly less than -1. The second function has no zeros, and the third, only one, $x = 3$. (See page 178.)

73. *Maximum or minimum value of a quadratic function.* In the previous article we stated that the vertex of a parabola was the highest or lowest point on the curve. The abscissa of the vertex is

Examples

1. $y = \frac{1}{2}x^2 - 2x - 3$ (Fig. 10)

x	-4	-2	0	2	4	6	8
y	13	3	-3	-5	-3	3	13

2. $y = -x^2 - 4x - 5$ (Fig. 11)

x	-6	-5	-4	-3	-2	-1	0	1	2
y	-17	-10	-5	-2	-1	-2	-5	-10	-17

3. $y = x^2 - 6x + 9$ (Fig. 12)

x	0	1	2	3	4	5	6
y	9	4	1	0	1	4	9

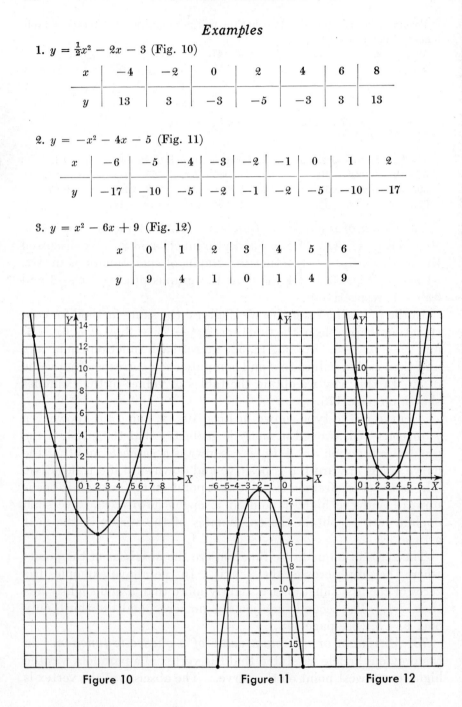

Figure 10   Figure 11   Figure 12

the value of x for which the function has the greatest or least value. This value of x may be obtained by the method of completing the square explained in Art. 63, and we shall illustrate the procedure in the following examples.

Example 1

In the function

$$y = 2x^2 - 4x + 10$$

the coefficient of x^2 is positive. Hence, the curve opens upward, and there is a least but no greatest value of y. We may obtain the value of x for which y is a minimum by the method below.

$$
\begin{aligned}
y &= 2x^2 - 4x + 10 \\
&= 2[(x^2 - 2x) + 5] \\
&= 2[(x^2 - 2x + 1) + 5 - 1] \\
&= 2[(x - 1)^2 + 4]
\end{aligned}
$$

(completing the square in the expression in parentheses by adding and subtracting the square of one-half the coefficient of x)

If the first expression in the brackets in the last line above is not zero, it is positive since it is a square. Hence, the value of y increases as the numerical value of $x - 1$ increases, and is least when this expression is zero, or when $x = 1$. Hence, the minimum value of y is $y = 2[(1 - 1)^2 + 4] = 8$.

Example 2

If we apply the above method to the function

$$y = -3x^2 - 12x + 4$$

we get

$$
\begin{aligned}
y &= -3[(x^2 + 4x) - \tfrac{4}{3}] \\
&= -3[(x^2 + 4x + 4) - \tfrac{4}{3} - 4] \\
&= -3[(x + 2)^2 - \tfrac{16}{3}] \\
&= -3(x + 2)^2 + 16
\end{aligned}
$$

The expression $(x + 2)^2$ is positive except for $x = -2$, and its value increases as x increases or decreases from -2. Hence the value of y is greatest when $x = -2$, and then $y = -3(-2 + 2)^2 + 16 = 16$.

The above method is useful for solving some types of practical problems such as the following example.

Example 3

A farmer wishes to build a rectangular pen along one side of his barn. If he has 80 ft. of fencing, find the dimensions that will yield a maximum area.

Solution

We shall let x = the width of the pen

z = the length

and

y = the area

Since no fence is required along the barn, the total length of the fence is $2x + z$. Hence,

$$2x + z = 80$$

and

$$z = 80 - 2x$$

Furthermore,

$$
\begin{aligned}
y &= (\text{length})(\text{width}) \\
&= (80 - 2x)(x) \\
&= -2x^2 + 80x \\
&= -2(x^2 - 40x) \\
&= -2(x^2 - 40x + 400) + 800 \\
&= -2(x - 20)^2 + 800
\end{aligned}
$$

Hence, y is greatest when $x = 20$, and for this value of x, $z = 80 - 2(20) = 40$. Hence the largest pen that can be built is 40 ft. long and 20 ft. wide.

EXERCISE 36

Construct the graph of the function given in each of Problems 1 to 10, and estimate the value of its zeros to one decimal place.

1. $y(x) = x^2 + 2x - 1$
2. $y(x) = x^2 + 2x + 1$.
3. $y(x) = x^2 + 2x + 2$.
4. $y(x) = x^2 + 5x + 6$.
5. $y(x) = x^2 + 4x + 6$.
6. $y(x) = x^2 - 4x + 2$.
7. $y(x) = -2x^2 + 4x + 3$.
8. $y(x) = -2x^2 + 7x - 1$.
9. $y(x) = -3x^2 + 6x - 7$.
10. $y(x) = -3x^2 - 2x + 5$.

Without constructing the graph, find the maximum or minimum values of $y(x)$ in Problems 11 to 20, and determine the number of points at which the graph contacts the X axis.

11. $y(x) = x^2 + 5x - 2$.
12. $y(x) = x^2 + 5x + 7$.
13. $y(x) = -x^2 + 6x - 9$.
14. $y(x) = -x^2 - 4x - 4$.
15. $y(x) = 2x^2 + 5x - 3$.
16. $y(x) = 3x^2 - 5x + 2$.
17. $y(x) = 4x^2 + 6x + 1$.
18. $y(x) = -3x^2 - 7x + 2$.
19. $y(x) = -5x^2 + 7x - 3$.
20. $y(x) = 6x^2 + 8x + 3$.

21. Find the dimensions of the largest rectangular pen that can be enclosed by 1600 ft. of fencing.

22. What number exceeds its square by the greatest possible quantity?

23. Divide 144 into two parts such that their product is the largest possible number.

24. A rectangular plot was enclosed and then divided into two equal parts with a fence parallel to one side. If 6000 ft. of fencing was required and the area enclosed was the largest possible, find the outside dimensions of the plot.

CHAPTER 9

SIMULTANEOUS QUADRATIC EQUATIONS

74. Introduction. The most general quadratic equation in two variables is an equation of the type

$$(1) \qquad Ax^2 + Bxy + Cy^2 + Dx + Ey + F = 0$$

in which at least one of A, B, and C is not zero. In this chapter we shall discuss the graphs of certain special cases of Eq. (1) and shall present methods for solving pairs of such equations simultaneously.

75. Graphs of quadratic equations in two variables. It is proved in analytic geometry that the graph of a quadratic equation in two variables, if it exists, is either a circle, an ellipse, a hyperbola, or a parabola (see Fig. 13). In certain special cases, the graph may degenerate into a point or a pair of straight lines.

We shall discuss the graphs of the following special cases of the general quadratic:

(a) $x^2 + y^2 = r^2$ *circle*
(b) $ax^2 + by^2 = c$ (a, b, and c positive)   *ellipse*
(c) $ax^2 - by^2 = c$ (a and b positive)   *hyperbola*
(d) $y = ax^2 + bx + c$ ($a \neq 0$)
(e) $x = ay^2 + by + c$ ($a \neq 0$)   *parabola*

As in Art. 34, the steps in constructing the graph are:

1. *Solve*[1] *the equation for **y** in terms of **x**.*

2. *Assign several values to **x**, compute each corresponding value of **y**, and arrange the associated pairs of values in tabular form.*

---

[1] If the equation is easier to solve for x than for y, we solve it for x. Then in reading the succeeding steps, we interchange x and y.

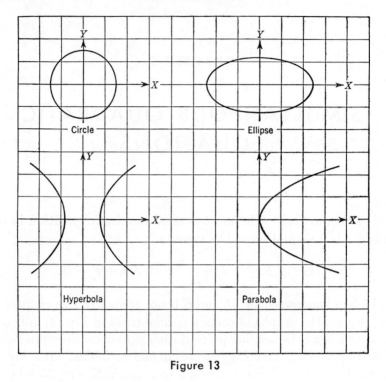

Figure 13

3. *Plot the points determined by the above pairs of values and then draw a smooth curve through them.*

Graphs of equations of the type $x^2 + y^2 = r^2$

Example 1

As our first example, we shall consider the equation

(1) $$x^2 + y^2 = 25$$

If we perform the operations suggested by the above steps, we have

1. $$y = \pm \sqrt{25 - x^2}$$

2. Assign the integers from -5 to 5, inclusive, to x and compute each corresponding value of y. For example, if $x = -5$, then

$$y = \pm \sqrt{25 - (-5)^2} = \pm \sqrt{25 - 25} = 0$$

Similarly, if $x = 2$,

$$y = \pm \sqrt{25 - (2)^2} = \pm \sqrt{25 - 4} = \pm \sqrt{21} = \pm 4.6$$

When a similar computation is performed for each of the other values assigned to x and the results are arranged in tabular form, we have

x	-5	-4	-3	-2	-1	0	1	2	3	4	5
y	0	± 3	± 4	± 4.6	± 4.9	± 5	± 4.9	± 4.6	± 4	± 3	0

3. Note that in the above table we have two values of y for each x except $x = -5$ and $x = 5$. The pair of values $x = 3$, $y = \pm 4$ determines the two points $(3,4)$ and $(3,-4)$.

With this understanding, if we plot the points determined by the above table and join them by a smooth curve, we have the graph in Fig. 14.

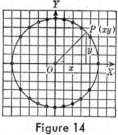

Figure 14

It may be seen readily that the curve is a circle, since the coordinates (x, y) of any point P on it satisfy (1); that is, the sum of their squares is 25. Furthermore, by looking at the figure, we see that the square of the distance OP of P from the center is $x^2 + y^2$. Hence, any point whose coordinates satisfy (1) is at a distance of 5 from the origin.

In general, by similar reasoning, we conclude that the graph of $x^2 + y^2 = r^2$ is a circle of radius r, and the graph of $ax^2 + ay^2 = c$ is a circle of radius $\sqrt{c/a}$.

Equations of the type $ax^2 + by^2 = c$

Example 2

As an example of the above type of equations, we shall construct the graph of

$$(2) \qquad\qquad 4x^2 + 9y^2 = 36$$

Solution

1. Solving for y, we have

$$y = \pm \sqrt{\frac{36 - 4x^2}{9}}$$
$$= \pm \tfrac{2}{3} \sqrt{9 - x^2}$$

2. We note here that if $x^2 > 9$, the radicand is negative and y is imaginary. Hence, the graph exists only for values of x from -3 to 3, inclusive. Therefore, we assign to x the integers 0, ± 1, ± 2, ± 3, compute each corresponding value of y, arrange the results in a table, and get

x	-3	-2	-1	0	1	2	3
y	0	±1.5	±1.9	±2	±1.9	±1.5	0

When we construct the graph determined by this table, we get the curve in Fig. 15.

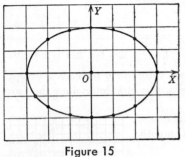

Figure 15

By referring to Fig. 13, we see that this curve is an ellipse. The proof that the equation $ax^2 + by^2 = c$, with a, b, and c positive, always defines an ellipse is beyond the scope of this book. However, the statement is true, and it is helpful to remember this fact when dealing with such an equation.

Equations of the type $ax^2 - by^2 = c$

Example 3

Here, we shall discuss the graph of the equation

(3) $$3x^2 - 4y^2 = 12$$

Solution

Proceeding as before, we have

1.
$$y = \pm \sqrt{\frac{3x^2 - 12}{4}}$$
$$= \pm\tfrac{1}{2}\sqrt{3(x^2 - 4)}$$

2. In this case, we notice that if $x^2 < 4$, the radicand is negative and y is imaginary. Hence, the graph does not exist between $x = -2$ and $x = 2$. However, if x is either 2 or -2, y is zero. Thus, the curve must extend to the right from $(2,0)$ and to the left from $(-2,0)$. Hence, we assign the values ±2, ±3, ±4, ±5, ±7, ±9 to x, proceed as in the previous example, and get the following table:

x	-9	-7	-5	-4	-3	-2	2	3	4	5	7	9
y	±7.6	±5.8	±4	±3	±2	0	0	±2	±3	±4	±5.8	±7.6

3. When the above points are plotted and the graph is drawn, we obtain the curve in Fig. 16.

Again, by referring to Fig. 13, we see that this curve is a hyperbola.

This example illustrates the fact that an equation of the type $ax^2 - by^2 = c$ defines a hyperbola. If c is positive, the curve is in the same general position as that in Fig. 16. However, if c is negative, the two branches of the curve cross the Y axis instead of the X axis and open upward and downward.

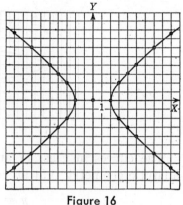

Equations of the type

$$y = ax^2 + bx + c$$

or

$$x = ay^2 + by + c$$

Example 4

By solving the equation

(4) $x^2 - 4x - 4y - 4 = 0$

for y, we have

(5) $y = \frac{1}{4}x^2 - x - 1$

Figure 16

and this is the first type mentioned above. We may avoid fractions here if we substitute only even values for x. If we use the values $-4, -2, 0, 2, 4, 6, 8$ for x and proceed as before, we get the following table of corresponding values of x and y:

x	-4	-2	0	2	4	6	8
y	7	2	-1	-2	-1	2	7

Plotting the above points and drawing the graph, we get the curve in Fig. 17.

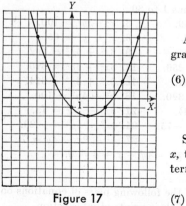

Figure 17

Example 5

As a final example, we shall construct the graph of

(6) $2y^2 + 1 = x + 4y$

Solution

Since this equation contains only one term in x, the computation is easier if we solve for x in terms of y and get

(7) $x = 2y^2 - 4y + 1$

Now we assign values to y and compute each corresponding value of x. The table below was obtained by using the values $-2, -1, 0, 1, 2, 3, 4$, for y.

x	17	7	1	-1	1	7	17
y	-2	-1	0	1	2	3	4

Now we plot the graph and obtain the curve in Fig. 18.

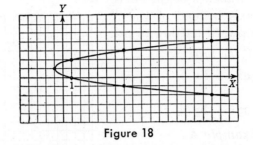

Figure 18

The curves in Figs. 17 and 18 are parabolas. It is proved in analytic geometry that an equation of the type

$$y = ax^2 + bx + c$$

defines a parabola opening upward if a is positive and a parabola opening downward if a is negative. Furthermore, an equation of the type

$$x = ay^2 + by + c$$

defines a parabola opening to the right if a is positive and a parabola opening to the left if a is negative.

EXERCISE 37

Plot the graphs of the equations in Problems 1 to 30.

1. $x^2 + y^2 = 25$.
2. $x^2 + y^2 = 169$.
3. $x^2 + y^2 = 100$.
4. $x^2 + y^2 = 13$.
5. $x^2 + y^2 = 50$.
6. $x^2 + y^2 = 65$.
7. $x^2 + 4y^2 = 100$.
8. $2x^2 + y^2 = 81$.
9. $3x^2 + 5y^2 = 192$.
10. $5x^2 + 4y^2 = 324$.
11. $7x^2 + 4y^2 = 256$.
12. $3x^2 + 5y^2 = 320$.
13. $3x^2 + 5y^2 = 192$.
14. $2x^2 + y^2 = 81$.
15. $5x^2 + 4y^2 = 324$.
16. $7x^2 + 4y^2 = 256$.
17. $3x^2 + 5y^2 = 320$.
18. $x^2 + 4y^2 = 100$.
19. $4x^2 - 5y^2 = 16$.
20. $x^2 - 9y^2 = 64$.
21. $3x^2 - 2y^2 = 75$.
22. $4x^2 - 5y^2 = -80$.
23. $2x^2 - 3y^2 = -75$.
24. $4x^2 - 5y^2 = -20$.
25. $y^2 = 4x$.
26. $x^2 = 9y$.
27. $x^2 - 2x - 4y = 7$.
28. $y^2 - 6y - 4x + 17 = 0$.
29. $y^2 - 4y + x + 4 = 0$.
30. $x^2 - 6x + y + 9 = 0$.

Plot the graphs of the members of each of the following pairs of equations on the same axes and estimate the coordinates of their points of intersection.

31. $x^2 + 3y^2 = 28$
   $5x - 3y = 14.$

32. $x^2 - 2y^2 = 7$
   $2x + 3y = 9.$

33. $2x^2 + 3y^2 = 35$
   $x - y = -1.$

34. $9x^2 - 5y^2 = -36$
   $8x - y = 12.$

35. $x^2 + y^2 = 13$
   $x^2 = 4y.$

36. $4x^2 + 5y^2 = 84$
   $y^2 = 4x.$

37. $8x^2 - 3y^2 = 5$
   $x^2 = 2y.$

38. $4x^2 - 5y^2 = -16$
   $y^2 = 8x.$

39. $y^2 - x - 8y + 12 = 0$
   $x^2 - y = 0.$

40. $x^2 - 10x + y + 16 = 0$
   $y^2 - 2x = 0.$

41. $y^2 - 2y - 4x = 7$
   $y^2 - 2y + 4x = 3.$

42. $x^2 - 2x - y - 1 = 0$
   $y^2 - x - 4y + 7 = 0.$

43. $9x^2 + y^2 = 90$
   $2x^2 + 15y^2 = 143.$

44. $3x^2 - 4y^2 = 8$
   $x^2 - 5y^2 = -16.$

45. $3x^2 + 8y^2 = 140$
   $3x^2 - y^2 = 2.$

46. $8x^2 + 3y^2 = 140$
   $7x^2 - 5y^2 = -13.$

76. Solution of pairs of equations involving quadratics in two variables. In the remainder of this chapter, we shall consider pairs of equations in two variables that consist either of a linear equation and a quadratic or of two quadratic equations. We obtain the solution of two such equations by first eliminating one of the variables and then solving the resulting equation for the unknown that remains. We then substitute this value into one of the original equations and solve for the other variable. If both equations are quadratic, the elimination of the first variable usually leads to an equation of the fourth degree, the solution of which is explained in Chap. 12. However, we shall present the method for solving several types of equation pairs which are completely solvable by the methods now available, and this will suffice until the student reaches more advanced fields.

77. Pairs of equations in two variables involving a linear and a quadratic equation. Since we can always solve a linear equation easily for one variable in terms of the other, the most logical method for solving a pair of equations in two variables in which one is linear and the other quadratic consists of the following steps:

1. *Solve the linear equation for one variable in terms of the other.*

2. *Substitute the solution in the quadratic equation, thus obtaining a quadratic equation in one variable.*

3. *Solve this equation for the variable involved.*

4. *Substitute each value obtained in step 3 into the solution obtained in step 1, thus obtaining the corresponding value of the second variable.*

5. *Pair[1] the solutions; thus,*

$$x = \underline{\hspace{1cm}} \qquad y = \underline{\hspace{1cm}}$$
$$x = \underline{\hspace{1cm}} \qquad y = \underline{\hspace{1cm}}$$

filling the blanks in each line with the value obtained in step 3 and the corresponding value obtained by using it in step 4.

Example 1

As a first example of the above method, we shall solve

(1) $$x^2 + 4y^2 = 25$$
(2) $$x \; - 2y \; = -1$$

simultaneously. The number on the left in the solution indicates which of the above steps is being applied.

1.	$x = 2y - 1$	[solving (2) for x in terms of y]
2.	$(2y - 1)^2 + 4y^2 = 25$	[substituting $2y - 1$ for x in (1)]
	$4y^2 - 4y + 1 + 4y^2 = 25$	(squaring $2y - 1$)
	$8y^2 - 4y - 24 = 0$	(transposing and collecting)
3.	$2y^2 - y - 6 = 0$	(dividing by 4)

$$y = \frac{-(-1) \pm \sqrt{(-1)^2 - 4(2)(-6)}}{2(2)} \qquad \text{(by the quadratic formula)}$$

$$= \frac{1 \pm \sqrt{1 + 48}}{4}$$

$$= \frac{1 \pm \sqrt{49}}{4}$$

$$= \frac{1 \pm 7}{4}$$

$$= \tfrac{8}{4} \text{ and } -\tfrac{6}{4}$$

$$= 2 \text{ and } -1\tfrac{1}{2}$$

Hence, $y = 2$ and $y = -1\tfrac{1}{2}$.

4. Substituting each of these values in the equation obtained in step 1, we have when $y = 2$, $x = 2(2) - 1 = 4 - 1 = 3$, and when $y = -1\tfrac{1}{2}$,

$$x = 2(-1\tfrac{1}{2}) - 1 = -3 - 1 = -4$$

[1] The graphs of a quadratic and a linear equation in two variables are one of the curves shown in Fig. 13 and a straight line. Since two such curves intersect at most in two points, we may, in general, expect two algebraic solutions for such a pair.

5. Hence, the solutions are

$$x = 3 \qquad y = 2$$
$$x = -4 \qquad y = -1\tfrac{1}{2}$$

These solutions may be checked by substituting in Eq. (1).

We shall next construct the graphs of the above equations and interpret the above solutions geometrically. If we solve Eq. (1) for y, we get

(3) $$y = \pm\tfrac{1}{2}\sqrt{25 - x^2}$$

Now we assign the values ± 5, ± 4, ± 3, ± 2, ± 1, and 0 to x, calculate the corresponding values of y, arrange the associated pairs of numbers in tabular form, and get

x	-5	-4	-3	-2	-1	0	1	2	3	4	5
y	0	± 1.5	± 2	± 2.3	± 2.4	± 2.5	± 2.4	± 2.3	± 2	± 1.5	0

When we construct the graph determined by the above table, we obtain the ellipse in Fig. 19.

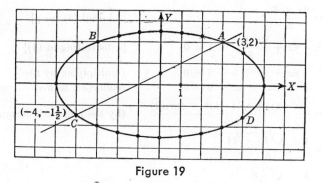

Figure 19

If we assign the values -3, 0, and 3 to x in (2) and calculate the corresponding values of y, we obtain the following:

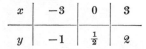

x	-3	0	3
y	-1	$\tfrac{1}{2}$	2

These pairs of values determine the straight line in Fig. 19.

The two graphs thus obtained intersect in the points whose coordinates are $(-4, -1\tfrac{1}{2})$ and $(3,2)$. We should expect this result since we obtain algebraically two real solutions of the equations.

The graphical situation offers an explanation for our procedure in step 4 of the algebraic solution. After we have found the values of one of the variables in step 3, we could find the values of the other by substituting in either of the given equations. However, if we look at Fig. 19, we see that there are *two* points

A and B on the ellipse whose y coordinate is 2.   Also there are two points C and D whose y coordinate is $-1\frac{1}{2}$.   Hence, if we had substituted in (1), we would have obtained four solutions, two of which would not be acceptable since they do not determine points on the line.   We avoid this difficulty by substituting the values obtained in step 3 in the linear equation instead of the quadratic.   Some work is avoided if we use the solved form of the linear equation obtained in step 1 for the substitution.

Example 2

As a second example of a pair of equations consisting of a linear and a quadratic, we shall solve

$$(4) \qquad\qquad x^2 - 2x + y - 1 = 0$$
$$(5) \qquad\qquad\qquad 2x - 3y = -5$$

simultaneously.   Again, the number at the left below indicates the step in the process of the solution.

1. $y = \dfrac{2x + 5}{3}$ [solving[1] (5) for y]

2. $x^2 - 2x + \dfrac{2x + 5}{3} - 1 = 0$ [substituting in (4)]

$3x^2 - 6x + 2x + 5 - 3 = 0$ (multiplying by 3)
$3x^2 - 4x + 2 = 0$ (collecting terms)

3. $x = \dfrac{-(-4) \pm \sqrt{(-4)^2 - 4(3)(2)}}{2(3)}$ (by the quadratic formula)

$= \dfrac{4 \pm \sqrt{16 - 24}}{6}$

$= \dfrac{4 \pm \sqrt{-8}}{6}$

$= \dfrac{4 \pm 2i\sqrt{2}}{6}$

$= \dfrac{2 \pm i\sqrt{2}}{3}$

Hence, $x = \dfrac{2 + i\sqrt{2}}{3}$ and $x = \dfrac{2 - i\sqrt{2}}{3}$.

4. Substituting each of these values for x in the equation in step 1, we see that for $x = \dfrac{2 + i\sqrt{2}}{3}$, the value of y is

[1] Note that (4) contains only one term involving y and it is a first-degree term. Hence the algebra in step 2 is simpler if (5) is solved for y instead of for x.

$$y = \frac{2\left(\dfrac{2 + i\sqrt{2}}{3}\right) + 5}{3}$$

$$= \frac{4 + 2i\sqrt{2} + 15}{9}$$

$$= \frac{19 + 2i\sqrt{2}}{9}$$

Similarly, when

$$x = \frac{2 - i\sqrt{2}}{3}$$

we have

$$y = \frac{2\left(\dfrac{2 - i\sqrt{2}}{3}\right) + 5}{3}$$

$$= \frac{4 - 2i\sqrt{2} + 15}{9}$$

$$= \frac{19 - 2i\sqrt{2}}{9}$$

5. Hence, the solutions are

$$x = \frac{2 + i\sqrt{2}}{3} \qquad y = \frac{19 + 2i\sqrt{2}}{9}$$

and

$$x = \frac{2 - i\sqrt{2}}{3} \qquad y = \frac{19 - 2i\sqrt{2}}{9}$$

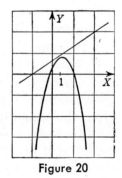

Figure 20

We may check these solutions by substituting in (4).

If we apply the usual methods for obtaining the graphs of these equations, we get the parabola in Fig. 20 for Eq. (4) and the straight line for Eq. (5). It should be noted that the two graphs do not intersect—a situation that we should expect since the algebraic solutions of the two equations were imaginary.

EXERCISE 38

Solve the following pairs of equations simultaneously for x and y:

1. $x^2 + y = 3$
   $5x + y = 7.$

2. $x + 3y = 5$
   $x + y^2 = 3.$

3. $y^2 + y = 2x - 4$
   $x - 4y = 6.$

4. $x^2 - 2x + 4y + 1 = 0$
   $2x - y = 7.$

5. $x^2 + y^2 = 25$
   $x - y = -1.$

6. $x^2 + y^2 = 13$
   $x + y = 1.$

7. $x^2 + y^2 = 17$
   $3x - 5y = -17.$

8. $x^2 + y^2 = 20$
   $3x - y = 10.$

9. $8x^2 + 5y^2 = 77$
   $4x - y = 11.$

10. $3x^2 + 16y^2 = 91$
    $x + 8y = 13.$

11. $3x^2 + 2y^2 = 35$
    $3x - 2y = -5.$

12. $2x^2 + y^2 = 33$
    $2x + 3y = -11.$

13. $3x^2 - 16y^2 = 11$
    $3x - 8y = 1.$

14. $7x^2 - 12y^2 = -80$
    $x + 6y = 20.$

15. $3x^2 - 20y^2 = 28$
    $3x - 10y = 2.$

16. $20x^2 - 7y^2 = 68$
    $10x - 7y = 2.$

17. $7y^2 - 12x - 19y = 0$
    $3x - 4y = -7.$

18. $12y^2 - 5x - 11y - 11 = 0$
    $x - 5y = -7.$

19. $7x^2 + x - 6y - 6 = 0$
    $4x - 3y = -4.$

20. $7x^2 - 11x - 6y - 6 = 0$
    $x - 2y = -5.$

21. $x^2 + 2y^2 + 3xy + x = 2$
    $2x + 5y = -4.$

22. $x^2 + 2xy - x - y + 1 = 0$
    $2x + 3y = 1.$

23. $6x^2 - 12xy - 5y^2 - 5x - 5 = 0$
    $x + 3y = -5.$

24. $x^2 + xy + 2x - 3y + 1 = 0$
    $x - y = -1.$

25. $2x^2 - 3y^2 = -a^2$
    $2x + y = 3a.$

26. $ax^2 - b^2(a + b)y + a^2b^3 = 0$
    $ax - by = 0.$

27. $ay^2 - (a + 2b)x + 2a^2b = 0$
    $x - ay = 0.$

28. $x^2 - 2y^2 = -a^2 + 2b^2$
    $x + 2y = a.$

29. $a^2x^2 - abxy + b^2y^2 = a^2 + 3b^2$
    $ax + by = 2a.$

30. $b^2x^2 - 2b^2xy - a^2y^2 = b^2$
    $bx - ay = b.$

31. $ax - by = -b^2$
    $xy - ay = -ab.$

32. $x^2 + xy + y^2 = 3a^2 + b^2$
    $x + y = 2a.$

78. *Elimination by addition or subtraction.* If one of the unknowns occurs in only one term of each member of a pair of quadratic equations and if these two terms are of the same type, then they may be eliminated by addition or subtraction.

This method can always be applied to two equations of the type $ax^2 + by^2 = c$. As we pointed out in Art. 75, the graph of an equation of the type $ax^2 + by^2 = c$ is either a circle, an ellipse, or a hyperbola, and in each case the center[1] is at the origin. Except when there are points of tangency, two such curves, whether they are different in nature or are of the same kind, intersect either in four points or not at all. If two such curves are tangent to each other at one point, they are also tangent to each other at another point. Hence, we may expect four solutions when two such equations are solved simultaneously. Either all four solutions are real, or all of them are imaginary. If there are points of tangency, we have two pairs of equal solutions. We shall illustrate each case by means of an example.

[1] The center of an ellipse is the intersection of the longest and shortest chords that can be drawn in it. The center of a hyperbola is the mid-point of the shortest line that can be drawn from one branch of the curve to the other.

Example 1

Solve the equations

(1) $$x^2 + 4y^2 = 36$$
(2) $$2x^2 - y^2 = 8$$

simultaneously.

Solution

We can solve Eqs. (1) and (2) simultaneously by first eliminating either x^2 or y^2 by addition or subtraction.   We shall eliminate y^2 and then complete the solution by the method below.

(1) $$x^2 + 4y^2 = 36$$
(3) $$8x^2 - 4y^2 = 32 \qquad \text{[Eq. (2) } \times 4]$$
(4) $$9x^2 \qquad\quad = 68 \qquad \text{[Eq. (1) + Eq. (3)]}$$
$$x^2 = \tfrac{68}{9} \qquad \text{[solving (4) for } x^2]$$
$$x = \pm \sqrt{\tfrac{68}{9}}$$
$$= \pm \tfrac{2}{3} \sqrt{17}$$

Hence, $x = \tfrac{2}{3} \sqrt{17}$ and $x = -\tfrac{2}{3} \sqrt{17}$.   The square of each of these values is $\tfrac{68}{9}$. Thus, when we substitute either of them in (1), we get

(5) $$\tfrac{68}{9} + 4y^2 = 36$$

Solving (5) for y, we get

$$68 + 36y^2 = 324 \qquad \text{(clearing of fractions)}$$
$$36y^2 = 324 - 68$$
$$36y^2 = 256$$
$$y^2 = \tfrac{256}{36}$$
$$= \tfrac{64}{9}$$

Hence,

$$y = \pm \tfrac{8}{3}$$

Thus, if x is either $\tfrac{2}{3} \sqrt{17}$ or $-\tfrac{2}{3} \sqrt{17}$, y is both $\tfrac{8}{3}$ and $-\tfrac{8}{3}$.   Thus, the solutions of the given pair of equations are

$$x = \tfrac{2}{3} \sqrt{17} \qquad y = \tfrac{8}{3}$$
$$x = \tfrac{2}{3} \sqrt{17} \qquad y = -\tfrac{8}{3}$$
$$x = -\tfrac{2}{3} \sqrt{17} \qquad y = \tfrac{8}{3}$$

and

$$x = -\tfrac{2}{3} \sqrt{17} \qquad y = -\tfrac{8}{3}$$

Since $\sqrt{17} = 4.12$ (to two decimal places), the approximate values of the above solutions to two decimal places are

$$x = 2.75 \qquad y = 2.67$$
$$x = 2.75 \qquad y = -2.67$$
$$x = -2.75 \qquad y = 2.67$$
$$x = -2.75 \qquad y = -2.67$$

If we apply the usual method of graphing to Eqs. (1) and (2) we obtain Fig. 21 in which the ellipse is the graph of (1) and the hyperbola is the graph of (2). These two curves intersect at four points whose coordinates are approximately

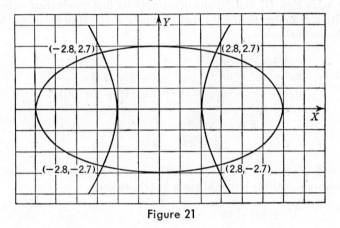

Figure 21

(2.8, 2.7), (2.8, −2.7), (−2.8, 2.7), (−2.8, −2.7). To one decimal place, these coordinates agree with the approximate solutions obtained above.

This method may also be applied to systems of equations that involve xy terms or first-degree terms, or both, provided that one unknown is involved in only one term of each equation and that these two terms are of the same type.

Example 2

Solve the equations

$$(6) \qquad x^2 + 2xy - 2x = 15$$
$$(7) \qquad xy - 3x = -3$$

simultaneously.

Solution

We shall eliminate the xy term and complete the solution by performing the following steps.

(6) $x^2 + 2xy - 2x = 15$ [rewriting Eq. (6)]
(8) $2xy - 6x = -6$ [Eq. (7) × 2]

$x^2 \qquad\quad + 4x = 21$ [Eq. (6) − Eq. (8)]
$\quad x^2 + 4x - 21 = 0$ (transposing 21)
$\quad (x + 7)(x - 3) = 0$ (factoring)
$$x = -7$$ (setting each factor equal to zero
and solving for x)

$$x = 3$$
$(-7)y - 3(-7) = -3$ [substituting $x = -7$ in (7)]
$\qquad -7y + 21 = -3$
$\qquad\quad -7y = -3 - 21$
$\qquad\quad -7y = -24$
$\qquad\quad\quad y = 3\tfrac{3}{7}$
$(3)y - 3(3) = -3$ [substituting $x = 3$ in (7)]
$\quad 3y - 9 = -3$
$\qquad 3y = -3 + 9$
$\qquad 3y = 6$
$\qquad\; y = 2$

Hence the solutions are

$$x = -7 \qquad y = 3\tfrac{3}{7}$$
$$x = 3 \qquad y = 2$$

The graphs of Eqs. (6) and (7) and their points of intersection are shown in Fig. 22.

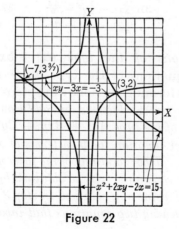

Figure 22

EXERCISE 39

Solve the following pairs of equations simultaneously.

1. $3x^2 + 4y^2 = 39$
   $5x^2 - 2y^2 = -13.$

2. $2x^2 + 5y^2 = 53$
   $4x^2 + 3y^2 = 43.$

3. $3x^2 - 4y^2 = -37$
   $5x^2 - 2y^2 = 13.$

4. $2x^2 + 5y^2 = 70$
$3x^2 - 7y^2 = 47.$

5. $5x^2 - 11y^2 = 69$
$2x^2 - 7y^2 = 25.$

6. $4x^2 - 3y^2 = 69$
$7x^2 - 2y^2 = 202.$

7. $6x^2 + 5y^2 = 341$
$4x^2 + 7y^2 = 407.$

8. $5x^2 + 3y^2 = 347$
$6x^2 + 7y^2 = 447.$

9. $24x^2 - 16y^2 = -3$
$16x^2 + 16y^2 = 13.$

10. $18x^2 + 36y^2 = 83$
$72x^2 - 108y^2 = -235.$

11. $288x^2 + 144y^2 = 137$
$36x^2 - 48y^2 = 13.$

12. $150x^2 - 180y^2 = 49$
$75x^2 - 180y^2 = 22.$

13. $x^2 - y^2 + 2y = 1$
$5x^2 - 3y^2 = -7.$

14. $x^2 - y^2 + 2x = -1$
$7x^2 - 5y^2 = -17.$

15. $x^2 + 12y^2 - 36y = 1$
$3x^2 + 35y^2 - 103y = 9.$

16. $13x^2 + 8y^2 - 58x = 8$
$27x^2 + 16y^2 - 122x = 8.$

17. $28x^2 + 12y^2 - 24x = 7$
$6x^2 + 4y^2 - 3x = 4.$

18. $5x^2 + 6y^2 + 3y = 23$
$10x^2 + 10y^2 + 3y = 44.$

19. $x^2 + 23y^2 - 14y = 1$
$3x^2 + 3y^2 + 35y = 25.$

20. $3x^2 - 4y^2 + 6y = 3$
$4x^2 + 8y^2 - 22y = -11.$

21. $4x^2 + 4xy + 3x = 15$
$5x^2 + 4xy + 5x = 18.$

22. $7y^2 + 7xy - 4y = 72$
$18y^2 + 7xy + 7y = 204.$

23. $5x^2 + 5xy + 4x = -18$
$48x^2 + 25xy - 3x = 48.$

24. $x^2 + xy - 3x = 6$
$12x^2 + 17xy - 36x = 12.$

25. $4x^2 + 2xy - 6x = 1$
$4x^2 + 4xy - 4x = 5.$

26. $x^2 + 3xy - 2x = -10$
$2xy + x = -14.$

27. $4xy - y^2 + 3y = 8$
$3xy - y^2 = -3.$

28. $5xy - 2y^2 + 4y = -1$
$4xy + y^2 - 6y = 4.$

29. $\frac{3}{2}x^2 + \frac{5}{3}y^2 = 8$
$\frac{3}{8}x^2 + \frac{5}{9}y^2 = \frac{29}{12}.$

30. $\frac{3}{4}x^2 - \frac{2}{9}y^2 = 5$
$\frac{5}{6}x^2 - \frac{1}{3}y^2 = 4.$

31. $\frac{3}{5}x^2 - \frac{1}{2}y^2 = \frac{25}{9}$
$\frac{5}{3}x^2 - 3y^2 = 7.$

32. $\frac{2}{3}x^2 + \frac{4}{9}y^2 = \frac{5}{9}$
$\frac{1}{6}x^2 - \frac{3}{4}y^2 = \frac{1}{32}.$

79. *Two equations of the type $ax^2 + bxy + cy^2 = d$.* The solution of two equations of the type $ax^2 + bxy + cy^2 = d$ may be obtained by performing the following steps.

1. *Eliminate the constant terms by addition or subtraction and obtain an equation of the type $Ax^2 + Bxy + Cy^2 = 0$.*

2. *Solve*[1] *the latter equation for y in terms of x by use of one of the methods of Chap. 8. Two*[2] *solutions of the form $y = Kx$ and $y = Gx$, where K and G are constants, will be obtained by this process.*

3. *Substitute each value of y obtained in step 2 in one of the original equations, thus obtaining two equations that involve x only.*

---

[1] The computation is sometimes easier if this equation is solved for x in terms of y. If this is done, then x and y should be interchanged in reading steps 3, 4, and 5.

[2] If $(Bx)^2 - 4ACx^2 = 0$, these two values of y will be equal. The constants K and G may involve radicals.

4. *Solve each of these equations for* **x**, *obtaining two solutions for each equation.*

5. *Substitute each solution of the equation obtained by use of* **y** = **Kx** *for* **x** *in* **y** = **Kx**, *thus obtaining each corresponding value of* **y**. *Similarly, substitute each solution of the equation obtained by use of* **y** = **Gx** *for* **x** *in* **y** = **Gx**.

6. *Arrange solutions in the form*

$$x = \underline{\quad} \qquad y = \underline{\quad}$$
$$x = \underline{\quad} \qquad y = \underline{\quad}$$
$$x = \underline{\quad} \qquad y = \underline{\quad}$$
$$x = \underline{\quad} \qquad y = \underline{\quad}$$

filling the blanks with the corresponding values of **x** *and* **y**.

Example 1

Solve the equations

(1) $$3x^2 + 4xy + y^2 = -8$$
(2) $$7x^2 + 2xy - y^2 = -28$$

simultaneously.

Solution

Step 1.

(3) $$21x^2 + 28xy + 7y^2 = -56 \qquad [\text{Eq. (1)} \times 7]$$
(4) $$\underline{14x^2 + 4xy - 2y^2 = -56} \qquad [\text{Eq. (2)} \times 2]$$
(5) $$7x^2 + 24xy + 9y^2 = 0 \qquad [\text{Eq. (3)} - \text{Eq. (4)}]$$

Step 2.

$$y = \frac{-24x \pm \sqrt{576x^2 - 252x^2}}{18}$$

[solving (5) for y by the quadratic formula with $a = 9$, $b = 24x$, and $c = 7x^2$]

$$= \frac{-24x \pm \sqrt{324x^2}}{18}$$

$$= \frac{-24x \pm 18x}{18}$$

$$= -\frac{x}{3} \text{ and } -\frac{7x}{3}$$

Hence,

(6) $$y = -\frac{x}{3}$$

and

(7) $$y = -\frac{7x}{3}$$

Steps 3, 4, and 5.

$$3x^2 + 4x\left(-\frac{x}{3}\right) + \left(\frac{x}{3}\right)^2 = -8$$ 　　[substituting (6) in (1)]

$$3x^2 - \frac{4x^2}{3} + \frac{x^2}{9} = -8$$ 　　(performing the indicated operations)

$$27x^2 - 12x^2 + x^2 = -72$$ 　　(clearing of fractions)

$$16x^2 = -72$$

$$x^2 = -\tfrac{72}{16} = -\tfrac{18}{4}$$

$$x = \pm\sqrt{-\frac{18}{4}} = \pm\frac{3\sqrt{2}}{2}\,i$$

$$y = -\frac{1}{3}\left(\pm\frac{3\sqrt{2}}{2}\,i\right) = \mp\frac{\sqrt{2}}{2}\,i$$ 　　$\left[\text{substituting } \pm\dfrac{3\sqrt{2}}{2}\,i \text{ for } x \text{ in (6)}\right]$

Hence, two solutions are

$$x = \pm\frac{3\sqrt{2}}{2}\,i \qquad y = \mp\frac{\sqrt{2}}{2}\,i$$

$$3x^2 + 4x\left(-\frac{7x}{3}\right) + \left(-\frac{7x}{3}\right)^2 = -8$$ 　　[substituting (7) in (1)]

$$3x^2 - \frac{28x^2}{3} + \frac{49x^2}{9} = -8$$ 　　(performing the indicated operations)

$$27x^2 - 84x^2 + 49x^2 = -72$$

$$-8x^2 = -72$$

$$x^2 = 9$$

$$x = \pm 3$$

$$y = -\tfrac{7}{3}(\pm 3) = \mp 7$$ 　　[substituting ±3 for x in (7)].

Therefore, two additional solutions are

$$x = \pm 3 \qquad y = \mp 7$$

Step 6.

Hence the four solutions are

$$x = \frac{3\sqrt{2}}{2}\,i \qquad\qquad y = -\frac{\sqrt{2}}{2}\,i$$

$$x = -\frac{3\sqrt{2}}{2}\,i \qquad\qquad y = \frac{\sqrt{2}}{2}\,i$$

$$x = 3 \qquad\qquad y = -7$$

$$x = -3 \qquad\qquad y = 7$$

If one of the equations in a given system contains no constant term, as in the pair

$$3x^2 - 2xy - y^2 = 0$$
$$2x^2 + xy - 2y^2 = 9$$

then step 1 is unnecessary. We apply step 2 to the first of these equations and then proceed with the other steps.

If the given system of equations has irrational roots, troublesome operations with radicals will probably be necessary in obtaining the solutions. Example 2 illustrates the method of dealing with such situations.

Example 2

If we apply the preceding six steps necessary to solve the equations

(8) $$3x^2 + 3xy + 2y^2 = 100$$
(9) $$x^2 - 4xy - y^2 = -40$$

simultaneously, we obtain the following.

(10) $\quad 6x^2 + 6xy + 4y^2 = 200 \qquad$ [Eq. (8) × 2]

(11) $\quad 5x^2 - 20xy - 5y^2 = -200 \qquad$ [Eq. (9) × 5]

(12) $\quad 11x^2 - 14xy - y^2 = 0 \qquad$ [Eq. (10) + Eq. (11)]

$$y = \frac{14x \pm \sqrt{196x^2 + 44x^2}}{-2} \qquad \begin{array}{l}\text{[solving (12) for } y \text{ by the quadratic}\\\text{formula]}\end{array}$$

$$= \frac{14x \pm \sqrt{240x^2}}{-2}$$

$$= \frac{14x \pm 4x\sqrt{15}}{-2}$$

Hence the two solutions of (12) for y in terms of x are

(13) $$y = (-7 - 2\sqrt{15})x$$

and

(14) $$y = (-7 + 2\sqrt{15})x$$

Now we substitute (13) in (9) and solve for x as follows.

$$x^2 - 4x[(-7 - 2\sqrt{15})x] - [(-7 - 2\sqrt{15})x]^2 = -40$$
$$x^2 + x^2(28 + 8\sqrt{15}) - x^2(49 + 28\sqrt{15} + 60) = -40$$
$$x^2(1 + 28 - 49 - 60 + 8\sqrt{15} - 28\sqrt{15}) = -40$$
$$x^2(-80 - 20\sqrt{15}) = -40$$

$$x^2 = \frac{-40}{-80 - 20\sqrt{15}}$$

$$= \frac{2}{4 + \sqrt{15}}$$

$$= \frac{8 - 2\sqrt{15}}{16 - 15} \quad \text{(rationalizing the denominator)}$$

$$= 8 - 2\sqrt{15}$$

$$x = \pm\sqrt{8 - 2\sqrt{15}}$$

$$= \pm(\sqrt{5} - \sqrt{3})^*$$

Substituting these values of x in (13), we get

$$y = (-7 - 2\sqrt{15})[\pm(\sqrt{5} - \sqrt{3})]$$

$$= \pm(-7 - 2\sqrt{15})(\sqrt{5} - \sqrt{3})$$

$$= \pm(-7\sqrt{5} + 7\sqrt{3} - 2\sqrt{75} + 2\sqrt{45})$$

$$= \pm(-7\sqrt{5} + 7\sqrt{3} - 10\sqrt{3} + 6\sqrt{5})$$

$$= \pm(-\sqrt{5} - 3\sqrt{3})$$

Hence, two solutions of (8) and (9) are

$$x = \sqrt{5} - \sqrt{3} \qquad y = -\sqrt{5} - 3\sqrt{3}$$
$$x = -\sqrt{5} + \sqrt{3} \qquad y = \sqrt{5} + 3\sqrt{3}$$

We obtain two additional solutions of (8) and (9) by carrying out the same procedure with (14). These two solutions are

$$x = \sqrt{5} + \sqrt{3} \qquad y = -\sqrt{5} + 3\sqrt{3}$$
$$x = -\sqrt{5} - \sqrt{3} \qquad y = \sqrt{5} - 3\sqrt{3}$$

EXERCISE 40

Solve the following pairs of equations simultaneously for x and y.

1. $x^2 + xy - 2y^2 = 0$
   $11x^2 + 3xy - 11y^2 = 27.$

2. $4x^2 - 8xy + 3y^2 = 0$
   $2x^2 + 17xy - 2y^2 = 28.$

3. $9x^2 - 9xy - 4y^2 = 0$
   $45x^2 - 69xy + 17y^2 = 45.$

4. $3x^2 + 4xy - 4y^2 = 0$
   $x^2 - 22xy + 16y^2 = 16.$

5. $3x^2 + 6xy + 4y^2 = 4$
   $2x^2 + 3xy + 2y^2 = 4.$

6. $11x^2 - 23xy - 19y^2 = 11$
   $9x^2 - 13xy - 9y^2 = 33.$

7. $x^2 - 2xy + y^2 = 1$
   $2x^2 - xy - 2y^2 = 4.$

8. $x^2 + 4xy - y^2 = 5$
   $x^2 - 2xy + y^2 = 1.$

9. $2x^2 - xy + y^2 = 1$
   $4x^2 + 16xy - 4y^2 = 5.$

10. $28x^2 + 114xy - 28y^2 = 9$
    $36x^2 - 12xy + y^2 = 1.$

---

* A radical of the form $\sqrt{a \pm 2\sqrt{b}} = \sqrt{u} \pm \sqrt{v}$, $a > 0, b > 0$, if $u + v = a$, and $uv = b$. Also, the radical $\sqrt{a + 2\sqrt{b}}\, i = \sqrt{u} \pm \sqrt{v}\, i$ if $u - v = a$ and $uv = b$.

11. $4x^2 - 4xy + y^2 = 1$
$18x^2 + 17xy - 18y^2 = 12.$

12. $12x^2 + 29xy - 12y^2 = -4$
$108x^2 - 27xy - 4y^2 = -4.$

13. $x^2 + 5xy + y^2 = -5$
$7x^2 + 3xy + 3y^2 = 25.$

14. $2x^2 + 7xy + 2y^2 = -16$
$2x^2 + xy + y^2 = 16.$

15. $x^2 + xy + 2y^2 = 28$
$2x^2 + 7xy - y^2 = -64.$

16. $8x^2 + 29xy + 24y^2 = 36$
$13x^2 + 40xy + 20y^2 = 68.$

17. $288x^2 - 45xy + 18y^2 = 95$
$36x^2 + 360xy + 36y^2 = -95.$

18. $112x^2 + 32xy + 16y^2 = 55$
$16x^2 + 96xy - 32y^2 = -35.$

19. $36x^2 + 72xy + 36y^2 = 49$
$108x^2 + 324xy - 36y^2 = 119.$

20. $160x^2 + 9xy + 27y^2 = 55$
$192x^2 + 36xy + 45y^2 = 80.$

21. $82x^2 - 3xy - 9y^2 = 80$
$20x^2 + xy - 3y^2 = 20.$

22. $3x^2 - xy - 8y^2 = 6$
$9x^2 - 94xy + 144y^2 = -24.$

23. $5x^2 - xy + 4y^2 = 95$
$8x^2 + 41xy - 32y^2 = -190.$

24. $27x^2 - 98xy - 88y^2 = -88$
$18x^2 - 77xy - 72y^2 = -77.$

25. $x^2 - 2xy + y^2 = -4$
$3x^2 - 8xy + 6y^2 = 1.$

26. $2x^2 + 3xy - 2y^2 = 50$
$3x^2 + 3xy - y^2 = 50.$

27. $2x^2 + xy + y^2 = 6$
$x^2 + 2xy + y^2 = 16.$

28. $4x^2 + 4xy + 3y^2 = 21$
$2x^2 - 8xy - y^2 = -27.$

29. $4x^2 + 4xy + 3y^2 = 30$
$x^2 - 6xy - y^2 = -3.$

30. $6x^2 + 4xy + 3y^2 = 55$
$4x^2 + 4xy + y^2 = 25.$

31. $8x^2 + 4xy + 5y^2 = 99$
$x^2 + 2xy + y^2 = 18.$

32. $x^2 - 4xy - y^2 = -68$
$x^2 + 5xy + 2y^2 = 130.$

80. Pairs of quadratic equations solvable by substitution. The method of substitution is advisable for solving a pair of equations if one of them is readily solvable for one of the variables in terms of the other, or if, after eliminating one or more terms from the equations by addition or subtraction, we obtain an equation that can be easily solved for one variable in terms of the other. The method for solving each of these cases is illustrated in Examples 1 and 2, respectively.

Example 1

In order to solve the equations

(1)
$$xy = 6$$

(2)
$$x^2 + y^2 = 13$$

simultaneously, we first solve (1) for y in terms of x and obtain

(3)
$$y = \frac{6}{x}$$

Now we substitute (3) in (2) and get

$$x^2 + \frac{36}{x^2} = 13$$

If we clear this equation of fractions, we have

$$x^4 + 36 = 13x^2$$

which is a fourth-degree equation in quadratic form, and we can solve it as follows:

$$x^4 - 13x^2 + 36 = 0 \qquad \text{(transposing } 13x^2)$$
$$(x^2 - 9)(x^2 - 4) = 0$$
$$x^2 - 9 = 0$$
$$x = \pm 3$$
$$x^2 - 4 = 0$$
$$x = \pm 2$$

We now substitute $x = \pm 3$ in (3) and get $y = 6/\pm 3 = \pm 2$. Similarly, if $x = \pm 2$, $y = \pm 3$.

Hence, the solutions are

$$x = 3 \qquad y = 2$$
$$x = -3 \qquad y = -2$$
$$x = 2 \qquad y = 3$$
$$x = -2 \qquad y = -3$$

Example 2

If, in the equations

$$(4) \qquad \qquad x^2 + y^2 + \ x - 2y = 9$$
$$(5) \qquad \qquad x^2 + y^2 - 2x \qquad = 1$$

we subtract (5) from (4), we get

$$(6) \qquad \qquad 3x - 2y = 8$$

This is a linear equation, and if we solve it for x in terms of y, we get

$$(7) \qquad \qquad x = \frac{2y + 8}{3}$$

Now, we substitute this value for x in (5) and obtain

$$(8) \qquad \left(\frac{2y + 8}{3}\right)^2 + y^2 - 2\left(\frac{2y + 8}{3}\right) = 1$$

and we can complete the solution by performing the following operations.

$$\frac{4y^2 + 32y + 64}{9} + y^2 - \frac{4y + 16}{3} = 1 \qquad \text{[performing the indicated operations in (8)]}$$

$$4y^2 + 32y + 64 + 9y^2 - 12y - 48 = 9 \qquad \text{(clearing of fractions)}$$

$$13y^2 + 20y + 7 = 0 \qquad \text{(transposing and collecting terms)}$$

$$y = \frac{-20 \pm \sqrt{400 - 364}}{26} \qquad \text{(solving for } y \text{ by the quadratic formula)}$$

$$= \frac{-20 \pm \sqrt{36}}{26}$$

$$= \frac{-20 \pm 6}{26}$$

$$= -1 \text{ and } -1\tfrac{7}{13}$$

Substituting these values in (7), we have

$$x = \frac{-2 + 8}{3} = \frac{6}{3}$$

$$= 2 \quad \text{(when } y = -1)$$

and

$$x = \frac{-\frac{14}{13} + 8}{3}$$

$$= \frac{-14 + 104}{39} = \frac{90}{39}$$

$$= \frac{30}{13} \quad \text{(when } y = -\frac{7}{13})$$

Hence, the solutions are

$$x = 2 \qquad y = -1$$
$$x = \frac{30}{13} \qquad y = -\frac{7}{13}$$

81. Symmetric equations. An equation is symmetric in two variables if the equation is not altered when the two variables are interchanged. For example, if in equation

$$x^2 + y^2 + 2xy + x + y = 2$$

we change x to y and y to x, we obtain the same equation. The solution of two such equations is simplified by first substituting $u + v$ for x and $u - v$ for y, and then solving the resulting equations for u and v. We then add v to u to get x, and subtract v from u to get y. The method is illustrated in the following example.

Example

Solve the equations

(1) $$x^2 + y^2 + 3xy + x + y = -4$$
(2) $$4xy + x + y = -23$$

simultaneously.

Solution

We first let

(3) $$x = u + v$$
(4) $$y = u - v$$

then substitute these values in (1) and get

$$u^2 + 2uv + v^2 + u^2 - 2uv + v^2 + 3u^2 - 3v^2 + u + v + u - v = -4$$

Collecting terms, we have

$$5u^2 - v^2 + 2u = -4$$

Similarly, from (2), we obtain

$$4u^2 - 4v^2 + u + v + u - v = -23$$

or

$$4u^2 - 4v^2 + 2u = -23$$

Hence, we have the two following equations in u and v.

(5) $5u^2 - v^2 + 2u = -4$
(6) $4u^2 - 4v^2 + 2u = -23$

Each of these equations involves v in only one term, and these terms can be eliminated by addition. Then the solution can be completed. The remainder of the solution follows.

(7) $20u^2 - 4v^2 + 8u = -16$ [Eq. (5) × 4]
(6) $\underline{4u^2 - 4v^2 + 2u = -23}$ [Eq. (6) recopied]
          $16u^2 \qquad + 6u = 7$ [Eq. (7) − Eq. (6)]
          $16u^2 + 6u - 7 = 0$ (transposing 7)

$$u = \frac{-6 \pm \sqrt{36 + 448}}{32} \qquad \text{(by the quadratic formula)}$$

$$u = \frac{-6 \pm 22}{32} = \frac{16}{32} \text{ and } -\frac{28}{32}$$

Hence, $u = \frac{1}{2}$, and $u = -\frac{7}{8}$.

Now we substitute $\frac{1}{2}$ for u in (6) and get

$$4(\tfrac{1}{4}) - 4v^2 + 2(\tfrac{1}{2}) = -23$$

or

$$1 - 4v^2 + 1 = -23$$
$$-4v^2 = -25$$
$$v^2 = \tfrac{25}{4}$$
$$v = \pm \tfrac{5}{2}$$

Hence, two solutions of (5) and (6) are

$$u = \tfrac{1}{2} \qquad v = \tfrac{5}{2}$$
$$u = \tfrac{1}{2} \qquad v = -\tfrac{5}{2}$$

For the first pair of values of u and v, we have, by use of (3) and (4),

$$x = \tfrac{1}{2} + \tfrac{5}{2} = 3 \qquad y = \tfrac{1}{2} - \tfrac{5}{2} = -2$$

and, for the second pair, we get

$$x = \tfrac{1}{2} - \tfrac{5}{2} = -2 \qquad y = \tfrac{1}{2} + \tfrac{5}{2} = 3$$

Next, we substitute $u = -\tfrac{7}{8}$ in (6) and get

$$4(\tfrac{49}{64}) - 4v^2 + 2(-\tfrac{7}{8}) = -23$$

Performing the indicated multiplication and clearing of fractions, we have

$$196 - 256v^2 - 112 = -1472$$

Transposing and collecting, we obtain

$$-256v^2 = -1556$$

Hence,

$$v^2 = \frac{1556}{256} = \frac{389}{64}$$

$$v = \pm \frac{\sqrt{389}}{8}$$

Hence, two additional solutions of (5) and (6) are

$$u = -\frac{7}{8} \qquad v = \frac{\sqrt{389}}{8}$$

$$u = -\frac{7}{8} \qquad v = -\frac{\sqrt{389}}{8}$$

When these values are substituted successively in (3) and (4), we obtain

$$x = -\frac{7}{8} + \frac{\sqrt{389}}{8} \qquad y = -\frac{7}{8} - \frac{\sqrt{389}}{8}$$

and

$$x = -\frac{7}{8} - \frac{\sqrt{389}}{8} \qquad y = -\frac{7}{8} + \frac{\sqrt{389}}{8}$$

Hence, the four simultaneous solutions of (1) and (2) are

$$x = 3 \qquad\qquad y = -2$$
$$x = -2 \qquad\qquad y = 3$$
$$x = \tfrac{1}{8}(-7 + \sqrt{389}) \qquad y = \tfrac{1}{8}(-7 - \sqrt{389})$$
$$x = \tfrac{1}{8}(-7 - \sqrt{389}) \qquad y = \tfrac{1}{8}(-7 + \sqrt{389})$$

EXERCISE 41

Solve the following pairs of equations for x and y.

1. $2x^2 - 7x - 5y = 2$
   $x^2 \qquad\quad + y = 8.$

2. $y^2 + 8x + 16y = 1$
   $7y^2 - 8x \qquad\quad = 23.$

3. $x^2 + 2x - 14y = 1$
   $x^2 \qquad - 10y = -1.$

4. $18y^2 - 56x + 57y = 18$
   $45y^2 - 64x \qquad = -12.$

5. $4x^2 + 9y^2 = 37$
   $xy = 1.$

6. $x^2 + 4y^2 = 25$
   $xy = -6.$

7. $4x^2 + 144y^2 = 153$
   $2xy = -3.$

8. $576x^2 + y^2 = 45$
   $4xy = -3.$

9. $10x^2 - y^2 = 4$
   $3x^2 - 2y = 0.$

10. $5x^2 - 4y^2 = 4$
    $2y = x^2.$

11. $37x^2 - y^2 = 4$
    $3x^2 \qquad = y.$

12. $4x^2 - 45y^2 = -144$
    $4x = 3y^2.$

13. $11x + xy = 48$
    $11y - 4xy = -5.$

14. $14x + xy = 60$
    $28y - 5xy = 8.$

15. $28x + 24xy = 9$
    $21y - 36xy = 4.$

16. $24x - 3xy = 10$
    $4y - 5xy = 2.$

17. $7xy - x - 11y = 7$
    $xy - x - 2y = -2.$

18. $xy - 8x + 7y = 1$
    $8xy - 19x - 10y = -10.$

19. $8xy + 11x - 14y = 8$
$2xy - 11x - 20y = -20.$

20. $10xy - 12x - y = 10$
$8xy - 14x - 3y = -3.$

21. $x^2 + y^2 + 12x - 24y = 1$
$x^2 + y^2 - 11x - y = -22.$

22. $x^2 + y^2 + 4x + 12y = 1$
$x^2 + y^2 - 9x - y = -12.$

23. $x^2 + y^2 - x + 11y + 18 = 0$
$x^2 + y^2 - 20x - 8y - 1 = 0.$

24. $2x^2 + 2y^2 + 9x - 37y = 2$
$x^2 + y^2 - 13x - y = -34.$

25. $2x^2 + 2y^2 + 7xy = -16$
$2x + 2y - 3xy = 20.$

26. $17x^2 + 17y^2 + 29xy = 143$
$17x + 17y - xy = 49.$

27. $x^2 + y^2 - 15x - 15y = 40$
$3x^2 + 3y^2 + 5xy = 15.$

28. $4x^2 + 4y^2 - 29x - 29y = -19$
$13x^2 + 13y^2 + 58xy = -11.$

29. $2x^2 + 2y^2 - 5x - 5y = 30$
$4xy + 5x + 5y = -22.$

30. $12x^2 + 12y^2 - 5x - 5y = 5$
$24xy - 5x - 5y = -7.$

31. $2x^2 + 3xy + 2y^2 + 2x + 2y = 6$
$x^2 + y^2 + 4x + 4y = 9.$

32. $x^2 + 3xy + y^2 + x + y = 2$
$x^2 + y^2 - 2x - 2y = 23.$

EXERCISE 42

1. Find two numbers whose sum is 56 and whose product is 768.

2. Find two numbers whose product is 270 and whose quotient is 1.2.

3. The sum of two numbers is 17, and the sum of their squares is 145. Find the numbers.

4. The sum of two numbers is 19, and the difference of their squares is 57. Find the numbers.

5. The area of a rectangle is 224 sq. yd. Find the dimensions if the lengths of the sides differ by 2 yd.

6. Find the dimensions of a rectangle if its diagonal is 10 ft. in length and its area is 48 sq. ft.

7. Find the lengths of the sides of a right triangle if its area is 30 sq. ft. and its hypotenuse is 13 ft. in length.

8. A group of citizens decided to donate playground equipment to the community school. Before the order was delivered, two more men entered the project and thereby reduced the cost of each share by $15. If the price of the equipment was $360, find the number of men that were in the project at the start and the amount each expected to pay.

9. A rectangular pasture containing 3200 sq. yd. was divided into three smaller plots by running two fences parallel to the shorter side. If the widths of two plots were the same and the width of the third was twice that of the others, find the dimensions if the perimeter of the pasture was 240 yd.

10. A rectangular garden with an area of 1600 sq. ft. is surrounded by a walk 4 ft. in width. If the area of the walk is 720 sq. ft., find the dimensions of the garden.

11. A tin box is made by cutting 2-in. squares from the corners of a rectangular piece of tin containing 320 sq. in. and then turning up the sides. Find the dimensions of the sheet of tin if the box contained 384 cu. in.

12. Two circles are tangent externally and have a combined area of 80π sq. in. Find the radius of each circle if their centers are 12 in. apart.

13. A truck left A at 6 A.M. on a trip to B 200 miles away. At 7 A.M. a car left A, overtook the truck at C, delivered a message, and returned to A. Find the speed of the truck and the distance from A to C if the car reached A at the same time that the truck reached B, and the speed of the car was 60 miles per hr.

14. New Orleans is 480 miles east of San Antonio. Two planes made a round trip from San Antonio to New Orleans in 7 hr. and 10 hr., respectively, with the wind blowing at a constant speed from the west during the entire trip. If the airspeed of the second plane was $\frac{5}{7}$ of that of the first, find the airspeed of both planes and the speed of the wind.

15. A Norman window in the shape of a rectangle surmounted by a semicircle has an area of $57\frac{1}{7}$ sq. ft. and a perimeter of $28\frac{4}{7}$ ft. Find the dimensions. (Use $3\frac{1}{7}$ for π.)

16. The cost of the material for a rectangular bin with a square base and an open top was 12 cents per square foot for the base and 8 cents per square foot for the sides and amounted to $13.92 all together. Find the dimensions of the bin if it contained 156 sq. ft. of material.

17. Two circles are tangent internally, and the area between them is 28π sq. in. If the distance between their centers is 2 in., find the radius of each.

18. A rectangle is constructed in a right triangle by drawing a perpendicular from a point on the hypotenuse to each of the other sides. If the legs of the triangle are 6 cm. and 8 cm. in length, respectively, find the dimensions of the rectangle if its area is 12 sq. cm.

19. A man and a boy whose heights are 6 ft. and 4 ft., respectively, are standing on opposite sides of a lamppost and each is 6 ft. from it. Find the height of the post and the lengths of their shadows if that of the man is twice that of the boy.

20. In the trapezoid $ABCD$, the bases AB and DC are perpendicular to AD. The side DC is 6 in. shorter than AB and 2 in. longer than BC. Find the lengths of the sides if the perimeter is 48 in.

21. A ladder 25 ft. long leans against the wall of a house and passes over and just touches the top of a fence 9 ft. high that is parallel to the wall. If the foot of the ladder is 12 ft. from the fence, find the distance from the fence to the house and the height of the top of the ladder.

22. A cotton buyer declined an offer of $15,000 for a consignment of baled cotton. Two months later, when the price of cotton had increased $5 per bale, he sold the consignment for $15,190. If in the meantime 2 bales had been destroyed by fire, find the number of bales in the original consignment and the price per bale in the original offer.

23. A man bought a block of stock for. $7500. At the end of 6 months he received a cash dividend of $1 per share and a stock dividend of 5 additional shares. He then sold the stock for $1 more per share than he paid. If the total profit on the transaction was $555, find the number of shares in the original block and the price paid per share.

24. A piece of wire 42 in. in length is cut into two pieces. One piece is bent into a square and the other into a circle. If the combined area of the two figures is $63\frac{1}{2}$ sq. in., find the side of the square and the radius of the circle. (Use $3\frac{1}{7}$ for π.)

Express the following radicals as the sum of two radicals.

25. $\sqrt{2 + \sqrt{3}}$.

Hint: If $x + y = 2$, and $4xy = 3$, then $(\sqrt{x} + \sqrt{y})^2 = 2 + \sqrt{3}$.

26. $\sqrt{\frac{17}{4} + \sqrt{15}}$.   **27.** $\sqrt{5 + \sqrt{24}}$.   **28.** $\sqrt{\frac{33}{20} + \sqrt{2}}$.

29. $\sqrt{3 + \frac{\sqrt{35}}{2}}$.   **30.** $\sqrt{\frac{7}{2} + \sqrt{12}}$.

31. $\sqrt{8 + \sqrt{55}}$.   **32.** $\sqrt{7 + \sqrt{33}}$.

CHAPTER 10

RATIO, PROPORTION, AND VARIATION

82. Ratio. The ratio of any number a to a second number b is the quotient obtained by dividing a by b. Thus, the *ratio of a to b is a/b* or, as it is often written, $a:b$, where the colon indicates division. Hence, the ratio of 10 to 2 feet is $\frac{10}{2} = 5$, and the ratio of 6 to 15 pounds is $\frac{6}{15} = \frac{2}{5}$.

If a and b are magnitudes of the same kind, then they must be expressed in the same unit if a/b is to have a meaning. Thus, in order to find the ratio of 3 inches to 2 feet, we reduce 2 feet to 24 inches; then the desired ratio is $\frac{3}{24} = \frac{1}{8}$. In such cases, the ratio a/b represents an abstract number and is the answer to the question "The number a is what multiple of b, or what fractional part of b?"

Although we ordinarily think of a ratio as an operation that involves quantities of the same kind, we frequently see a ratio expressed between magnitudes that are entirely different in their nature. For example, in physics the velocity v of a body is expressed thus:

$$v = \frac{s}{t}$$

The value of the ratio is the number of feet, or the part of s, that a body moves in 1 second. Also, the price P per acre of a farm is equal to the ratio of the total cost C to the number of acres n or

$$P = \frac{C}{n}$$

Again, the value of the ratio is the portion of C that corresponds to 1 acre.

Thus if a and b do not represent magnitudes of the same kind, the ratio $a:b$ represents a portion of a that corresponds to one unit of b.

83. Proportion. One of the most frequent applications of the ratio relation occurs in situations involving numbers that can be separated into pairs in which the ratios of the members are equal. For example, if a car is traveling at a speed that is double that of another, it will cover twice as great a distance in a given time. In fact, if S and s are the average speeds of the two cars and D and d are the respective distances covered in a given time, we have

$$\frac{S}{s} = \frac{D}{d}$$

We call an equation of the above type a *proportion*, and it is an illustration of the following definition:

Definition. *A **proportion** is a statement that two ratios are equal.* Proportions are written in two[1] ways;

(1)
$$\frac{a}{b} = \frac{c}{d}$$

or

(2)
$$a:b = c:d$$

In either (1) or (2), the terms b and c are called the *means* and a and d the *extremes*. Also, a and c are called the *antecedents* and b and d the *consequents*.

Many important relationships in mathematics and in the other sciences are stated as proportions, and hence some familiarity with them will be helpful to one entering a technical field. We shall present below several properties that are useful in dealing with proportions.

If we multiply each member of (1) by bd we obtain

$$\frac{abd}{b} = \frac{cbd}{d}$$

Now, dividing each member of the fraction on the left by b and each member on the right by d, we have

(3)
$$ad = cb$$

Hence, we have the important property stated below.

[1] In older algebras and arithmetics, proportions were usually written $a:b::c:d$.

PROPERTY I. *In any proportion, the product of the means is equal to the product of the extremes.*

Example 1

Find x if $3:4 = x:12$.

Solution

Applying Property I, we have

$$4x = 36$$

Hence,

$$x = 9$$

If we divide each member of (3) by cd, we get

$$\frac{ad}{cd} = \frac{cb}{cd}$$

or

$$\frac{a}{c} = \frac{b}{d}$$

Furthermore, by dividing each member of (3) by ac, we obtain

$$\frac{ad}{ac} = \frac{cb}{ac}$$

or

$$\frac{d}{c} = \frac{b}{a}$$

Hence, we have

PROPERTY II. *If $a/b = c/d$, then $a/c = b/d$ and also $b/a = d/c$.*
The second proportion is said to be derived from the first by *alternation*, and the third is derived from the first by *inversion*.

Example 2

If $a/b = c/d$ and $n/d = m/c$, show that $a/b = m/n$.

Solution

Since $n/d = m/c$, we have first by alternation

$$\frac{n}{m} = \frac{d}{c}$$

and then by inversion,

$$\frac{m}{n} = \frac{c}{d}$$

Hence,

$$\frac{a}{b} = \frac{m}{n}$$

We may derive two other proportions from (1) by first adding 1 to each member of (1) and simplifying, and then by adding -1 to each member of (1) and simplifying. In the first case, we get

$$\frac{a}{b} + 1 = \frac{c}{d} + 1$$

Hence,

(4) $$\frac{a + b}{b} = \frac{c + d}{d}$$

In the second, we have

$$\frac{a}{b} - 1 = \frac{c}{d} - 1$$

Simplifying, we get

(5) $$\frac{a - b}{b} = \frac{c - d}{d}$$

Now, dividing corresponding members of (4) and (5), we obtain

$$\frac{a + b}{a - b} = \frac{c + d}{c - d}$$

Consequently, we have

PROPERTY III. *If $a/b = c/d$, then $(a + b)/b = (c + d)/d$, $(a - b)/b = (c - d)/d$, and $(a + b)/(a - b) = (c + d)/(c - d)$.*

In Property III, the second and third proportions are said to be derived from the first by addition and subtraction, respectively. The fourth is said to be derived from the first by addition and subtraction.

Example 3

If $a/b = c/d$, $a + b = 60$, $c = 3$, and $d = 2$, find a and b.

Solution

If $a/b = c/d$, we have by addition,

$$\frac{a + b}{b} = \frac{c + d}{d}$$

Hence, when we substitute the given values for $a + b$, c and d, we have

$$\frac{60}{b} = \frac{3 + 2}{2}$$

or

$$\frac{60}{b} = \frac{5}{2}$$

Hence, by Property I,

$$5b = 120$$
$$b = 24$$

Furthermore, since

$$a + b = 60$$

it follows that

$$a = 36$$

If, in any proportion, the two means are equal, we have a *mean proportion*. Thus, in (1), if $c = b$, we have $a/b = b/d$ or $a:b = b:d$. Then b is called the *mean proportional* to (or between) a and d, and d is called the *third proportional* to a and b. However, if $b \neq c$ in (1), d is called the *fourth proportional* to a, b, and c.

Example 4

Find the mean proportional between 12 and 3.

Solution

If we let x represent the desired mean proportional, we have

$$12:x = x:3$$

Hence,

$$x^2 = 36 \qquad \text{(by Property I)}$$

and

$$x = \pm 6$$

Example 5

Find the third proportional to 16 and 12.

Solution

If we let x represent the third proportional, we have

$$16:12 = 12:x$$

Hence,

$$16x = 144 \qquad \text{(by Property I)}$$

and

$$x = 9$$

Example 6

Find x if 7 is the fourth proportional to 35, 28, and x.

Solution

By definition we have

$$35:28 = x:7$$

Hence,

$$28x = 245 \qquad \text{(by Property I)}$$

and

$$x = \tfrac{245}{28} = \tfrac{35}{4}$$

A symbolic statement resembling a proportion is frequently used to indicate that three ratios are equal. For example,

(6) $$a:b:c = x:y:z$$

is a short way of stating that

(7) $$a:b = x:y \qquad a:c = x:z \qquad b:c = y:z$$

or that

(8) $$\frac{a}{x} = \frac{b}{y} = \frac{c}{z}$$

If in (8) each of the ratios is equal to a constant k, we have

(9) $$a = kx \qquad b = ky \qquad \text{and} \qquad c = kz$$

From (9), it follows at once that

$$a + b + c = k(x + y + z)$$

Hence,

$$\frac{a + b + c}{x + y + z} = k$$

or

(10) $$\frac{a + b + c}{x + y + z} = \frac{a}{x} = \frac{b}{y} = \frac{c}{z}$$

Example 7

If the sides of two triangles are A, B, C and a, b, c, respectively, and if

$$\frac{A}{a} = \frac{B}{b} = \frac{C}{c}$$

find A, B, and C if the perimeter of the first triangle is 176 and if $a = 5$, $b = 18$, and $c = 21$.

Solution

It is given that

$$\frac{A}{a} = \frac{B}{b} = \frac{C}{c}$$

Hence, by (10),

$$\frac{A + B + C}{a + b + c} = \frac{A}{a}$$

Now, if we substitute the value of the perimeter for $A + B + C$ and the given values for a, b, and c, we have

$$\frac{176}{5 + 18 + 21} = \frac{A}{5}$$

or

$$\frac{176}{44} = \frac{A}{5}$$

Hence, by Property I,

$$44A = 880$$
$$A = 20$$

Then, since

$$\frac{A}{a} = \frac{B}{b}$$

we have

$$\frac{20}{5} = \frac{B}{18}$$
$$5B = 360$$

and

$$B = 72$$

Finally, since

$$A + B + C = 176$$
$$C = 176 - (A + B)$$
$$= 176 - 92$$
$$= 84$$

EXERCISE 43

In each of Problems 1 to 8, express the indicated ratio as a fraction and simplify.

1. 5 ft. to 8 in.
2. $2\frac{1}{3}$ yd. to 2 ft.
3. $3\frac{3}{4}$ yd. to 6 in.
4. $2\frac{1}{4}$ miles to 120 yd.
5. 2 weeks to 5 days.
6. $\frac{3}{4}$ of a day to 20 min.
7. $10 to 5 cents.
8. $2.40 to 3 dimes.

In each of Problems 9 to 12, find the value of the indicated ratio and interpret the result.

9. 1200 miles to 24 hr.
10. $3 to 4 doz. eggs.
11. 4080 lb. to 8 bales of cotton.
12. $5400 to 12 months.

13. The pitch of a roof is the distance the roof rises per unit of horizontal distance covered. Find the pitch of a roof if a rafter is 13 ft. in length and one of its ends is 5 ft. higher than the other.

14. The grade of a highway is the distance it rises per unit length along the surface. Find the average grade of a highway that rises 264 ft. in a mile.

15. The specific gravity of a body is the ratio of the weight of the body to the weight of an equal body of water. If a cubic foot of water weighs 62.5 lb. and a cubic foot of iron weighs 487.5 lb., what is the specific gravity of iron?

16. The density of a body is defined as the ratio of the mass of the body to its volume. If the mass of 120 cc. of aluminum is 224 g., find its density.

17. The floor areas of two corresponding rooms have the same ratio as the squares of two corresponding dimensions. Compare the floor areas of two rooms whose lengths are 19 ft. 6 in. and 13 ft.

By use of Property I, find the value of x in Problems 18 to 24.

18. $x:5 = 9:20$.   **19.** $\dfrac{5}{2x} = \dfrac{15}{18}$.

20. $2:3 = 1:x$.   **21.** $3:4 = x:7$.

22. $(1 + x):(1 - x) = 2:3$.   **23.** $(x - 1):2 = 5:(x + 2)$.

24. $9:(2x - 1) = (x - 2):3$.

25. What number must be added to 3 and to 4 to obtain numbers whose ratio is $11:13$?

26. What number must be added to 7 and subtracted from 3 to obtain two numbers whose ratio is $3:1$?

Find the mean proportional to the pair of numbers in each of Problems 27 to 30.
27. 4, 9.   **28.** 3, 27.   **29.** 4, 36.   **30.** 5, 120.

Find the third proportional to the pair of numbers in each of Problems 31 to 34.
31. 1, 2.   **32.** 4, 12.   **33.** 2, 5.   **34.** 3, 10.

Find the fourth proportional to each set of numbers in Problems 35 to 38.
35. 2, 3, 6.   **36.** 5, 9, 10.   **37.** 4, 7, 8.   **38.** 5, 3, 15.

39. If $x:y = 3:4$ and $x + y = 14$, find x and y.

40. If $x:y = 1:5$ and $x + y = 12$, find x and y.

41. If $x:y = 7:3$ and $x - y = 8$, find x and y.

42. If $x/8 = y/3$ and $x - y = 5$, find x and y.

43. If two bodies are balanced on a lever, then their weights are inversely proportional to their respective distances from the fulcrum (or center of support). If two boys weighing 60 and 75 lb. are balanced on a teeterboard, how far is each from the fulcrum if they are 12 ft. apart?

44. What weight on one end of a lever 2 ft. from the fulcrum will exactly balance a force of 40 lb. applied to the other end, if the lever is 10 ft. in length?

45. If an airplane flies 525 miles in $2\frac{1}{2}$ hr., how far will it travel in 3 hr. and 20 min.?

84. *Variation.* We are continually dealing with situations involving two quantities which vary in such a way that their ratio does not change. For example, if the price of cotton does not change during one day, then at any time during this day the ratio of the amount paid for one bale of a certain grade of cotton to the weight of the bale always has the same value, and this value is the price per pound.

In such cases, the first quantity is said to vary as the second, or, stated more precisely, to vary directly as the second. Thus, if a varies directly as b, then the ratio a/b is equal to a constant. If k represents this constant, we have $a/b = k$ or $a = kb$.

Many scientific laws that deal with relations between physical quantities use the above terminology. We shall state below two such laws and show how the laws are translated into equations.

Charles's law states that if the pressure is constant, the volume of a given mass of gas varies as the absolute temperature. If we let V represent the volume and t the temperature, then the law states that $V = kt$, where k is a constant.

Boyle's law states that if the temperature is constant, the volume of a mass of gas varies *inversely* as the pressure to which it is subjected. Hence, if V is the volume and p is the pressure, then V varies inversely as p. This means that V is at all times the product of a constant k and $1/p$ or $V = k(1/p)$.

The above examples illustrate two of the three types of variation defined below.

DIRECT VARIATION. *If one quantity **varies directly** as another, then the first quantity is equal to a constant times the second.*

INVERSE VARIATION. *If one quantity **varies inversely** as another, then the first quantity is equal to a constant times the reciprocal of the second.*

JOINT VARIATION. *If one quantity **varies jointly** as two or more others, then the first is equal to a constant times the product of the remaining quantities.*

In each of the above definitions, the constant is known as the *constant of variation*.

Frequently situations involve relations that are combinations of the above types. For example, Newton's law of gravitation states that the gravitational attraction between two bodies varies directly as the product of their masses and inversely as the square of the distance between their centers of gravity. If we let G, M, m, and d, respectively, represent the gravitational attraction, the two masses, and the distance, then the law states that

$$G = k\left(\frac{Mm}{d^2}\right)$$

Example 1

The pressure on the bottom of a swimming pool varies directly as the depth. If the pressure is 624,000 lb. when the water is 2 ft. deep, find the pressure when it is $4\frac{1}{2}$ ft. deep.

Solution

If we let P represent the pressure and d the depth, then P varies directly as d. Hence,

$$P = kd$$

Now, when $P = 624,000$ lb., $d = 2$ ft., then

$$624,000 = 2k$$

Hence,

$$k = \frac{624000}{2}$$
$$= 312,000$$

Thus,

$$P = (312,000)d$$

Consequently, if $d = 4\frac{1}{2}$ ft., then

$$P = (312,000)4\frac{1}{2}$$
$$= 1,404,000 \text{ lb.}$$

Example 2

The amount of coal used by a steamship traveling at a uniform speed varies jointly as the distance traveled and the square of the speed. If a steamship uses 45 tons of coal traveling 80 miles at 15 miles per hr., how many tons will it use if it travels 120 miles at 20 miles per hr.?

Solution

We shall let

$T =$ the number of tons used

$s =$ the distance in miles

and

$v =$ the speed in miles per hour

then

(1) $\qquad T = k(sv^2) \qquad$ (by the definition of joint variation)

Hence, when $T = 45$, $s = 80$, and $v = 15$, we have

$$45 = k(80)(15^2)$$

Therefore,

$$k = \frac{45}{(80)(225)}$$
$$= \frac{1}{400}$$

If we substitute this value for k in (1), we have

$$T = \frac{1}{400}(sv^2)$$

Now, when $s = 120$ and $v = 20$, it follows that

$$T = \tfrac{1}{400}(120)(20^2)$$
$$= \tfrac{48000}{400} = 120 \text{ tons}$$

Example 3

If the volume of a mass of gas at a given temperature is 56 cu. in. when the pressure is 18 lb., use Boyle's law to find the volume when the pressure is 16 lb.

Solution

Boyle's law states that the volume varies inversely as the pressure.   Hence, if we let

$$V = \text{the volume}$$

and

$$p = \text{the pressure}$$

we have

(2) $V = k\left(\dfrac{1}{p}\right)$ (by the definition of inverse variation)

Thus, if $V = 56$ when p is 18, we have

$$56 = k(\tfrac{1}{18})$$

Therefore,

$$k = (56)(18)$$
$$= 1008$$

Now we substitute this value for k in (2) and get

$$V = 1008 \left(\dfrac{1}{p}\right)$$

Hence, when $p = 16$, we have

$$V = 1008(\tfrac{1}{16}) = 63 \text{ cu. in.}$$

Example 4

The safe load for a horizontal beam supported at both ends varies jointly as the breadth and the square of the depth, and inversely as the distance between the supports.   If a 4- by 6-in. beam 15 ft. long supports 1470 lb. when standing on edge, what is the safe load if the beam is turned on its side?

Solution

If we let

$$L = \text{the load}$$
$$w = \text{the width}$$
$$d = \text{the depth}$$

and

$$l = \text{the distance between supports}$$

we have

(3)
$$L = k \left(\frac{wd^2}{l} \right)$$

When the beam is on its edge, $w = 4$, $d = 6$, $l = 15$, and $L = 1470$. After substituting these values in (3), we have

$$1470 = k \left[\frac{(4)(6^2)}{15} \right]$$

Hence,

$$22,050 = 144k$$

and

$$k = \frac{22050}{144}$$
$$= \frac{1225}{8}$$

Now, if the beam is turned on its side, $w = 6$, $d = 4$, and $l = 15$. If we substitute these values and the value of k in (3), we have

$$L = \left[\frac{1225}{8} \right] \left[\frac{(6)(4^2)}{15} \right]$$
$$= \left[\frac{1225}{8} \right] \left[\frac{(6)(16)}{15} \right]$$
$$= 980 \text{ lb.}$$

Problems that can be solved by the methods illustrated in the above examples consist of three parts. First, we have a statement of the law that operates in the problem from which we can write the equation of variation. Second, we have a set of data that enables us to find the value of the constant of variation. Third, we have another set of data in which all but one of the quantities in the problem are given. Using the information contained in the first two parts, we can find the unknown quantity in the third.

EXERCISE 44

1. Express the following statements as equations: (a) m varies directly as n; (b) s varies inversely as t; (c) r varies jointly as s and m; (d) w varies directly as x and inversely as the square of y.

2. If y varies directly as x and is 10 when $x = 5$, find the value of y if $x = 7$.

3. If w varies directly as x and is 10 when $x = 5$, find the value of w if $x = 3$.

4. Given that y varies inversely as x. If $y = 3$ when $x = 4$, find the value of y when $x = 6$.

5. If w varies inversely as y and is equal to 2 when $y = 3$, find the value of w if $y = 6$.

6. If y varies jointly as x and w and is 30 when $x = 2$ and $w = 3$, find the value of y if $x = 4$ and $w = 5$.

7. Given that x varies jointly as w and y, and also that $x = 24$ when $w = 3$ and $y = 4$, find the value of x if $w = 4$ and $y = 5$.

8. Given that w varies directly as the product of x and y and inversely as the square of z. If $w = 9$ when $x = 6$, $y = 27$, and $z = 3$, find the value of w when $x = 4$, $y = 7$, and $z = 2$.

9. The volume of a right circular cylinder varies jointly as the height and the square of the radius. If the volume of a right circular cylinder of radius 4 in. and height 7 in. is 352 cu. in., find the volume of another of radius 8 in. and height 14 in.

10. In comparing centigrade and Fahrenheit thermometers, it has been found that the centigrade reading varies directly as the difference between the Fahrenheit reading and 32°F. If a centigrade thermometer reads 100° when a Fahrenheit reads 212°, what will the centigrade read when the Fahrenheit reads 100°?

11. The intensity of light varies inversely as the square of the distance from the source. Compare the intensity on a screen that is 5 ft. from a given source with that on a screen 7 ft. from the source.

12. The weight of wire used for a clothesline varies directly as the length. If 25 ft. of the wire weighs $1\frac{1}{4}$ lb., what is the weight of 55 ft.?

13. The time necessary to make an enlargement from a photographic negative varies directly as the area. If 6 sec. are required for an enlargement that is 4 by 5 in., how many seconds are required to make an enlargement that is 8 by 10 in. from the same negative?

14. The amount of oil used by a ship traveling at a uniform speed varies jointly as the distance traveled and the square of the velocity. If a certain ship used 600 bbl. of oil on a 300-mile trip at 20 knots, how much oil would it use on a trip of 1200 miles at 10 knots?

15. How much oil would be used by the ship described in Problem 14 on a trip of 200 miles at 30 knots?

16. The weight of a dam of a certain design varies as the cube of its height. Compare the weights of two such dams if the height of the first is $1\frac{1}{2}$ times that of the second.

17. The wind force on a flat vertical surface varies jointly as the area of the surface and the square of the wind velocity. If the pressure on 1 sq. ft. is 1 lb. when the wind velocity is 15 miles per hr., find the force on an 8- by 10-ft. sign in a storm with a wind velocity at 60 miles per hr.

18. On the ocean, the square of the distance in miles to the horizon varies as the height in feet that the observer is above the surface of the water. If a 6-ft. man on a surfboard can see 3 miles, how far can one see if he is in a plane that is 1000 ft. above the water?

19. The exposure time necessary to obtain a good negative varies directly as the square of the f-numbers of the camera shutter. If $\frac{1}{25}$ of a second is required when the shutter is set at $f/16$, what exposure is required under the same conditions if the shutter is set at $f/8$?

20. The horsepower that a rotating shaft can safely transmit varies jointly as the cube of the radius of the shaft and the number of revolutions through which it turns per minute. Compare the safe load of a shaft of radius 4 in. which turns 1000 revolutions per min. with that of another which has a radius of 6 in. and revolves 440 times per minute.

21. The force of attraction between two spheres varies directly as the product of their masses and inversely as the square of the distance between them. Compare the attraction between two bodies with masses m_1 and m_2 that are separated by the distance d with that between two other bodies of masses $2m_1$ and $8m_2$ that are separated by the distance $4d$.

22. If the kinetic energy of a body varies as the square of its velocity, compare the kinetic energy of a car traveling at 10 miles per hr. with that of the same car traveling at 50 miles per hr.

23. One of Kepler's laws states that the square of the time required by a planet to make one revolution about the sun varies directly as the cube of the average distance of the planet from the sun. If Mars is $1\frac{1}{2}$ times as far from the sun, on the average, as the earth, find the approximate length of time required for it to make a revolution about the sun.

24. The gravitational attraction of the earth for an object varies inversely as the square of the distance of the object from the center of the earth. If a meteor weighs 100 lb. on the earth's surface, how much did it weigh when it was 1000 miles from the earth's surface? (Assume the radius of the earth to be 4000 miles.)

25. The strength of a rectangular horizontal beam that is supported at the ends varies jointly as the width w and the square of the depth d and inversely as the length L. Compare the strengths of two beams if one of them is 20 ft. long, 4 in. wide, and 6 in. deep and the other is 10 ft. long, 2 in. wide, and 4 in. deep.

26. The electric resistance of a uniform wire varies directly as the length and inversely as the area of the cross section. Compare the resistance of 100 ft. of wire of diameter $\frac{1}{16}$ in. with that of 50 ft. of wire of diameter $\frac{1}{32}$ in.

CHAPTER 11

COMPLEX NUMBERS

85. *Introduction.* In Chap. 8, we defined complex numbers and then employed them in the solution of quadratic equations. However, very limited use of them was made and practically none of their properties were discussed. In this chapter, we shall present a more complete discussion of complex numbers and shall include their most important properties.

For the convenience of the reader, we shall repeat the definition and a portion of the discussion presented there.

DEFINITION. *A **complex number** is a number of the type **a + bi** where **a** and **b** are real and **i**² = −1 (or **i** = √−1).*

The letter a is called the *real part* of $a + bi$ and bi is called the imaginary part. If a is zero, the complex number reduces to a *pure imaginary number.* If b is zero, it reduces to a real number. Hence, real numbers and pure imaginary numbers are special cases of complex numbers. If b is different from zero, we shall refer to $a + ib$ as an imaginary number.

*The two complex numbers **a + bi** and **c + di** are equal if and only if **a** = **c** and **b** = **d**.*

Example

If
$$x - 2 + 4yi = 3 + 12i$$
then
$$x - 2 = 3$$
and
$$4y = 12$$
Hence,
$$x = 5 \quad \text{and} \quad y = 3$$

86. *The four fundamental operations on complex numbers.* We find the sum, the difference, and the product of two complex numbers by using the methods of Chap. 1. For example, we

223

obtain the sum and the difference of $2 + 3i$ and $4 - 5i$ in exactly the same way that we find the sum and difference of $2 + 3x$ and $4 - 5x$. Hence, $(2 + 3i) + (4 - 5i) = 6 - 2i$, and

$$(2 + 3i) - (4 - 5i) = (2 - 4) + i(3 + 5) = -2 + 8i$$

If we apply the usual method of multiplication for finding the product $(2 + 3i)(4 - 5i)$, we obtain

$$(2 + 3i)(4 - 5i) = 8 + 2i - 15i^2$$

and if we replace i^2 by -1, we get

$$(2 + 3i)(4 - 5i) = 8 + 2i + 15 = 23 + 2i$$

The quotient obtained by dividing $2 + 3i$ by $4 - 5i$ is written as the fraction $(2 + 3i)/(4 - 5i)$ and this fraction can be expressed as a fraction with a real denominator by multiplying each member by $4 + 5i$. Thus we obtain

$$\frac{2 + 3i}{4 - 5i} = \frac{(2 + 3i)(4 + 5i)}{(4 - 5i)(4 + 5i)} = \frac{8 + 22i + 15i^2}{16 - 25i^2} = \frac{8 - 15 + 22i}{16 + 25}$$
$$= \frac{-7 + 22i}{41}$$

We call the last fraction the quotient of $2 + 3i$ and $4 - 5i$.

In general, the sum, difference, product, and quotient of two complex numbers $a + bi$ and $c + di$ are expressed by the following formulas.

(1) $\qquad (a + bi) + (c + di) = (a + c) + i(b + d)$

(2) $\qquad (a + bi) - (c + di) = (a - c) + i(b - d)$

(3) $\qquad (a + bi)(c + di) = (ac - bd) + i(ad + bc)$

(4) $\qquad \dfrac{a + bi}{c + di} = \dfrac{(a + bi)(c - di)}{(c + di)(c - di)}$

$$= \frac{(ac + bd) + i(bc - ad)}{c^2 + d^2}$$

In obtaining the quotient in (4), we multiplied the dividend, $a + bi$, and the divisor, $c + di$, by $c - di$. This multiplier, $c - di$, is called the conjugate of $c + di$, and this relationship is defined in the following definition.

DEFINITION. *Two complex numbers are called the* **conjugates** *of each other if their real parts are equal and their imaginary parts differ only in sign.*

The conjugate of a complex number is designated by placing a horizontal line segment, or vinculum, above it. Thus,

$$\overline{x + iy} = x - iy$$

Examples

(1) $(3 + 4i) + (2 - 7i) = 3 + 2 + i(4 - 7) = 5 - 3i$

(2) $(3 + 4i) - (2 - 7i) = 3 - 2 + i(4 + 7) = 1 + 11i$

(3) $(3 + 4i)(2 - 7i) = 6 + i(8 - 21) - 28i^2 = 34 - 13i$

(4)
$$\frac{3 + 4i}{2 - 7i} = \frac{(3 + 4i)(2 + 7i)}{(2 - 7i)(2 + 7i)}$$
$$= \frac{6 + i(21 + 8) + 28i^2}{4 - 49i^2}$$
$$= \frac{-22 + 29i}{53}$$

(5) $3 + 4i + \overline{3 + 4i} = 3 + 4i + 3 - 4i = 6$

(6) $(3 + 4i)(\overline{3 + 4i}) = (3 + 4i)(3 - 4i) = 9 + 16 = 25$

EXERCISE 45

Perform the operations indicated in Problems 1 to 40.

1. $(4 + 5i) + (2 + 3i)$.
2. $(5 - 2i) + (1 + 3i)$.
3. $(3 + 5i) + (4 - i)$.
4. $(7 - 6i) + (2 + 3i)$.
5. $(3 + 2i) - (1 - 2i)$.
6. $(2 + 5i) - (3 + 4i)$.
7. $(5 + i) - (2 - 3i)$.
8. $(4 - 3i) - (3 - 4i)$.
9. $(2 + 3i) + (6 - 2i) + (5 + 4i)$.
10. $(4 - 6i) + (7 + 10i) + (3 - 2i)$.
11. $(12 + 3i) + (2 - 4i) + (-10 + i)$.
12. $(9 - 5i) + (3 + 8i) + (-9 - 3i)$.
13. $(15 + 3i) + (5 + 8i) - (12 + 10i)$.
14. $(6 - 7i) + (4 - 3i) - (10 + 10i)$.
15. $(5 + 11i) + (3 - 8i) - (4 + 2i)$.
16. $(7 - 2i) + (5 - 4i) - (10 - 2i)$.
17. $(4 + 5i)(1 - 2i)$.
18. $(5 - 2i)(3 + 4i)$.
19. $(3 + 5i)(2 - 3i)$.
20. $(2 + 5i)(3 + 4i)$.
21. $(3 - 4i)^2$.
22. $(2 + 5i)^2$.
23. $(4 + 3i)^2$.
24. $(6 - 2i)^2$.
25. $(1 + i)(1 - i)(2 + 3i)$.
26. $(2 + 3i)(2 - 3i)(1 + i)$.
27. $(3 + 4i)(3 - 4i)(\frac{1}{5} + \frac{3}{5}i)$.
28. $(\frac{1}{2} + \frac{1}{2}i)(\frac{1}{2} - \frac{1}{2}i)(8 + 12i)$.
29. $\dfrac{2 + 3i}{3 + 2i}$.
30. $\dfrac{1 + 3i}{2 + 5i}$.
31. $\dfrac{4 - i}{5 + i}$.
32. $\dfrac{7 - 6i}{3 + 4i}$.
33. $\dfrac{4 - i}{1 + 4i}$.
34. $\dfrac{3 + i}{1 + 3i}$.
35. $\dfrac{6 + 2i}{3 - i}$.
36. $\dfrac{8 - 2i}{4 + i}$.
37. $\dfrac{(2 + i)(2 - i)}{1 + i}$.
38. $\dfrac{(3 + 4i)(3 - 4i)}{5 + 5i}$.
39. $\dfrac{(2 + 3i)(3 - 2i)}{2 - 3i}$.
40. $\dfrac{(5 - 2i)(2 + 5i)}{5 + 2i}$.

Find the conjugate of the complex number in each of Problems 41 to 52.

41. $2 + 3i.$ **42.** $7 + i.$ **43.** $6i.$ **44.** $6.$ **45.** $3 - 2i.$

46. $7 - 4i.$ **47.** $5 - 3i.$ **48.** $1 - 7i.$ **49.** $i(1 + i).$

50. $(1 + i)^2.$ **51.** $(1 + i)(1 - i).$ **52.** $\dfrac{1 + i}{1 - i}.$

If $z = x + iy$ and $w = u + iv$, prove that the statement in each of Problems 53 to 56 is true.

53. $\overline{z + w} = \bar{z} + \bar{w}.$ **54.** $\overline{z - w} = \bar{z} - \bar{w}.$

55. $\overline{zw} = \bar{z}\,\bar{w}.$ **56.** $\overline{\left(\dfrac{z}{w}\right)} = \dfrac{\bar{z}}{\bar{w}}.$

Find the product indicated in each of Problems 57 to 60.

57. $(3 + 4i)\overline{(2 - 3i)}.$ **58.** $(4 - 5i)\overline{(3 - i)}.$

59. $(2 + 5i)\overline{(4 + 3i)}.$ **60.** $(5 - 7i)\overline{(2 + 5i)}.$

By use of the conditions under which two complex numbers are equal, find the value of x and of y in each of the following equations.

61. $x + 2yi + 3 = 5 - 4i.$ **62.** $2x + yi - i = 6 + 3i.$

63. $2xi - 3y + 4 = 6i - 2.$ **64.** $5xi + 3i + 2y = 8 - 2i.$

65. $xi + 2y = 6 + yi.$ **66.** $3x + 2yi = 9 + xi + i.$

67. $3x + 4yi + 1 = 2xi - 5.$ **68.** $5x + 3y - yi = 2x + i.$

69. $xi + y + 4 = yi - 2i + 3x.$ **70.** $3xi - y - 3i = x - 5 + yi.$

71. $3xi + 4y + 2 = 6yi + 3x.$ **72.** $2x + y + xi = 1 + 3i + 2yi.$

73. $(x - yi)(3 + 2i) = 12 - 5i.$ **74.** $(x + yi)(1 - 2i) = 7 - 4i.$

75. $(x + iy)(4 - i) = 31 + 5i.$ **76.** $(x - yi)(2 + 3i) = 18i - 1.$

87. Geometrical representation. In Art. 2 we represented a real number by a point on a line and explained several properties

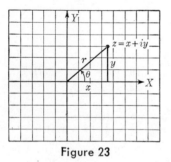

Figure 23

of a real number by means of this representation. A geometrical interpretation of a complex number is equally useful. In order to associate a complex number $z = x + iy$ with a point, we use a pair of rectangular coordinate axes; then the point that represents $x + iy$ is the point whose coordinates are (x,y) (see Fig. 23).

When used as a frame of reference for complex numbers, the X and Y axes are usually referred to as the *real* and the *imaginary* axes respectively.

If, in Fig. 23, we join the point z with the origin, we obtain the line segment r and the angle θ. We call r the *absolute value* or *modulus* of z, and θ the *amplitude* or *argument*. Thus we obtain the following definition.

DEFINITION. *The length of the line segment from the origin to the point that represents the complex number is called the **modulus** or **absolute value** of the number. The angle from the positive real axis to this line is called the **argument** or **amplitude** of the number.*

By use of the Pythagorean theorem, we have

$$(1) \qquad r = \sqrt{x^2 + y^2}$$

and it should be noted that r is always positive. Furthermore, since $\tan \theta = y/x$, it follows that

$$(2) \qquad \theta = \arctan \frac{y}{x}$$

The absolute value of z is also designated by $|z|$.

Example

In the complex number $3 + 4i$, $r = \sqrt{9 + 16} = \sqrt{25} = 5$, and

$$\theta = \arctan \frac{y}{x} = \arctan \tfrac{4}{3}$$

Likewise, in the complex number $\sqrt{3} + i$,

$$r = \sqrt{(\sqrt{3})^2 + 1^2} = \sqrt{3 + 1} = \sqrt{4} = 2$$

and $\theta = \arctan 1/\sqrt{3} = 30°$.

88. *Geometric addition and subtraction.* If we plot the points that represent

$$z = x + iy$$
$$w = u + iv$$

and

$$z + w = (x + u) + i(y + v)$$

we obtain the points designated by z, w, and $w + z$, in Fig. 24.

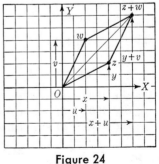

Now, if we join the points z and w to the origin and to $z + w$, we obtain the quadrilateral whose vertices are 0, z, $z + w$, and w, and it is easy to prove that this quadrilateral is a parallelogram. Furthermore, the absolute value of $z + w$, or $|z + w|$ is equal to the diagonal of the parallelogram.

Thus, we may obtain the geometrical representation of the sum of the com-

Figure 24

plex numbers $z = x + iy$ and $w = u + iv$ by first plotting the points which represent the two numbers, and then completing the parallelogram which has the origin, and the points representing z and w as three vertices. The point that represents $z + w$ is the fourth vertex of this parallelogram.

The difference of the two complex numbers z and w is

$$z - w = (x + iy) - (u + iv)$$
$$= (x + iy) + (-u - iv)$$

and we may obtain this difference geometrically by applying the above procedure to $x + iy$ and $-u - iv$. Thus we obtain Fig. 25.

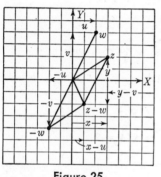

Figure 25

89. Polar representation. By referring to Fig. 23, we see that $\cos \theta = x/r$ and $\sin \theta = y/r$. Hence, $x = r \cos \theta$, and $y = r \sin \theta$. Therefore, the complex number

$$z = x + iy$$
$$= r \cos \theta + ir \sin \theta$$

Factoring the right member of the above, we get

$$(1) \qquad z = r(\cos \theta + i \sin \theta)$$

The right member of (1) is called the *trigonometric* or *polar* form of z, and it is very useful in obtaining the powers and roots of a complex number and also in the processes of multiplication and division.[1]

[1] The following facts from trigonometry will be useful in dealing with problems involving the polar form.

$$\sin 0° = 0 = \cos 90°$$
$$\sin 30° = \tfrac{1}{2} = \cos 60°$$
$$\sin 45° = \frac{\sqrt{2}}{2} = \cos 45°$$
$$\sin 60° = \frac{\sqrt{3}}{2} = \cos 30°$$
$$\sin (180° \pm \theta) = \mp \sin \theta$$
$$\cos (180° \pm \theta) = -\cos \theta$$
$$\sin (360° - \theta) = -\sin \theta$$

$$\sin 90° = 1 = \cos 0°$$
$$\sin 180° = 0 = \cos 270°$$
$$\sin 270° = -1 = \cos 180°$$
$$\sin 360° = 0$$
$$\cos (360° - \theta) = \cos \theta$$
$$\sin (-\theta) = -\sin \theta$$
$$\cos (-\theta) = \cos \theta.$$

Example 1

In order to express the complex number $1 + i\sqrt{3}$ in polar form, we notice that by (1) and (2) respectively of Art. 87

$$r = \sqrt{1^2 + (\sqrt{3})^2} = 2$$

and

$$\theta = \arctan \frac{\sqrt{3}}{1} = 60°$$

Hence,

$$1 + i\sqrt{3} = 2(\cos 60° + i \sin 60°)$$

Example 2

Express $4 - 5i$ in polar form.

Solution

The absolute value of $4 - 5i$ is $r = \sqrt{4^2 + (-5)^2} = \sqrt{41}$, its argument is $\theta = \arctan(-5/4)$. Consequently,

$$4 - 5i = \sqrt{41}\left[\cos\left(\arctan \frac{-5}{4}\right) + i \sin\left(\arctan \frac{-5}{4}\right)\right]$$

If we use a table of trigonometric functions, we find that

$$\arctan \frac{-5}{4} = 308°40'$$

hence,

$$4 - 5i = \sqrt{41}\,(\cos 308°40' + i \sin 308°40')$$

EXERCISE 46

In each of Problems 1 to 16, plot the given complex number and its conjugate.

1. $2 + 3i$.	**2.** $3 - 4i$.	**3.** $5 + 12i$.	**4.** $4 + 7i$.
5. $1 - 3i$.	**6.** $7 - 6i$.	**7.** $1 - i$.	**8.** $1 + i$.
9. i.	**10.** $-2i$.	**11.** -3.	**12.** 4.
13. $-2 - 3i$.	**14.** $-3 + 5i$.	**15.** $-5 - 7i$.	**16.** $-6 + 2i$.

Express the complex number given in each of Problems 17 to 36 in polar form.

17. $1 + i$.	**18.** $1 - i$.	**19.** $-1 - i$.	**20.** $-1 + i$.
21. $\sqrt{3} + i$.	**22.** $1 - \sqrt{3}\,i$.	**23.** $-\sqrt{3} - i$.	**24.** $-1 + \sqrt{3}\,i$.
25. 2.	**26.** i.	**27.** $-3i$.	**28.** -3.
29. $3 + 4i$.	**30.** $5 + 12i$.	**31.** $12 - 5i$.	**32.** $-4 - 3i$.
33. $2 - 4i$.	**34.** $1 + 2i$.	**35.** $-3 + 5i$.	**36.** $-5 - 7i$.

Perform the operation indicated in each of Problems 37 to 52 graphically and check the result algebraically.

37. $(1 + 2i) + (2 - i)$.   **38.** $(3 + 4i) + (5 - 3i)$.
39. $(4 - 3i) + (2 - 3i)$.   **40.** $(5 - 2i) + (-5 + 3i)$.
41. $(3 + 5i) + (3 - 5i)$.   **42.** $(4 - 3i) + (5 + 3i)$.
43. $(2 + 3i) + (2 - 3i)$.   **44.** $(5 + 8i) + (3 - 6i)$.
45. $(7 + 2i) - (1 + 3i)$.   **46.** $(8 + 10i) - (2 - 4i)$.
47. $(12 - 9i) - (-6 - 3i)$.   **48.** $(-15 - 12i) - (-7 + 3i)$.
49. $(-13 + 8i) - (-5 - 3i)$.   **50.** $(17 + 12i) - (12 - 6i)$.
51. $(11 - 7i) - (6 - 7i)$.   **52.** $(8 - 3i) - (2 + 4i)$.

90. *The product of two complex numbers.* The product of two complex numbers

$$C = r(\cos \theta + i \sin \theta)$$

and

$$C' = r'(\cos \theta' + i \sin \theta')$$

is

$$
\begin{aligned}
CC' &= r(\cos \theta + i \sin \theta)r'(\cos \theta' + i \sin \theta') \\
&= rr'(\cos \theta \cos \theta' + i \cos \theta \sin \theta' + i \sin \theta \cos \theta' \\
&\qquad\qquad\qquad\qquad\qquad\qquad\qquad + i^2 \sin \theta \sin \theta') \\
&= rr'[(\cos \theta \cos \theta' - \sin \theta \sin \theta') + i(\sin \theta \cos \theta' \\
&\qquad\qquad\qquad\qquad\qquad\qquad\qquad\qquad + \cos \theta \sin \theta')]
\end{aligned}
$$

By making use of the formulas for the cosine and the sine of the sum of two angles, we have

(1) $CC' = rr'[\cos (\theta + \theta') + i \sin (\theta + \theta')]$

Hence we have the following theorem:

THEOREM. *The **absolute value** of the product of two complex numbers is the product of their absolute values. The **argument** of the product of two complex numbers is the sum of their arguments.*

Since the product of two complex numbers is a complex number, we may find the product of any number of complex numbers by repeated applications of this theorem.

Example

In order to obtain the product of $1 + i$, $1 + \sqrt{3}\, i$, and $\sqrt{3} - i$, we shall first express each of these numbers in polar form and get

$$1 + i = \sqrt{2} \ (\cos \arctan 1 + i \sin \arctan 1)$$
$$= \sqrt{2} \ (\cos 45° + i \sin 45°)$$
$$1 + \sqrt{3} \, i = 2(\cos \arctan \sqrt{3} + i \sin \arctan \sqrt{3})$$
$$= 2(\cos 60° + i \sin 60°)$$
$$\sqrt{3} - i = 2\left(\cos \arctan \frac{-1}{\sqrt{3}} + i \sin \arctan \frac{-1}{\sqrt{3}} \right)$$
$$= 2(\cos 330° + i \sin 330°)$$

Hence, their product is

$$\sqrt{2} \ (\cos 45° + i \sin 45°)2(\cos 60° + i \sin 60°)2(\cos 330° + i \sin 330°)$$
$$= (\sqrt{2})(2)(2)[\cos (45° + 60° + 330°) + i \sin (45° + 60° + 330°)]$$
$$= 4 \sqrt{2} \ (\cos 435° + i \sin 435°)$$
$$= 4 \sqrt{2} \ (\cos 75° + i \sin 75°)$$

since the trigonometric functions of 435° are equal to those of $435° - 360° = 75°$.

We can get an approximate value of this number by using a table of values of trigonometric functions and a decimal approximation for $\sqrt{2}$.

91. The quotient of two complex numbers. As pointed out in Art. 86, we obtain the quotient of two complex numbers by multiplying each by the conjugate of the divisor. Hence, the quotient of $C = r(\cos \theta + i \sin \theta)$ and $C' = r'(\cos \theta' + i \sin \theta')$ is

$$\frac{C}{C'} = \frac{r(\cos \theta + i \sin \theta)}{r'(\cos \theta' + i \sin \theta')}$$
$$= \frac{r(\cos \theta + i \sin \theta)}{r'(\cos \theta' + i \sin \theta')} \frac{\cos \theta' - i \sin \theta'}{\cos \theta' - i \sin \theta'}$$
$$= \frac{r(\cos \theta + i \sin \theta)}{r'(\cos \theta + i \sin \theta')} \frac{\cos (-\theta') + i \sin (-\theta')}{\cos \theta' - i \sin \theta'}$$
$$[\text{since } \cos (-\theta') = \cos \theta' \text{ and } \sin (-\theta') = - \sin \theta']$$
$$= \frac{r\{\cos [\theta + (-\theta')] + i \sin [\theta + (-\theta')]\}}{r'(\cos^2 \theta' - i^2 \sin^2 \theta')} \qquad [\text{by (1), Art. 90}]$$
$$= \frac{r \cos (\theta - \theta') + i \sin (\theta - \theta')}{r'(\cos^2 \theta' + \sin^2 \theta)}$$
$$= \frac{r \cos (\theta - \theta') + i \sin (\theta - \theta')}{r'} \qquad (\text{since } \cos^2 \theta' + \sin^2 \theta' = 1)$$

Therefore the formula for the quotient of the two complex numbers C and C' is

(1)
$$\frac{C}{C'} = \frac{r}{r'} \ [\cos (\theta - \theta') + i \sin (\theta - \theta')]$$

Hence we have the following theorem:

THEOREM. *The **absolute value** of the quotient of two complex numbers is the absolute value of the dividend divided by the absolute value of the divisor. The **amplitude** of the quotient of two complex numbers is the amplitude of the dividend minus the amplitude of the divisor.*

Example

In order to obtain the quotient of

$$1 + \sqrt{3}\,i \quad \text{and} \quad 1 + i$$

we express each of these numbers in polar form and get

$$\frac{1 + \sqrt{3}\,i}{1 + i} = \frac{2(\cos \arctan \sqrt{3} + i \sin \arctan \sqrt{3})}{\sqrt{2}\ (\cos \arctan 1 + i \sin \arctan 1)}$$

$$= \frac{2}{\sqrt{2}} \left[\frac{\cos 60° + i \sin 60°}{\cos 45° + i \sin 45°} \right]$$

$$= \frac{2}{\sqrt{2}} [\cos (60° - 45°) + i \sin (60° - 45°)]$$

$$= \sqrt{2}\ (\cos 15° + i \sin 15°)$$

An approximate value of this number can be obtained by use of a table of values of trigonometric functions and a decimal approximation of $\sqrt{2}$.

EXERCISE 47

Perform the operation indicated in each of Problems 1 to 28. Express the result in both polar and rectangular form.

1. $[2(\cos 20° + i \sin 20°)][4(\cos 10° + i \sin 10°)]$.
2. $[3(\cos 25° + i \sin 25°)][2(\cos 35° + i \sin 35°)]$.
3. $[4(\cos 23° + i \sin 23°)][\frac{1}{2}(\cos 22° + i \sin 22°)]$.
4. $[5(\cos 65° + i \sin 65°)][3(\cos 25° + i \sin 25°)]$.
5. $[2(\cos 70° + i \sin 70°)][2(\cos 50° + i \sin 50°)]$.
6. $[6(\cos 85° + i \sin 85°)][3\ (\cos 50° + i \sin 50°)]$.
7. $[10(\cos 80° + i \sin 80°)][\frac{1}{2}(\cos 70° + i \sin 70°)]$.
8. $[12(\cos 65° + i \sin 65°)][\frac{1}{3}(\cos 55° + i \sin 55°)]$.
9. $[5(\cos 70° + i \sin 70°)][7(\cos 20° + i \sin 20°)]$.
10. $[7(\cos 85° + i \sin 85°)][2(\cos 95° + i \sin 95°)]$.
11. $[2(\cos 140° + i \sin 140°)][5(\cos 130° + i \sin 130°)]$.
12. $[7(\cos 170° + i \sin 170°)][2(\cos 190° + i \sin 190°)]$.
13. $\dfrac{8(\cos 50° + i \sin 50°)}{2(\cos 20° + i \sin 20°)}$.
14. $\dfrac{9(\cos 60° + i \sin 60°)}{3(\cos 15° + i \sin 15°)}$.
15. $\dfrac{12(\cos 75° + i \sin 75°)}{3(\cos 15° + i \sin 15°)}$.
16. $\dfrac{21(\cos 80° + i \sin 80°)}{7(\cos 50° + i \sin 50°)}$.

17. $\dfrac{15(\cos 20° + i \sin 20°)}{5(\cos 50° + i \sin 50°)}.$

18. $\dfrac{28(\cos 20° + i \sin 20°)}{14(\cos 65° + i \sin 65°)}.$

19. $\dfrac{24(\cos 10° + i \sin 10°)}{8(\cos 130° + i \sin 130°)}.$

20. $\dfrac{18(\cos 20° + i \sin 20°)}{6(\cos 110° + i \sin 110°)}.$

21. $[3(\cos 10° + i \sin 10°)][2(\cos 16° + i \sin 16°)][4(\cos 4° + i \sin 4°)].$

22. $[4(\cos 15° + i \sin 15°)][\tfrac{1}{2}(\cos 20° + i \sin 20°)][2(\cos 10° + i \sin 10°)].$

23. $[6(\cos 60° + i \sin 60°)][2(\cos 80° + i \sin 80°)][3(\cos 40° + i \sin 40°)].$

24. $[\tfrac{1}{2}(\cos 20° + i \sin 20°)][6(\cos 40° + i \sin 40°)][3(\cos 60° + i \sin 60°)].$

25. $\dfrac{[6(\cos 75° + i \sin 75°)][2(\cos 25° + i \sin 25°)]}{12(\cos 40° + i \sin 40°)}.$

26. $\dfrac{36(\cos 100° + i \sin 100°)}{[3(\cos 50° + i \sin 50°)][4(\cos 20° + i \sin 20°)]}.$

27. $\dfrac{45(\cos 80° + i \sin 80°)}{[3(\cos 25° + i \sin 25°)][5(\cos 55° + i \sin 55°)]}.$

28. $\dfrac{[72(\cos 70° + i \sin 70°)][2(\cos 40° + i \sin 40°)]}{[4(\cos 20° + i \sin 20°)][3(\cos 80° + i \sin 80°)]}.$

Express the complex numbers in each of Problems 29 to 40 in polar form, perform the indicated operations, and reduce the answer to the rectangular form.

29. $(1 - i)(1 + \sqrt{3}\,i)(\sqrt{3} - i).$

30. $(-1 + i)(1 - \sqrt{3}\,i)(-\sqrt{3} - i).$

31. $(-1 + \sqrt{3}\,i)(\sqrt{3} + i)(1 + i).$

32. $(1 - i)(-1 + i)(\sqrt{3} - i).$

33. $(\sqrt{3} - i)^2.$

34. $(1 - \sqrt{3}\,i)^2.$

35. $(-1 + i)^3.$

36. $(-1 - i)^4.$

37. $\dfrac{(1 + i)(1 - \sqrt{3}\,i)}{-\sqrt{3} + i}.$

38. $\dfrac{(1 - i)(\sqrt{3} + i)}{-1 + i}.$

39. $\dfrac{(1 + i)(1 + \sqrt{3}\,i)}{i(-1 - i)}.$

40. $\dfrac{(-1 - \sqrt{3}\,i)(\sqrt{3} - i)(i)}{(-i)(-2)(1 + i)}.$

92. De Moivre's theorem. If we square the complex number

$$C = r(\cos \theta + i \sin \theta)$$

we get

$$C^2 = [r(\cos \theta + i \sin \theta)][r(\cos \theta + i \sin \theta)]$$
$$= r^2(\cos 2\theta + i \sin 2\theta) \qquad \text{[by (1), Art 90]}$$

Furthermore,

$$C^3 = C(C^2)$$
$$= [r(\cos \theta + i \sin \theta)][r^2(\cos 2\theta + i \sin 2\theta)]$$
$$= r^3(\cos 3\theta + i \sin 3\theta)$$

A repeated application of this process leads to the following theorem.

Theorem.   *If*

(1) $C = r(\cos \theta + i \sin \theta)$

then

(2) $C^n = r^n(\cos n\theta + i \sin n\theta)$

This statement is known as De Moivre's theorem.

The proof of this theorem for integral values of n requires the use of mathematical induction and will be given as Example 2 in Chap. 16. At this point we shall assume that the theorem holds for integral values of n and shall prove that it holds for any rational number p/q.

Let

$$r^{p/q} = R \qquad \text{and} \qquad \frac{p}{q}\theta = \phi$$

Then,

$$r = R^{q/p} \qquad \text{and} \qquad \theta = \frac{q}{p}\phi$$

Furthermore,

$$r^p = R^q \qquad \text{and} \qquad p\theta = q\phi$$

Now

$$\begin{aligned}
[r(\cos \theta + i \sin \theta)]^{p/q} &= \{[r(\cos \theta + i \sin \theta)]^p\}^{1/q} \\
&= [r^p(\cos p\theta + i \sin p\theta)]^{1/q} \\
&= [R^q(\cos q\phi + i \sin q\phi)]^{1/q} \\
&= \{[R(\cos \phi + i \sin \phi)]^q\}^{1/q} \\
&= R(\cos \phi + i \sin \phi) \\
&= r^{p/q}\left(\cos \frac{p}{q}\theta + i \sin \frac{p}{q}\theta\right)
\end{aligned}$$

Example

Raise $\sqrt{3} + i$ to the fifth power.

Solution

$$\begin{aligned}
(\sqrt{3} + i)^5 &= \left[2\left(\cos \arctan \frac{1}{\sqrt{3}} + i \sin \arctan \frac{1}{\sqrt{3}}\right)\right]^5 \\
&= [2(\cos 30° + i \sin 30°)]^5 \\
&= 2^5[\cos 5(30°) + i \sin 5(30°)] \\
&= 32(\cos 150° + i \sin 150°) \\
&= 32\left(\frac{-\sqrt{3}}{2} + i\frac{1}{2}\right) \\
&= -16\sqrt{3} + 16i
\end{aligned}$$

93. *Roots of complex numbers.* There is no square root of
-9, no fourth root of -16, in fact, no even root of any negative
number and only one odd root of a negative number in the realm
of real numbers. However, if we employ complex numbers, we
can obtain m mth roots of any number by use of De Moivre's
theorem with $n = 1/m$.

Thus, we get

$$C^{1/m} = [r(\cos \theta + i \sin \theta)]^{1/m}$$

$$= r^{1/m} \left(\cos \frac{1}{m} \theta + i \sin \frac{1}{m} \theta \right)$$

Furthermore, if we make use of the fact that

$$\sin (\theta + k360°) = \sin \theta \quad \text{and} \quad \cos (\theta + k360°) = \cos \theta$$

where k is an integer, we have

$$C^{1/m} = [r(\cos \theta + i \sin \theta)]^{1/m}$$
$$= \{r[\cos (\theta + k360°) + i \sin (\theta + k360°)]\}^{1/m}$$
$$= r^{1/m} \left(\cos \frac{\theta + k360°}{m} + i \sin \frac{\theta + k360°}{m} \right)$$

The m mth roots are now obtained by assigning the m consecutive
integral values $0, 1, 2, 3, \ldots , m - 1$ to k. It should be noted
that the same roots are obtained if any m consecutive integral
values are assigned to k.

Example 1

Find the three cube roots of 64.

Solution

$$64^{\frac{1}{3}} = (64 + 0i)^{\frac{1}{3}}$$
$$= 64^{\frac{1}{3}}(\cos \arctan 0 + i \sin \arctan 0)^{\frac{1}{3}}$$
$$= 4(\cos 0 + i \sin 0)^{\frac{1}{3}}$$
$$= 4[\cos (0 + k360°) + i \sin (0 + k360°)]^{\frac{1}{3}}$$
$$= 4 \left(\cos \frac{k360°}{3} + i \sin \frac{k360°}{3} \right)$$
$$= 4(\cos k120° + i \sin k120°)$$

Therefore,

$$64^{\frac{1}{3}} = 4(\cos 0 + i \sin 0) \qquad \text{(for } k = 0)$$
$$= 4(1 + 0i)$$
$$= 4$$
$$64^{\frac{1}{3}} = 4(\cos 120° + i \sin 120°) \qquad \text{(for } k = 1)$$
$$= 4 \left(-\frac{1}{2} + i \frac{\sqrt{3}}{2} \right)$$
$$= -2 + 2 \sqrt{3} i$$

$$64^{\frac{1}{3}} = 4(\cos 240° + i \sin 240°) \qquad \text{(for } k = 2\text{)}$$
$$= 4\left(-\frac{1}{2} - i\frac{\sqrt{3}}{2}\right)$$
$$= -2 - 2\sqrt{3}\,i$$
$$64^{\frac{1}{3}} = 4(\cos 360° + i \sin 360°) \qquad \text{(for } k = 3\text{)}$$
$$= 4(1 + i0)$$
$$= 4$$

Hence, the cube roots of 64 are 4, $-2 + 2\sqrt{3}\,i$, $-2 - 2\sqrt{3}\,i$.

Example 2

Find the four fourth roots of $1 + \sqrt{3}\,i$.

Solution

$$(1 + \sqrt{3}\,i)^{\frac{1}{4}} = [2(\cos \arctan \sqrt{3} + i \sin \arctan \sqrt{3})]^{\frac{1}{4}}$$
$$= 2^{\frac{1}{4}}(\cos 60° + i \sin 60°)^{\frac{1}{4}}$$
$$= 2^{\frac{1}{4}}[\cos (60° + k360°) + i \sin (60° + k360°)]^{\frac{1}{4}}$$
$$= 2^{\frac{1}{4}}\left(\cos \frac{60° + k360°}{4} + i \sin \frac{60° + k360°}{4}\right)$$
$$= 2^{\frac{1}{4}}[\cos (15° + k90°) + i \sin (15° + k90°)]$$

Hence,
$$(1 + \sqrt{3}\,i)^{\frac{1}{4}} = 2^{\frac{1}{4}}(\cos 15° + i \sin 15°) \qquad \text{(for } k = 0\text{)}$$
$$(1 + \sqrt{3}\,i)^{\frac{1}{4}} = 2^{\frac{1}{4}}(\cos 105° + i \sin 105°) \qquad \text{(for } k = 1\text{)}$$
$$(1 + \sqrt{3}\,i)^{\frac{1}{4}} = 2^{\frac{1}{4}}(\cos 195° + i \sin 195°) \qquad \text{(for } k = 2\text{)}$$
$$(1 + \sqrt{3}\,i)^{\frac{1}{4}} = 2^{\frac{1}{4}}(\cos 285° + i \sin 285°) \qquad \text{(for } k = 3\text{)}$$

There are no other fourth roots of $1 + \sqrt{3}\,i$ since any other integral value of k will yield one of the values already obtained. Each of these roots can be approximated by use of a table of values of trigonometric functions and a decimal approximation of $2^{\frac{1}{4}}$.

It is interesting to note that the four fourth roots of $1 + \sqrt{3}\,i$ are equally spaced about the circumference of a circle of radius $r^{\frac{1}{4}} = 2^{\frac{1}{4}}$. This is a special case of the following general statement:

*The **m** mth roots of **a** + **bi** are equally spaced about the circumference of a circle of radius $r^{1/m} = \sqrt{(a^2 + b^2)}^{1/m}$, the argument of the first one being θ/m.*

EXERCISE 48

Raise the number in each of Problems 1 to 20 to the indicated power by use of De Moivre's theorem. Express each angle to the nearest degree. Use Table II in the back of the book when necessary.

   1. $(1 + i)^3$.　　　　　**2.** $(1 - i)^2$.　　　　　**3.** $(-1 + i)^4$.

4. $(1 - \sqrt{3}\,i)^3.$ **5.** $(-1 - \sqrt{3}\,i)^5.$ **6.** $(-1 + \sqrt{3}\,i)^6.$
7. $(\sqrt{3} + i)^6.$ **8.** $(-\sqrt{3} + i)^4.$ **9.** $(\sqrt{3} - i)^3.$
10. $(2i)^5.$ **11.** $(-3i)^6.$ **12.** $(-2)^9.$ **13.** $(3 - 4i)^3.$
14. $(-5 + 12i)^4.$ **15.** $(7 + 24i)^2.$ **16.** $(3 - 2i)^5.$ **17.** $(1 + 2i)^7.$
18. $(5 - i)^4.$ **19.** $(-2 + 3i)^5.$ **20.** $(4 - 2i)^3.$

Find the values of the roots indicated in Problems 21 to 44.
21. The cube roots of $1 + i.$ **22.** The fifth roots of $1 - i.$
23. The ninth roots of $-1 + i.$ **24.** The fourth roots of $1 + \sqrt{3}\,i.$
25. The sixth roots of $-1 - \sqrt{3}\,i.$ **26.** The eighth roots of $-1 + \sqrt{3}\,i.$
27. The cube roots of $\sqrt{3} + i.$ **28.** The fifth roots of $-\sqrt{3} + i.$
29. The sixth roots of $\sqrt{3} - i.$ **30.** The fifth roots of $2 + 2i.$
31. The fourth roots of $-\sqrt{3} - 3i.$ **32.** The square roots of $3 - \sqrt{3}\,i.$
33. The cube roots of $(1 - i)^2.$ **34.** The fourth roots of $(1 + \sqrt{3}\,i)^3.$
35. The fifth roots of $(-\sqrt{3} + i)^2.$ **36.** The cube roots of $(1 + i)^4.$
37. The fourth roots of $16.$ **38.** The fifth roots of $32i.$
39. The cube roots of $-8.$ **40.** The square roots of $-i.$
41. The square roots of $3 + 4i.$ **42.** The eighth roots of $2 - 3i.$
43. The sixth roots of $-3 + i.$ **44.** The fourth roots of $-5 - 12i.$

Find all roots of each of the following equations. Locate each root on a circle.
45. $x^4 - 16 = 0.$ **46.** $x^3 - 27 = 0.$ **47.** $x^5 + 32 = 0.$
48. $x^3 + 8 = 0.$ **49.** $x^4 - i = 0.$ **50.** $x^5 - i = 0.$
51. $x^3 + 27i = 0.$ **52.** $x^4 + 16 = 0.$

CHAPTER 12

HIGHER-DEGREE EQUATIONS

94. *Introduction.* This chapter will be devoted to methods for solving equations of the type

$$(1) \qquad a_0x^n + a_1x^{n-1} + a_2x^{n-2} + \cdots + a_{n-1}x + a_n = 0$$

where n is an integer and a_0, a_1, a_2, $\ldots$ a_n are constants. We have dealt with the cases where $n = 1$ and $n = 2$ in earlier chapters, and in this chapter we shall consider the cases in which n is greater than two.

The left member of (1) is called a *rational integral function* or a *polynomial*, and equations of the type in (1) are called *rational integral* or *polynomial* equations.

The degree of a polynomial equation is equal to the exponent of the highest power of the unknown that occurs in it.

We shall make extensive use of the functional notation introduced in Art. 32. For example, if $f(x) = 2x^3 + x^2 - 2x + 4$, then $f(2) = 2(2)^3 + (2)^2 - 2(2) + 4$, and $f(r) = 2r^3 + r^2 - 2r + 4$.

95. *The remainder theorem.* The computation involved in finding the roots of (1), Art. 94, is greatly simplified if the left member is factored into linear factors or even if one or more linear factors are found. The remainder theorem stated and proved below is useful for this purpose, and is also fundamental for the method of finding the roots of (1) when the left member is not readily factorable.

REMAINDER THEOREM. *If a polynomial $f(x)$ is divided by $x - r$ until a remainder independent of x is obtained, then the remainder is equal to $f(r)$.*

Before proving the remainder theorem, we shall illustrate its meaning in the following example.

Example

If we divide $x^3 - 2x^2 - 4x + 5$ by $x - 3$, using the method of Art. 10, we obtain $x^2 + x - 1$ as the quotient and 2 as the remainder. Note that the remainder is independent of x. In this problem $x - r = x - 3$. Hence $r = 3$. Since

$$f(x) = x^3 - 2x^2 - 4x + 5$$
$$f(3) = 3^3 - 2(3)^2 - 4(3) + 5 = 27 - 18 - 12 + 5 = 2$$

and this is equal to the remainder obtained above.

In a division process we have the following relation between the dividend, the divisor, the quotient, and the remainder:

$$\text{Dividend} = (\text{quotient})(\text{divisor}) + \text{remainder}$$

Hence, if the quotient obtained by dividing $f(x)$ by $x - r$ is $Q(x)$ and if the remainder is R, we have

(1) $$f(x) = Q(x)(x - r) + R$$

Equation (1) is true for all values of x including $x = r$. Hence, if we substitute r for x in (1), we have

$$f(r) = Q(r)(r - r) + R$$

Hence,

$$f(r) = R$$

This proves the remainder theorem.

96. *The factor theorem and its converse.* If r is a root of $f(x) = 0$, then $f(r) = 0$. Hence, by the remainder theorem, R, in (1) of the previous article, is zero, and then (1) becomes

$$f(x) = Q(x)(x - r)$$

Therefore, $x - r$ is a factor of $f(x)$, and we have the factor theorem stated below.

FACTOR THEOREM. *If r is a root of the polynomial equation $f(x) = 0$ then $x - r$ is a factor of $f(x)$.*

Conversely, if $x - r$ is a factor of $f(x)$, then the remainder obtained by dividing $f(x)$ by $x - r$ is equal to zero. Hence, by the remainder theorem, $f(r) = 0$. Therefore, r is a root of $f(x) = 0$. Hence we have the converse of the factor theorem stated below.

CONVERSE OF FACTOR THEOREM. *If $x - r$ is a factor of the polynomial $f(x)$, then r is a root of $f(x) = 0$.*

EXERCISE 49

By use of the remainder theorem, find the remainder that would be obtained by dividing the first expression in each of Problems 1 to 16 by the second.

1. $x^3 + 7x^2 - 3x - 2$, $x - 1$.   2. $x^3 - 8x^2 + 6x + 3$, $x - 2$.
3. $x^3 + 3x^2 - x + 1$, $x - 3$.   4. $x^3 - 2x^2 - x - 1$, $x - 2$.
5. $2x^3 + 3x^2 - 5x - 8$, $x + 2$.   6. $3x^3 - 2x^2 + 2x - 3$, $x + 3$.
7. $2x^3 + 8x^2 - 6x - 10$, $x + 1$.   8. $4x^3 + 12x^2 - 10x - 7$, $x + 4$.
9. $-3x^3 + 5x^2 - 2x + 1$, $x - 2$.   10. $-5x^3 - 3x^2 + 10x - 2$, $x - 1$.
11. $-7x^3 - 12x^2 + 13x + 3$, $x + 1$.
12. $-x^4 + 3x^3 + 2x^2 - 5x + 2$, $x - 3$.
13. $x^5 + 3x^4 + 2x^3 + 5x^2 - 2x - 3$, $x + 3$.
14. $2x^4 - 3x^2 + 5$, $x + 4$.   15. $16x^3 - 12x^2 + 6x - 3$, $x - \frac{1}{2}$.
16. $-3x^6 - 5x^5 + 4x^4 + 7x^3 + 3x^2 + x - 3$, $x - 3$.

By use of the factor theorem, show that the second expression in each of Problems 17 to 36 is a factor of the first.

17. $x^3 + 4x^2 - 8x + 3$, $x - 1$.   18. $-x^3 + 5x^2 + 8x + 2$, $x + 1$.
19. $2x^3 + x^2 - 7x - 2$, $x + 2$.   20. $3x^3 - 2x^2 - 13x + 10$, $x - 2$.
21. $3x^4 + 2x^3 - 7x^2 + 4x - 2$, $x - 1$.
22. $2x^4 + 3x^3 - 11x^2 - x + 15$, $x + 3$.
23. $-2x^5 + 11x^4 - 12x^3 - 5x^2 + 22x - 8$, $x - 4$.
24. $3x^5 + 17x^4 + 17x^3 + 35x^2 - 4x - 20$, $x + 5$.
25. $2x^3 - 5x^2 - 4x + 3$, $x - \frac{1}{2}$.   26. $3x^3 - 7x^2 - 7x + 3$, $x - \frac{1}{3}$.
27. $3x^3 - 2x^2 - 17x - 12$, $x + \frac{4}{3}$.   28. $4x^4 - 3x^3 - 4x + 3$, $x - \frac{3}{4}$.
29. $x^3 - 4ax^2 + 2a^2x + a^3$, $x - a$.   30. $2x^3 + bx^2 - 5b^2x + 2b^3$, $x + 2b$.
31. $x^3 - x^2(2a + 3) + x(6a - 2) + 4a$, $x - 2a$.
32. $x^3 - x^2(2a + b) + x(3a + 2ab) - 3ab$, $x - b$.
33. $x^n - a^n$, $x - a$.   34. $x^n - a^n$, n even, $x + a$.
35. $x^n + a^n$, n odd, $x + a$.   36. $x^n - a^{2n}$, $x - a^2$.

Using the converse of the factor theorem, find the roots of the equations in Problems 37 to 44.

37. $(x - 1)(x - 2)(x + 3) = 0$.   38. $(x + 2)(x - 4)(x + 5) = 0$.
39. $(x - \frac{1}{2})(x + \frac{2}{3})(x - \frac{3}{4}) = 0$.   40. $(x - a)(x - b)(x + a) = 0$.
41. $(x^2 - x - 2)(x + 3) = 0$.   42. $(x^2 - 3x - 4)(x - 1) = 0$.
43. $(x^2 - 5x + 6)(x + 4) = 0$.   44. $(x^2 - 2x - 8)(x + 5) = 0$.

97. Synthetic division. We may materially decrease the amount of labor involved in the problem of finding the quotient and remainder when a polynomial in x is divided by $x - r$ by use of a process known as *synthetic division*.

Illustrative Example

The procedure to be followed can be understood more readily by considering an example. If we use the ordinary long-division method for dividing $2x^3 + x^2 - 18x - 7$ by $x - 3$, we have

$$2x^2 + 7x + 3$$

$$\overline{2x^3 + x^2 - 18x - 7}\big| x - 3$$

$$\underline{(2x^3) - 6x^2}$$

$$7x^2 - [18x]$$

$$\underline{(7x^2) - 21x}$$

$$3x - [7]$$

$$\underline{(3x) - 9}$$

$$2$$

Now let us examine this problem in order to see what can be omitted without interfering with the essential steps. In the first place, the division process requires that each term written in parentheses in the problem be exactly the same as the term just above it. Furthermore, the terms in brackets are the terms in the dividend written in a new position. If these two sets of terms are omitted, we have

$$2x^2 + 7x + 3$$

$$\overline{2x^3 + x^2 - 18x - 7}\big| x - 3$$

$$\underline{- 6x^2}$$

$$7x^2$$

$$\underline{- 21x}$$

$$3x$$

$$\underline{- 9}$$

$$2$$

We can save space by placing $-21x$ and -9 on the same line with $-6x^2$, and $3x$ and 2 on the same line with $7x^2$. Furthermore, it is not necessary to write the variable since the problem tells us what this is. Hence, a shorter form of the work is

$$2 + 7 + 3$$

$$\overline{2 + 1 - 18 - 7}\big| 1 - 3$$

$$\underline{- 6 - 21 - 9}$$

$$7 + 3 + 2$$

Since the method we are developing applies only to division problems in which the divisor is $x - r$, it is not necessary for the coefficient of x to appear. Moreover, in subtraction, we change the sign of the subtrahend and add. This latter change becomes automatic if we replace the -3 in the divisor by $+3$. Carrying out these suggestions, we have

$$\frac{2 + 7 + 3}{}$$
$$\overline{2 + 1 - 18 - 7\lfloor 3}$$
$$\frac{+ 6 + 21 + 9}{+ 7 + 3 + 2}$$

The final step in the process is to rewrite the 2 in the dividend as the first term in the third line.   Then the first three terms in this line are the same as the coefficients in the quotient.   Hence the latter can be omitted, and the problem becomes

$$2 + 1 - 18 - 7\lfloor 3$$
$$\frac{+ 6 + 21 + 9}{2 + 7 + 3 + 2}$$

Consequently, the essential steps in the process can be carried out mechanically as follows: Write the first 2 in the third line, multiply by 3, place the product 6 under 1, and add, obtaining 7; then multiply 7 by 3, obtaining 21 which is placed under -18 and added to it; finally, multiply the last sum by 3, and add the product to -7, getting 2.   Hence the coefficients in the quotient are 2, $+7$, $+3$ and the remainder is 2.

RULE FOR SYNTHETIC DIVISION.   *In order to divide $F(x)$ by $x - r$ synthetically,*

(1) *Arrange the coefficients of $F(x)$ in order of descending powers of x, supplying zero as the coefficient of each missing power.*

(2) *Replace the divisor $x - r$ by $+r$.*

(3) *Bring down the coefficient of the largest power of x, multiply it by r, place the product beneath the coefficient of the second largest power of x, and add the product to that coefficient, multiply this sum by r and place it beneath the coefficient of the next largest power of x, continue this procedure until there is a product added to the constant term.*

The last number in the third row is the remainder, and the others, reading from left to right, are the coefficients of the quotient which is of degree one less than $F(x)$.

Example

Determine the quotient and the remainder obtained by dividing $2x^4 + x^3 - 16x^2 + 18$ by $x + 2$ synthetically.

Solution

Since $x - r = x + 2$, we have $r = -2$. Writing the coefficients of the dividend in a line, supplying zero as the coefficient of the missing term in x, and carrying out the steps of synthetic division, we have

$$2 + 1 - 16 \quad\quad 0 + 18 \underline{|-2}$$
$$\underline{\quad - 4 + \ \ 6 + 20 - 40}$$
$$2 - 3 - 10 + 20 - 22$$

Hence, the quotient is $2x^3 - 3x^2 - 10x + 20$, and the remainder is -22.

EXERCISE 50

By use of synthetic division, find the quotient and remainder when the first expression in each of Problems 1 to 32 is divided by the second.

1. $x^3 - 2x^2 + 3x - 5,\ x - 3$.
2. $x^3 - 3x^2 + 2x + 1,\ x - 2$.
3. $2x^3 + 5x^2 + 7x + 3,\ x + 1$.
4. $3x^3 + 6x^2 + 4x + 7,\ x + 2$.
5. $-3x^3 + 11x^2 + 5x - 4,\ x - 4$.
6. $-5x^3 - 3x^2 + 9x - 8,\ x + 1$.
7. $-x^3 - 8x^2 - 12x - 9,\ x + 3$.
8. $-2x^3 - 9x^2 - 5x + 6,\ x + 4$.
9. $x^4 + 3x^3 - 5x^2 + 7x - 9,\ x - 1$.
10. $x^4 - 7x^3 - 6x^2 - 10x + 7,\ x + 1$.
11. $-2x^4 + 5x^3 + 6x^2 - 11x + 2,\ x + 2$.
12. $-3x^4 - 8x^3 - 5x^2 + 3x - 1,\ x + 2$.
13. $x^5 + x^4 - 7x^3 + 2x^2 + x - 1,\ x - 1$.
14. $x^5 - 3x^4 + 2x^3 - 5x^2 - 3x + 1,\ x - 3$.
15. $2x^5 + 4x^4 - 3x^3 - 7x^2 + 3x - 2,\ x + 2$.
16. $-3x^5 - 10x^4 + 8x^3 - 4x^2 + 5x - 1,\ x - 3$.
17. $3x^3 - x + 1,\ x - 5$.
18. $2x^4 - x^2 + x,\ x + 2$.
19. $x^5 - x + 1,\ x - 1$.
20. $2x^5 + x^2 + x,\ x + 2$.
21. $4x^4 - 5x^2 + 1,\ x - \frac{1}{2}$.
22. $6x^3 - 2x^2 - x - 1,\ x + \frac{2}{3}$.
23. $12x^3 + 3x^2 - x + 3,\ x - \frac{3}{4}$.
24. $6x^4 + x^3 + 16x - 3,\ x + \frac{3}{2}$.
25. $x^6 + 27x - 10,\ x + 2$.
26. $2x^6 - x^3 + x,\ x - 1$.
27. $3x^4 + 82x,\ x + 3$.
28. $2x^4 - 9x^2 + 2,\ x + 2$.
29. $x^3 + ax^2 + x + 3a,\ x + a$.
30. $2x^3 - ax^2 + 3a^2x - 4a^3,\ x - a$.
31. $2x^4 + 4ax^3 - 2a^2x^2 - 3a^3x + 6a^4,\ x + 2a$.
32. $x^4 - 5a^2x^2 - 2a^3x,\ x - 2a$.

Find the value of k such that when the first expression in each of the following problems is divided by the second, the remainder will have the indicated value.

33. $x^3 - 3x^2 + 7x + 2k,\ x - 2$; remainder, 4.
34. $x^3 - 5x^2 + x + k,\ x - 5$; remainder, 1.
35. $x^3 + x^2 + kx + 3,\ x + 1$; remainder, -3.
36. $x^3 + 4x^2 + kx + 6,\ x + 2$; remainder, 10.
37. $x^3 + kx^2 + 2kx + 30,\ x + 3$; remainder, 3.
38. $2x^3 + kx^2 - (k + 7)x - 2,\ x - 2$; remainder, 0.
39. $2x^3 - kx^2 - (k^2 - k)x - 2k - 4,\ x - k$; remainder, -1.
40. $x^4 - (k - 2)x^3 - 2kx^2 + kx + 6k + 3,\ x - k$; remainder, -2.

98. *The graph of a polynomial.* The roots of a polynomial equation $f(x) = 0$ are the abscissas of the points where the graph of $y = f(x)$ crosses the X axis, for, at these points, $y = 0$. We shall make extensive use of the graph in the process of obtaining the roots of polynomial equations. In this article we shall discuss the graphs of polynomials.

The method of obtaining the graph of a polynomial is the same as that used in Arts. 34 and 72 except that we shall use synthetic division for obtaining the corresponding values of x and y. We shall illustrate the process in the following example.

Example 1

In order to obtain the graph of $x^3 + 3x^2 - x - 3$, we shall set this function equal to y and obtain

$$(1) \qquad y = x^3 + 3x^2 - x - 3$$

Next, we obtain a table of corresponding values of x and y by use of synthetic division and the remainder theorem. For example, the value of the right member of (1) when $x = 2$ is the remainder when this function is divided by $x - 2$. Performing this operation, we get

$$\begin{array}{r} 1 + 3 - 1 - 3 \underline{|2} \\ + 2 + 10 + 18 \\ \hline 1 + 5 + 9 + 15 \end{array}$$

The remainder is 15. Hence, when $x = 2$, $y = 15$. In the same way, we obtain the table of corresponding values of x and y below.

x	-4	-3	-2	-1	0	1	2
y	-15	0	3	0	-3	0	15

These points are plotted and shown in Fig. 26. Since the points $(-4, -15)$ and $(-3,0)$, also $(1,0)$ and $(2,15)$, are rather far apart, we need to use two fractional values, $x = -3\frac{1}{2}$ and $x = 1\frac{1}{2}$, to determine the shape of the curve more accurately. When $x = 1\frac{1}{2}$, $y = 5\frac{5}{8}$, and when $x = -3\frac{1}{2}$, $y = -5\frac{5}{8}$. When these points are plotted we have the nine points indicated in the figure. Now we join these points with a smooth curve and obtain the graph in Fig. 26.

Except for a comparatively short range, the values of a rational integral function of x change much more rapidly than the corresponding values of x. For example, in Example 1, when x changes from 1 to 2, y changes from 0 to 15. Furthermore, when $x = 3$, $y = 48$. For this reason, it is usually advisable to use different scales on the X and Y axes.   This is done in the following example.

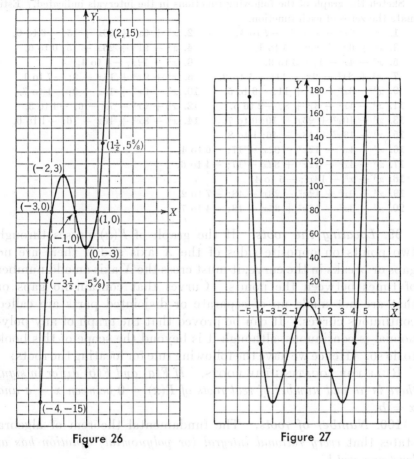

Figure 26   Figure 27

Example 2

A table of corresponding values of x and y for the function

$$y = x^4 - 18x^2$$

is given below.

x	-5	-4	-3	-2	-1	0	1	2	3	4	5
y	175	-32	-81	-56	-17	0	-17	-56	-81	-32	175

In order to construct the graph by use of these values, we shall select a scale so that one unit on the X axis is equal to 10 units on the Y axis.   The graph is shown in Fig. 27.

EXERCISE 51

Sketch the graph of the following functions in the intervals indicated. Estimate the zeros of each function.

1. $x^3 - 3x^2 - x + 3$; -2 to 4.   2. $x^3 + 9x^2 + 23x + 15$; -6 to 0.

3. $x^3 + 6x^2 + 8x$; -5 to 1.   4. $x^4 - 9x^2 + 23x - 15$; 0 to 6.

5. $x^3 - 4x - 1$; -3 to 3.   6. $x^3 - 12x$; -4 to 4.

7. $x^3 + 3x^2 - 9x - 11$; -5 to 3.   8. $x^3 + 9x^2 + 15x - 9$; -7 to 1.

9. $x^3 - 3x^2 - 9x + 11$; -3 to 5.   10. $x^3 - 9x^2 + 15x + 9$; -1 to 7.

11. $x^3 - 4x^2 - 3x + 8$; -2 to 5.   12. $x^3 + 2x^2 - 7x - 6$; -4 to 3.

13. $x^3 - 10x^2 + 25x - 10$; 0 to 7.   14. $x^3 - 8x^2 + 16x - 16$; -1 to 6.

15. $x^3 - 13x^2 + 48x - 46$; 1 to 8.

16. $x^4 + 4x^3 - 12x^2 - 32x - 17$; -6 to 4.

17. $x^4 - 4x^3 - 12x^2 + 32x - 17$; -4 to 6.

18. $x^4 + x^3 - 18x^2$; -5 to 4.

19. $x^4 + 9x^3 + 12x^2 - 28x - 48$; -7 to 2.

20. $x^4 - 3x^3 - 15x^2 + 35x - 18$; -4 to 7.

99. Locating the roots. If the graph of $F(x)$ passes through two points on opposite sides of the X axis and if there are no gaps or breaks in the curve, it must cross the X axis an odd number of times between the points. Curves that contain no gaps or that are not made up of separate or disjointed parts are called continuous curves. It can be proved that the graph of any polynomial is continuous, although it is beyond the scope of this book to do so. Hence we have the following rule for locating the roots:

RULE FOR LOCATING THE ROOTS. *If $F(a)$ and $F(b)$ differ in sign, there is an odd number of real roots of $F(x) = 0$ between $x = a$ and $x = b$.*

100. Number of roots. The fundamental theorem of algebra states that *every rational integral (or polynomial) equation has at least one root.*[1]

We shall consider the rational integral equation

$$(1) \qquad f(x) = a_0x^n + a_1x^{n-1} + \cdots + a_{n-1}x + a_n = 0$$

and let r_1 be a root. Then, by the factor theorem,

$$f(x) = Q_1(x)(x - r_1)$$

where $Q_1(x)$ is of degree $n - 1$. The equation $Q_1(x) = 0$ also has at least one root, and we shall let it be r_2. Then $x - r_2$ is a

---

[1] For proof, see Dickson's "First Course in Theory of Equations," p. 155.

factor of $Q_1(x)$ and $Q_1(x) = Q_2(x)(x - r_1)$, where $Q_2(x)$ is of degree $n - 2$. Thus $f(x) = (x - r_1)(x - r_2)Q_2(x)$. If we continue this process, we can find $n - 2$ additional factors, $(x - r_3)$, $(x - r_4)$, . . . , $(x - r_n)$, of $f(x)$ and have

$$(2) \qquad f(x) = (x - r_1)(x - r_2)(x - r_3) \cdot \cdot \cdot (x - r_n)Q_n(x)$$

where $Q_n(x)$ is of degree $n - n = 0$, and is therefore a constant. Obviously, $Q_n(x)$ is the coefficient of x^n in the right member of (2). Hence it is equal to a_0. Then the factored form of $f(x)$ is

$$(3) \qquad f(x) = a_0(x - r_1)(x - r_2)(x - r_3) \cdot \cdot \cdot (x - r_n)$$

Obviously by the converse of the factor theorem, r_1, r_2, r_3, . . . , r_n are roots of $f(x) = 0$. Furthermore, $f(x) = 0$ has no other roots, since no one of the factors in (3) is equal to zero for any value r_{n+1} of x not equal to $r_1, r_2, r_3, . . . , r_n$.

If s values of $r_1, r_2, r_3, . . . , r_s$ are equal, that is, suppose $r_1 = r_2 = r_3 = \cdot \cdot \cdot = r_s$, then (3) becomes

$$f(x) = a_0(x - r_s)^s(x - r_{s+1}) \cdot \cdot \cdot (x - r_n)$$

and r_s is called a root of multiplicity s of $f(x) = 0$. Hence we have the following theorem.

THEOREM. *A rational integral equation of degree **n** has exactly **n** roots where a root of multiplicity **s** is counted as **s** roots.*

Example

In the equation
$$2x^3 - x^2 - 6x + 3 = 0$$

$f(x) = 2x^3 - x^2 - 6x + 3$. Furthermore, it can be verified that $f(-2) = -5$, $f(-1) = 6$. $f(0) = 3, f(1) = -2$, and $f(2) = 3$. Hence, there is an odd number of roots between -2 and -1, between 0 and 1, and between 1 and 2. Since the degree of the equation is three, it has only three roots. Hence, there is exactly one root in each of the above intervals.

101. *Limits of the real roots.* The theorem given in this article enables us to find a number that is greater than or equal to the largest real root of an equation and another number that is smaller than or equal to the least root of the equation. Thus we can restrict the range in which the real roots must lie.

DEFINITION. *Any number that is larger than or equal to the greatest root of an equation is called **an upper limit of the roots.***

*Any number that is smaller than or equal to the least root of an equation is called a **lower limit of the roots**.*

We shall now state and then prove the theorem that enables us to determine these limits.

THEOREM. *If the coefficient of x^n in the polynomial equation $f(x) = 0$ is positive, and if there are no negative terms in the third line of the synthetic division of $f(x)$ by $x - k$, $k > 0$, then k is an upper limit of the real roots of $f(x) = 0$. Furthermore, if the signs in the third line of the synthetic division of $f(x)$ by $x - (-k) = x + k$ are alternately plus and minus,[1] then $-k$ is a lower limit of the real roots.*

Example

The synthetic division processes of the left member of $x^3 - 2x^2 + 3x + 3 = 0$ by $x - 3$ and also by $x + 1$ are given below.

$$1 - 2 + 3 + 3 \underline{| 3}$$
$$3 + 3 + 18$$
$$\overline{1 + 1 + 6 + 21}$$

$$1 - 2 + 3 + 3 \underline{| -1}$$
$$-1 + 3 - 6$$
$$\overline{1 - 3 + 6 - 3}$$

In the first case, the terms in the third row are all positive. Hence, 3 is an upper limit. In the second case, the terms in the third row are alternately plus and minus. Therefore -1 is a lower limit of the roots.

In order to prove the first part of the theorem, we shall use (1) of Art. 95 with $r = k$ and have

$$(1) \qquad f(x) = Q(x)(x - k) + R$$

By Art. 97, the coefficients in $Q(x)$ and the value of R are the numbers in the third row of the division of $f(x)$ by $x - k$. If these numbers are positive or zero, and if x is greater than k, then $Q(x)(x - k) + R > 0$. Hence there are no real roots of $f(x) = 0$ that are greater than k.

---

[1] If one or more zeros occur in the third line of the synthetic division of $f(x)$ by $x + k$, $-k$ is a lower limit of the real roots if, after each zero is replaced by either a plus or a minus sign, the signs in the third line of the synthetic division are alternately plus or minus.

If the quotient obtained by dividing $f(x)$ by $x + k$ is $q(x)$ and if the remainder is R', then

(2)
$$f(x) = q(x)(x + k) + R'$$

Furthermore if the terms in the third line of the synthetic division are alternately plus and minus, then the coefficients in $q(x)$ and R' are alternately plus and minus. The expression $q(x)$ is of degree $n - 1$, and its first coefficient is the same as the coefficient of x^n in $f(x)$ and therefore is positive. Furthermore, since R' is the last term of the third line of the synthetic division, and since there are $n + 1$ terms in this line, then R' is negative when n is odd, and positive when n is even.

We now choose a positive number h such that $-h < -k$, or $-h + k < 0$, substitute $-h$ for x in (2), and get

(3)
$$f(-h) = q(-h)(-h + k) + R'$$

The substitution of $-h$ for x in $q(x)$ will change the signs of the terms of odd degree only. Since the terms in $q(x)$ are alternately plus and minus, then the terms in $q(-h)$ are all plus or all minus. If the degree n of $f(x)$ is odd, then the degree of $q(x)$ is $n - 1$ and is therefore even. Hence, the first term in $q(-h)$, as well as all the other terms, are plus. Thus, since $-h + k$ is negative, $q(-h)(-h + k)$ is negative. Furthermore, when n is odd, R' is negative. Consequently, $f(-h)$ is the sum of two negative quantities and hence is not zero.

If n is even, $n - 1$ is odd, and then all terms in $q(-h)$ are negative and R' is positive. Therefore, since $q(-h)(-h + k)$ is positive, $f(-h)$ is the sum of two positive numbers and is not zero.

Thus in either case, $-h$ is not a root of $f(x)$. This completes the proof of the theorem.

EXERCISE 52

State the degree of the equation in each of Problems 1 to 8, then find all the roots and give the multiplicity of each.

1. $(x + 2)^3(x - 3)^2 = 0$.   2. $(x - 1)(x + 3)(x - 4)^3 = 0$.
3. $(x + 5)^4(x - 2)^3 = 0$.   4. $(x - 1)^2(x - 2)^4(x + 1)(x - 3)^3 = 0$.
5. $(2x - 5)^4(3x + 7)^3 = 0$.   6. $(5x + 9)^{10}(2x - 1)^3(x + 4)^7 = 0$.
7. $(3x - 2)^6(2x + 3)^3(x - 3)^2(x + 2) = 0$.
8. $(4x - 1)^4(3x + 5)^3(2x - 3)^2(x - 4)^4 = 0$.

Find upper and lower limits of the real roots of the equations in Problems 9 to 32, and locate all real roots of each.

9. $2x^3 - x^2 - 4x + 2 = 0.$ **10.** $3x^3 + x^2 - 9x - 3 = 0.$

11. $x^3 - 2x^2 - 7x + 13 = 0.$ **12.** $x^3 + x^2 - 5x - 4 = 0.$

13. $2x^3 - 3x^2 - 26x + 39 = 0.$ **14.** $3x^3 + 3x^2 - 36x - 35 = 0.$

15. $x^3 + 5x^2 - x - 4 = 0.$ **16.** $2x^3 - 3x^2 - 13x - 5 = 0.$

17. $x^4 + 3x^3 - 15x^2 - 9x + 31 = 0.$

18. $3x^4 - 20x^3 + 28x^2 + 19x - 13 = 0.$

19. $x^4 - x^3 - 24x^2 + 4x + 78 = 0.$ **20.** $x^4 - 4x^2 + 5 = 0.$

21. $6x^4 + 11x^3 - 25x^2 - 33x + 21 = 0.$

22. $6x^4 + x^3 - 43x^2 - 7x + 7 = 0.$

23. $3x^4 + 2x^3 - 41x^2 - 26x + 26 = 0.$

24. $x^4 - 18x^2 + 80 = 0.$ **25.** $2x^3 + x^2 + 8x + 4 = 0.$

26. $x^3 + 3x^2 + x - 4 = 0.$ **27.** $x^3 + 4x^2 - 2x - 18 = 0.$

28. $2x^3 + 5x^2 + 2x - 15 = 0.$ **29.** $6x^4 + 23x^3 + 25x^2 - 9x - 5 = 0.$

30. $x^4 + 5x^3 + 7x^2 - 3x - 9 = 0.$ **31.** $x^4 + 5x^3 + 3x^2 - 19x - 32 = 0.$

32. $x^4 + 7x^3 + 13x^2 - 23x + 78 = 0.$

The equation in each of the following problems has two roots between consecutive integers. Locate these roots by use of a value halfway between the two consecutive integers. Also locate the other roots of each equation.

33. $16x^3 + 16x^2 - 29x + 5 = 0.$ **34.** $8x^3 - x^2 - 8x + 2 = 0.$

35. $4x^3 - 28x^2 + 57x - 35 = 0.$ **36.** $6x^3 - 13x^2 - 5x + 1 = 0.$

37. $8x^3 - x^2 - 7x - 1 = 0.$ **38.** $2x^3 + 10x^2 + 12x - 1 = 0.$

39. $4x^3 - 12x^2 + 8x + 1 = 0.$ **40.** $x^3 - x + 1 = 0.$

102. Rational roots of a polynomial equation.

If a polynomial equation has one or more rational roots, the work involved in finding the others is greatly reduced if the rational roots are found first. The process of identifying a rational root is a matter of trial. Hence, the following theorem is very useful since it enables us to find a set of numbers which include the rational roots.

THEOREM. *If the coefficients of*

$$(1) \qquad a_0x^n + a_1x^{n-1} + \cdots + a_{n-1}x + a_n = 0$$

are integers, then each of its rational roots, after being reduced to lowest terms, has a factor of a_n for its numerator and a factor of a_0 for its denominator.

Proof. We shall assume that q/p is a rational root of (1) and that q and p do not have a common factor greater than one. Now, if we substitute q/p for x in (1) and multiply by p^n, we obtain

$$(2) \qquad a_0q^n + a_1q^{n-1}p + \cdots + a_{n-1}qp^{n-1} + a_np^n = 0$$

Transposing $a_n p^n$ and dividing by q, we have

$$(3) \qquad a_0 q^{n-1} + a_1 q^{n-2} p + \cdots + a_{n-1} p^{n-1} = - \frac{a_n p^n}{q}$$

The left number of (3) is made up of the sum, product, and integral powers of integers; hence, it is an integer. Therefore, the right member must be an integer. Consequently, q is a factor of a_n since by hypothesis q and p have no common factor greater than one.

If we transpose $a_0 q^n$ from the left to the right member of (2) and divide by p, we obtain

$$(4) \qquad a_1 q^{n-1} + \cdots + a_{n-1} q p^{n-2} + a_n p^{n-1} = - \frac{a_0 q^n}{p}$$

Hence, p is a factor of a_0, since q and p have no common factor greater than one, and the left member of (4) is an integer.

If $a_0 = 1$ in (1), we get the following corollary:

COROLLARY. *Each rational root of an equation*

$$(5) \qquad x^n + a_1 x^{n-1} + \cdots + a_{n-1} x + a_n = 0$$

with integral coefficients is an integer and a factor of a_n.

Example

In the equation

$$2x^4 + x^3 - 9x^2 - 4x + 4 = 0$$

the numerators of the rational roots must be factors of 4, and the denominators factors of 2. Hence the possibilities for the rational roots are

$$\pm 1, \ \pm 2, \ \pm 4, \ \pm \tfrac{1}{2}, \ \pm \tfrac{2}{2}, \ \pm \tfrac{4}{2}$$

If we eliminate repetitions, this set of quotients becomes

$$-4, \ -2, \ -1, \ -\tfrac{1}{2}, \ \tfrac{1}{2}, \ 1, \ 2, \ 4$$

We may use synthetic division and the remainder theorem in order to determine which of these possibilities are actually roots.

103. The depressed equation. DEFINITION. *If r is a root of the polynomial equation $F(x) = 0$, then*

$$(1) \qquad \frac{F(x)}{x - r} = 0$$

*is called the **depressed equation** of $F(x)$ corresponding to r.*

The quotient indicated in the definition may be obtained by synthetic division.

The depressed equation corresponding to a given root is very useful in the process of investigating the remaining roots of the original equation since any root, other than r, of $F(x) = 0$ is a root of (1); furthermore, if r is a root of multiplicity m of $F(x) = 0$, it is a root of multiplicity $m - 1$ of (1).

The degree of the depressed equation is one less than the degree of the given equation. It is often possible to reduce an equation to a quadratic by repeatedly depressing it.

Example

If in the equation of the example of the previous article we use synthetic division to determine whether or not 2 is a root, we have

$$
\begin{array}{r}
2 + 1 - \ 9 - 4 + 4\underline{|2} \\
+ 4 + 10 + 2 - 4 \\
\hline
2 + 5 + \ 1 - 2 \quad 0
\end{array}
$$

Hence 2 is a root. Furthermore, all roots of the given equation, except possibly $x = 2$, are roots of the depressed equation

$$2x^3 + 5x^2 + x - 2 = 0$$

We shall next try $x = -2$ in the depressed equation above and obtain

$$
\begin{array}{r}
2 + 5 + 1 - 2\underline{|-2} \\
- 4 - 2 + 2 \\
\hline
2 + 1 - 1 \quad 0
\end{array}
$$

Hence -2 is a root. The depressed equation, corresponding to $x = 2$ and $x = -2$, is the quadratic

$$2x^2 + x - 1 = 0$$

We may solve it by use of the quadratic formula and get

$$
\begin{aligned}
x &= \frac{-1 \pm \sqrt{1 + 8}}{4} \\
&= \frac{-1 \pm 3}{4} \\
&= \tfrac{1}{2}, \ -1
\end{aligned}
$$

Hence the four roots of the given equation are 2, -2, -1, and $\tfrac{1}{2}$.

104. The process of obtaining all rational roots.
We shall now outline the steps that should be followed in determining the rational roots of a polynomial equation.

1. *List all possible rational roots in order of magnitude.*

2. *Test the smallest possible positive integral root, then the next larger, and so on until each integral root or a limit to the roots is found.*

(a) *If a limit is found, discard all larger possible roots.*

(b) *If a root is found, use the depressed equation in further calculations.*

3. *Test the fractional possibilities that remain after considering any limit that has been found.*

4. *Repeat steps 2 and 3 for negative roots.*

NOTE: If a quadratic is obtained by use of the depressed equation, its roots should be found by use of the quadratic formula.

Example

Find the rational roots of

$$F(x) = 4x^4 - 4x^3 - 25x^2 + x + 6 = 0$$

Solution

The possible numerators of rational roots are ± 6, ± 3, ± 2, ± 1, and the possible denominators are ± 4, ± 2, ± 1. The possible rational roots in order of numerical value are $\pm \frac{1}{4}$, $\pm \frac{1}{2}$, $\pm \frac{3}{4}$, ± 1, $\pm \frac{3}{2}$, ± 2, ± 3, ± 6. We shall now test the positive integral possibilities.

$$
\begin{array}{rrrrr|r}
4 & -4 & -25 & 1 & 6 & 1 \\
  & +4 & 0 & -25 & -24 & \\
\hline
4 & 0 & -25 & -24 & -18 &
\end{array}
$$

Hence, 1 is neither a root nor a limit.

$$
\begin{array}{rrrrr|r}
4 & -4 & -25 & +1 & +6 & 2 \\
  & +8 & +8 & -34 & -66 & \\
\hline
4 & +4 & -17 & -33 & -60 &
\end{array}
$$

Therefore, 2 is neither a root nor a limit.

$$
\begin{array}{rrrrr|r}
4 & -4 & -25 & +1 & +6 & 3 \\
  & +12 & +24 & -3 & -6 & \\
\hline
4 & +8 & -1 & -2 & 0 &
\end{array}
$$

Consequently, 3 is a root and the corresponding depressed equation is

$$4x^3 + 8x^2 - x - 2 = 0$$

It has all the roots of the original equation with the possible exception of 3. Since the constant term is different from that of the original equation, the number of possible rational roots may be decreased by using only those possibilities common to the original equation and the depressed equation corresponding to the root 3. The possible rational roots of the depressed equation are ± 1, ± 2, $\pm \frac{1}{2}$, $\pm \frac{1}{4}$. Not all of these need be considered since we found that 1 and 2 are not roots of the original equation.

It is readily seen that $\frac{1}{4}$ is not a root and $\frac{1}{2}$ is a root and that $4x^2 + 10x + 4 = 0$ is the corresponding depressed equation. This is a quadratic and can be solved by means of the quadratic formula. Its roots are -2 and $-\frac{1}{2}$. Hence, the roots of the original equation are 3, $\frac{1}{2}$, $-\frac{1}{2}$, and -2.

EXERCISE 53

Find all rational roots of the equation in each of Problems 1 to 20.

1. $x^3 - x^2 - 4x + 4 = 0$.
2. $x^3 - 4x^2 + x + 6 = 0$.
3. $x^3 + 6x^2 + 3x - 10 = 0$.
4. $x^3 - x^2 - 10x - 8 = 0$.
5. $4x^3 - 7x - 3 = 0$.
6. $6x^3 + 13x^2 + x - 2 = 0$.
7. $2x^3 - 5x^2 - x + 6 = 0$.
8. $4x^3 + 16x^2 + 9x - 9 = 0$.
9. $12x^3 - 4x^2 - 3x + 1 = 0$.
10. $8x^3 - 12x^2 - 18x + 27 = 0$.
11. $16x^3 - 28x^2 + 16x - 3 = 0$.
12. $8x^3 - 12x^2 + 6x - 1 = 0$.
13. $x^4 - 3x^3 + x^2 + 3x - 2 = 0$.
14. $x^4 + x^3 - 15x^2 + 23x - 10 = 0$.
15. $x^4 - x^3 - 13x^2 + x + 12 = 0$.
16. $x^4 - x^3 - 6x^2 + 4x + 8 = 0$.
17. $3x^4 - x^3 - 21x^2 - 11x + 6 = 0$.
18. $3x^4 - 17x^3 + 27x^2 - 7x - 6 = 0$.
19. $8x^4 + 6x^3 - 51x^2 + 11x + 6 = 0$.
20. $2x^4 + 7x^3 - 2x^2 - 13x + 6 = 0$.

Find all roots of the following equations.

21. $2x^3 + 3x^2 - 4x - 5 = 0$.
22. $2x^3 + 3x^2 - 6x - 8 = 0$.
23. $2x^3 + x^2 + 11x - 6 = 0$.
24. $3x^3 + 4x^2 + 5x - 6 = 0$.
25. $x^3 - 1 = 0$.
26. $2x^3 - x^2 + 2x - 1 = 0$.
27. $3x^3 + 7x^2 + 8x + 2 = 0$.
28. $2x^3 - 11x^2 + 22x - 15 = 0$.
29. $x^4 - x^3 - x^2 - x - 2 = 0$.
30. $x^4 - 2x^3 + x^2 + 2x - 2 = 0$.
31. $4x^4 - 8x^3 + 19x^2 + 2x - 5 = 0$.
32. $2x^4 + x^3 + 7x^2 + 4x - 4 = 0$.
33. $x^4 + x^3 - x - 1 = 0$.
34. $6x^5 + 19x^4 + 25x^3 + 25x^2 + 19x + 6 = 0$.
35. $x^5 - x^4 - x + 1 = 0$.
36. $12x^5 + 25x^4 - 23x^3 - 16x^2 + x + 1 = 0$.

105. Descartes' rule of signs. In this article we shall present a criterion or rule that enables us to determine the maximum number of positive and the maximum number of negative roots of a rational integral equation.

If the terms of a polynomial are arranged according to the ascending or descending powers of the variable, we say that a *variation of signs* occurs when the signs of two consecutive terms differ.

Example

In the polynomial $2x^4 - 5x^3 - 6x^2 + 7x + 3$, the signs of the terms are $+ - - + +$. Hence, there are two variations of signs, since the sign changes from positive to negative and back again to positive. Furthermore, there are three variations of sign in $x^4 - 2x^3 + 3x^2 + 6x - 4$.

We shall next state Descartes' rule of signs, then illustrate it, and finally give the proof.

DESCARTES' RULE OF SIGNS. *The number of positive roots of a rational integral equation* $f(x) = 0$ *does not exceed the number of variations of signs in* $f(x)$. *The number of negative roots of the equation does not exceed the number of variations of signs in* $f(-x)$.

Example

There are three variations of sign in $f(x) = x^4 - 3x^3 - 5x^2 + 7x - 3$. Hence, the maximum number of positive roots of the equation

$$x^4 - 3x^3 - 5x^2 + 7x - 3 = 0$$

is three. Furthermore, $f(-x) = x^4 + 3x^3 - 5x^2 - 7x - 3$, and this polynomial has one variation of sign. Therefore, the maximum number of negative roots of the above equation is one.

In order to prove Descartes' rule of signs, we shall first establish the following statement.

The number of variations of sign in the product of $f(x)(x - r)$, $r > 0$, is at least one greater than the number of variations of sign in $f(x)$.

Since we are interested in the signs of the product of $f(x)$ and $x - r$, we shall consider only the behavior of the signs in the multiplication. Suppose the signs of the terms in $f(x)$ are those in the first line below, and the signs of $x - r$, $r > 0$, are those in the second row. The signs in the third and fourth rows are those in the products of $f(x)$ by x and $-r$, respectively, and the fifth line consists of the signs of the sums of the terms in these products.

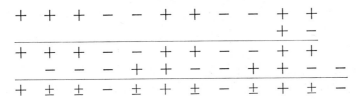

We use the double sign where a positive and negative number are added, since we cannot tell what the sign is unless we know the two numbers involved in the sum. Now the only signs clearly defined in the sum are the first, the last, and those where the signs immediately above them are the same. Each term in the fifth line is the sum of the product of a term in $f(x)$ by x and the product of the term immediately preceding it by $-r$. Hence, these two products will have the same sign if the two consecutive terms in $f(x)$ occur where there is a variation of sign, and the two products are minus when the variation is from minus to plus and positive when it is from plus to minus. Thus, in addition to the first and last terms, there will be as many signs clearly defined as there are variations of sign in $f(x)$. Now, if we change all the double signs in each sequence to the unambiguous sign that precedes the sequence, we clearly do not increase the number of variations of sign in the product. When this is done, the fifth line becomes

$$+ \quad + \quad + \quad - \quad - \quad + \quad + \quad - \quad - \quad + \quad + \quad -$$

Then, with the exception of the last term, these signs change only when there is a variation in $f(x)$; furthermore, these signs are exactly the same as those in $f(x)$. Clearly, the product of the last term in $f(x)$ by $-r$ differs in sign from this term. So we have at least one additional variation of sign in the product.

Now, suppose that r_1, r_2, r_3, . . . , r_k are the positive roots of $f(x) = 0$. Then,

(1) $f(x) = q(x)(x - r_1)(x - r_2)(x - r_3) \cdots (x - r_k)$

In the right member of (1), $q(x)(x - r_1)$ has at least one more variation of sign than $q(x)$; $q(x)(x - r_1)(x - r_2)$ has at least one more than $q(x)(x - r_1)$ and hence at least two more than $q(x)$. Continuing this argument, we conclude that the number of variations in the right member of (1) is at least k greater than those in $q(x)$. Since the minimum of variations of signs in $q(x)$ is zero, the minimum number of variations in $f(x)$ is k. Thus, the number of positive roots of $f(x) = 0$, does not exceed the number of variations of sign in $f(x)$.

The second statement in the theorem follows from the fact that the negative roots of $f(x) = 0$ are the positive roots of $f(-x) = 0$.

106. *Imaginary roots.* It can be readily verified that $x = 2$ is a root of the rational integral equation

$$x^3 - 4x^2 + 9x - 10 = 0$$

and that the depressed equation is $x^2 - 2x + 5 = 0$. If we solve this quadratic, we obtain $x = 1 + 2i$ and $x = 1 - 2i$. Hence, the roots of the given equation are the real number, 2, and the conjugate imaginary numbers $1 + 2i$ and $1 - 2i$.

The above equation illustrates the fact that the imaginary roots of a rational integral equation with real coefficients occur in pairs and that the members of each pair are conjugates of each other. We shall prove that this is true for all rational integral equations with real coefficients.

We shall let $F(x) = 0$ be a rational integral equation with real coefficients and one that has $a + bi$ as a root. If we divide $F(x)$ by the quadratic function

$$(x - a)^2 + b^2 = (x - a - ib)(x - a + ib)$$

until we reach a linear remainder $rx + s$ and call the quotient $Q(x)$, we have the identity

(1) $$F(x) = Q(x)[(x - a)^2 + b^2] + rx + s$$

Since (1) is true for all values of x, it is true for $x = a + ib$. Consequently,

$$\begin{aligned} F(a + ib) &= Q(a + ib)[(a + ib - a)^2 + b^2] + (r)(a + ib) + s \\ &= Q(a + ib)(-b^2 + b^2) + (r)(a + ib) + s \\ &= Q(a + ib)0 + (r)(a + ib) + s \\ &= ra + s + ibr = 0 \end{aligned}$$

since $a + ib$ is a root of $F(x) = 0$ by hypothesis.

Hence, by Art. 85, the coefficient br of the imaginary part is zero and the real part $ra + s$ is zero. That is,

(2) $$br = 0$$

and

(3) $$ra + s = 0$$

However, $b \neq 0$, and hence, $r = 0$ and (3) becomes $s = 0$. Therefore, (1) becomes

$$F(x) = Q(x)[(x - a)^2 + b^2]$$

Hence,
$$F(a - ib) = Q(a - ib)[(a - ib - a)^2 + b^2]$$
$$= Q(a - ib)(-b^2 + b^2) = 0$$

and $a - ib$ is a root of $F(x) = 0$.

Hence we have the following theorem.

THEOREM. *If $a + bi$ is a root of the rational integral equation $F(x) = 0$ with real coefficients, its conjugate $a - bi$ is also a root.*

Example

Form a cubic equation with 2 and $3 - i$ as roots.

Solution

If the equation is to have real coefficients, the conjugate $3 + i$ of $3 - i$ must be a root. Hence, by (3), Art. 100, the desired equation is

$$(x - 3 + i)(x - 3 - i)(x - 2) = 0$$

or

$$x^3 - 8x^2 + 22x - 20 = 0$$

As a consequence of the theorem of this article and (3), Art. 100, we can now state the following corollary:

COROLLARY. *A polynomial can be expressed as the product of distinct or repeated linear and irreducible quadratic factors with real coefficients.*

EXERCISE 54

By use of Descartes' rule of signs, find the maximum number of positive and negative roots of the equation in each of Problems 1 to 12.

1. $3x^3 + 5x^2 - x + 1 = 0$.
2. $4x^3 - 3x^2 - 5x + 2 = 0$.
3. $7x^3 + 3x^2 + 2x - 1 = 0$.
4. $8x^3 - x^2 + 2x - 4 = 0$.
5. $x^3 + 1 = 0$.
6. $x^3 + x^2 + 1 = 0$.
7. $x^3 - x^2 - 1 = 0$.
8. $x^4 + 1 = 0$.
9. $x^4 + x^3 - 3x^2 - 2x + 5 = 0$.
10. $3x^4 - 2x^3 + 4x^2 - 2x + 2 = 0$.
11. $x^4 + x^2 + 1 = 0$.
12. $x^4 + x^3 + 1 = 0$.

13. Show that $x^6 + x^4 + 1 = 0$ has six imaginary roots.
14. Show that $x^5 + x^3 + x + 1 = 0$ has four imaginary roots.
15. Show that $x^7 + 5x + 3 = 0$ has six imaginary roots.
16. Show that $x^3 - x^2 - 1 = 0$ has two imaginary roots.

Form a polynomial equation of lowest possible degree that has the numbers in each of the following problems as roots.

17. $1 + i, 2$.
18. $2 + 3i, 1$.
19. $3 + 4i, -3$.
20. $4 - i, -2$.
21. $i, 1, -1$.
22. $i, 2i$.
23. $1 + i, 2 - i$.
24. $1 - i, 3 + 2i$.
25. $i, -2i, -1$.
26. $-i, 1 + i, 1$.
27. $3 - i, 1, 2, -1$.
28. $1 + 2i, 2 - i, 1$.

107. *Irrational roots by successive magnification.* In this article, we shall illustrate a graphical method for approximating an irrational root to any desired degree of accuracy. The method is based on the fact that if two values of the variable are sufficiently near to one another, the part of the graph between these values is approximately a straight line.

Example 1

Find, to two decimal places, the least positive root of

$$(1) \qquad y(x) = x^3 - 4x + 1 = 0$$

Solution

We first construct the graph of $y(x) = x^3 - 4x + 1$ by use of the accompanying table of corresponding values of x and y. The graph is shown in Fig. 28.

x	-2.5	-2	-1	0	1	2
$y(x)$	$-\frac{37}{8}$	1	4	1	-2	1

From this graph, we see that the roots of (1) lie between -2.5 and -2, 0 and 1, and 1 and 2.

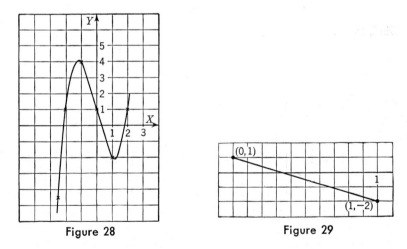

Figure 28   Figure 29

In order to calculate the value of the root that lies between 0 and 1 to one decimal place, we construct the graph of $y(x)$ in this interval under the assumption that it is a straight line, using a horizontal scale that is 10 times the vertical scale (see Fig. 29). This graph indicates that the root is approximately .3; however, if we look at Fig. 28, we see that the actual curve between $(0,1)$ and $(1,-2)$ is slightly to the left of the straight line from one to the other. Consequently,

$x = .3$ is probably larger than the root. By substitution, we find that

$$y(.3) = -.173$$

and $y(.2) = .208$; hence, the root is between $x = .2$ and $x = .3$ and is nearer the latter than the former.

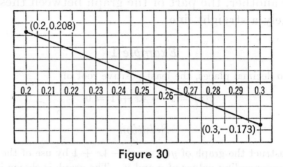

Figure 30

In order to obtain the value of the root to two decimal places, we repeat the process for the portion of the graph in the interval from $x = .2$ to $x = .3$, using the scale indicated in Fig. 30.

We see that the root is approximately $x = .25$. Again, by calculation, we find that $y(.25) = .015625$ and $y(.26) = -.022424$. Hence, to two decimal places, the root is $x = .25$.

Example 2

Find, to one decimal place, the largest root of

$$y(x) = 2x^3 - 2x^2 - 8x + 9 = 0$$

Solution

The graph shows that there are two roots between $x = 1$ and $x = 2$, and that the larger of these is between $x = 1.5$ and $x = 2$ (see Fig. 31), which was constructed by use of the accompanying table.

x	-2.5	-2	-1	0	1	1.5	2	2.5
$y(x)$	$-\frac{59}{4}$	1	13	9	1	$-\frac{3}{4}$	1	$\frac{31}{4}$

If we enlarge the graph in the interval from $x = 1.5$ to $x = 2$ and use the scale in Fig. 32, we see that the root appears to be between $x = 1.7$ and $x = 1.8$.

However, since in this interval the curve lies to the right of the straight line, the root is probably nearer $x = 1.8$. By actual trial, we see that $y(1.8) = -.216$ and, hence, that $x = 1.8$ is less than the root. However, we find that

$$y(1.9) = .298$$

hence, the value of the root to one decimal place is $x = 1.8$.

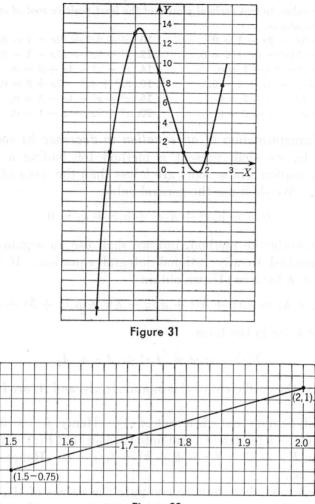

Figure 31

Figure 32

EXERCISE 55

Find the value, to one decimal place, of each root of the equations in Problems 1 to 8. Indicate by placing a plus or minus sign after each, whether each value found is smaller or larger than the root.

1. $x^3 - x^2 - 2x + 1 = 0$.
2. $2x^3 + 3x^2 - 2x - 1 = 0$.
3. $3x^3 - 7x^2 - x + 1 = 0$.
4. $3x^3 - 5x^2 - 8x - 2 = 0$.
5. $6x^3 - 16x^2 + 5x + 2 = 0$.
6. $x^3 - 4x^2 + 2 = 0$.
7. $3x^3 - 8x^2 + 1 = 0$.
8. $3x^3 - 5x^2 - 5x - 1 = 0$.

Find the value, to two decimal places, of the least positive root of each of the following equations.

9. $x^3 + 3x^2 + 3x - 1 = 0.$ **10.** $x^3 + 6x^2 + 12x - 7 = 0.$
11. $3x^3 - 11x^2 + 2x + 2 = 0.$ **12.** $x^3 + 9x^2 + 27x - 1 = 0.$
13. $x^3 - x^2 - 2x + 1 = 0.$ **14.** $x^3 - x^2 - 4x + 3 = 0.$
15. $2x^3 + x^2 - 5x + 1 = 0.$ **16.** $3x^3 + 2x^2 - 7x + 3 = 0.$
17. $x^3 - 4x^2 - x + 5 = 0.$ **18.** $x^3 + x^2 - 4x - 5 = 0.$
19. $x^3 - 3x^2 - x + 2 = 0.$ **20.** $x^3 + 2x^2 - x - 1 = 0.$

108. *Transformation of an equation to decrease its roots.* In this article, we shall present a method for finding a rational integral equation whose roots are h less than the roots of a given equation. We shall use the general cubic

$$(1) \qquad f(x) = a_0x^3 + a_1x^2 + a_2x + a_3 = 0$$

to demonstrate the method, but we shall use an argument that can be applied to any rational integral equation. If we substitute $z + h$ for x in (1), we obtain

$$(2) \quad f(z + h) = a_0(z + h)^3 + a_1(z + h)^2 + a_2(z + h) + a_3$$

which we write in the form

$$(3) \qquad\qquad F(z) = a_0z^3 + A_1z^2 + A_2z + A_3$$

Obviously, the coefficient of z^3 is a_0 and A_1, A_2, and A_3 are functions of h.

We shall assume that r is a root of (1). Hence, $f(r) = 0$. If we substitute $r - h$ for z in (3), and note the fact that $F(z) = f(z + h)$, we obtain $F(r - h) = f(r - h + h) = f(r) = 0$. Hence $r - h$ is a root of (3).

We shall next show how to compute the values of A_1, A_2, and A_3 in (3) without expanding the binomials in (2). Since $F(z)$ was obtained by substituting $z + h$ for x in (1), then if we reverse the process and substitute $x - h$ for z in (3), we obtain (1). This substitution yields the following result:

$$(4) \quad f(x) = F(x - h) = a_0(x - h)^3 + A_1(x - h)^2$$
$$+ A_2(x - h) + A_3$$

Obviously, if we divide the right member of (4) by $x - h$, we obtain the quotient $a_0(x - h)^2 + A_1(x - h) + A_2$ and a remainder, A_3. Hence, A_3 is the last term in the third line of the synthetic division of $f(x)$ by $x - h$. Similarly, A_2 is the last term in the third line of the synthetic division of the above quotient by $x - h$; and finally, continuing the argument, A_1 is the remainder, when the second quotient is divided by $x - h$. In the example below, we shall show how the above steps are carried out in a specific problem. The above process is called *decreasing the roots* of an equation, and the transformed equation is called the *diminished equation*.

Example 1

If $f(x) = 2x^3 - 5x^2 + 3x - 1$, and $h = 2$, then we perform the above computation as follows.

$$\begin{array}{llr}
\text{(first division)} & 2 - 5 + 3 - 1\underline{|2} \\
& 4 - 2 + 2 \\
\text{(second division)} & 2 - 1 + 1 + (1) = A_3 \\
& 4 + 6 \\
\text{(third division)} & 2 + 3 + (7) = A_2 \\
& 4 \\
& 2 + (7) = A_1
\end{array}$$

Then $a_0 = 2$ and the diminished equation is $2x^3 + 7x^2 + 7x + 1 = 0$.

Example 2

In this example, we shall decrease the roots of

$$2x^3 - x^2 - 7x + 6 = (x - 1)(x + 2)(2x - 3) = 0$$

by 2. The work is shown below.

$$\begin{array}{r}
2 - 1 - 7 + 6\underline{|2} \\
4 + 6 - 2 \\
\hline
2 + 3 - 1 + 4 \\
4 + 14 \\
\hline
2 + 7 + 13 \\
4 \\
\hline
2 + 11
\end{array}$$

Hence, the diminished equation is $2x^3 + 11x^2 + 13x + 4 = 0$. It can be readily verified that the roots of this equation are -1, -4, and $-\frac{1}{2}$, and each of these is two less than the corresponding root of the original equation.

109. *Horner's method for determining irrational roots*. By means of Horner's method, we can obtain an irrational root of a polynomial equation to any desired degree of accuracy. The labor involved is rather tedious at times; however, the method is straightforward and simple. The amount of labor involved will be somewhat decreased if we obtain all rational roots before attempting to determine the irrational roots.

The procedure consists of

1. *Determining the root to one significant figure by means of the location theorem of Art. 99.*

2. *Deriving the equation whose roots are those of the original decreased by the smaller of the numbers used in the application of the theorem mentioned in step 1.*

3. *Repeating this process until the desired degree of accuracy is obtained.*

Example

Calculate a positive irrational root of

(1) $F(x) = x^4 + 4x^3 - x^2 - 12x - 6 = 0$

to four significant figures.

Solution

The possible rational roots are ± 6, ± 3, ± 2, and ± 1. If we test each of these possibilities, we find that none of them are roots. It is readily seen by use of synthetic division that $F(1) = -14$ and $F(2) = 14$. Hence, there is a root between 1 and 2.

We shall now decrease the roots by $h_1 = 1$, thus obtaining an equation that has a root between 0 and 1. Using the method of Art. 108, we get

$$
\begin{array}{rrrrr}
1 & +4 & -\ 1 & -12 & -\ 6\underline{|1} \\
  & 1 & +\ 5 & +\ 4 & -\ 8 \\
\hline
1 & +5 & +\ 4 & -\ 8 & -14 = A_4 \\
  & 1 & +\ 6 & +10 & \\
\hline
1 & +6 & +10 & +\ 2 = A_3 & \\
  & 1 & 7 & & \\
\hline
1 & +7 & +17 = A_2 & & \\
  & +1 & & & \\
\hline
1 & +8 = A_1 & & &
\end{array}
$$

Therefore, the equation

(2) $F_1(x) = x^4 + 8x^3 + 17x^2 + 2x - 14 = 0$

has a root between 0 and 1. It is readily seen by means of synthetic division that $F_1(.7) = -1.2859$ and $F_1(.8) = 2.9856$. Hence, there is a root of $F_1(x) = 0$ between .7 and .8 and we now derive the equation whose roots are $h_2 = .7$ less than those of (2).

$$
\begin{array}{rrrrr}
1 & +\ 8 & +17 & +\ 2 & -14 & \underline{\lfloor.7} \\
& .7 & +\ 6.09 & +16.163 & +12.7141 \\
\hline
1 & +\ 8.7 & +23.09 & +18.163 & -\ 1.2859 = A_4 \\
& .7 & +\ 6.58 & +20.769 \\
\hline
1 & +\ 9.4 & +29.67 & +38.932 = A_3 \\
& .7 & +\ 7.07 \\
\hline
1 & +10.1 & +36.74 = A_2 \\
& .7 \\
\hline
1 & +10.8 = A_1
\end{array}
$$

Therefore,

(3) $$F_2(x) = x^4 + 10.8x^3 + 36.74x^2 + 38.932x - 1.2859 = 0$$

has a root between 0 and .1. By means of synthetic division, we find that $F_2(.03) = -.08458159$ and $F_2(.04) = .33085776$; hence, there is a root of $F_2(x)$ between .03 and .04, and we derive an equation each of whose roots is $h_3 = .03$ less than those of (3).

$$
\begin{array}{rrrrr}
1 & +10.8 & +36.74 & +38.932 & -1.2859 & \underline{\lfloor.03} \\
& +\ .03 & +\ .3249 & +\ 1.111947 & +1.20131841 \\
\hline
1 & +10.83 & +37.0649 & +40.043947 & -\ .08458159 = A_4 \\
& .03 & +\ .3258 & +\ 1.121721 \\
\hline
1 & +10.86 & +37.3907 & +41.165668 = A_3 \\
& .03 & +\ .3267 \\
\hline
1 & +10.89 & +37.7174 = A_2 \\
& +\ .03 \\
\hline
1 & +10.92 = A_1
\end{array}
$$

Therefore,

$$F_3(x) = x^4 + 10.92x^3 + 37.7174x^2 + 41.165668x - .08458159 = 0$$

has a root between 0 and .01.

Since x is very near zero, x^4, x^3, and x^2 are negligible in comparison to it; hence, we omit those terms and write

$$F_4(x_4) = 41.165668x_4 - .08458159$$

Setting this equal to zero and solving for x_4, we get

$$x_4 = .002$$

Consequently,

$$
\begin{aligned}
x &= h_1 + h_2 + h_3 + x_4 \\
&= 1 + .7 + .03 + .002 \\
&= 1.732
\end{aligned}
$$

The other irrational roots of Eq. (1) can be found in a similar manner. Furthermore, each irrational root may be computed to any desired degree of accuracy.

The calculation of the root to the first two decimal places in the foregoing example may be placed in the condensed form below.

1	+ 4	− 1	−12	− 6	$\underline{1}$
	1	+ 5	+ 4	− 8	
1	+ 5	+ 4	− 8	−14	
	1	+ 6	+10		
1	+ 6	+10	+ 2		
	1	7			
1	+ 7	+17			
	1				
1	+ 8	+17	+ 2	−14	$\underline{.7}$
	.7	+ 6.09	+16.163	+12.7141	
1	+ 8.7	+23.09	+18.163	− 1.2859	
	.7	+ 6.58	+20.769		
1	+ 9.4	+29.67	+38.932		
	.7	+ 7.07			
1	+10.1	+36.74			
	.7				
1	+10.8	+36.74	+38.932	− 1.2859	$\underline{.03}$
	.03	+ .3249	+ 1.111947	+ 1.20131841	
1	+10.83	+37.0649	+40.043947	− .08458159	
	+ .03	+ .3258	+ 1.121721		
1	+10.86	+37.3907	+41.165668		
	+ .03	+ .3267			
1	+10.89	+37.7174			
	+ .03				
1	+10.92	+37.7174	+41.165668	− .08458159	

The digit for the last decimal place of the root may be obtained by taking the negative of the quotient of the final number in the last line and the one immediately preceding it. However, if the root is to be calculated to more than three decimal places, the foregoing procedure must be continued until the next to the last digit in the root is obtained.

EXERCISE 56

In each of Problems 1 to 12, obtain an equation whose roots are those of the given equation diminished by the number given at the right of the equation.

1. $x^3 - 2x^2 - 5x + 4 = 0, 2$.
2. $x^3 + 5x^2 - 6x + 3 = 0, 3$.
3. $2x^3 - 3x^2 + 4x - 3 = 0, 4$.
4. $3x^3 - 7x^2 - 2x + 4 = 0, 1$.
5. $x^4 + 5x^3 - 8x^2 - 3x + 2 = 0, 2$.
6. $2x^4 - x^3 + 3 = 0, 1$.
7. $3x^4 - 8x^3 - 9x + 1 = 0, 2$.
8. $4x^4 - 9x^3 - 8x^2 - 2 = 0, 1$.
9. $x^3 - 2x^2 + x - 1 = 0, .1$.
10. $3x^3 - x^2 + 2x - 3 = 0, .3$.
11. $2x^3 + x^2 - 3x + 1 = 0, .2$.
12. $x^3 - 3x^2 + x + 1 = 0, .4$.

By use of Horner's method, find to two decimal places, the value of the least positive root of the equations in Problems 13 to 24.

13. $x^3 + 8x^2 + 15x - 2 = 0$.
14. $x^3 - x^2 + 4x - 2 = 0$.
15. $x^3 - 8x + 5 = 0$.
16. $x^3 - 3x^2 - x + 1 = 0$.

17. $3x^3 + 9x^2 - 3x - 16 = 0.$ **18.** $x^3 + 4x^2 - x - 6 = 0.$
19. $2x^3 - 9x^2 + x + 11 = 0.$ **20.** $3x^3 - 10x^2 - 3x + 11 = 0.$
21. $x^3 + 3x^2 - 6x - 3 = 0.$ **22.** $x^3 - 4x^2 + 3x + 1 = 0.$
23. $x^3 + 6x^2 + 3x - 7 = 0.$ **24.** $x^3 - 6x^2 + 7x + 3 = 0.$

Find, to three decimal places, the value of the irrational roots of the equations in Problems 25 to 32.

25. $x^3 + 3x^2 + 3x - 12 = 0.$ **26.** $x^3 + 3x^2 + 2x - 7 = 0.$
27. $x^3 - x^2 + x + 37 = 0.$ **28.** $x^3 - 6x^2 + 13x - 11 = 0.$
29. $x^4 - 2x^3 - 2x - 1 = 0.$ **30.** $4x^4 - 8x^3 + 5x^2 - 8x + 1 = 0.$
31. $x^4 - x^3 + 2x^2 - 3x - 3 = 0.$ **32.** $2x^4 - 2x^3 + 9x^2 - 10x - 5 = 0.$

By use of Horner's method, find, to three decimal places, the value of the indicated real root in the following problems.

33. $\sqrt[3]{3}.$ HINT: Solve the equation $x^3 - 3 = 0.$
34. $\sqrt[3]{2}.$ **35.** $\sqrt[3]{7}.$ **36.** $\sqrt[3]{4}.$ **37.** $\sqrt[4]{2}.$ **38.** $\sqrt[4]{5}.$ **39.** $\sqrt[5]{3}.$ **40.** $\sqrt[5]{7}.$

110. Identical polynomials. The following theorem is the basis for the work on partial fractions in Chap. 22.

THEOREM. *If two polynomials of degree* **n** *are equal for more than* **n** *values of the variable, they are identical; that is, the coefficients of equal powers of the variables are equal.*

Proof. We are given that

$$a_0 x^n + a_1 x^{n-1} + \cdots + a_n = b_0 x^n + b_1 x^{n-1} + \cdots + b_n$$

for the n distinct values $x = x_1, x_2, \ldots, x_n$ and for $x = x_{n+1}$ which is different from $x_1, x_2, \ldots, x_n$. Hence,

$$\begin{aligned} f(x) &= (a_0 - b_0)x^n + (a_1 - b_1)x^{n-1} + \cdots + (a_n - b_n) \\ &= (a_0 - b_0)(x - x_1)(x - x_2) \cdots (x - x_n) \\ &= 0 \end{aligned}$$

for $x = x_1, x_2, \ldots, x_n$ and for $x = x_{n+1}$. Since $f(x_{n+1}) = 0$ and no one of the factors involving x is zero for $x = x_{n+1}$, it follows that $a_0 - b_0$, the leading coefficient of x, is zero. Therefore, $a_0 = b_0$. Hence,

$$\begin{aligned} f(x) &= (a_0 - b_0)x^n + (a_1 - b_1)x^{n-1} + \cdots + (a_n - b_n) \\ &= 0 \end{aligned}$$

for $x = x_1, x_2, \ldots, x_n$ and for $x = x_{n+1}$ and is of degree $n - 1$. Consequently, we have the same situation as above, and the leading coefficient $a_1 - b_1$ is zero. Therefore, $a_1 = b_1$. We can show by $(n - 1)$ more repetitions of this process that $a_2 = b_2$, $a_3 = b_3$, $\ldots, a_n = b_n$; and the proof of the theorem is complete.

111. *The cubic equation.* [1] We shall now consider the general cubic equation

(1) $$x^3 + b_1 x^2 + b_2 x + b_3 = 0$$

If we let

(2) $$x = y - \frac{b_1}{3}$$

we get

$$\left(y - \frac{b_1}{3}\right)^3 + b_1 \left(y - \frac{b_1}{3}\right)^2 + b_2 \left(y - \frac{b_1}{3}\right) + b_3 = 0$$

or

(3) $$y^3 + \left(b_2 - \frac{b_1{}^2}{3}\right) y + \frac{2b_1{}^3}{27} - \frac{b_1 b_2}{3} + b_3 = 0$$

which is an equation without a second-degree term and is called the *reduced cubic*. This equation can be further simplified by making the substitution

(4) $$b_2 - \frac{b_1{}^2}{3} = p \quad \text{and} \quad \frac{2b_1{}^3}{27} - \frac{b_1 b_2}{3} + b_3 = q$$

Thus, (3) becomes

(5) $$y^3 + py + q = 0$$

In order to solve the reduced cubic (5), we introduce two new variables u and v whose sum is a root of (5). Consequently, we let

(6) $$y = u + v$$

in (5) and obtain

$$(u + v)^3 + p(u + v) + q = 0$$

or

(7) $$u^3 + v^3 + (p + 3uv)(u + v) + q = 0$$

This gives us one equation in u and v. However, we must have a second equation in order to determine their values uniquely. We may obtain a second equation and further simplify (7) by requiring that u and v satisfy the equation

(8) $$p + 3uv = 0$$

[1] For a more complete discussion of the cubic, see Chap. V of Dickson's "New First Course in the Theory of Equations."

Hence, (7) becomes

(9) $$u^3 + v^3 + q = 0$$

If we eliminate v between (8) and (9) by solving the former for v in terms of u and p and then substituting in (9), we obtain

$$u^3 - \frac{p^3}{27u^3} + q = 0$$

or

(10) $$27u^6 + 27qu^3 - p^3 = 0$$

This equation is a quadratic in u^3, and its solutions are

$$u^3 = \frac{-27q \pm \sqrt{729q^2 + 108p^3}}{54}$$

$$= \frac{-q \pm \sqrt{q^2 + \dfrac{4p^3}{27}}}{2}$$

$$= \frac{-q}{2} \pm \sqrt{\frac{q^2}{4} + \frac{p^3}{27}}$$

(11) $$= \frac{-q}{2} \pm \sqrt{R}$$

where

(12) $$R = \frac{q^2}{4} + \frac{p^3}{27}$$

If we let

(13) $$u^3 = \frac{-q}{2} + \sqrt{R} = A$$

then, from (9),

(14) $$v^3 = \frac{-q}{2} - \sqrt{R} = B$$

Furthermore, if we had let $u^3 = -q/2 - \sqrt{R}$, we would have obtained $v^3 = -q/2 + \sqrt{R}$. Hence, the values of u and v would have been interchanged.

Since $u^3 = A$ and $v^3 = B$, the values of u and v are

(15) $$u = \sqrt[3]{A},\ \omega \sqrt[3]{A},\ \omega^2 \sqrt[3]{A}$$

and

(16) $$v = \sqrt[3]{B}, \, \omega \sqrt[3]{B}, \, \omega^2 \sqrt[3]{B}$$

where

$$\omega = -\tfrac{1}{2} + \tfrac{1}{2}i \sqrt{3} \qquad \text{and} \qquad \omega^2 = -\tfrac{1}{2} - \tfrac{1}{2}i \sqrt{3}$$

If we make use of the fact that $\omega^3 = 1$, we see that

$$\sqrt[3]{A} \text{ and } \sqrt[3]{B}, \quad \omega \sqrt[3]{A} \text{ and } \omega^2 \sqrt[3]{B}, \quad \omega^2 \sqrt[3]{A} \text{ and } \omega \sqrt[3]{B}$$

are the only pairs of values of u and v that satisfy the condition (8).

If now we substitute these pairs of values of u and v in (6), we obtain

$$y_1 = \sqrt[3]{A} + \sqrt[3]{B}$$
$$y_2 = \omega \sqrt[3]{A} + \omega^2 \sqrt[3]{B}$$

and

$$y_3 = \omega^2 \sqrt[3]{A} + \omega \sqrt[3]{B}$$

Since $x = y - \dfrac{b_1}{3}$, we see that the roots of (1) are

$$x_1 = \sqrt[3]{A} + \sqrt[3]{B} - \frac{b_1}{3}$$

(17) $$x_2 = \omega \sqrt[3]{A} + \omega^2 \sqrt[3]{B} - \frac{b_1}{3}$$

$$x_3 = \omega^2 \sqrt[3]{A} + \omega \sqrt[3]{B} - \frac{b_1}{3}$$

Example 1

In the equation

$$x^3 - 3x^2 + 21x - 19 = 0$$

$b_1 = -3, \, b_2 = 21, \, b_3 = -19$. Hence, by (4), $p = 21 - 3 = 18$ and

$$q = -2 + 21 - 19 = 0$$

Furthermore, by (12), $R = 216$. Therefore, by (13) and (14), $A = \sqrt{216}$ and $B = -\sqrt{216}$. Finally, $\sqrt[3]{A} = \sqrt[3]{\sqrt{216}} = \sqrt{\sqrt[3]{216}} = \sqrt{6}$, and

$$\sqrt[3]{B} = -\sqrt{6}$$

Hence, by (17) we have

$$x_1 = \sqrt{6} - \sqrt{6} + 1 = 1$$
$$x_2 = \omega \sqrt{6} + \omega^2(- \sqrt{6}) + 1 = 3 \sqrt{2} \, i + 1$$
$$x_3 = \omega^2 \sqrt{6} + \omega(-6) + 1 = -3 \sqrt{2} \, i + 1$$

If R is negative, $\sqrt{R}$ is imaginary, and A and B are conjugate complex numbers. In this case, we use De Moivre's theorem to find the cube roots of A and B and choose these roots so that they are also conjugate imaginary numbers.

Example 2

In the equation

$$x^3 - 3x^2 - 24x + 26 = 0$$

$b_1 = -3$, $b_2 = -24$, $b_3 = 26$. Substituting these values in (4), we get $p = -27$ and $q = 0$. Hence, from (12), $R = -729$, and therefore $A = 27i$ and $B = -27i$. In order to find the cube root of A we write

$$\sqrt[3]{A} = A^{\frac{1}{3}} = [27(\cos 90° + i \sin 90°)]^{\frac{1}{3}}$$
$$= 3(\cos 30° + i \sin 30°)$$
$$= \tfrac{1}{2}(3 \sqrt{3} + 3i)$$

Similarly,

$$\sqrt[3]{B} = \tfrac{1}{2}(3 \sqrt{3} - 3i)$$

When these values are substituted in (17), we get

$$x = 1 + 3 \sqrt{3}, \; x = 1 - 3 \sqrt{3}, \; x = 1$$

112. The quartic equation. We shall now consider the general quartic

(1) $$x^4 + bx^3 + cx^2 + dx + e = 0$$

If we transpose the last three terms, (1) becomes

$$x^4 + bx^3 = -cx^2 - dx - e$$

The left member contains two terms of the square of $(x^2 + \tfrac{1}{2}bx)$, and we shall complete the square by adding $\tfrac{1}{4}b^2x^2$. Thus,

$$(x^2 + \tfrac{1}{2}bx)^2 = (\tfrac{1}{4}b^2 - c)x^2 - dx - e$$

Now, adding $(x^2 + \tfrac{1}{2}bx)y + \tfrac{1}{4}y^2$ to each member, we have

(2) $$(x^2 + \tfrac{1}{2}bx + \tfrac{1}{2}y)^2 = (\tfrac{1}{4}b^2 - c + y)x^2$$
$$+ (-d + \tfrac{1}{2}by)x - e + \tfrac{1}{4}y^2$$

The left member is a perfect square; hence, the right member must be a perfect square also. Consequently, its discriminant is zero. Thus,

$$(-d + \tfrac{1}{2}by)^2 - 4(\tfrac{1}{4}b^2 - c + y)(-e + \tfrac{1}{4}y^2) = 0$$

or, if we expand, collect coefficients of like terms, and change signs,

(3) $\qquad$ $y^3 - cy^2 + (bd - 4e)y - b^2e + 4ce - d^2 = 0$

This equation is known as the *resolvent cubic*. If we choose *any* root y of (3) and substitute it in (2), the right member becomes a perfect square of a linear function of x, say $mx + n$. Hence,

$$(x^2 + \tfrac{1}{2}bx + \tfrac{1}{2}y)^2 = (mx + n)^2$$

and, therefore,

(4) $\qquad$ $x^2 + \tfrac{1}{2}bx + \tfrac{1}{2}y = mx + n$

and

$$x^2 + \tfrac{1}{2}bx + \tfrac{1}{2}y = -mx - n$$

Hence, we have reduced the solution of the quartic (1) to solving the two quadratics (4).

Example

Solve

(1) $\qquad$ $x^4 + 2x^3 - x^2 + x + \tfrac{1}{4} = 0$

Solution

Transposing the last three members, we have

$$x^4 + 2x^3 = x^2 - x - \tfrac{1}{4}$$

Completing the square of the left member by adding x^2, we get

$$(x^2 + x)^2 = 2x^2 - x - \tfrac{1}{4}$$

Now adding $(x^2 + x)y + \tfrac{1}{4}y^2$ to each member, we have

$$(x^2 + x)^2 + (x^2 + x)y + \tfrac{1}{4}y^2 = 2x^2 - x - \tfrac{1}{4} + (x^2 + x)y + \tfrac{1}{4}y^2$$

or

(2) $\qquad$ $(x^2 + x + \tfrac{1}{2}y)^2 = x^2(2 + y) + x(-1 + y) - \tfrac{1}{4} + \tfrac{1}{4}y^2$

Since the left member is a perfect square, the right member must be. Hence, its discriminant is zero. Thus,

$$(-1 + y)^2 - 4(2 + y)(-\tfrac{1}{4} + \tfrac{1}{4}y^2) = 0$$
$$1 - 2y + y^2 + 2 + y - 2y^2 - y^3 = -y^3 - y^2 - y + 3 = 0$$

One solution of this is 1. Hence, $y = 1$ in (2) must make the right member a perfect square. Substituting $y = 1$ in (2) gives

$$(x^2 + x + \tfrac{1}{2})^2 = 3x^2$$

Therefore, taking the square root of each member,

$$x^2 + x + \tfrac{1}{2} = \sqrt{3}\,x \quad \text{and} \quad x^2 + x + \tfrac{1}{2} = -\sqrt{3}\,x$$

Consequently, the roots of (1) are those of

$$x^2 + (1 - \sqrt{3})x + \tfrac{1}{2} = 0 \quad \text{and} \quad x^2 + (1 + \sqrt{3})x + \tfrac{1}{2} = 0$$

Hence,

$$x = \frac{-1 + \sqrt{3} \pm \sqrt{1 - 2\sqrt{3} + 3 - 2}}{2} \quad \text{and}$$

$$\frac{-1 - \sqrt{3} \pm \sqrt{1 + 2\sqrt{3} + 3 - 2}}{2}$$

$$= \frac{-1 + \sqrt{3} \pm \sqrt{2 - 2\sqrt{3}}}{2} \quad \text{and} \quad \frac{-1 - \sqrt{3} \pm \sqrt{2 + 2\sqrt{3}}}{2}$$

$$= \frac{-1 + \sqrt{3} \pm \sqrt{2}\sqrt{1 - \sqrt{3}}}{2} \quad \text{and} \quad \frac{-1 - \sqrt{3} \pm \sqrt{2}\sqrt{1 + \sqrt{3}}}{2}$$

EXERCISE 57

Solve the equations in Problems 1 to 16 by the method of Art. 111.

1. $x^3 - 3x^2 + 12x - 10 = 0$.
2. $x^3 + 6x^2 + 21x + 26 = 0$.
3. $x^3 - 3x^2 + 15x - 13 = 0$.
4. $x^3 + 6x^2 + 20x + 14 = 0$.
5. $x^3 - 9x^2 + 39x - 63 = 0$.
6. $x^3 + 3x^2 + 30x + 28 = 0$.
7. $x^3 - 3x^2 + 30x - 28 = 0$.
8. $x^3 - 6x^2 + 39x - 62 = 0$.
9. $x^3 + 9x^2 + 21x + 13 = 0$.
10. $x^3 - 6x^2 + 6x + 8 = 0$.
11. $x^3 - 9x^2 + 21x - 5 = 0$.
12. $x^3 + 3x^2 - 21x + 9 = 0$.
13. $x^3 - 3x^2 - 9x + 11 = 0$.
14. $x^3 - 6x^2 + 9x - 2 = 0$.
15. $x^3 - 9x^2 + 54 = 0$.
16. $x^3 + 6x^2 + 9x + 2 = 0$.

Solve the following equations by the method of Art. 112.

17. $x^4 + x^3 - 7x^2 - x + 6 = 0$.
18. $x^4 + 2x^3 - 7x^2 - 8x + 12 = 0$.
19. $2x^4 - 11x^3 + 16x^2 - x - 6 = 0$. NOTE: Divide by the coefficient of x^4 before applying Art. 112.
20. $2x^4 + 3x^3 - 12x^2 - 7x + 6 = 0$.
21. $x^4 - 3x^3 - x^2 + 9x - 6 = 0$.
22. $x^4 - x^3 - 4x^2 + 2x + 4 = 0$.
23. $x^4 + x^3 - 3x^2 - 2x + 2 = 0$.
24. $x^4 + 2x^3 - 7x^2 - 6x + 12 = 0$.
25. $x^4 + 2x^3 - 3x^2 - 4x + 3 = 0$.
26. $x^4 + x^3 - 3x^2 + 10x - 12 = 0$.
27. $x^4 + 3x^3 + 5x^2 + 4x + 2 = 0$.
28. $x^2 + 5x^3 + 14x^2 + 19x + 15 = 0$.

CHAPTER 13

INEQUALITIES

113. Definitions and fundamental principles. It was proved in Art. 69 that a quadratic equation has real and unequal roots if and only if its discriminant is greater than zero. For example, the roots of $x^2 + kx - 1 = 0$ are real and unequal if and only if

$$(1) \qquad\qquad k^2 + 4 > 0$$

Likewise, the roots of $x^2 + 2x + k = 0$ are real and unequal if and only if

$$(2) \qquad\qquad 4 - 4k > 0$$

Statements (1) and (2) illustrate situations in which it is necessary to determine values of the variable for which one function is greater than or less than another. Such situations occur frequently in mathematics, and in this chapter we shall study methods for dealing with them.

DEFINITION. *An **inequality** is a statement that one real quantity is greater than or less than another.*

The signs $>$ and $<$ introduced in Art. 2 indicate the relationships of "greater than" and "less than," respectively. Note that the inequality sign always points to the smaller quantity.

Two inequalities have the *same sense* or the *opposite sense* according as the signs in them point in the same or in opposite directions.

In (1), k^2 is never negative for real values of k. Hence $k^2 + 4$ is positive for all real values of k. On the other hand, the left member of (2) is greater than zero only when k is less than one. Hence, statements (1) and (2) illustrate the following definitions.

DEFINITION. *An inequality that is true for all real values of the variable is an **absolute inequality.***

DEFINITION. *An inequality that is true for some real values of the variable and is not true for others is a* **conditional inequality.**

The *solution* of an inequality is a range of values of the variable for which the inequality is true. The process of solving inequalities is based on the following theorems.

THEOREM 1. *The sense of an inequality is not changed if the same number is added to, or subtracted from, each member.*

THEOREM 2. *The sense of an inequality is not changed if each member is multiplied, or divided, by the same positive number.*

THEOREM 3. *The sense of an inequality is reversed if each member is multiplied, or divided, by the same negative number.*

The proof of these theorems involves repeated applications of an argument similar to the one presented below.

We shall assume that $a < b$ and shall prove

$$(3) \qquad a + c < b + c$$
$$(4) \qquad ap < bp, \; p > 0$$
$$(5) \qquad am > bm, \; m < 0$$

If $a < b$, then

$$(6) \qquad a - b = n, \; n < 0$$

Adding $c - c \; (= 0)$ to the left member of (6), we have

$$a - b + c - c = n$$

or,

$$(a + c) - (b + c) = n$$

Hence,

$$a + c < b + c$$

If we multiply each member of (6) by $p > 0$, we have

$$ap - bp = pn$$

Furthermore, since $p > 0$ and $n < 0$, it follows that $pn < 0$. Hence, $ap < bp$.

Likewise, if we multiply each member of (6) by $m < 0$, we obtain $am - bm = mn$. In this case, mn is positive, since $m < 0$ and $n < 0$. Hence, $am > bm$.

The steps necessary for the completion of the proof of these theorems appear as the first four problems of Exercise 58.

THEOREM 4. *If a and b are two unequal positive numbers and n is a positive integer, then a^n and b^n, also $\sqrt[n]{a}$ and $\sqrt[n]{b}$* are unequal in the same sense as a and b.*

Proof. By section 4 of Art. 16, we have

(7) $\quad a^n - b^n = (a - b)(a^{n-1} + a^{n-2}b + \cdots + ab^{n-2} + b^{n-1})$

(8) $\quad a - b = (\sqrt[n]{a})^n - (\sqrt[n]{b})^n$
$$= (\sqrt[n]{a} - \sqrt[n]{b})[(\sqrt[n]{a})^{n-1} + (\sqrt[n]{a})^{n-2}(\sqrt[n]{b}) + \cdots$$
$$+ (\sqrt[n]{a})(\sqrt[n]{b})^{n-2} + (\sqrt[n]{b})^{n-1}]$$

Since a and b are positive, the second factor in the second member of each of (7) and (8) is positive. Hence $a^n - b^n$, $\sqrt[n]{a} - \sqrt[n]{b}$, and $a - b$ have the same algebraic sign.

Example

As an example illustrating the use of the above theorems, we shall show that if $x \neq y$, then $x^2 + y^2 > 2xy$.

Since $x \neq y$, then both are not zero. Hence, $x - y = n$, $n \neq 0$. Therefore, $(x - y)^2 = n^2$. Thus, since n^2 is positive, we have

$$(x - y)^2 > 0$$

or

$$x^2 - 2xy + y^2 > 0$$

Hence,

$$x^2 + y^2 > 2xy, \text{ by Theorem 1}$$

EXERCISE 58

1. If $a < b$, prove that $a - c < b - c$, and $a/p < b/p$ with $p > 0$.

2. If $a > b$, prove that $a + c > b + c$ and $a - c > b - c$.

3. If $a > b$ and $p > 0$, prove that $ap > bp$ and $a/p > b/p$.

4. If $a > b$ and $m < 0$, prove that $am < bm$ and $a/m < b/m$.

5. Use the method for proving Theorem 4 to show that if $a > b$, then $\sqrt{a} > \sqrt{b}$.

6. Show that $x^2 < x$ if $0 < x < 1$, and $x^2 > x$ if $x > 1$.

7. Show that if $0 < x < y$, then $x/y + y/x > 2$.

8. If $x < y < 0$, show that $\frac{1}{2}(x + y) > \sqrt{xy}$.

9. If x is positive and not equal to 1, show that $x + (1/x) > 2$.

10. If $0 < x < y$, show that $(x + 1)/(y + 1) > x/y$.

11. If $0 < x < y$, prove that $\sqrt{xy} > 2xy/(x + y)$.

12. If $x > 1$, prove that $(x - 1)/(x + 1) < (x^2 - 1)/(x^2 + 1)$.

* Note that $\sqrt[n]{a}$ and $\sqrt[n]{b}$ denote the principal roots of a and b, respectively, and since a and b are positive, these roots are positive.

114. Conditional inequalities. As we stated in the previous article, the solution of a conditional inequality is a range of values of the variable for which the inequality is true. In this article we shall present both the graphical and the algebraic methods for obtaining this solution.

Graphical method. We shall first illustrate and then present the formal steps in the method of obtaining the graphical solution of an inequality.

In order to solve the inequality

(1) $$6x^2 - 2 > -x$$

we transpose $-x$ and obtain

(2) $$6x^2 + x - 2 > 0$$

By Theorem 1, any value of x that satisfies (2) satisfies (1) also. Now we set the left member of (2) equal to y and obtain

(3) $$y = 6x^2 + x - 2$$

and we seek the values of x for which $y > 0$. Next we construct the graph of (3), using the table of corresponding values below.

x	-2	-1	0	1	2
y	20	3	-2	5	24

The graph shown in Fig. 33 crosses the X axis at the points whose abscissas are approximately .5 and $-.7$, respectively. Obviously y is positive for all values of x greater than .5 and also for all values of x less than $-.7$. Hence, the solutions of (1) are $x > .5$ and $x < -.7$.

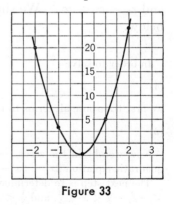

Figure 33

The formal steps for obtaining the solution of an inequality by the graphical method are given below.

1. *Transpose all terms to one member.*

2. *Set the resulting expression equal to a new variable.*

3. *Draw the graph of the equation thus obtained.*

4. *The solution consists of those values of x for which the graph*

*is above or below the **X** axis according as the expression in step 1 is positive or negative.*

Algebraic method. The steps presented below for obtaining the algebraic solution of a linear inequality are formally the same as those used in solving a linear equation.

1. *Transpose the terms that involve the variable to the left member of the inequality and the constants to the right member.*

2. *Combine all terms in each member.*

3. *Divide both members of the inequality obtained in step 2 by the coefficient of the unknown, bearing in mind that if this coefficient is negative, the inequality sign is reversed.*

Example 1

The solution of

$$2x + 3 > 5x - 9$$

consists of the following steps.

1.	$2x - 5x > -9 - 3$	(transposing terms)
2.	$-3x > -12$	(combining terms)
3.	$x < 4$	(dividing both members by -4 and reversing the inequality sign)

In the solution of nonlinear inequalities, we make use of the fact that a rational integral function of x changes sign only at the zeros of the function. For example, if the zeros of $f(x)$ are r_1, r_2, and r_3, with $r_1 < r_2 < r_3$, then $f(x)$ will not change signs in any one of the intervals $-\infty < x < r_1$, $r_1 < x < r_2$, $r_2 < x < r_3$, and $r_3 < x < \infty$. We shall illustrate the method in the examples below.

Example 2

In order to solve

$$(4) \qquad\qquad 2x^2 < 2 - 3x$$

we first transpose all terms to the left and get

$$(5) \qquad\qquad 2x^2 + 3x - 2 < 0$$

Now we obtain the zeros, -2, and $\frac{1}{2}$ of $f(x) = 2x^2 + 3x - 2$ by solving the quadratic equation $2x^2 + 3x - 2 = 0$.

The next step is to determine the sign of $f(x)$ in each of the intervals $-\infty < x < -2$, $-2 < x < \frac{1}{2}$, and $\frac{1}{2} < x < \infty$ by assigning a value in each of them to x. Since $-\infty < -3 < -2$, and

$$f(-3) = 2(-3)^2 + 3(-3) - 2 = 18 - 9 - 2 = 7$$

$f(x) > 0$ in the first interval. Similarly, $f(x) < 0$ in the second since $f(0) = -2$, and $f(x) > 0$ in the third since $f(1) = 3$. Hence, since $f(x) < 0$ in the second interval, the solution of (4) is $-2 < x < \frac{1}{2}$.

Example 3

As a second example, we shall solve the inequality

$$x^3 + 3x^2 > x + 3$$

1. $$x^3 + 3x^2 - x - 3 > 0 \qquad \text{(transposing } x + 3\text{)}$$

2. The zeros of the function

$$
\begin{aligned}
f(x) &= x^3 + 3x^2 - x - 3 \\
&= x^2(x + 3) - (x + 3) \\
&= (x^2 - 1)(x + 3)
\end{aligned}
$$

are $x = -3$, $x = -1$, and $x = 1$.

3. The intervals to be considered are $-\infty < x < -3$, $-3 < x < -1$, $-1 < x < 1$, and $1 < x < \infty$.

4. In the first, $f(x) < 0$, since $f(-4) = -64 + 48 + 4 - 3 = -15$. In the second, $f(x) > 0$, since $f(-2) = -8 + 12 + 2 - 3 = 3$. In the third, $f(x) < 0$, since $f(0) = -3$. In the fourth, $f(x) > 0$, since $f(2) = 15$.

5. Hence, the solution of the given inequality is $-3 < x < -1$, and $1 < x < \infty$.

These examples illustrate the following formal steps in the solution of a nonlinear inequality.

1. *Transpose all terms to the left member.*
2. *Find the zeros of the function obtained in step 1.*
3. *Determine the sign of the function in the intervals:*
   (a) *All values of **x** less than the smallest zero.*
   (b) *All values of **x** between consecutive zeros.*
   (c) *All values of **x** greater than the largest zero.*
4. *Select the intervals in step 3 that satisfy the given inequality.*

115. Conditional inequalities that involve absolute values. If we use the definition of absolute value given in Art. 2, we see that an inequality of the type

(1) $$|ax + b| < c$$

requires that $ax + b$ shall be between c and $-c$ as indicated on the line given below.

$$-c \qquad 0 \qquad c$$

Hence, if a value of x satisfies both $ax + b < c$ *and* $ax + b > -c$, it will satisfy (1).

Furthermore, the inequality $|rx + t| > c$ requires that $rx + t$ represent a point that is to the right of c or one that is to the left of $-c$. Hence, a value of x satisfies $|rx + t| > c$ if it satisfies $rx + t > c$ *or* satisfies $rx + t < -c$.

Example 1

Solve

$$\left| \frac{x}{3} + 2 \right| < 4$$

Solution

This inequality is satisfied if, and only if, both

$$\frac{x}{3} + 2 < 4 \quad \text{and} \quad \frac{x}{3} + 2 > -4$$

are satisfied. Transposing 2 in each of these inequalities, we get

$$\frac{x}{3} < 2 \quad \text{and} \quad \frac{x}{3} > -6$$

Hence, multiplying by 3 in each case, we see that the original inequality is satisfied by values of x that satisfy both $x < 6$ and $x > -18$. Therefore, the solution of the given inequality is $-18 < x < 6$.

Example 2

Solve

$$\left| \frac{4x}{5} - 1 \right| > 3$$

Solution

This inequality is satisfied if either

$$\frac{4x}{5} - 1 > 3 \quad \text{or} \quad \frac{4x}{5} - 1 < -3$$

is satisfied. Transposing -1 in each of these inequalities, we get

$$\frac{4x}{5} > 4 \quad \text{and} \quad \frac{4x}{5} < -2$$

Hence, multiplying by $\frac{5}{4}$ in each case, we see that the original inequality is satisfied by values of x that are greater than 5 and by values of x that are less than $-\frac{5}{2}$, that is, by $x > 5$ and by $x < -\frac{5}{2}$.

EXERCISE 59

Solve the inequalities in Problems 1 to 16 graphically.

1. $2x - 1 > x + 2.$
2. $x - 2 < 3x.$
3. $4x > 2x - 7.$
4. $8x - 1 < 6x + 3.$
5. $3x + 4 > x - 2.$
6. $9x < 4 + 7x.$
7. $5x - 7 > 3x + 2.$
8. $11x - 5 < 7x - 2.$
9. $x^2 - x - 2 < 0.$
10. $x^2 > x + 6.$
11. $x^2 + 3x > -2.$
12. $x^2 - 3x < -4.$
13. $2x - 3 > 2x^2.$
14. $6x^2 < x + 2.$
15. $x^3 + x^2 > 4x + 4.$
16. $x^3 + 2x^2 + 2x + 1 > 0.$

Solve the inequalities in Problems 17 to 60 algebraically.

17. $x + 3 < 5.$
18. $x + 4 < 7.$
19. $-x + 2 < 3.$
20. $-x - 3 > -1.$
21. $2x - 5 > 0.$
22. $3x - 4 < 0.$
23. $-3x - 9 < 0.$
24. $-5x > -15.$
25. $2x + 3 < 5.$
26. $3x - 2 > 3.$
27. $-2x + 1 < -3.$
28. $-3x + 4 < 11.$
29. $3x + 5 > x + 1.$
30. $5x - 7 < 2x + 2.$
31. $x + 3 < 3x - 2.$
32. $2x - 4 > 5x - 1.$
33. $\dfrac{2x}{3} + 1 > x + \tfrac{1}{2}.$
34. $\dfrac{5x}{6} - \dfrac{1}{3} < \dfrac{2x}{3} - 1.$

35. $\dfrac{x}{5} - \dfrac{2x - 1}{3} > \dfrac{x - 3}{3}.$
36. $\dfrac{x}{6} - \dfrac{3x + 2}{3} < \dfrac{x + 2}{2}.$

37. $|x + 1| < 2.$
38. $|x - 3| < 1.$
39. $|x + 2| > 1.$

40. $|x - 1| > 3.$
41. $\left|\dfrac{2x}{3} - 1\right| < 2.$
42. $|\tfrac{3}{4}x + 3| < 5.$

43. $\left|\dfrac{3x}{5} + 1\right| > 3.$
44. $\left|\dfrac{5x}{6} - 2\right| > 3.$
45. $(x - 3)(3x + 4) < 0.$

46. $(2x - 1)(1 - x) > 0.$
47. $(3x + 2)(2x - 5) > 0.$
48. $(4x - 3)(3x + 5) > 0.$
49. $6x^2 + 7x - 3 < 0.$
50. $2x^2 - 5x - 3 < 0.$
51. $6x^2 - 7x - 3 > 0.$
52. $4x^2 + 5x - 6 > 0.$
53. $(x - 1)(2x + 3)(3x + 2) < 0.$
54. $(2x + 1)(3x - 2)(x + 2) < 0.$
55. $(3x + 4)(2x - 3)(x - 2) > 0.$
56. $(5x - 2)(3x + 5)(x - 5) > 0.$
57. $2x^3 - x^2 - 13x - 6 < 0.$
58. $2x^3 - 3x^2 - 5x + 6 < 0.$
59. $6x^3 + x^2 - 19x + 6 > 0.$
60. $6x^3 - 11x^2 - 12x + 5 > 0.$

Find the values of x for which the following expressions represent real numbers.

61. $\sqrt{x^2 - a^2}.$
62. $\sqrt{x^2 + a^2}.$
63. $\sqrt{a^2 - x^2}.$
64. $\sqrt{-x^2 - a^2}.$
65. $\dfrac{(x - 2)(x + 3)}{\sqrt{x + 1}}.$
66. $\dfrac{(x - 1)(x + 2)\sqrt{2 - x}}{\sqrt{x + 3}}.$
67. $\sqrt{(2x - 1)(1 - x)}.$
68. $\sqrt{(3x + 2)(2 - 5x)}.$

CHAPTER 14

LOGARITHMS

116. *Introduction*. In the statement

(1) $$2^3 = 8$$

we use the term *exponent* to indicate the relationship that exists between 3 and 2. However, 3 is also related to 8 in (1), and we indicate this relationship by the term *logarithm*. In other words, in (1), 3 is the exponent of 2 and also the logarithm of 8, or more precisely, the logarithm to the base 2 of 8. Hence, this chapter will be a continuation of the discussion of exponents. In particular, we shall show how exponents, or logarithms, may be used to simplify numerical computation and to solve certain types of equations that are not solvable by more elementary methods. Since we shall employ the definitions and laws of Chap. 7, the reader is advised to review that chapter before proceeding further.

As a basis for our subsequent discussion, we shall next present the following definition:

DEFINITION I. *The **logarithm** to a given base of any number is the exponent that indicates the power to which the base must be raised in order to obtain the number.*

The abbreviated form of the statement "The logarithm to the base b of N is L" is $\log_b N = L$. If we use this notation we may express definition I in symbolic form as

(2) $$\log_b N = L \quad implies \quad b^L = N$$

Note that the abbreviation "log" appears without a period and that the symbol for the base appears as a subscript.

Examples

1.	$\log_8 64 = 2$	since	$8^2 = 64$
2.	$\log_4 64 = 3$	since	$4^3 = 64$
3.	$\log_{81} 9 = \frac{1}{2}$	since	$81^{\frac{1}{2}} = 9$
4.	$\log_a 1 = 0$	since	$a^0 = 1$

In many cases, if two of the three letters in (2) are known, the third can be found by inspection.

Example 5

Find the value of N if $\log_7 N = 2$.

Solution

If we convert the above logarithmic statement to the exponential form, we have

$$7^2 = N$$

and then it is obvious that $N = 49$.

Example 6

If $\log_b 125 = 3$, find the value of b.

Solution

By use of (2), we

$$b^3 = 125$$

Hence,

$$b = \sqrt[3]{125} = 5$$

Example 7

Find a if $\log_{27} 3 = a$.

Solution

Again, using (2), we have

$$27^a = 3$$

Hence, since $27^{\frac{1}{3}} = 3$, it follows that

$$a = \tfrac{1}{3}$$

EXERCISE 60

By use of (2) of Art. 116, express the statements in Problems 1 to 18 in exponential form.

1. $\log_5 25 = 2$.
2. $\log_4 16 = 2$.
3. $\log_3 27 = 3$.
4. $\log_5 125 = 3$.
5. $\log_2 32 = 5$.
6. $\log_4 64 = 3$.
7. $\log_3 \frac{1}{9} = -2$.
8. $\log_2 \frac{1}{16} = -4$.
9. $\log_3 \frac{1}{27} = -3$.
10. $\log_{16} 4 = \frac{1}{2}$.
11. $\log_{27} 243 = \frac{5}{3}$.
12. $\log_4 8 = \frac{3}{2}$.
13. $\log_{\frac{1}{4}} \frac{1}{8} = \frac{3}{2}$.
14. $\log_{\frac{1}{8}} \frac{1}{4} = \frac{2}{3}$.
15. $\log_{\frac{9}{16}} \frac{3}{4} = \frac{1}{2}$.
16. $\log_{a^2} a^8 = 4$.
17. $\log_{a^{\frac{1}{2}}} a^4 = 8$.
18. $\log_{a^2} a^3 = \frac{3}{2}$.

By use of (2) of Art. 116, express the statements in Problems 19 to 30 in logarithmic form.

19. $2^3 = 8$.
20. $4^3 = 64$.
21. $5^2 = 25$.
22. $32^{\frac{2}{5}} = 4$.
23. $8^{\frac{2}{3}} = 4$.
24. $64^{\frac{1}{3}} = 4$.

25. $3^{-1} = \frac{1}{3}$.   **26.** $2^{-3} = \frac{1}{8}$.   **27.** $\left(\frac{1}{2}\right)^{-4} = 16$.
28. $\left(\frac{1}{3}\right)^{-2} = 9$.   **29.** $27^{-\frac{2}{3}} = \frac{1}{9}$.   **30.** $32^{-\frac{3}{5}} = \frac{1}{8}$.

Find the value of each logarithm in Problems 31 to 51.

31. $\log_4 16$.   **32.** $\log_5 25$.   **33.** $\log_7 49$.
34. $\log_9 81$.   **35.** $\log_3 27$.   **36.** $\log_5 125$.
37. $\log_{10} 1000$.   **38.** $\log_2 32$.   **39.** $\log_{36} 6$.
40. $\log_{64} 8$.   **41.** $\log_{144} 12$.   **42.** $\log_{121} 11$.
43. $\log_8 2$.   **44.** $\log_{216} 6$.   **45.** $\log_{125} 5$.
46. $\log_{81} 3$.   **47.** $\log_{a^2} a^6$.   **48.** $\log_{b^8} b^6$.
49. $\log_{b^{\frac{1}{2}}} b^4$.   **50.** $\log_{b^{\frac{1}{3}}} b^6$.   **51.** $\log_{b^{\frac{2}{3}}} b^6$.

Find the value of the unknown letter in Problems 52 to 66.

52. $\log_2 n = 2$.   **53.** $\log_3 n = 4$.   **54.** $\log_5 n = 3$.
55. $\log_4 n = 4$.   **56.** $\log_b 8 = 3$.   **57.** $\log_b 16 = 4$.
58. $\log_b 32 = 5$.   **59.** $\log_b 81 = 4$.   **60.** $\log_b 4 = \frac{1}{2}$.
61. $\log_b 6 = \frac{1}{2}$.   **62.** $\log_b 3 = \frac{1}{3}$.   **63.** $\log_b 3 = \frac{1}{5}$.
64. $\log_b 125 = \frac{3}{2}$.   **65.** $\log_b 8 = \frac{3}{5}$.   **66.** $\log_b 81 = \frac{4}{3}$.

117. Common or Briggs logarithms. Examples 1, 2, 3, 4, and 7 of the previous article are illustrations of situations in which the logarithm of a number can be determined by inspection. In general, this is not possible. For example, we cannot determine the value of L by elementary methods in $\log_{10} 32.71 = L$. However, since $10 < 32.71 < 10^2$, we know that the value of L is between 1 and 2. Tables have been prepared from which the logarithm of any number to the base ten can be obtained. Furthermore, these tables may be used to find a number if its logarithm to the base ten is known. The method for using these tables will be explained in the next three articles.

If the base is 10, the logarithm of a number is called the *common* or *Briggs* logarithm. It is customary to omit the symbol for the base when dealing with common logarithms. Hence, hereafter in the statement $\log N = L$, it is understood that the base is ten.

118. The characteristic and mantissa. As we stated in the previous article, $\log 32.71$ is between 1 and 2. Actually, this logarithm is irrational and cannot be expressed exactly in decimal form, but to four decimal places its value is 1.5146. Thus, $\log 32.71 = 1.5146$, and therefore, by (2) of Art. 116, $32.71 = 10^{1.5146}$. Obviously,

$$3271 = 32.71(10)^2 = (10^{1.5146})(10^2) = 10^{1.5146+2} = 10^{3.5146}$$

Hence, $\log 3271 = 3.5146$. Similarly,

$$3.271 = \frac{32.71}{10} = \frac{10^{1.5146}}{10} = 10^{0.5146}$$

and

$$.03271 = \frac{32.71}{10^3} = \frac{10^{1.5146}}{10^3} = 10^{1.5146-3} = 10^{-2+.5146}$$

Hence,

$$\log 3.271 = 0.5146$$

and

$$\log .03271 = -2 + .5146^*$$

The above examples illustrate the following definition:

DEFINITION. *The common logarithm of any number can be expressed approximately as an integer, either positive, zero, or negative, plus a positive decimal fraction. When the logarithm is in this form, the integer is called the* **characteristic** *and the positive fraction is called the* **mantissa.**

The mantissa of a logarithm is obtained from a table by use of a method explained in Art. 120.

If the characteristic of a logarithm is positive, then the characteristic and the mantissa are written as a single number, as in $\log 32.71 = 1.5147$. However, when the characteristic is negative, as in the case of $\log .03271 = -2 + .5147$, the characteristic and mantissa cannot be expressed as a single positive number, since the former is negative and the latter is positive and the former is greater than the latter. Since it is desirable to keep the fractional part of a logarithm positive, it is customary to write a logarithm such as $-2 + .5147$ in the form $8.5147 - 10$.†
In general, if the characteristic of a logarithm is $-c$, it is customary to express $-c$ in the form $n - 10$, and then to write the mantissa preceded by a decimal point at the right of n.

If the decimal point in a number is shifted to the right or to the left, the number is multiplied by a positive or negative integral power of ten. Thus, the logarithm is either increased or decreased by an integer. Such an operation affects the characteristic only.

---

* The reason for using this notation instead of the equivalent negative number -1.4853 will be explained later.

† A logarithm of the type $-2 + .5147$ is sometimes written $\bar{2}.5147$. However, we shall not employ this notation.

Thus, the characteristic of the logarithm of any number depends upon the position of the decimal point, and the mantissa depends upon the digits and their arrangement in the number.

The decimal point in a number that is between one and ten is located at the right of the first digit in it. Since such a number is between 10^0 and 10^1, the characteristic of its common logarithm is zero. If the decimal point is shifted n places to the right, the number is multiplied by 10^n, and hence the characteristic of its logarithm is $0 + n$. Similarly, if the decimal point is shifted n places to the left, the characteristic of the logarithm is

$$0 - n = -n$$

We shall now define the *reference position for the decimal point in a number as the position immediately to the right of the first nonzero digit in the number*. For example, the reference position in 6234 is between 6 and 2, and the reference position in .003621 is between 3 and 6. Using this terminology, we are now in position to state the following rule for obtaining the characteristic of the common logarithm of any number.

RULE. *The characteristic of the common logarithm of a number is numerically equal to the number of digits between the reference position and the decimal point. It is positive or negative according as the decimal point is to the right or the left of the reference position.*

Examples

1. The reference position in 236.78 is between 2 and 3. Hence, there are two digits, 3 and 6, between the reference position and the decimal point. Furthermore, the decimal point is to the right of the reference position. Hence, the characteristic of the logarithm of 236.78 is 2.

2. The characteristic of the logarithm of 3.124 is zero, since the decimal point is in the reference position.

3. The decimal point in .003271 is three places to the left of the reference position. Hence, the characteristic of the logarithm of .003271 is -3. As we stated earlier in this article, it is customary to write the characteristic, -3, as $7 - 10$.

119. *Rounding off a number.* The tables in this book enable us to obtain the mantissa of a logarithm to four places only. By use of these tables, we can obtain results that are correct to only four places. Hence, we shall frequently resort to the practice of *rounding off a number* or, stated more precisely, rounding off a number to n places. This practice consists of the following steps:

1. We replace all digits after the nth by zeros. If the number is a decimal fraction, we do not count the zeros between the decimal point and the first nonzero digit.

2. We consider the decimal fraction made by placing a decimal point before the number made up of the digits replaced. If this number is greater than .5, we increase the nth digit by one. If the fraction is less than .5, we leave the nth digit unchanged.

3. If the above fraction is exactly .5 and the nth digit is odd, we increase it by one. If the nth digit is even, we leave it unchanged. In other words, in this case, the "rounded-off" number should always be even.

Examples

1. 63276 rounded off to three places is 63,300 since .76 > .5.

2. 8142183 rounded off to four places is 8,142,000 since .183 < .5.

3. 10.365 rounded off to four places is 10.36 since the fourth digit 6 is even; and 3.275 rounded off to three places is 3.28 since the third digit 7 is odd.

4. .006258461 rounded off to two places is .00063 since .58461 > .5.

120. *Use of the table to obtain the mantissa.* In this article, we shall explain the method of finding the mantissa of a logarithm by use of the table on page 416. We shall first discuss numbers of only three digits[1] and as a specific example shall consider 3.27. As we stated in the preceding article, the mantissa of the logarithm of a number is not affected by the position of the decimal point in the number. Hence, for the present, we shall disregard the decimal point. We now turn to the table on page 416 and look in the column headed by N on the left side of the page for the first two digits 32 of the number 327. Then in line with this and across the page in the column headed by the third digit 7 we find the entry 5145. Except for the decimal point[2] before it, this is the desired mantissa. Since the decimal point in 3.27 is in the reference position, the characteristic of the logarithm is zero. Hence, $\log 3.27 = 0.5145$.

As a second example, we shall consider .00634. Again, we temporarily disregard the decimal point and find 63 in the column

---

[1] In this article, when we count the number of digits in a decimal fraction, we start with the first nonzero digit.

[2] No decimal points are printed in the table of mantissas. Hence, when a mantissa is obtained from the table, a decimal point must be placed to the left of it.

headed by N. In line with this and in the column headed by 4, we find the entry 8021. By the rule in Art. 118, the characteristic of the logarithm of .00634 is -3, which we write as $7 - 10$. Hence, log .00634 = $7.8021 - 10$.

If a number is composed of less than three digits, we mentally annex one or two zeros at the right and proceed as before. For example, to get the mantissa of the logarithm of 72, we look up 720, and to get the mantissa of the logarithm of 3, we look up 300.

If all the digits in a number after the third are zeros, we disregard them in the process of getting the mantissa.

In the discussion that follows, it will be necessary to use the expression "the mantissa of the logarithm of N" frequently. For the sake of brevity, we shall abbreviate the expression to ml N.

If a number is composed of four digits, we obtain the mantissa by a method known as *linear interpolation*. We shall explain and illustrate the method by employing it in two examples.

Example 1

As a first example, we shall use the interpolation method to find ml 412.8. Since 412.8 is between 412 and 413, ml 412.8 is between ml 412 and ml 413. Furthermore, 413 differs from 412 by 1, and 412.8 differs from 412 by .8. Hence, 412.8 differs from 412 by .8 of the difference between 412 and 413. We now assume that ml 412.8 differs from ml 412 by .8 of the difference between ml 412 and ml 413. We now turn to the table and find that ml 413 = .6160 and that ml 412 = .6149.

Hence, since .6160 $-$ .6149 = .0011, ml 412.8 differs from ml 412 by

$$.8 \times .0011 = .00088 = .0009 \quad \text{(to one digit)}$$

Therefore, ml 412.8 = .6149 + .0009 = .6158.

The above procedure can be condensed into the following form in which the calculations can be easily performed:

$$1\left[.8\left[\begin{matrix} \text{ml } 413 &= .6160 \\ \text{ml } 412.8 &= \\ \text{ml } 412 &= .6149 \end{matrix} \right].0011 \right.$$

$$.8 \times .0011 = .00088 = .0009 \quad \text{(to one digit)}$$
$$\text{ml } 412.8 = .6149 + .0009 = .6158$$

Hence, since the decimal point in 412.8 is two places to the right of the reference position, we have log 412.8 = 2.6158.

Example 2

As a second example in interpolation, we shall find ml .006324. Since the position of the decimal point has no effect on the mantissa, it follows that

$$\text{ml } .006324 = \text{ml } 632.4$$

Then the process of obtaining the latter mantissa is the same as in Example 1. We note that 632.4 is between 632 and 633. Hence, we have

$$1 \left[.4 \begin{bmatrix} \text{ml } 633 \quad = .8014 \\ \text{ml } 632.4 = \\ \text{ml } 632 \quad = .8007 \end{bmatrix} .0007 \right.$$

$$.4 \times .0007 = .00028 = .0003 \quad \text{(to one digit)}$$

Consequently,

$$\text{ml } 632.4 = .8007 + .0003 = .8010$$

Since the decimal point in .006324 is three places to the left of the reference position, we have log .006324 = 7.8010 − 10.

The interpolation process consists of simple operations which, after some practice, can be performed mentally, thus saving considerable time. We suggest the following steps that can be carried forward rapidly.

1. Temporarily place the decimal point between the third and fourth digits of the given number.

2. Subtract the mantissas of the logarithms of the two numbers between which the above number lies.

3. Multiply this difference by the fourth digit of the given number considered as a decimal fraction.

4. Add the above product to the smaller of the mantissas in step 2.

If a number contains more than four digits, we round it off to four places and proceed as before. For example, to get ml 17.6352, we find ml 17.64.

EXERCISE 61

Determine the characteristic of the common logarithm of the number in each of Problems 1 to 16.

1. 34.	**2.** 4.7.	**3.** 58.6.	**4.** 2.96.
5. 893.	**6.** 94.7.	**7.** 9.87.	**8.** 4725.
9. 362.04.	**10.** .863.	**11.** .032.	**12.** .531.
13. .0029.	**14.** .0503.	**15.** .00021.	**16.** 43,000.

Find the common logarithm of each of the problems below.

17. 58.3.	**18.** 9.72.	**19.** 8.32.	**20.** 470.
21. 5.98.	**22.** .382.	**23.** .025.	**24.** .709.
25. .002.	**26.** .037.	**27.** .0033.	**28.** .371.
29. .012.	**30.** 5.02.	**31.** 20.7.	**32.** .0402.
33. 2130.	**34.** 32,100.	**35.** 806,000.	**36.** 42,000.
37. 10,200.	**38.** 71,000,000.	**39.** 816,000.	**40.** 91,000.
41. 61.34.	**42.** 849.7.	**43.** .1628.	**44.** .04623.
45. 39.72.	**46.** .03175.	**47.** .006007.	**48.** 823.4.
49. .7243.	**50.** 214.8.	**51.** .0006149.	**52.** 5.019.
53. 10.46.	**54.** 77,470.	**55.** .6245.	**56.** .03249.
57. 12.384.	**58.** 46.8752.	**59.** 9.9818.	**60.** 100,467.

121. *Use of the tables to find N when* log N *is given.* The next problem in the use of the tables is the process of finding a number when its logarithm is given. We shall illustrate the process in several examples and shall explain each step as we proceed.

Example 1

In this example, we shall find N when $\log N = 1.6191$. The first step is to find the mantissa, .6191, in the body of the tables. Hence, we look through the tables until we find the mantissas starting with 61, and then we look through these until we locate 6191. We see that it is in line with 41 (in the column headed by N) and in the column headed by 6. Thus, N is made up of the digits 416, and the next step is to place the decimal point. Since the characteristic of $\log N$ is 1, the decimal point is one place to the right of the reference position, and hence is between 1 and 6. Therefore, $N = 41.6$.

If ml N is not listed in the tables, we must resort to interpolation. By the use of a four-place table, we cannot obtain accurately more than the first four digits in N. We shall show in the following discussion that the first three digits are obtained from the table and the fourth is determined by interpolation. If the characteristic of $\log N$ indicates that N contains more than four digits, then zeros are added after the fourth.

Example 2

We shall illustrate the process by obtaining N when $\log N = 5.4978$. We shall let T represent the number composed of the first four digits in N and shall determine T. Finally, we shall place the decimal point by considering the characteristic, and thus get N. The mantissa .4978 is not listed in the table, but the two nearest to it are .4969 and .4983. These two mantissas are ml 3140 and ml 3150, respectively. (We add the zero in each case in order to obtain four places for use in interpolation.)   Furthermore, since $4983 - 4969 = 14$ and

$$4978 - 4969 = 9$$

it follows that 4978 is $\frac{9}{14}$ of the way from 4969 to 4983.   Hence, T is approximately $\frac{9}{14}$ of the way from 3140 to 3150.   Furthermore,

$$\tfrac{9}{14} \times 10 = \tfrac{90}{14} = 6.4 = 6 \text{ (to one digit)}$$

and $3140 + 6 = 3146$.   Hence, $T = 3146$.   Since the characteristic of log N is 5, the decimal point in N is 5 places to the right of the reference position.   Hence, $N = 314,600$.

The steps in the above process are shown in the condensed form given below.

$$\log N = 5.4978$$

$$14 \left[\begin{array}{c} 4983 = \text{ml } 3150 \\ 9 \left[\begin{array}{c} 4978 = \text{ml } T \\ 4969 = \text{ml } 3140 \end{array} \right] \end{array} \right] 10$$

$$\tfrac{9}{14} \times 10 = 6.4 = 6 \quad \text{(to one digit)}$$

$$3140 + 6 = 3146 = T$$

Hence,

$$N = 314,600$$

since the characteristic of log N is 5.

Example 3

As a third example, we shall determine N if log $N = 8.6736 - 10$.   We shall again let T represent the number composed of the first four digits in N.   The two entries in the table that are nearest to 6736 are $6730 = \text{ml } 4710$ and

$$6739 = \text{ml } 4720$$

Using these in the interpolation process, we have

$$9 \left[\begin{array}{c} 6739 = \text{ml } 4720 \\ 6 \left[\begin{array}{c} 6736 = \text{ml } T \\ 6730 = \text{ml } 4710 \end{array} \right] \end{array} \right] 10$$

$$\tfrac{6}{9} \times 10 = 6.6 = 7 \quad \text{(to the nearest integer)}$$

Hence,

$$4710 + 7 = 4717 = T$$

Therefore,

$$N = .04717$$

since the characteristic of log N is $8 - 10 = -2$

EXERCISE 62

Find the value of N if log N is equal to the number in each of Problems 1 to 16.

1. 3.8075.   **2.** 1.2856.   **3.** $8.4857 - 10$.   **4.** 0.7738.
5. 4.5775.   **6.** $7.9058 - 10$.   **7.** 2.6304.

8. 9.8645 − 10.	**9.** 3.6920.	**10.** 2.8692.
11. 6.7796 − 10.	**12.** 5.7101.	**13.** 5.3560 − 10.
14. 1.1004.	**15.** 3.7427.	**16.** 0.3766.

If the number in each of Problems 17 to 32 is the value of log N, find the value of N to three places by using the mantissa in the table nearest to the given one.

17. 1.2371.	**18.** 2.3462.	**19.** 0.9785.	**20.** 1.7385.
21. 2.5862.	**22.** 1.8427.		**23.** 9.3849 − 10.
24. 8.4239 − 10.	**25.** 9.6184 − 10.		**26.** 7.3942 − 10.
27. 8.9692 − 10.	**28.** 9.7287 − 10.		**29.** 0.5710.
30. 1.1250.	**31.** 9.2000 − 10.		**32.** 8.2999 − 10.

Find the value of N to four digits by use of interpolation if log N is the number in each of Problems 33 to 48.

33. 1.4850.	**34.** 3.8823.	**35.** 2.6047.	**36.** 0.2017.
37. 8.5520 − 10.	**38.** 9.9038 − 10.	**39.** 1.6510.	
40. 3.3316.	**41.** 2.7180.	**42.** 7.9203 − 10.	
43. 0.6742.	**44.** 6.3653 − 10.	**45.** 9.4512 − 10.	
46. 3.5818.	**47.** 8.1050.	**48.** 1.2191.	

122. *Properties of logarithms.* In this article, we shall employ the laws of exponents (see Chap. 7) and the definition of a logarithm to derive three important properties of logarithms. In the next article, we shall show how to use these properties in numerical computation.

We shall first show how to find the logarithm of a product of two numbers in terms of the logarithms of the two numbers.

If we are given

$$(1) \qquad \log_b M = m \qquad \text{and} \qquad \log_b N = n$$

then by (2) of Art. 116, we have

$$(2) \qquad M = b^m \qquad \text{and} \qquad N = b^n$$

Hence,

$$MN = (b^m)(b^n)$$
$$= b^{m+n} \qquad \text{[by (2) of Art. 46]}$$

and

$$\log_b MN = m + n \qquad \text{[by (2) of Art. 116]}$$
$$= \log_b M + \log_b N \qquad \text{[by (1) of this article]}$$

Consequently, we have

PROPERTY I. *The logarithm of the product of two numbers is equal to the sum of the logarithms of the numbers.*

Example 1

$$\begin{aligned}
\log 6 &= \log (3 \times 2) \\
&= \log 3 + \log 2 \\
&= .4771 + .3010 \\
&= .7781
\end{aligned}$$

Property I can be extended to three or more numbers by the following process:

$$\begin{aligned}
\log_b MNP &= \log_b (MN)(P) \\
&= \log_b M + \log_b N + \log_b P
\end{aligned}$$

Again, using relations (2) of this article, we have

$$\begin{aligned}
\frac{M}{N} &= \frac{b^m}{b^n} \\
&= b^{m-n} \qquad \text{[by (5) of Art. 46]}
\end{aligned}$$

Hence,

$$\begin{aligned}
\log_b \frac{M}{N} &= m - n \qquad \text{[by (2) of Art. 116]} \\
&= \log_b M - \log_b N \qquad \text{[by (1) of this article]}
\end{aligned}$$

Therefore, we have

PROPERTY II. *The logarithm of the quotient of two numbers is equal to the logarithm of the dividend minus the logarithm of the divisor.*

Example 2

$$\begin{aligned}
\log 1.5 &= \log \frac{3}{2} \\
&= \log 3 - \log 2 \\
&= .4771 - .3010 \\
&= .1761
\end{aligned}$$

Finally, if we raise both members of $M = b^m$ to the kth power, we have

$$\begin{aligned}
M^k &= (b^m)^k \\
&= b^{km} \qquad \text{[by (4), Art. 46]}
\end{aligned}$$

Therefore,

$$\begin{aligned}
\log_b M^k &= km \qquad \text{[by (2), Art. 116]} \\
&= k \log_b M \qquad \text{[by (1) of this article]}
\end{aligned}$$

Thus, we have

PROPERTY III.   *The logarithm of a power of a number is equal to the product of the exponent of the power and the logarithm of the number.*

Example 3

$$\log 3^2 = 2 \log 3$$
$$= 2(.4771)$$
$$= .9542$$

NOTE: Since a root of a number can be expressed as a fractional power, Property III can be used to find the logarithm of a root of a number.   Thus,

$$\log_b \sqrt[r]{M} = \log_b (M)^{\frac{1}{r}} = \frac{1}{r} \log_b M$$

Example 4

$$\log \sqrt[3]{2} = \log 2^{\frac{1}{3}}$$
$$= \tfrac{1}{3} \log 2$$
$$= \tfrac{1}{3}(.3010)$$
$$= .1003$$

For the convenience of the reader, we shall restate the above properties in symbolic form.

I. $\log_b MN = \log_b M + \log_b N$

II. $\log_b \dfrac{M}{N} = \log_b M - \log_b N$

III. $\log_b M^k = k \log_b M$

123. *Logarithmic computation.* As we stated previously, one of the most useful applications of logarithms is in the field of numerical computation.   We shall explain presently the methods involved by means of several examples.   However, before considering special problems, we wish to call attention again to the fact that results obtained by the use of four-place tables are correct at most to four places.   If the numbers in any computation problem contain only three places, the result is dependable to only three places.   If a problem contains a mixture of three-place and four-place numbers, we cannot expect more than three places of the result to be correct, so we round it off to three places. Hence, in the problems that follow, we shall not obtain any answer to more than four nonzero places, and sometimes not that far.[1] Tables exist from which logarithms may be obtained to five, six, seven, and even more places. If results that are correct to more than four places are desired, longer tables should be used. The methods which we have presented may be applied to a table of any length.

We shall now present examples with explanations that illustrate the methods for using logarithms to obtain (1) products and quotients, (2) powers and roots, (3) miscellaneous computation problems.

In all computation problems, we use the properties of logarithms in Art. 122 to find the logarithm of the result. Then the value of the result can be obtained from the table.

1. *Products and quotients*

Example 1

As our first example, we shall show how logarithms may be used to find the value of R if $R = (8.56)(3.47)(198)$.

Since R is equal to the product of three numbers, by Property I, Art. 122, log R is equal to the sum of the logarithms of the three factors. Hence, we shall obtain the logarithm of each of the factors, add them together, and thus have log R. Then we may use the table to get R. Before we turn to the table, it is advisable to make an outline leaving blanks in which to enter the logarithms as they are found. It is also advisable to arrange the outline so that the logarithms to be added are in a column. We suggest the following plan:

$$\begin{aligned}
\log 8.56 &= \text{_____} \\
\log 3.47 &= \text{_____} \\
\log 198 &= \text{_____} \\
\hline
\log R &= \text{_____} \\
&\quad \text{(enter sum here)} \\
R &= \text{_____}
\end{aligned}$$

Next we enter the characteristics in each of the blanks and have

$$\begin{aligned}
\log 8.56 &= 0.\text{_____} \\
\log 3.47 &= 0.\text{_____} \\
\log 198 &= 2.\text{_____} \\
\hline
\log R &= \text{_____} \\
R &= \text{_____}
\end{aligned}$$

---

[1] The above remarks are based on the theory of significant figures. A discussion of this theory is found in most trigonometries. For example Sparks and Rees, "Plane Trigonometry," 3d ed., Prentice-Hall, Inc., New York 1952, p. 20.

Now we turn to the tables, get the mantissas, and, as each is found, enter it in the proper place in the outline. Then we perform the addition, and, finally, determine R by the method of Art. 121. The completed solution then appears as

$$\log 8.56 = 0.9325$$
$$\log 3.47 = 0.5403$$
$$\underline{\log 198 = 2.2967}$$
$$\log R = 3.7695$$
$$R = 5880$$

NOTE: Each of the numbers in the problem contains only three digits. Hence, we can determine only three digits in R. Since the mantissa 7695 is between the two entries 7694 and 7701 and nearer the former than the latter, the first three digits in R are 588, the number corresponding to the mantissa .7694. The characteristic of $\log R$ is 3. Hence, the decimal point is three places to the right of the reference position. Therefore, we add one zero and place the decimal point.

We have written the outline of the solution 3 times in order to show how the outline appears at the conclusion of each step. In practice, it is necessary to write the outline only once, since each operation requires the filling of separate blanks.

Example 2

As our second example, we shall use logarithms to find R where

$$R = \frac{(337)(2.68)}{(521)(.763)}$$

In this problem, R is a quotient in which the dividend and divisor are each the product of two numbers. Hence, we shall add the logarithms of the two numbers in the dividend and also add the logarithms of the two in the divisor, subtract the latter sum from the former, thus obtaining $\log R$. We suggest the following outline for the solution:

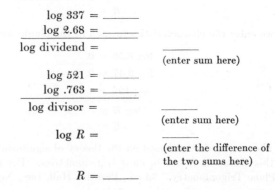

$$\log 337 = \underline{\hspace{1cm}}$$
$$\underline{\log 2.68 = \underline{\hspace{1cm}}}$$
$$\log \text{dividend} = \underline{\hspace{1cm}}$$
$$\qquad\qquad\text{(enter sum here)}$$
$$\log 521 = \underline{\hspace{1cm}}$$
$$\underline{\log .763 = \underline{\hspace{1cm}}}$$
$$\log \text{divisor} = \underline{\hspace{1cm}}$$
$$\qquad\qquad\text{(enter sum here)}$$
$$\log R = \underline{\hspace{1cm}}$$
$$\qquad\qquad\text{(enter the difference of}$$
$$\qquad\qquad\text{the two sums here)}$$
$$R = \underline{\hspace{1cm}}$$

After the characteristics are entered and the mantissas are found and listed in the proper places, the problem can be completed as below.

$$\log 337 = 2.5276$$
$$\log 2.68 = 0.4281$$
$$\log \text{dividend} = \qquad\qquad 2.9557$$
$$\log 521 = 2.7168$$
$$\log .763 = 9.8825 - 10$$
$$\log \text{divisor} = \qquad 12.5993 - 10$$
$$\log R = \qquad\qquad 0.3564$$
$$R = 2.27$$

NOTE: The logarithm of the divisor turned out to be 12.5993 − 10. Hence, the characteristic is 2. Therefore, in the above outline, we cancel the 10 and the first digit in 12 before completing the solution.

Example 3

If we use logarithms to evaluate $R = \dfrac{2.68}{33.2}$, we have

$$\log 2.68 = 0.4281$$
$$\log 33.2 = 1.5211$$
$$\log R = \underline{\qquad}$$

where $\log R$ is obtained by subtracting the second logarithm from the first. If we perform this subtraction, we get $\log R = -1.0930$. This is a correct value of $\log R$, but since the fractional part 0930 is negative, it is not a mantissa, and the value of R cannot be obtained from the table. We avoid this type of difficulty by adding $10 - 10$ to $\log 2.68$ before performing the subtraction. Then we have

$$\log 2.68 = 10.4281 - 10$$
$$\log 33.2 = 1.5211$$
$$\log R = 8.9070 - 10$$
$$R = .0807$$

We use the device shown in Example 3 whenever a necessary subtraction of one logarithm from another leads to a negative remainder. Thus, in order to subtract $9.2368 - 10$ from 2.6841, we add $10 - 10$ to the latter and have

$$12.6841 - 10$$
$$9.2368 - 10$$
$$3.4473$$

Similarly, in performing the indicated subtraction in $(7.3264 - 10) - (9.4631 - 10)$, we would again obtain a negative number,

-2.1367.   Hence, we add $10 - 10$ to $7.3264 - 10$ and proceed with the subtraction as below.

$$17.3264 - 20$$
$$\underline{9.4631 - 10}$$
$$7.8633 - 10$$

2. *Powers and roots*

Example 4

In order to obtain the value of $R = (3.74)^5$ by use of logarithms, we use Property, III, Art. 122, and have

$$\log R = \log (3.74)^5$$
$$= 5(\log 3.74)$$
$$= 5(0.5729)$$
$$= 2.8645$$

Hence,

$$R = 732$$

We may also use Property III to obtain the root of a number by means of logarithms.   The method is illustrated in the following example:

Example 5

If $R = \sqrt[3]{62.3}$, we rewrite the problem in the exponential form and get

$$R = (62.3)^{\frac{1}{3}}$$

Hence,

$$\log R = \tfrac{1}{3} \log 62.3$$
$$= \tfrac{1}{3}(1.7945)$$
$$= 0.5982$$

Therefore,

$$R = 3.96$$

In the application of Property III to the problem of extracting a root of a decimal fraction, we employ a device similar to that described in Example 3 in order to avoid a troublesome situation.

Example 6

If $R = \sqrt[6]{.0628}$, we have

$$\log R = \tfrac{1}{6} \log .0628$$
$$= \frac{8.7980 - 10}{6}$$

If we perform the division indicated above, we get

$$\log R = 1.4663 - 1.6667$$
$$= -.2004$$

Thus, we have a negative logarithm and cannot obtain R from the table. We avoid a situation of this sort by adding $50 - 50$ to $\log .0628$, obtaining $\log .0628 = 58.7980 - 60$. Now we have

$$\log R = \frac{58.7980 - 60}{6}$$
$$= 9.7997 - 10$$

The last logarithm is in the customary form, and by referring to the table we find that

$$R = .631$$

3. *Miscellaneous problems*

Many computation problems require a combination of the processes of multiplication, division, raising to powers, and the extraction of roots. We shall illustrate the general procedure for solving such problems by an example.

Example 7

Use logarithms to find R if

$$R = \sqrt[5]{\frac{\sqrt{2.689}(3.478)}{(52.18)^2(51.67)}}$$

Solution

Since all the numbers in this problem contain four digits, we must obtain the value of R to four places. Furthermore, we must use interpolation to obtain the mantissas. The steps in the solution are indicated in the following suggested outline:

$\log \sqrt{2.689} = \frac{1}{2} \log 2.689 = \frac{1}{2}(\underline{\quad}) = \underline{\quad}$
$\log 3.478 \qquad\qquad\qquad\qquad = \underline{\quad}$

$\qquad\qquad\qquad \log \text{dividend} = $
$\qquad\qquad\qquad\qquad\qquad\qquad\qquad \underline{\quad}$
$\qquad\qquad\qquad\qquad\qquad\qquad\qquad \text{(sum here)}$

$\log (52.18)^2 = 2 \log 52.18 = 2(\underline{\quad}) = \underline{\quad}$
$\log 51.67 \qquad\qquad\qquad\qquad = \underline{\quad}$

$\qquad\qquad\qquad \log \text{divisor} = $
$\qquad\qquad\qquad\qquad\qquad\qquad\qquad \underline{\quad}$
$\qquad\qquad\qquad\qquad\qquad\qquad\qquad \text{(sum here)}$

$5\,|\,\underline{\qquad}$
$\qquad\qquad\qquad\qquad\qquad\qquad\qquad \text{(difference)}$

$\qquad\qquad\qquad\qquad \log R = \underline{\quad}$
$\qquad\qquad\qquad\qquad\quad R = \underline{\quad}$

We now enter the characteristics in the proper places, then turn to the table, get the mantissas and enter each in the space left for it, and complete the solution. Then the outline appears as below.

$$\log \sqrt{2.689} = \tfrac{1}{2} \log 2.689 = \tfrac{1}{2}(0.4296) = 0.2148$$
$$\log 3.478 \qquad\qquad\qquad\qquad = 0.5413$$

$$\log \text{ dividend } = \qquad\qquad 10.7561^* - 10$$

$$\log (52.18)^2 = 2 \log 52.18 = 2(1.7175) = 3.4350$$
$$\log 51.67 \qquad\qquad\qquad\qquad = 1.7132$$

$$\log \text{ divisor } = \qquad\qquad 5.1482$$

$$\qquad\qquad\qquad\qquad\qquad 5\,\overline{|45.6079} \quad - 50\dagger$$
$$\log R = \qquad\qquad 9.1216 \quad - 10$$
$$R = .1323$$

EXERCISE 63

Use logarithms to perform the computation indicated in Problems 1 to 48. In Problems 1 to 32, obtain the answer to three digits. In the others, obtain the answers to four digits.

1. $(47.1)(2.83)(.125)$ **2.** $(5.94)(39.2)(.0624)$ **3.** $(4.25)(1.96)(.938)$

4. $(897)(.359)(.0621)$ **5.** $(7.34)(.0417)(.00231)$

6. $(.574)(.923)(.241)$ **7.** $(.593)(.841)(.728)$ **8.** $(.616)(3.14)(.0167)$

9. $\dfrac{(49.6)(3.88)}{123}.$ **10.** $\dfrac{(8.48)(7.37)}{6.16}.$ **11.** $\dfrac{(8.95)(41.7)}{305}.$ **12.** $\dfrac{(6.63)(71.2)}{543}.$

13. $\dfrac{9.83}{(4.71)(37.2)}.$ **14.** $\dfrac{5.96}{(2.34)(3.09)}.$ **15.** $\dfrac{78.2}{(38.1)(4.05)}.$ **16.** $\dfrac{67.5}{(416)(.831)}.$

17. $\sqrt[3]{482}.$ **18.** $\sqrt{59.4}.$ **19.** $\sqrt[4]{.678}.$ **20.** $\sqrt[3]{(82.3)^2}.$

21. $\sqrt{\dfrac{(326)(41.2)}{(136)(1.21)}}.$ **22.** $\left[\dfrac{(.0413)(3.62)}{(.613)(711)}\right]^2.$ **23.** $\sqrt[3]{\dfrac{(7.42)(41.2)}{(.503)(3.18)}}.$

24. $\sqrt[3]{\left[\dfrac{(1.25)(31.4)}{(4.21)(61.3)}\right]^2}.$ **25.** $(\sqrt{71.4})\sqrt[3]{(4.79)^2}.$ **26.** $\sqrt[3]{8.08}\sqrt{66.2}.$

27. $\sqrt{99.1}\sqrt[3]{3.05}.$ **28.** $\sqrt[4]{.237}\sqrt{.865}.$ **29.** $\dfrac{\sqrt{762}}{\sqrt[3]{903}}.$

30. $\dfrac{\sqrt[3]{84.7}}{\sqrt{47.5}}.$ **31.** $\dfrac{(384)^{\frac{2}{3}}}{(24.7)\sqrt{53.9}}.$ **32.** $\dfrac{596}{\sqrt[3]{847}\sqrt{29.6}}.$

33. $(6.728)^5.$ **34.** $\sqrt{362.8}.$ **35.** $\sqrt[5]{.7196}.$ **36.** $\sqrt{(87.62)^3}.$

37. $\dfrac{4.342}{25.77}.$ **38.** $\dfrac{\sqrt{739.6}}{21.82}.$ **39.** $\dfrac{\sqrt[3]{240.7}}{\sqrt{37.46}}.$

* Note that we add $10 - 10$ here so we can subtract 5.1482.

† We add $40 - 40$ here so that we can divide by 5.

40. $\dfrac{(297.3)^{\frac{2}{3}}}{(234.7)^{\frac{1}{4}}}.$

41. $\dfrac{(838.7)(9.234)}{(214.7)(7.893)}.$

42. $\dfrac{(476.1)(3.812)}{(57.63)(27.92)}.$

43. $\dfrac{(21.62)(3.412)}{(47.18)(562.3)}.$

44. $\dfrac{(4.061)(.8426)}{(9837)(.07381)}.$

45. $\sqrt{\dfrac{(47.83)(162.1)}{(37.81)^2}}.$

46. $\left[\dfrac{(.6837)(83.41)}{\sqrt[3]{.1126}}\right]^2.$

47. $\sqrt[3]{\dfrac{(.07243)^2}{\sqrt{3784}(12.46)}}.$

48. $\sqrt{\dfrac{(.6241)\sqrt{4728}}{(1247)(8.732)^3}}.$

Express the functions in Problems 49 to 56 as the sum or difference of logarithms of quantities to the first power by use of the computation theorems.

49. $y = \log \dfrac{cx}{x+1}.$

50. $y = \log \dfrac{cx^2}{x-2}.$

51. $y = \log cx^2 \sqrt{x-1}.$

52. $z = \log \dfrac{(x+y)c}{\sqrt{x-2y}}.$

53. $z = \log \dfrac{\sqrt{x+y}}{c(x-y)^2}.$

54. $z = \log \dfrac{cx^2y}{\sqrt{x-2y}}.$

55. $z = \log \dfrac{c\sqrt{x}}{y(x+3y)^2}.$

56. $z = \log \dfrac{y^2c}{\sqrt{x}\,(2x-y)^3}.$

Express as the logarithm of a product, quotient, or power by use of the computation theorems.

57. $\log c - \log x.$

58. $\log c + \log x - \log (x-1).$

59. $\log c - \log x + 2 \log (x+1).$

60. $3 \log c + 2 \log x.$

61. $\log (x+y) - \frac{1}{2} \log x.$

62. $\log c + \frac{1}{2} \log (2x+y).$

63. $\log x + 2 \log c - \log (3x - 2y).$

64. $2 \log y - \frac{1}{4} \log (c-x) + \frac{1}{2} \log (x - 2y + c).$

124. *Logarithms to bases other than* 10. As we implied in the first article of this chapter, any real number can be used as a base for a system of logarithms. However, there are only two in general use, the common or Briggs system, and the natural or Napierian system. The former is the system more convenient for numerical computation, and the latter is very important in more advanced mathematics and its applications. The base for the Napierian system is the irrational number $e = 2.718 \ldots$ to three decimal places. Tables of Napierian logarithms may be found in most technical handbooks and manuals of mathematical tables. However, the logarithm of a number to any base can be expressed in terms of the logarithm of the number to another base. In particular, the logarithm of a number to any base can be obtained by use of a table of common logarithms, and it is the purpose of the present article to explain how this can be done.

THEOREM: *If a and b are any two bases, then*

(1)
$$\log_a N = \frac{\log_b N}{\log_b a}$$

Proof. We shall let

$$N = a^y$$

then

$$\log_a N = \log_a a^y$$
$$= y$$

Furthermore,

$$\log_b N = \log_b a^y$$
$$= y \log_b a \qquad \text{(by Property III of Art. 122)}$$
$$= \log_a N \log_b a \qquad \text{(since } y = \log_a N)$$

Now, solving this equation for $\log_a N$, we have

$$\log_a N = \frac{\log_b N}{\log_b a}$$

COROLLARY. *The relation between $\log_{10} N$ and $\log_e N$ is given by*

(2)
$$\log_e N = \frac{\log_{10} N}{\log_{10} e}$$

Proof. If, in (1), we let $a = e$ and $b = 10$, we have the equations as stated in the corollary.

Since $\log_{10} e = .4343$ and $1/.4343 = 2.3026$, (2) can be expressed in the form

(3)
$$\log_e N = 2.3026 \log_{10} N$$

Example

By means of (1), find the value of $\log_7 236$.

Solution

If we substitute in (1), we get

$$\log_7 236 = \frac{\log_{10} 236}{\log_{10} 7}$$
$$= \frac{2.3729}{.8451} = 2.808$$

EXERCISE 64

By use of a table of common logarithms, find the value of each of the following to four digits.

1. $\log_e 57.3$.	**2.** $\log_e 6.37$.	**3.** $\log_e 1.48$.	**4.** $\log_e .693$.
5. $\log_2 17.3$.	**6.** $\log_2 3.46$.	**7.** $\log_2 38.5$.	**8.** $\log_2 97.3$.
9. $\log_3 9.23$.	**10.** $\log_3 87.8$.	**11.** $\log_5 631$.	**12.** $\log_5 247$.
13. $\log_7 419$.	**14.** $\log_7 162$.	**15.** $\log_{11} 119$.	**16.** $\log_{11} 987$.
17. $\log_{11} 1334$.	**18.** $\log_5 1492$.	**19.** $\log_5 1066$.	**20.** $\log_{11} 2379$.
21. $\log_7 1776$.	**22.** $\log_7 1891$.	**23.** $\log_{e^2} 1902$.	**24.** $\log_{e^3} 1937$.

125. Exponential and logarithmic equations. *An **exponential equation** is an equation in which the unknown occurs in one or more exponents. A **logarithmic equation** is an equation which involves the logarithm of a function of the unknown.*

Examples

In the examples below, (1) and (2) are exponential equations, and (3) is a logarithmic equation.

1. $$3^x = 7$$
2. $$3^{x+1} = 5^{x-2}$$
3. $$\log x + \log (x - 1) = 2$$

In general, exponential and logarithmic equations cannot be solved by the methods heretofore discussed, but many such equations can be solved by use of the properties of logarithms. The following examples illustrate the procedure.

Example 4

Solve the equation

$$3^{x+4} = 5^{x+2}$$

Solution

If we take the common logarithm of each member of the above equation we have, by Property III, Art. 122,

$$(x + 4) \log 3 = (x + 2) \log 5$$

and we complete the solution as follows:

$$x \log 3 + 4 \log 3 = x \log 5 + 2 \log 5$$
$$x(\log 3 - \log 5) = 2 \log 5 - 4 \log 3 \qquad \text{(transposing and collecting)}$$
$$= \log 25 - \log 81 \qquad \text{(by III, Art. 122)}$$
$$x = \frac{\log 25 - \log 81}{\log 3 - \log 5} \qquad \text{(solving for } x\text{)}$$
$$= \frac{1.3979 - 1.9085}{.4771 - .6990}$$
$$= \frac{-.5106}{-.2219}$$
$$= 2.301$$

Example 5

Solve

$$\log_6 (x + 3) + \log_6 (x - 2) = 1$$

Solution

By applying I, Art. 122, to the left member of the given equation, we have

$$\log_6 (x + 3)(x - 2) = 1$$

Hence,

$$(x + 3)(x - 2) = 6^1 \qquad \text{[by (2), Art. 116]}$$
$$x^2 + x - 6 = 6 \qquad \text{(performing the indicated operations)}$$
$$x^2 + x - 12 = 0 \qquad \text{(transposing and collecting terms)}$$
$$(x + 4)(x - 3) = 0$$

Solving this equation, we get

$$x = -4 \quad \text{and} \quad x = 3$$

Example 6

Solve

$$y = \log_e (x + \sqrt{x^2 + 1})$$

for x.

Solution

By use of Eq. (2), Art. 116, we can change the given equation to the exponential form and obtain

$$e^y = x + \sqrt{x^2 + 1}$$

We next rationalize the above equation and solve for x by performing the following steps.

$$e^y - x = \sqrt{x^2 + 1} \qquad \text{(isolating the radical)}$$
$$e^{2y} - 2e^y x + x^2 = x^2 + 1 \qquad \text{(squaring each member)}$$
$$-2e^y x + x^2 - x^2 = -e^{2y} + 1 \qquad \text{(transposing and collecting terms)}$$
$$x = \frac{-e^{2y} + 1}{-2e^y}$$
$$= \frac{e^y - e^{-y}}{2} \qquad \text{(dividing each member of the fraction by } -e^y\text{)}$$

Example 7

Solve

(1) $5^{x-2y} = 100$

and

(2) $3^{2x-y} = 10$

for x and y.

Solution

If we take the logarithm of each member of (1) and of (2), we get

(3) $(x - 2y) \log 5 = 2$
(4) $(2x - y) \log 3 = 1$

Therefore,

(3') $x - 2y = \dfrac{2}{\log 5}$

and

(4') $2x - y = \dfrac{1}{\log 3}$

If we perform the computation indicated in the right member we have

(3'') $x - 2y = 2.86$
(4'') $2x - y = 2.10$

Multiplying each member of (4'') by 2 and subtracting from the corresponding member of (3''), we obtain

$$-3x = -1.34$$
$$x = .447$$

Substituting this value for x in (3'') and solving for y, we get

$$-2y = 2.86 - .447$$
$$= 2.413$$

Therefore,

$$y = -1.206$$

Therefore the solution of the system is $x = .447$ and $y = -1.206$.

EXERCISE 65

Solve the equations in Problems 1 to 12 for x or n.

1. $y = e^x$.   **2.** $y = 3e^x$.   **3.** $y = e^{-x}$.

4. $y = ae^{-bx}$.   **5.** $y = ar^n$.   **6.** $L = ar^{n-1}$.

7. $S = A(1 + r)^n$.   **8.** $A = S(1 + r)^{-n}$.   **9.** $y = \log_e (\sqrt{1 + x^2} - x)$.

10. $y = \log_e (x - \sqrt{x^2 - 1})$, $x \geq 1$.

11. $y = \log_e \sqrt{(x - 1)(x + 2)}$, $x > 1$.

12. $y = \log_e \sqrt{\dfrac{x+3}{3-x}}$, $-3 < x < 3$.

Solve the equations in Problems 13 to 32.

13. $3^x = 81 = 3^4$.   **14.** $6^{x-1} = 216$.   **15.** $5^{2x-1} = 25$.

16. $7^{x+2} = 343$.   **17.** $e^x e^{x+1} = e^3$.   **18.** $3^{x^2-2} = 3^{4-x}$.

19. $2^{x^2+2} = 2^{3x}$.   **20.** $5^{x^2-3x} = 5^{x-3}$.   **21.** $2^{x+3} = 3^{x-1}$.

22. $3^{4x} = 4^{3x+1}$.   **23.** $2^{5x+2} = 5^{3x}$.   **24.** $3^{3x+1} = 7^{4x}$.

25. $\log_8 (x + 1) + \log_8 (x + 3) = 1$.

26. $\log_5 (x - 1) + \log_5 (x + 3) = 1$.

27. $\log_6 (x + 2) + \log_6 (x + 7) = 2$.

28. $\log_5 (2x + 1) + \log_5 (3x - 1) = 2$.

29. $\log_2 (x + 4) - \log_2 (x + 1) = 1$.

30. $\log_3 (13x + 3) - \log_3 (x + 1) = 2$.

31. $\log_5 (x^2 + 21x - 10) - \log_5 (5x - 1) = 1$.

32. $\log_3 (2x^2 + 3x + 7) - \log_3 1 = 3$.

Solve the following pairs of equations simultaneously.

33. $3^{x+y} = 2$ **34.** $4^{2x-3y} = 2$ **35.** $3^{x+3y} = 27$ **36.** $3^{x+3y} = 81$

     $2x - y = 3$. $x + y = 1$. $x + 2y = 4$. $x + 2y = 4$.

37. $10^{x+2y} = 2$ **38.** $6^{x-y} = 2^x$

     $\log 3x - \log 2y = 1$. $6^y = 4^{x-1}$.

39. $\log x + \log y = 2$ **40.** $e^{x+2y} = e^2$

     $\log 2x - \log y = 1$. $e^{2x-y} = 2$.

126. *The graphs of* $\log_a x$ *and* a^x. The graphs of $\log_a x$ and a^x reveal several important properties of this function. Further-

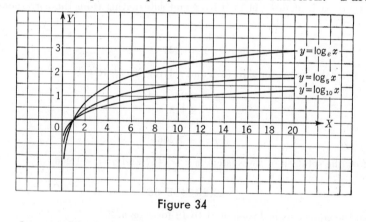

Figure 34

more, the graphical method must be applied to logarithmic and exponential equations that are not solvable by algebraic methods. Hence, it is important to be able to sketch the graph of the above function rapidly. In Fig. 34 we show the graph of the function $y = \log_a x$ with $a = 10$, $a = e$, and $a = 5$. The following table of values computed to one decimal place was used for constructing the graph. These values were obtained by use of a table of common logarithms and formulas (3) and (1) of Art. 124.

x	.2	.4	.6	.8	1	2	4	6	8	10	20
$\log_{10} x$	$-.7$	$-.4$	$-.2$	$-.1$	0	.3	.6	.8	.9	1	1.3
$\log_e x$	-1.6	$-.9$	$-.5$	$-.2$	0	.7	1.4	1.8	2.1	2.3	3.0
$\log_5 x$	$-.1$	$-.6$	$-.3$	$-.14$	0	.4	.9	1.1	1.3	1.4	1.8

These graphs reveal the following properties of the function $\log_a x$:

1. The function is not defined for negative values of x.
2. The function is negative for values of x less than one and positive for values of x greater than one.
3. The function is equal to zero when x is equal to one.
4. The value of the function increases as x increases.
5. The larger the value of a, the nearer the curve is to the x axis for a given value of x.

In order to illustrate the method for obtaining the graph of the exponential function, we shall show how to compute a table of corresponding values for the equation $y = e^x$, using a table of common logarithms, and shall construct the graph of this equation. For example, if $x = 1.5$, then

$$y = e^{1.5}$$

and

$$\log y = 1.5(\log e)$$
$$= 1.5(\log 2.718)$$
$$= 1.5(.4343)$$
$$= .6514$$

Hence,

$$y = 4.5$$

Furthermore, if $x = -2$,

$$\log y = -2(\log e)$$
$$= -2(.4343)$$
$$= -.8686$$
$$= 9.1314 - 10$$

Therefore,

$$y = .14 \text{ (or .1 for plotting purposes)}$$

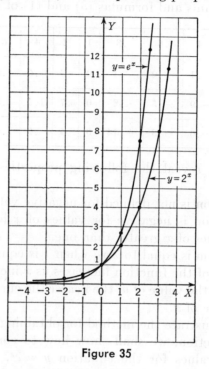

Figure 35

In a similar manner, we obtained the following table which was used in constructing the graph in Fig. 35. This figure also shows the graph of $y = 2^x$.

x	-4	-2	-1	0	1	1.5	2	2.5	3
e^x	.02	.1	.4	1	2.7	4.5	7.4	12.2	20

The following example illustrates the application of graphical methods to systems of equations that involve logarithms.

Example

The equations

$$y = \log x$$
$$3x + 2y = 6$$

cannot be solved simultaneously by algebraic methods. However, if we construct the graphs of the two equations (see Fig. 36), we may estimate their point of intersection and thus obtain an approximate solution. In this figure the abscissa of the point of intersection is between 1.8 and 1.9. In the first equation, when $x = 1.8$, $y = .26$; and when $x = 1.9$, $y = .28$. Furthermore, between these two points, the graph is approximately a straight line. In the second equation, if $x = 1.8$, $y = .3$; and if $x = 1.9$, $y = .15$. We now enlarge the scale, plot the above points, and join the two corresponding pairs with straight lines

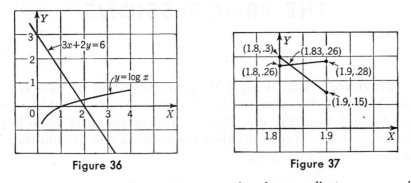

Figure 36   Figure 37

(see Fig. 37). These two lines intersect at a point whose coordinates are approximately $x = 1.83$, $y = .26$. By substituting in the original equations, it can be verified that this pair of values is an approximate solution.

EXERCISE 66

Construct the graph of the equation in each of Problems 1 to 12.

1. $y = \log_{12} x$.
2. $y = \log_{15} x$.
3. $y = \log_7 x$.
4. $y = \log_5 x$.
5. $y = \log_{10} 2x$.
6. $y = \log_{10} 4x$.
7. $y = \log_{10} x^2$.
8. $y = \log_{10} x^3$.
9. $y = 3^x$.
10. $y = 5^x$.
11. $y = 4^x$.
12. $y = 2^{2x}$.

Use the graphical method to find the solution of the following systems of equations. Find the solution to one decimal place.

13. $y = 10^x$.
    $x + y = 6$.
14. $y = 10^x$
    $x + y = 4$.
15. $y = 10^x$
    $y = x^2 - 4x + 4$.
16. $y = 10^x$
    $y = x^2$.
17. $y = \log_{10} x$
    $x + y = 0$.
18. $y = \log_{10} x$
    $x + y = 2$.
19. $y = \log_8 x$
    $y^2 = x$.
20. $y = \log_3 x$
    $2x + 3y = 6$.

CHAPTER 15

THE PROGRESSIONS

127. *Introduction.* Frequently in mathematics, we have occasion to deal with a sequence of numbers each of which can be obtained from the preceding by the operation of some law. Sequences of this type are called progressions and are illustrated in the following examples:

Example 1

The distances in feet that a body falls from rest during each of the first 5 sec. are

(1)   16.1,   48.3,   80.5,   112.7,   144.9

If we add 32.2 to any number in this sequence, we obtain the next number.

Example 2

Each person has two parents, four grandparents, eight great-grandparents, and so on. Hence, if there are no duplications, we may list the number of ancestors that any person has in each of the five generations that precede him in the sequence

(2)   2,   4,   8,   16,   32

Here, each term after the first is double the preceding.

The two above examples are illustrations of arithmetic progressions and geometric progressions. These two progressions are met frequently in mathematics and in applied fields, and we shall devote the remainder of this chapter to a discussion of them.

128. *Arithmetic progressions.* DEFINITION. *An **arithmetic progression** is a sequence of numbers so related that each term after the first can be obtained from the preceding by adding a fixed quantity called the **common difference.***

Examples

1. If the first term is 2 and the common difference is 5, then the first eight terms of an arithmetic progression are

$$2, \quad 7, \quad 12, \quad 17, \quad 22, \quad 27, \quad 32, \quad 37$$

2. In the sequence

$$16, \quad 14\tfrac{1}{2}, \quad 13, \quad 11\tfrac{1}{2}, \quad 10, \quad 8\tfrac{1}{2}$$

each term after the first is $1\tfrac{1}{2}$ less than the preceding. Hence, this is an arithmetic progression with the common difference equal to $-1\tfrac{1}{2}$.

Most problems in arithmetic progressions deal with three or more of the following five quantities: the first term, the last term, the number of terms, the common difference, and the sum of all the terms. Hence, we shall derive formulas which enable us to determine any one of these five quantities if we know the values of three of the others.

We shall let[1]

$$a = \text{the first term in the progression}$$
$$l = \text{the last term}$$
$$d = \text{the common difference}$$
$$n = \text{the number of terms}$$

and

$$s = \text{the sum of all the terms}$$

129. The last term of an arithmetic progression. In terms of the above notation, the first four terms of an arithmetic progression are

$$a \qquad a + d \qquad a + 2d \qquad \text{and} \qquad a + 3d$$

We notice that d enters with the coefficient one in the second term and that this coefficient increases by one as we move from one term to the next. Hence, the coefficient of d in any term is one less than the number of that term in the progression. Therefore, the sixth term is $a + 5d$, the ninth is $a + 8d$, and finally the last, or nth, term is $a + (n - 1)d$. Hence, we have the formula

$$(1) \qquad\qquad l = a + (n - 1)d$$

---

[1] Note that these symbols can be arranged so that they spell the word "lands."

Example 1

If the first three terms of an arithmetic progression are 2, 6, and 10, find the eighth term.

Solution

Since the first and second terms, as well as the second and third, differ by 4, it follows that $d = 4$. Furthermore, $a = 2$ and $n = 8$. Hence, if we substitute these values in (1), we have

$$l = 2 + (8 - 1)4$$
$$= 2 + 28$$
$$= 30$$

Example 2

If the first term of an arithmetic progression is -3 and the eighth term is 11, find d and write the eight terms of the progression.

Solution

In this problem, $a = -3$, $n = 8$, and $l = 11$. If these values are substituted in (1), we have

$$11 = -3 + (8 - 1)d$$

or

$$11 = -3 + 7d$$

Hence,

$$-7d = -14$$

and

$$d = 2$$

Therefore, since $a = -3$, the first eight terms of the desired progression are -3, -1, 1, 3, 5, 7, 9, 11.

130. The sum of an arithmetic progression. In order to obtain the formula for the sum s of the n terms of an arithmetic progression in which the first term is a and the common difference is d, we note that the terms in the progression are a, $a + d$, $a + 2d$, and so on until we reach the last term which by (1), Art. 129, is $l = a + (n - 1)d$. Hence,

$$(1) \quad s = a + (a + d) + (a + 2d) + \cdots + [a + (n - 1)d]$$

Since there are n terms in (1) and each term contains a, we may rearrange the terms and write s as

$$(2) \quad s = na + [d + 2d + \cdots + (n - 1)d]$$

Now, if we reverse the order of the terms in the progression by writing l as the first term, then the second term is $l - d$, the third $l - 2d$, and so on to the nth term, which by (1), Art. 129, is $l + (n - 1)(-d)$. Hence, we can write the sum as

$$s = l + (l - d) + (l - 2d) + \cdots [l + (n - 1)(-d)]$$

Next, combining the l's and the d's, we get

(3) $$s = nl - [d + 2d + \cdots + (n - 1)d]$$

Finally, if we add the corresponding members of (2) and (3), we see that the terms containing d cancel and we have

$$2s = na + nl$$
$$= n(a + l)$$

Hence, dividing by 2, we obtain the formula

(4) $$s = \frac{n}{2}(a + l)$$

We obtain a second form for the sum of the terms in an arithmetic progression by substituting the value of l in formula (1), Art. 129, in (4). Thus we obtain

$$s = \frac{n}{2}[a + a + (n - 1)d]$$

or

(5) $$s = \frac{n}{2}[2a + (n - 1)d]$$

Example 1

Find the sum of all the even integers from 2 to 1000, inclusive.

Solution

Since the even integers 2, 4, 6, etc., taken in order form an arithmetic progression with $d = 2$, we may use (4) with $a = 2$, $n = 500$, and $l = 1000$ to obtain the desired sum. The substitution of these values in (4) yields

$$s = \frac{500}{2}(2 + 1000)$$
$$= 250(1002) = 250,500$$

Example 2

A man buys a used car for $600 and agrees to pay $100 down and $100 per month plus interest at 6 per cent on the outstanding indebtedness until the car is paid for. How much will the car cost him?

Solution

The rate of 6 per cent per year is .5 per cent per month. Hence, when he makes his first payment, he will owe 1 month's interest on $500, or

$$(.005)(\$500) = \$2.50$$

Since he pays $100 on the principal, his interest from month to month is reduced by .5 per cent of $100 or by $.50 per month. The final payment will be $100 plus interest on $100 for 1 month, which is $100.50. Hence, his payments constitute an arithmetic progression with $a = \$102.50$, $l = \$100.50$, and $n = 5$. Therefore, by (4), the sum of his payments is

$$s = \tfrac{5}{2}(\$102.50 + \$100.50)$$
$$= \tfrac{5}{2}(\$203) = \$507.50$$

Thus, the total cost of the car will be $607.50.

131. Simultaneous use of the formulas for l and s. If any three of the quantities l, a, n, d, and s are known, the other two can be found by use of formulas (1) of Art. 129 and (4) or (5) of Art. 130. If all three known quantities appear in either of the two formulas, the two unknowns can be found by use of the formulas separately. However, if only two of the three known quantities appear in each of the formulas, we get the other two by solving (1), Art. 129, and (4), Art. 130, simultaneously.

Example 1

If $a = 4$, $n = 10$, and $l = 49$, find d and s.

Solution

Since each of (1), Art. 129, and (4), Art. 130, contain a, n, and l, we may find d and s by using the formulas separately. If we substitute the given values for a, n, and l in (1), Art. 129, we get

$$49 = 4 + (10 - 1)d$$

or

$$49 = 4 + 9d$$

Hence,

$$9d = 45$$

and

$$d = 5$$

Similarly, substituting in (4), Art. 130, we have

$$s = \tfrac{10}{2}(4 + 49)$$
$$= 5(53)$$
$$= 265$$

Example 2

If $l = 23$, $d = 3$, and $s = 98$, find a and n.

Solution

If we substitute these values in (1), Art. 129, and (4), Art. 130, we obtain

(1) $23 = a + (n - 1)3$

from the former, and

(2) $98 = \dfrac{n}{2}(a + 23)$

from the latter. Each of these equations contains the two desired unknowns a and n. Hence, we may complete the solution by solving (1) and (2) simultaneously. If we solve (1) for a, we get

$$a = 23 - (n - 1)3$$

or

(3) $a = 26 - 3n$

Substituting the above value for a in (2), we obtain

$$98 = \dfrac{n}{2}(26 - 3n + 23)$$

which we may solve for n as follows:

$$196 = n(49 - 3n) \qquad \text{(clearing of fractions and combining)}$$
$$196 = 49n - 3n^2 \qquad \text{(performing the indicated operations)}$$
$$3n^2 - 49n + 196 = 0 \qquad \text{(transposing)}$$
$$n = \frac{49 \pm \sqrt{(49)^2 - (4)(3)(196)}}{6} \qquad \text{(by the quadratic formula)}$$
$$= \frac{49 \pm \sqrt{2401 - 2352}}{6}$$
$$= \frac{49 \pm \sqrt{49}}{6}$$
$$= \frac{49 \pm 7}{6}$$
$$= 9\tfrac{1}{3} \text{ and } 7$$

Since n cannot be a fraction, we discard $9\frac{1}{3}$ and have

$$n = 7$$

If we substitute 7 for n in (3), we obtain

$$a = 26 - 3(7)$$
$$= 5$$

Hence, the progression consists of the seven terms 5, 8, 11, 14, 17, 20, and 23.

132. Arithmetic means. The terms between the first and last terms of an arithmetic progression are called *arithmetic means*. If the progression contains only three terms, the middle term is called *the arithmetic mean* of the first and last term. We may obtain the arithmetic means between two numbers by first using (1) Art. 129, to find d, and then the means can be computed. If the progression consists of the three terms a, m, and l, then by formula (1), Art. 129,

$$l = a + (3 - 1)d = a + 2d$$

Hence,

$$d = \frac{l - a}{2}$$

and

$$m = a + \frac{l - a}{2} = \frac{a + l}{2}$$

Therefore, *the arithmetic mean of two numbers is equal to one-half their sum.*

Example 1

Insert five arithmetic means between 6 and -10.

Solution

Since we are to find five means between 6 and -10, we shall have seven terms in all. Hence, $n = 7$, $a = 6$, and $l = -10$. Thus, by (1), Art. 129, we have

$$-10 = 6 + (7 - 1)d$$

Hence,

$$6d = -16,$$
$$d = -\frac{16}{6} = -\frac{8}{3}$$

and the progression consists of the terms, 6, $\frac{10}{3}$, $\frac{2}{3}$, $-\frac{6}{3}$, $-\frac{14}{3}$, $-\frac{22}{3}$, $-\frac{30}{3}$.

EXERCISE 67

Write the n terms of the arithmetic progressions that have the elements given in Problems 1 to 12.

1. $a = 2, d = 3, n = 6.$ **2.** $a = 3, d = 2, n = 5.$
3. $a = 3, d = -2, n = 7.$ **4.** $a = -2, d = -3, n = 6.$
5. First term 2, second term 5, $n = 4.$
6. First term 4, second term 1, $n = 8.$
7. First term 4, third term 10, $n = 5.$
8. First term 3, third term -1, $n = 6.$
9. Second term 7, fourth term 11, $n = 7.$
10. Third term 8, sixth term 2, $n = 6.$
11. First term -1, fifth term 11, $n = 5.$
12. Second term 20, sixth term 0, $n = 6.$

Find the last term of the arithmetic progression described in each of Problems 13 to 20.

13. $a = 2, d = 3, n = 4.$ **14.** $a = 3, d = -1, n = 5.$
15. $a = -7, d = 2, n = 6.$ **16.** $a = -13, d = -2, n = 8.$
17. $a = 8, d = \frac{1}{2}, n = 9.$ **18.** $a = \frac{2}{3}, d = \frac{1}{6}, n = 5.$
19. $a = \frac{3}{4}, d = -\frac{5}{4}, n = 10.$ **20.** $a = .5, d = .01, n = 8.$

Find the sum of the terms of the arithmetic progression described in each of Problems 21 to 28.

21. $a = 5, l = 9, n = 6.$ **22.** $a = -2, l = 14, n = 5.$
23. $a = 6, l = -7, n = 8.$ **24.** $a = 11, l = -5, n = 7.$
25. $a = 3, d = 4, n = 5.$ **26.** $a = -6, d = 1, n = 13.$
27. Second term 5, $d = 2, n = 6.$ **28.** Third term 4, $d = -2, n = 7.$

Find the two of the five quantities l, a, n, d, and s that are missing in each of Problems 29 to 44.

29. $l = -11, n = 4, d = -4.$ **30.** $l = 14, n = 5, d = 6.$
31. $n = 8, l = -19, s = -96.$ **32.** $n = 7, l = 9, s = 21.$
33. $a = \frac{1}{2}, n = 6, s = 25\frac{1}{2}.$ **34.** $a = 11, n = 7, s = 14.$
35. $a = 6, l = 26, s = 96.$ **36.** $a = 4, l = -4, s = 0.$
37. $a = -9, d = 2, l = 5.$ **38.** $a = \frac{3}{4}, d = \frac{1}{2}, l = 4\frac{1}{4}.$
39. $n = 6, d = 2, s = 42.$ **40.** $n = 6, d = 1\frac{1}{2}, s = -7\frac{1}{2}.$
41. $a = -9, d = 1, s = -42.$ **42.** $a = -10, d = 1, s = -54.$
43. $l = -7, d = -2, s = -7.$ **44.** $l = 17, d = 4, s = 45.$

45. Insert three arithmetic means between 2 and 14.
46. Insert four arithmetic means between 3 and 13.
47. Insert four arithmetic means between -5 and 15.
48. Insert eight arithmetic means between -8 and 1.
49. Find the sum of all even integers between 5 and 29.
50. Find the sum of all odd integers between 5 and 29, inclusive.

51. Find the sum of all multiples of 3 between 2 and 43.

52. Find the sum of all multiples of 7 between 5 and 55.

53. A man worked for 11 years and received a raise of $200 at the beginning of each year after the first. If his salary was $2700 the first year, find his salary the last year and the total amount received for the entire 11 years.

54. If the man in Problem 53 saved his increase and 7 per cent of his salary, how much did he save in the 11 years?

55. The value of an automobile depreciated from $2100 to $1130 in 4 years. Find the value at the end of each year if the depreciation during each of the 4 years was $105 less than that of the preceding year.

56. If a compact body falls 16.1 ft. during the first second, 48.3 ft. during the second, and 80.5 ft. during the third, how far will it fall in 7 sec.?

57. A man bought a house on Jan. 1, 1941, for $7000 and sold it on Jan. 1, 1949, for $15,400. If the increase in value of the house each year was $100 more than the increase the previous year, find the value of the house at the first of each of the 9 years.

58. A machine that cost $5800 depreciated 15 per cent the first year, 13.5 per cent the second year, 12 per cent the third, and so on. What was the value at the end of 9 years if all percentages apply to the original cost?

59. The three consecutive digits of a number form an arithmetic progression whose sum is 15. The number obtained by reversing the digits is 594 less than the original. Find the number.

60. Find the approximate length of a motion-picture film .01 in. thick that can be wound on a reel 6 in. in diameter and that has a central core 2 in. in diameter. HINT: Consider the film as being wound in concentric circles.

61. On June 1, Mr. Brown bought a piano for $500. If he paid $50 in cash and $50 plus accrued interest on the first of each month, find the amount of interest paid if the rate was 6 per cent.

62. A bomb was dropped from a plane flying at an altitude of 10,000 ft. If the resistance of the air is neglected, find to the nearest second the time required for the bomb to reach the earth (see Problem 56).

63. Find the relation between x and y if $x - 2y$, $2x + y$, and $5x - y$ are three successive terms of an arithmetic progression.

64. If a, b, c and x, y, z are two arithmetic progressions, show that $a + x$, $b + y$, and $c + z$ is an arithmetic progression.

133. Geometric progressions. DEFINITION. *A geometric progression is a sequence of numbers so related that each one after the first can be obtained from the preceding by multiplying it by a fixed constant called the* **common ratio.**

Examples

Each of the sequences below is a geometric progression with the indicated common ratio.

1. 2, 6, 18, 54, 162; common ratio 3.
2. 3, −3, 3, −3, 3; common ratio −1.
3. 96, 24, 6, $\frac{3}{2}$, $\frac{3}{8}$; common ratio $\frac{1}{4}$.

In order to obtain formulas for dealing with a geometric progression we shall let[1]

$$a = \text{the first term}$$
$$l = \text{the last term}$$
$$r = \text{the common ratio}$$
$$n = \text{the number of terms}$$

and

$$s = \text{the sum of the terms}$$

134. The last term of a geometric progression. In terms of the above notation, the first six terms of a geometric progression in which the first term is a and the common ratio is r are

$$a, \quad ar, \quad ar^2, \quad ar^3, \quad ar^4, \quad ar^5$$

We notice here that the exponent of r in the second term is one, and that this exponent increases by one as we proceed from each term to the next. Hence, the exponent of r in any term is one less than the number of that term in the progression. Therefore, the nth term is ar^{n-1}. Thus, we have the formula

(1) $$l = ar^{n-1}$$

Example 1

Find the seventh term of the geometric progression 36, −12, 4, ...

Solution

In this progression, each term, after the first, is obtained by multiplying the preceding term by $-\frac{1}{3}$. Hence, $r = -\frac{1}{3}$. Obviously, $a = 36$, $n = 7$, and the seventh term is l. Hence, if we substitute these values in (1), we have

[1] Note that the letters used here can be arranged so as to spell the word "snarl."

$$l = 36(-\tfrac{1}{3})^{7-1}$$
$$= \frac{36}{(-3)^6}$$
$$= \tfrac{36}{729}$$
$$= \tfrac{4}{81}$$

135. *The sum of a geometric progression.* If we add the terms of the geometric progression

$$a,\ ar,\ ar^2,\ \ldots,\ ar^{n-2},\ ar^{n-1}$$

we have

(1) $\qquad s = a + ar + ar^2 + \cdots + ar^{n-2} + ar^{n-1}$

However, by use of an algebraic device, we can obtain a more compact formula for s. First, we multiply each member of (1) by r and get

(2) $\qquad rs = ar + ar^2 + ar^3 + \cdots + ar^{n-1} + ar^n$

Next we notice that if we subtract the corresponding members of (1) and (2), all the terms on the right cancel except the first term in (1) and the last term in (2). Hence, we have

$$s - rs = a - ar^n$$

or

$$s(1 - r) = a - ar^n$$

Solving the last equation for s, we obtain

(3) $\qquad s = \dfrac{a - ar^n}{1 - r}$

If we multiply each member of formula (1), Art. 134, by r, we get $rl = ar^n$. Now, if we replace ar^n by rl in (3), we get

(4) $\qquad\qquad\qquad s = \dfrac{a - rl}{1 - r}$

Example 1

Find the sum of the first six terms of the progression 2, −6, 18, ...

Solution

In this progression, $a = 2$, $r = -3$, and $n = 6$. Hence, if we substitute these values in (3), we have

$$s = \frac{2 - 2(-3)^6}{1 - (-3)}$$
$$= \frac{2 - 2(729)}{1 + 3}$$
$$= \frac{2 - 1458}{4}$$
$$= \frac{-1456}{4}$$
$$= -364$$

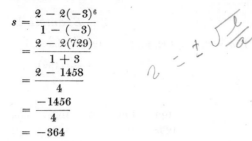

Example 2

The first term of a geometric progression is 3; the fourth term is 24. Find the tenth term and the sum of the first ten terms.

Solution

In order to find either the tenth term or the sum, we must have the value of r. We may obtain this value by considering the progression made up of the first four terms of the above. Then we have $a = 3$, $n = 4$, and $l = 24$. If we substitute these values in (1), Art. 134, we get

$$24 = 3r^{4-1}$$

or

$$3r^3 = 24$$

Hence,

$$r^3 = 8$$

and

$$r = 2$$

Now, using (1), Art. 134, again with $a = 3$, $r = 2$, and $n = 10$, we get

$$l = 3(2^{10-1})$$
$$= 3(2^9)$$
$$= 3(512)$$
$$= 1536$$

Hence, the tenth term is 1536.

In order to obtain s, we shall use (3), Art. 135, with $a = 3$, $r = 2$, and $n = 10$ and get

$$s = \frac{3 - 3(2)^{10}}{1 - 2} = \frac{3 - 3(1024)}{-1} = \frac{3 - 3072}{-1} = 3069$$

136. Simultaneous use of the formulas for l and s. If three of the quantities s, n, a, r, and l are given, the other two can be found by use of formula (1), Art. 134, and formula (3) or (4), Art. 135. For example, if a, l, and s are given, r can be found by means of (4), Art. 135; then n can be obtained by use of (1), Art. 134.

Example 1

If $a = 3$, $l = 192$, and $s = 129$, we have, by (4), Art. 135,

$$129 = \frac{3 - r(192)}{1 - r}$$

or

$$
\begin{aligned}
129 - 129r &= 3 - 192r &&\text{(clearing of fractions)} \\
-129r + 192r &= 3 - 129 &&\text{(transposing)} \\
63r &= -126 \\
r &= -2
\end{aligned}
$$

Now we substitute the values of a, l, and r in (1), Art. 134 and get

$$
\begin{aligned}
192 &= 3(-2)^{n-1} \\
(-2)^{n-1} &= 64 \\
&= (-2)^6
\end{aligned}
$$

Hence,

$$
\begin{aligned}
n - 1 &= 6 \\
n &= 7
\end{aligned}
$$

If s, l, and n are given, neither of the unknowns a and r can be found by any one of the three formulas. Hence, we must substitute the known values in two of them and solve the resulting equations simultaneously for a and r.

Example 2

If $s = 61$, $l = 81$, and $n = 5$, we may find a and r by use of any two of the three formulas. However, the work is easier if we use (1) of Art. 134, and (4) of Art. 135. Substituting the given values in these, we get

(1) $$81 = ar^4$$

(2) $$61 = \frac{a - 81r}{1 - r}$$

We shall solve these simultaneously by first solving (2) for a in terms of r, and then substituting in (1).

(3)
$$
\begin{aligned}
61 - 61r &= a - 81r &&\text{(clearing of fractions)} \\
a &= 61 + 20r &&\text{(solving for } a) \\
81 &= (61 + 20r)r^4 &&\text{[substituting the value of } a \text{ in (1)]} \\
20r^5 + 61r^4 - 81 &= 0 &&\text{(performing the indicated operations} \\
& &&\text{and transposing)}
\end{aligned}
$$

Now, by use of the method of Art. 104, we find the rational roots of this equation to be -3 and 1. The solution $r = 1$ must be discarded since, for this value, (2) is meaningless. However, if $r = -3$, then, by (3), $a = 1$. Hence, the solution is $a = 1$, $r = -3$.

137. Geometric means. The terms between the first and last terms of a geometric progression are called the *geometric means*. If the progression contains only three terms, the middle term is called the *geometric mean* of the other two. In order to obtain the geometric means between a and l, we use formula (1) of Art. 134 to find the value of r, and then the means can be computed. If there are only three terms in the progression, then, by (1), Art. 134,

$$l = ar^2$$

Hence,

$$r = \pm \sqrt{\frac{l}{a}}$$

Thus, the second term, or the geometric mean between a and l, is

$$a\left(\pm \sqrt{\frac{l}{a}}\right) = \pm \sqrt{\frac{a^2l}{a}} = \pm \sqrt{al}$$

Hence, *the geometric mean between two quantities is plus and minus the square root of their product.*

Example 1

Find the five geometric means between 3 and 192.

Solution

A geometric progression starting with 3 and ending with 192 with five intermediate terms contains seven terms. Hence, $n = 7$, $a = 3$, and $l = 192$. Therefore, by (1), Art. 134,

$$192 = 3(r^{7-1})$$

Hence,

$$r^6 = \frac{192}{3}$$
$$= 64$$

and

$$r = \pm \sqrt[6]{64} = \pm 2$$

Consequently, the two sets of geometric means of five terms each between 3 and 192 are 6, 12, 24, 48, 96, and -6, 12, -24, 48, -96.

Example 2

Find the geometric mean of $\frac{1}{2}$ and $\frac{1}{8}$.

Solution

By the statement just before Example 1, the geometric mean of $\frac{1}{2}$ and $\frac{1}{8}$ is
$\pm \sqrt{(\frac{1}{2})(\frac{1}{8})} = \pm \sqrt{\frac{1}{16}} = \pm\frac{1}{4}$.

EXERCISE 68

In each of Problems 1 to 8, write the progression that has the given elements.

1. $a = -3, r = -2, n = 5.$ **2.** $a = 2, r = \frac{1}{2}, n = 6.$

3. $a = 4, r = -\frac{1}{2}, n = 7.$ **4.** $a = 6, r = -1, n = 4.$

5. First term 1, second term 3, $n = 5.$

6. Third term 8, fourth term -4, $n = 6.$

7. Fifth term $1\frac{1}{2}$, sixth term $2\frac{1}{4}$, $n = 7.$

8. Third term 3, fourth term -1, $n = 5.$

Find the last term of the progression described in each of Problems 9 to 12.

9. $a = 1, r = 3, n = 5.$ **10.** $a = 2, r = \frac{1}{2}, n = 6.$

11. $a = 3, r = -2, n = 4.$ **12.** $a = 81, r = -\frac{1}{3}, n = 7.$

Find the sum of the terms in the geometric progression described in each of Problems 13 to 20.

13. $a = 4, r = -2, n = 4.$ **14.** $a = 2, r = 2, n = 10.$

15. $a = 8, r = \frac{1}{2}, n = 6.$ **16.** $a = 3, r = -\frac{1}{3}, n = 5.$

17. $a = 1, r = 2, l = 32.$ **18.** $a = 81, r = \frac{1}{3}, l = 1.$

19. $a = 18, r = \frac{1}{2}, l = \frac{9}{8}.$ **20.** $a = 8, r = -1, l = 8.$

In Problems 21 to 28, insert the indicated number of geometric means between the two given numbers.

21. Two between 1 and 8.   **22.** Three between 2 and $\frac{1}{8}$.

23. Two between 2 and 2.   **24.** Three between 3 and 48.

25. Three between 3 and 27.   **26.** Two between 9 and $-\frac{1}{3}$.

27. Five between $\frac{8}{27}$ and $\frac{27}{8}$.   **28.** Four between $\sqrt{2}$ and -8.

Find the two of the five quantities s, n, a, r, and l that are missing in Problems 29 to 48.

29. $a = 3, r = 2, n = 5.$ **30.** $a = 2, r = 3, n = 5.$

31. $a = 4, n = 6, l = -128.$ **32.** $a = 8, n = 7, l = \frac{1}{8}.$

33. $r = -3, n = 4, l = 54.$ **34.** $r = \frac{1}{3}, n = 5, l = 3.$

35. $a = -2, r = 2, l = -256.$ **36.** $a = -128, r = -\frac{1}{2}, l = -2.$

37. $s = -182, n = 6, r = -3.$ **38.** $s = \frac{211}{18}, n = 5, r = \frac{2}{3}.$

39. $a = 3, r = 3, s = 1092.$ **40.** $a = \frac{1}{4}, r = -2, s = 2\frac{3}{4}.$

41. $l = 1, s = 1, n = 7.$ **42.** $l = 12, s = 9, n = 3.$

43. $r = -1\frac{1}{2}, l = 40\frac{1}{2}, s = 27\frac{1}{2}.$ **44.** $r = \frac{2}{3}, l = \frac{2}{3}, s = \frac{211}{24}.$

45. $a = 1\frac{1}{2}, l = 48, s = 94\frac{1}{2}.$ **46.** $a = 8, l = \frac{1}{8}, s = \frac{127}{8}.$

47. $a = 5, n = 3, s = 65.$ **48.** $a = 2, n = 4, s = 80.$

49. Show that the sequence of geometric means of the consecutive pairs of terms of a geometric progression is a geometric progression.

50. Show that the product of the first and fourth terms of a geometric progression is equal to the product of the second and third.

51. Show that the products of the corresponding terms of two geometric progressions are a geometric progression.

52. Show that the quotients of the corresponding terms of two geometric progressions are a geometric progression.

53. If there were no duplications, how many ancestors did a person have in the seven generations immediately preceding him?

54. The number of bacteria in a culture doubles every 2 hr. If there were n bacteria present at the start, how many will there be in the culture at the end of 24 hr?

55. An air pump removes $\frac{1}{4}$ of the air in a bell jar at each stroke. Find the fractional part of the original volume of air that remained in the bell jar after the sixth stroke.

56. Suppose that it is possible for a person to save 1 cent on the first day of the month, 2 cents on the second day, 4 cents on the third, and so on. Find to the nearest million of dollars the amount he would save in a 30-day month.

57. A car depreciates by 20 per cent of its value each year. Find the value at the end of the fifth year of a car that cost $3000 new.

58. A person starts a chain letter by writing to three friends and requesting each to copy the letter and send it to three of his friends. Assuming that the chain was unbroken when the sixth set of letters, including that of the originator, was mailed, how much was spent for postage at 3 cents per letter?

59. A man traveling in a car with a leaking radiator refilled it with water at the end of each hour. His radiator holds 5 gal. and at the start was filled with a mixture containing 60 per cent alcohol. If he lost 1 gal. between fillings, how much alcohol was in the radiator at the end of the fifth hour?

60. A man deposits $100 at the beginning of each year in a bank that pays interest at the rate of 2 per cent compounded annually. How much will he have to his credit at the end of 7 years?

61. A man willed $\frac{1}{4}$ of his estate to his eldest child, $\frac{1}{4}$ of the remainder to the next, and so on until his sixth child received $1215. How large was the estate, and what was the residue after the children received their shares?

62. Twelve men are fishing from a pier. The first is worth $1000; the second, $2000; the third, $4000; and so on. How many millionaires are in the group?

138. Infinite geometric progressions. If the common ratio is between -1 and 1, the numerical values of the terms in a geometric progression decrease as n increases. Hence, if the number of terms of such a progression is large, we would not expect the addition of more terms to affect the sum very greatly. In fact, we shall show that if $-1 < r < 1$, the sum of the terms in a geometric progression approaches nearer and nearer to a fixed number as n increases.

Formula (3), Art. 135, can be expressed in the form

$$s \; \frac{\dfrac{a}{1-r}}{}$$

(1)
$$s = \frac{a}{1-r}(1 - r^n)$$

If $-1 < r < 1$, then the numerical value of r^n decreases as n increases and can be made arbitrarily small by choosing n sufficiently large. Hence, for increasing values of n, the quantity in the parentheses in (1) approaches nearer and nearer to 1. Thus, s approaches $a/(1 - r)$. In other words, the greater the value of n, the more nearly the value of s is equal to $a/(1 - r)$. Consequently, when the ratio in a geometric progression is between -1 and 1 and the number of terms is unlimited, we say that

(2)
$$s = \frac{a}{1 - r}$$

Example 1

Find the sum of $1 + \frac{1}{2} + \frac{1}{4} + \cdots$, where the dots indicate that there is no end to the progression.

Solution

In this progression, $a = 1$ and $r = \frac{1}{2}$. Hence, by (2),

$$s = \frac{1}{1 + \frac{1}{2}} = \frac{1}{\frac{1}{2}} = 2$$

A nonterminating, repeating decimal fraction is an illustration of an infinite geometric progression with $-1 < r < 1$. For example,

$$.232323 \cdots = .23 + .0023 + .000023 + \cdots$$

The sequence of terms on the right is a geometric progression with $a = .23$ and $r = \frac{1}{100}$.

By use of (2), we can express any repeating decimal fraction as a common fraction by the method illustrated in the following example.

Example 2

Show that $.333 \cdots = \frac{1}{3}$.

Solution

The decimal fraction $.333 \ldots$ can be expressed as the progression

$$.3 + .03 + .003 + \cdots$$

in which $a = .3$ and $r = .1$. Hence, by (2), the sum s is

$$s = \frac{.3}{1 - .1} = \frac{.3}{.9} = \frac{3}{9} = \frac{1}{3}$$

Example 3

Express .423423 . . . as a common fraction.

Solution

Expressing the given repeating decimal as a progression, we have

$$.423423423 \cdots = .423 + .000423 + .000000423 + \cdots$$

in which $a = .423$ and $r = .001$. Hence, by (2),

$$s = \frac{.423}{1 - .001} = \frac{.423}{.999} = \frac{423}{999} = \frac{47}{111}$$

EXERCISE 69

Assume that the number of terms is unlimited, and find the sum of the geometric progression having the elements in each of Problems 1 to 12.

1. $a = 3, r = \frac{1}{2}$. **2.** $a = 4, r = \frac{1}{3}$. **3.** $a = 6, r = \frac{2}{3}$. **4.** $a = 8, r = \frac{3}{4}$.

5. First term 5, second term $2\frac{1}{2}$. **6.** First term -6, second term -1.5.

7. First term 6, second term -3. **8.** First term -8, second term 6.

9. First term 4, second term -3. **10.** First term 7, second term, 1.4.

11. Second term 6, fourth term $\frac{8}{3}$. **12.** Second term 5, fourth term 1.25.

Express each of the following repeating decimals as rational fractions.

13. .222 . . . . **14.** .555 . . . . **15.** .666 . . . .

16. .888 . . . . **17.** .1515 . . . . **18.** .126126 . . . .

19. .540540 . . . . **20.** 142857142857 . . . . **21.** 3.2727 . . . .

22. 58.1818 . . . . **23.** 3.123123 . . . . **24.** 2.432432 . . . .

Find the sum of all numbers of the form indicated in Problems 25 to 28 where n is a positive integer.

25. $1/2^n$. **26.** $3/4^n$. **27.** $\left(\frac{3}{4}\right)^n$. **28.** 5^{-n}.

29. If a ball rebounds $\frac{3}{5}$ as far as it falls, how far will it travel before coming to rest if it is dropped from a height of 30 ft.?

30. The tip of a vibrating pendulum swings through arcs each of which is $\frac{3}{4}$ as long as the preceding. If the first arc is 8 in. in length, how far will the tip move before coming to rest?

31. A college received a block of stock as a gift to the endowment fund. The dividend the first year was $400, and each year thereafter it was $\frac{4}{5}$ of that of the preceding year. What is the maximum amount that the college can receive from these dividends.

32. A child receives $1500 from a certain source during the first year of his life; $750, the second year; $375, the third year, and so on. About how much will he receive from this source by the time his third grandchild is 3 years of age?

33. The motion of a ball rolling across a surface is retarded in such a way that it moves $\frac{2}{3}$ as far each second as in the preceding second. If the ball rolled 6 ft. the first second, what distance will it move before coming to rest?

34. A first square has an area of 64 sq. in. A second is drawn by connecting the mid-points of the sides of the first, and a third by connecting the mid-points of the sides of the second, and so on. Find the approximate sum of the areas.

35. Find the approximate sum of the perimeters of the squares in Problem 34.

36. Suppose the shrinkage per week in the weight of stored potatoes is $\frac{1}{2}$ of that of the preceding week. If a dealer stored 500 lb. of potatoes when the price was 5 cents per pound and the weight decreased to 480 lb. during the first week, could he afford to hold them until the price rises to 6 cents?

37. Find the sum

$$\frac{1}{x} + \frac{1}{x^2} + \frac{1}{x^3} + \cdots$$

if (a) $x > 1$, (b) $x < -1$. Why is it necessary to limit the range of x?

Find the range of x for which the sum in each of Problems 38 to 40 exists. Find the sum in each case.

38. $\dfrac{1}{2x-1} + \dfrac{1}{(2x-1)^2} + \dfrac{1}{(2x-1)^3} + \cdots$

39. $\dfrac{2}{3x-2} + \dfrac{4}{(3x-2)^2} + \dfrac{8}{(3x-2)^3} + \cdots$

40. $\dfrac{3}{2x-5} + \dfrac{9}{(2x-5)^2} + \dfrac{27}{(2x-5)^3} + \cdots$

139. Harmonic progressions. DEFINITION. *The series formed by the reciprocals of the terms of an arithmetic progression is called a harmonic progression.*[1]

Illustrative Example

Since two quantities are reciprocals if and only if their product is unity and since -5, -3, -1, 1, 3, 5, 7 is an arithmetic series, it follows that $-\frac{1}{5}$, $-\frac{1}{3}$, -1, 1, $\frac{1}{3}$, $\frac{1}{5}$, $\frac{1}{7}$ is a harmonic progression.

*In order to determine the **nth** term of a H.P., we transform it into an A.P., find the **nth** term of the A.P., and take its reciprocal.*

DEFINITION. *The terms of a harmonic progression between any two of its terms are called **harmonic means**.*

Example

What is the tenth term of a H.P. if the first and third terms are $\frac{1}{2}$ and $\frac{1}{6}$?

[1] It is interesting that strings of the same weight and subjected to the same tension will produce a harmonious sound if their lengths are in harmonic progression.

THE PROGRESSIONS

Solution

The first and third terms of the corresponding A.P. are 2 and 6. Hence, $l = a + (3 - 1)d$ becomes $6 = 2 + 2d$ and, consequently, $d = 2$. Therefore, when $n = 10$, $l = 2 + (10 - 1)2 = 20$. Taking the reciprocal of 20, we find that the tenth term of the H.P. is $\frac{1}{20}$.

EXERCISE 70

Determine the type of the progression in each of Problems 1 to 12. Extend the harmonic progressions by two more terms.

1. $1, \frac{1}{3}, \frac{1}{5}, \frac{1}{7}$. **2.** $\frac{1}{4}, 1, -\frac{1}{2}, -\frac{1}{5}$. **3.** $\frac{3}{4}, 1\frac{1}{2}, 2\frac{1}{4}, 3$.

4. $2, 3, 4\frac{1}{2}, 6\frac{3}{4}$. **5.** $\frac{1}{3}, \frac{1}{9}, \frac{1}{27}, \frac{1}{81}$. **6.** $\frac{1}{3}, 1, -1, -\frac{1}{3}$.

7. $\frac{1}{7}, \frac{1}{3}, -1, -\frac{1}{5}$. **8.** $\frac{2}{3}, 1\frac{1}{3}, 2, 2\frac{2}{3}$. **9.** $a, \dfrac{a^2 + 1}{a}, \dfrac{a^2 + 2}{a}, \dfrac{a^2 + 3}{a}$.

10. $\dfrac{x}{y}, 1, \dfrac{y}{x}, \dfrac{y^2}{x^2}$. **11.** $\frac{1}{7}, \frac{2}{11}, \frac{1}{4}, \frac{2}{5}$. **12.** $x, \dfrac{x}{1 + x}, \dfrac{x}{1 + 2x}$.

13. The first term of a harmonic progression is $1\frac{1}{2}$ and the second term is 1. Find the fifth term.

14. The first term of a harmonic progression is $\frac{1}{2}$ and the second term is $\frac{1}{5}$. Find the tenth term.

15. The third term of a harmonic progression is $\frac{1}{5}$ and the ninth term is $\frac{1}{8}$. Find the first term.

16. The third term of a harmonic progression is 12 and the seventh term is 2. Find the thirteenth term.

17. The fifth term of a harmonic progression is $\frac{1}{13}$ and the ninth term is $\frac{1}{23}$. Find the first term.

18. The second term of a harmonic progression is 2 and the fifth term is -2. Find the eighth term.

19. The third term of a harmonic progression is -1 and the eighth term is $\frac{1}{9}$. Find the sixth term.

20. The sixth term of a harmonic progression is $\frac{1}{2}$ and the tenth term is $\frac{1}{4}$. Find the third term.

21. Insert two harmonic means between $\frac{1}{2}$ and $\frac{1}{11}$.

22. Insert three harmonic means between $\frac{5}{8}$ and $\frac{1}{4}$.

23. Insert four harmonic means between $\frac{1}{5}$ and $\frac{1}{15}$.

24. Insert two harmonic means between $\frac{6}{7}$ and $\frac{3}{5}$.

$H.P. \quad \frac{2}{3}, 1$

$A.P. \quad \frac{2}{3}, 1,$

$d = 1 - \frac{2}{3} = \frac{1}{3}$

$l_N = a + (N-1)d \qquad l_5 = \frac{2}{3} + (5-1)\frac{1}{3} = \frac{2}{3} + \frac{4}{3} = 2$

CHAPTER 16

MATHEMATICAL INDUCTION

140. *Mathematical induction.* Frequently, scientific laws are discovered experimentally by observing and stating properties that are common to a large number of experiments. The statement of the common property may be called a law, but repeated laboratory verification of its truth does not constitute a mathematical proof of its general validity. For example, if we let $n = 0, 1, 2, 3$ in $q(n) = n^2 - n + 41$, we find that $q(n)$ becomes 41, 41, 43, and 47, respectively. These numbers are primes; that is, no one of them is divisible by any integer other than itself and unity. If we calculate the value of $q(n)$ for each integral value of n up to and including 40, we see that $q(n)$ represents the same type of integer, and this surely suggests that $q(n)$ represents a prime number for every integral value assigned to n. However, if n is equal to 41, $q(n) = 41^2 - 41 + 41 = 41^2$ which is not a prime.

On the other hand, $1 + 3 = 4 = 2^2$, $1 + 3 + 5 = 9 = 3^2$, $1 + 3 + 5 + 7 = 16 = 4^2$. These results suggest that the sum of the first n odd integers is n^2, that is

$$(1) \qquad 1 + 3 + 5 + \cdots + (2n - 1) = n^2$$

Since repeated verification of the truth of (1) for particular values of n does not constitute a proof, we must find some other means of demonstrating its general validity. A method known as *mathematical induction* can frequently be used for proving that certain statements which involve n are true for all integral values of n. The type of reasoning involved in mathematical induction is illustrated by the following hypothetical example. Suppose that a certain goal can be reached by a sequence of successive but unknown number of steps. Suppose, further, that a person in the process of achieving this goal can be assured that it will always be possible for him to take the next step. Then, regardless of all other circumstances, he knows that he can ultimately attain the goal.

In order to apply this method of reasoning to the proof of the statement in (1), we assume that the statement is true for some definite but unknown integral value of n, that is, for $n = k$. Then we shall show that it *necessarily* follows that the statement is true for the *next* integer, $k + 1$. Hence, if we can show that it is true for some number, say $k = 3$, we know that it is true for the next integer, $k = 4$, and thus for all following integers. We shall show how this is done in Example 1.

Example 1

Prove formula (1) by mathematical induction.

Solution

(a) We first assume that (1) is true for $n = k$ and obtain

$$(2) \qquad 1 + 3 + 5 + \cdots + (2k - 1) = k^2$$

(b) Next, we write the formula (1) with $n = k + 1$ and get

$$(3) \qquad 1 + 3 + 5 + \cdots + (2k + 1) = (k + 1)^2$$

Now we shall prove that the truth of (3) necessarily follows. The last term in the left member of (3) is the $(k + 1)$st term of (1); hence, the next to the last is the kth term and, therefore, is $(2k - 1)$. Consequently, we may write (3) in the form

$$(4) \qquad 1 + 3 + 5 + \cdots + (2k - 1) + (2k + 1) = (k + 1)^2$$

(c) In order to prove that (4) is true, provided we assume the truth of (2), we notice that the left member of (4) is the corresponding member of (2) increased by $(2k + 1)$, that is, by the $(k + 1)$st term of (1). Hence, we add $2k + 1$ to each member of (2), thus obtaining

$$1 + 3 + 5 + \cdots + (2k + 1) = k^2 + 2k + 1 = (k + 1)^2$$

which is the same as (4). Therefore, if (1) is true, (4) is true. That is, the formula is true for $n = k + 1$, if it is true for $n = k$.

(d) Evidently, (1) is true for $n = 1$.

(e) Hence, by step (c), (1) holds for $n = 1, 2, 3, 4, 5$, and so on.

The formal process of a mathematical induction proof consists of the following five steps.

1. *Assume that the theorem or statement to be proved is true for* **n** *equal to a particular but unspecified integer* **k**, *and express this assumption in symbolic form.*

2. *Obtain a symbolic statement of the theorem for* **n = k + 1**.

3. *Prove that if the equation in the statement in step 1 is true, the equation in the statement in step 2 is true also.*

4. *Verify the theorem for the least integral value* **q** *of* **n** *for which it has a meaning.*

5. *Using the conclusion in step 3, show by successive steps that the theorem is true for* **n = q + 1** *since it is true for the integer* **q** *of step 4; furthermore, that it is true for* **n = q + 2**, *since it is true for* **n = q + 1**; · · · ; *and, finally, that it is true for* **n = q + m**, *since it is true for* **n = q + (m − 1)**, *regardless of the positive integral value of* **m**.

No general directions can be given for carrying out the work of step 3. However, the following additional examples illustrate a procedure that can frequently be followed.

Example 2

Prove De Moivre's theorem, which states

(1) $$[r(\cos \theta + i \sin \theta)]^n = r^n(\cos n\theta + i \sin n\theta)$$

Solution

(a) According to step 1, we assume that (1) is true for $n = k$, thus obtaining

(2) $$[r(\cos \theta + i \sin \theta)]^k = r^k(\cos k\theta + i \sin k\theta)$$

(b) We write (1) with $n = k + 1$, and get

(3) $$[r(\cos \theta + i \sin \theta)]^{k+1} = r^{k+1} [\cos (k + 1)\theta + i \sin (k + 1)\theta]$$

(c) In order to prove that the truth of (3) follows from (2), we multiply each member of the latter by $r(\cos \theta + i \sin \theta)$, since this will give us a new equation whose left member is the same as that of (3). We thus have

$$[r(\cos \theta + i \sin \theta)]^{k+1} = [r(\cos \theta + i \sin \theta)][r^k(\cos k\theta + i \sin k\theta)]$$
$$= r^{k+1}[(\cos \theta \cos k\theta - \sin \theta \sin k\theta) + i(\sin \theta \cos k\theta + \cos \theta \sin k\theta)]$$
$$= r^{k+1}[\cos (\theta + k\theta) + i \sin (\theta + k\theta)], \text{ by the addition formulas of trigonometry}$$
$$= r^{k+1}[\cos (k + 1)\theta + i \sin (k + 1)\theta]$$

Hence, (1) is true for $n = k + 1$ if it is true for $n = k$.

(d) We next verify (2) for $k = 2$, obtaining

$$[r(\cos \theta + i \sin \theta)]^2 = r^2(\cos \theta + i \sin \theta)^2$$
$$= r^2[(\cos^2 \theta - \sin^2 \theta) + i(2 \sin \theta \cos \theta)]$$
$$= r^2(\cos 2\theta + i \sin 2\theta)$$

(e) Hence, by (c), (1) is true for $n = 3, 4, 5$, and so on.

Example 3

Prove that $x^n - y^n$ is divisible by $x - y$.

Solution

(a) We first assume that $x^k - y^k$ is divisible by $x - y$, or that

(1)
$$\frac{x^k - y^k}{x - y} = q(x,y)$$

where

(2)
$$q(x,y) = x^{k-1} + x^{k-2}y + \cdots + xy^{k-2} + y^{k-1}$$

(b) When $n = k + 1$, the quotient of $x^n - y^n$ and $x - y$ may be expressed in the form

$$\frac{x^{k+1} - y^{k+1}}{x - y} = \frac{x^{k+1} - xy^k + xy^k - y^{k+1}}{x - y}$$
$$= \frac{x(x^k - y^k) + y^k(x - y)}{x - y}$$
$$= x\left(\frac{x^k - y^k}{x - y}\right) + y^k\left(\frac{x - y}{x - y}\right)$$
$$= x[q(x,y)] + y^k$$
$$= x^k + x^{k-1}y + \cdots + x^2y^{k-2} + xy^{k-1} + y^k$$

substituting the value of $q(x,y)$ from (2).

(c) When $k = 2$, (1) becomes

$$\frac{x^2 - y^2}{x - y} = x + y$$

Hence, $x^n - y^n$ is divisible by $x - y$ when $n = 3, 4, 5$, and so on.

In most of the problems of Exercise 71, the work of step 3 can be carried out *by adding the $(k + 1)$st term of the formula under consideration to each member of the equation obtained in step 1.*

EXERCISE 71

Using mathematical induction, prove the following relations:

1. $1 + 2 + 3 + \cdots + n = \dfrac{n(n + 1)}{2}$.

2. $2 + 4 + 6 + \cdots + 2n = n(n + 1)$.

3. $3 + 5 + 7 + \cdots + (2n + 1) = n(n + 2)$.

4. $1 + 4 + 7 + \cdots + (3n - 2) = \dfrac{n}{2}(3n - 1).$

5. $4 + 7 + 10 + \cdots + (3n + 1) = \dfrac{n}{2}(3n + 5).$

6. $2 + 5 + 8 + \cdots + (3n - 1) = \dfrac{n}{2}(3n + 1).$

7. $3 + 6 + 9 + \cdots + 3n = \dfrac{3n}{2}(n + 1).$

8. $1 + 5 + 9 + \cdots + (4n - 3) = n(2n - 1).$

9. $2 + 2^2 + 2^3 + \cdots + 2^n = 2(2^n - 1).$

10. $2 + 6 + 18 + \cdots + 2(3^{n-1}) = 3^n - 1.$

11. $3 + 3^2 + 3^3 + \cdots + 3^n = \frac{3}{2}(3^n - 1).$

12. $\dfrac{1}{2} + \dfrac{1}{2^2} + \dfrac{1}{2^3} + \cdots + \dfrac{1}{2^n} = 1 - \dfrac{1}{2^n}.$

13. $(1)(2) + (2)(3) + (3)(4) + \cdots + n(n + 1) = \dfrac{n(n + 1)(n + 2)}{3}.$

14. $(2)(4) + (4)(6) + (6)(8) + \cdots + 2n(2n + 2) = \dfrac{4n(n + 1)(n + 2)}{3}.$

15. $(1)(3) + (2)(4) + (3)(5) + \cdots + n(n + 2) = \dfrac{n(n + 1)(2n + 7)}{6}.$

16. $\dfrac{1}{(1)(2)} + \dfrac{1}{(2)(3)} + \dfrac{1}{(3)(4)} + \cdots + \dfrac{1}{n(n + 1)} = \dfrac{n}{n + 1}.$

17. $1 + 3 + 6 + \cdots + \frac{1}{2}n(n + 1) = \dfrac{n(n + 1)(n + 2)}{6}.$

18. $1 + 4 + 10 + \cdots + \dfrac{n(n + 1)(n + 2)}{6} = \dfrac{(n)(n + 1)(n + 2)(n + 3)}{24}.$

19. $1 + r + r^2 + \cdots + r^{n-1} = \dfrac{1 - r^n}{1 - r}.$

20. $a + (a + d) + (a + 2d) + \cdots + [a + (n - 1)d] = \frac{1}{2}n[2a + (n - 1)d].$

21. Show that $x^{2n+1} + y^{2n+1}$ is divisible by $x + y$.

22. Show that $x^{2n-1} - y^{2n-1}$ is divisible by $x - y$.

CHAPTER 17

THE BINOMIAL THEOREM

141. *The binomial formula.* In this article, we shall develop a formula which enables us to express any positive integral power of a binomial as a polynomial. This polynomial is called the expansion of the power of the binomial.

By actual multiplication, we may obtain the following expansions of the first, second, third, fourth, and fifth powers of $x + y$:

$$(x + y)^1 = x + y$$
$$(x + y)^2 = x^2 + 2xy + y^2$$
$$(x + y)^3 = x^3 + 3x^2y + 3xy^2 + y^3$$
$$(x + y)^4 = x^4 + 4x^3y + 6x^2y^2 + 4xy^3 + y^4$$
$$(x + y)^5 = x^5 + 5x^4y + 10x^3y^2 + 10x^2y^3 + 5xy^4 + y^5$$

By referring to the above expansions, we may readily verify the fact that the following properties of $(x + y)^n$ exist when $n = 1, 2, 3, 4,$ and 5:

1. The first term in the expansion is x^n.

2. The second term is $nx^{n-1}y$.

3. The exponent of x decreases by one and the exponent of y increases by one as we proceed from term to term.

4. There are $n + 1$ terms in the expansion.

5. The $(n + 1)$st term or the last term is y^n.

6. The nth or the next to the last term of the expansion is nxy^{n-1}.

7. If we multiply the coefficient of any term by the exponent of x in that term and then divide the product by the number of the term in the expansion, we obtain the coefficient of the next term.

8. The sum of the exponents of x and y in any term is n.

If we assume that these properties hold for any integral power of n, we may write the first five terms in the expansion of $(x + y)^n$ as follows:

First term

$$x^n \qquad \qquad \text{(by Property 1)}$$

Second term

$$nx^{n-1}y \qquad \qquad \text{(by Property 2)}$$

Third term

$$\frac{n(n-1)}{2} x^{n-2}y^2 \qquad \qquad \text{(by Properties 7 and 3)}$$

Fourth term

$$\frac{n(n-1)(n-2)}{(3)(2)} x^{n-3}y^3 \qquad \qquad \text{(by Properties 7 and 3)}$$

Fifth term

$$\frac{n(n-1)(n-2)(n-3)}{(4)(3)(2)} x^{n-4}y^4 \qquad \qquad \text{(by Properties 7 and 3)}$$

We continue this process until we reach the nth term which is

nth term

$$nxy^{n-1} \qquad \qquad \text{(by Property 6)}$$

and, finally, we reach the last, or the

$(n + 1)$st term

$$y^n \qquad \qquad \text{(by Property 5)}$$

We are now in position to form the sum of the above terms and obtain the binomial formula. However, if we introduce a new notation at this point, we can write the expansion in a slightly more compact form.

DEFINITION. *The product of any integer n and all the integers less than n is called factorial n, and it is designated by the symbol $n!$.*

Examples

1. $3! = 3 \times 2 \times 1 = 6$.
2. $5! = 5 \times 4 \times 3 \times 2 \times 1 = 120$.

Now, if we notice that $4 \times 3 \times 2 = 4 \times 3 \times 2 \times 1 = 4!$,

$$3 \times 2 = 3 \times 2 \times 1 = 3!$$

and $2 = 2 \times 1 = 2!$, we may write the expansion of $(x + y)^n$ as follows:

(1)
$$(x + y)^n = x^n + nx^{n-1}y + \frac{n(n-1)}{2!} x^{n-2}y^2$$
$$+ \frac{n(n-1)(n-2)}{3!} x^{n-3}y^3$$
$$+ \frac{n(n-1)(n-2)(n-3)}{4!} x^{n-4}y^4$$
$$+ \cdots + nxy^{n-1} + y^n$$

Formula (1) is called the *binomial formula*, and the statement that it is true is called the *binomial theorem*.

Example 3

Use the binomial formula to obtain the expansion of $(2a + b)^6$.

Solution

We shall first apply (1) with $x = 2a$, $y = b$, and $n = 6$. Then we shall simplify each term in the expansion. By (1),

$$(2a + b)^6 = (2a)^6 + 6(2a)^5b + \frac{(6)(5)}{2!} (2a)^4b^2 + \frac{(6)(5)(4)}{3!} (2a)^3b^3$$
$$+ \frac{(6)(5)(4)(3)}{4!} (2a)^2b^4 + \frac{(6)(5)(4)(3)(2)}{5!} (2a)b^5$$
$$+ \frac{(6)(5)(4)(3)(2)(1)}{6!} b^6$$

Now we shall compute the coefficients and raise $2a$ to the indicated powers and obtain

$$(2a + b)^6 = 64a^6 + 6(32a^5)b + 15(16a^4)b^2 + 20(8a^3)b^3$$
$$+ 15(4a^2)b^4 + 6(2a)b^5 + b^6$$

Finally, we perform the indicated multiplication in each term above and get

$$(2a + b)^6 = 64a^6 + 192a^5b + 240a^4b^2 + 160a^3b^3 + 60a^2b^4 + 12ab^5 + b^6$$

The computation of the coefficients can, in most cases, be performed mentally by use of Property 7, and thus we can avoid writing the first step in the expansion in the above example.

Example 4

Expand $(a - 3b)^5$.

Solution

The first term in the expansion is a^5, and the second is $5a^4(-3b)$.   To get the coefficient of the third, we multiply 5 by 4 and divide the product by 2, obtaining 10.   Hence, the third term is $10a^3(-3b)^2$.   Similarly, the fourth term is

$$\tfrac{30}{3}a^2(-3b)^3 = 10a^2(-3b)^3$$

Continuing this process, we obtain the following expansion:

$$(a - 3b)^5 = a^5 + 5a^4(-3b) + 10a^3(-3b)^2 + 10a^2(-3b)^3 + 5a(-3b)^4 + (-3b)^5$$
$$= a^5 - 15a^4b + 90a^3b^2 - 270a^2b^3 + 405ab^4 - 243b^5$$

It should be noted that we carry the second term of the binomial $-3b$ through the first step of the expansion as a single term.   Then we raise $-3b$ to the indicated power and simplify the result.

Example 5

Expand $(2x - 5y)^4$.

Solution

We shall carry through the expansion with $2x$ as the first term and $-5y$ as the second and get

$$(2x - 5y)^4 = (2x)^4 + 4(2x)^3(-5y) + 6(2x)^2(-5y)^2 + 4(2x)(-5y)^3 + (-5y)^4$$
$$= 16x^4 + 4(8x^3)(-5y) + 6(4x^2)(25y^2) + 4(2x)(-125y^3) + 625y^4$$
$$= 16x^4 - 160x^3y + 600x^2y^2 - 1000xy^3 + 625y^4$$

142. The rth term of the binomial formula.   In the preceding examples, we explained the method for obtaining any term of a binomial expansion from the term just before it.   However, by use of this method, it is impossible to obtain any specific term of the expansion without first computing all the terms which precede it.   We shall next develop a formula for finding the general rth term without reference to the other terms.   Our development is an example of the method of inductive reasoning—a method that is very important in all scientific investigations.

We shall consider the fifth term in (1) of the previous article and note the following properties:

1. The exponent of y in the fifth term is one less than the number 5 of the term in the expansion.

2. The exponent of x is n minus the exponent of y.

3. The denominator of the coefficient is the exponent of y followed by the exclamation point or the factorial of the exponent of y.

4. The first factor in the numerator is n, and the last factor is n minus a number that is two less than the number of the term, or $n - (5 - 2)$; and the intervening factors are the consecutive integers between the first and the last factors.

We may also verify the fact that the above properties are true for the other terms of the expansion.

We now assume that the above properties hold for *any* term in the expansion, and hence for the rth term, we have:

1. The exponent of y is $r - 1$.
2. The exponent of x is $n - (r - 1) = n - r + 1$.
3. The denominator of the coefficient is $(r - 1)!$.
4. The last factor in the numerator is $n - (r - 2) = n - r + 2$, and hence the numerator is $n(n - 1)(n - 2) \cdots (n - r + 2)$.

Therefore, we have the formula

(1) *The rth term in the expansion of* $(x + y)^n$ *is*

$$\frac{n(n - 1)(n - 2) \cdots (n - r + 2)}{(r - 1)!} x^{n-r+1} y^{r-1}$$

It should be noted that this formula is based on the *assumption* that the four properties mentioned in the second paragraph of this article hold for *all* terms in the expansion. The proof of this fact depends upon the use of mathematical induction, and we shall present it in the next article.

Example 1

Find the sixth term in the expansion of $(2a - b)^9$.

Solution

In this problem, $x = 2a$, $y = -b$, $n = 9$, and $r = 6$. Hence, $r - 1 = 5$, $n - r + 1 = 9 - 6 + 1 = 4$, and $n - r + 2 = 5$. Hence, if we substitute these values in (1), we get

$$\text{6th term} = \frac{(9)(8)(7)(6)(5)}{(5)(4)(3)(2)(1)} (2a)^4 (-b)^5$$
$$= 126(16a^4)(-b^5)$$
$$= -2016a^4 b^5$$

EXERCISE 72

Expand the binomial to the indicated power in each of Problems 1 to 24.

1. $(x + y)^6$.
2. $(a + b)^7$.
3. $(u + v)^8$.
4. $(a + b)^{10}$.
5. $(x - y)^5$.
6. $(a - b)^9$.
7. $(c - d)^8$.
8. $(p - q)^{11}$.

9. $(x + 2y)^5$.　　**10.** $(3x + y)^4$.　　**11.** $(x + 4y)^5$.　　**12.** $(4x + 3y)^3$.

13. $(2x - 3y)^6$.　　**14.** $(3x - 4y)^4$.　　**15.** $(3x - 2y)^7$.　　**16.** $(5a - b)^6$.

17. $(x^2 + a)^9$.　　**18.** $(2x - a^2)^7$.　　**19.** $(x^2 + y^3)^6$.　　**20.** $(2a^4 - 3b^3)^5$.

21. $\left(x + \dfrac{1}{x}\right)^7$.　　**22.** $\left(2x - \dfrac{3}{x}\right)^5$.　　**23.** $\left(\dfrac{4}{a^4} + \dfrac{a^2}{2}\right)^6$.　　**24.** $\left(\dfrac{6}{c^3} - \dfrac{c^6}{3}\right)^5$.

Find the first four terms in the binomial expression of each of Problems 25 to 28.

25. $(x + 2y)^{50}$.　　**26.** $(a - 3b)^{100}$.　　**27.** $(c + 3d)^{40}$.　　**28.** $(10x + .001)^{10}$.

Use the binomial formula to obtain the value of the power in each of Problems 29 to 32.

29. $(101)^4 = (100 + 1)^4$.　　　　**30.** $98^3 = (100 - 2)^3$.

31. $(1.03)^5$.　　　　**32.** $(.96)^5$.

Find the specified term in the expansion of each of the following problems:

33. Fourth term of $(a + 2c)^6$.　　**34.** Fifth term of $(2x - y)^7$.

35. Fifth term of $(2a - 3b)^8$.　　**36.** Sixth term of $\left(x - \dfrac{y}{2}\right)^{12}$.

37. Fourth term of $\left(2x + \dfrac{y}{2}\right)^9$.　　**38.** Sixth term of $(x^2 + 3y)^9$.

39. Seventh term of $(x + y)^{11}$.　　**40.** Sixth term of $(a - b)^{12}$.

41. Seventh term of $(x - 2y)^{16}$.　　**42.** Ninth term of $\left(3a + \dfrac{b}{3}\right)^{17}$.

43. Fifth term of $(x^2 + x^{-1})^8$.　　**44.** Seventh term of $(x^{\frac{1}{2}} - 2)^9$.

45. Middle term of $\left(4a - \dfrac{1}{2a}\right)^8$.

46. Middle term of $\left(3x^3 + \dfrac{1}{9x^2}\right)^{10}$.

47. Middle term of $\left(\tfrac{3}{4}a^2b - \dfrac{2b}{9a^3}\right)^6$.

48. Middle term of $\left(\dfrac{5}{2}x^3y^2 + \dfrac{1}{10xy}\right)^4$.

49. The term that involves y^5 in the expansion of $(2x - y)^7$.

50. The term that involves b^6 in the expansion of $(a - 2b^2)^5$.

51. The term that involves y^3 in the expansion of $(2x - y^{\frac{1}{2}})^{10}$.

52. The term that involves b^2 in the expansion of $(a^{\frac{1}{2}} - b^{\frac{2}{3}})^9$.

143. Proof of the binomial formula. We have seen that the binomial formula is true for $n = 1, 2, 3, 4,$ and 5 and shall prove by mathematical induction that it is true for all integral values of n. In order to do this, we assume it is true for $n = k$ and show that it follows that it is true for $n = k + 1$; hence, for all positive integers. Under the assumption that it is true for $n = k$, we have

$$(1) \quad (x + y)^k = x^k + kx^{k-1}y + \cdots$$
$$+ \frac{k(k-1) \cdots (k-r+3)x^{k-r+2}y^{r-2}}{(r-2)!}$$
$$+ \frac{k(k-1)(k-2) \cdots (k-r+2)x^{k-r+1}y^{r-1}}{(r-1)!} + \cdots + y^k$$

This expansion shows the first, second, $(r-1)$st, rth, and last terms.

Multiplying each member of this assumed equation by $x + y$ and writing out the first and last terms and those which contain y^{r-1} [these are obtained by multiplying the term in the second line of (1) by y and the term of the next line by x], we have

$$(x + y)^{k+1} = x^{k+1} + \cdots$$
$$+ \frac{k(k-1) \cdots (k-r+3)x^{k-r+2}y^{r-1}}{(r-2)!}$$
$$+ \frac{k(k-1) \cdots (k-r+2)x^{k-r+2}y^{r-1}}{(r-1)!} + \cdots + y^{k+1}$$

Collecting coefficients of $x^{k-r+2}y^{r-1}$, we get

$$\frac{k(k-1) \cdots (k-r+3)}{(r-2)!} + \frac{k(k-1) \cdots (k-r+2)}{(r-1)!}$$
$$= \frac{k(k-1) \cdots (k-r+3)(r-1)}{(r-2)!(r-1)}$$
$$+ \frac{k(k-1) \cdots (k-r+3)(k-r+2)}{(r-1)!}$$

Dividing by the common factor $\dfrac{k(k-1) \cdots (k-r+3)}{(r-1)!}$, we see that the coefficient is

$$\frac{k(k-1) \cdots (k-r+3)[(r-1) + (k-r+2)]}{(r-1)!}$$
$$= \frac{k(k-1) \cdots (k-r+3)(k+1)}{(r-1)!}$$

Hence, the term in the product of $x + y$ and $(x + y)^k$ which involves y^{r-1} is

$$\frac{(k+1)k(k-1) \cdots (k-r+3)x^{k-r+2}y^{r-1}}{(r-1)!}$$

Using this as a formula for all terms after the first, we see that the product is

$$(x + y)^{k+1} = x^{k+1} + (k + 1)x^k y + \cdots$$
$$+ \frac{(k + 1)k(k - 1) \cdots (k - r + 3)x^{k-r+2}y^{r-1}}{(r - 1)!}$$
$$+ \cdots + y^{k+1}$$

This equation is readily seen to be the one obtained by replacing k by $k + 1$ in (1). Hence, we have shown that (1) is true for $n = k + 1$ if true for $n = k$. This fact along with our knowledge that it is true for $n = 1, 2, 3, 4,$ and 5 enables us to say that it is true for $n = 5 + 1 = 6$; hence, for $6 + 1 = 7; \cdots$; consequently, for all positive integers.

144. *The binomial theorem for fractional and negative exponents.* The proof of the binomial formula for fractional and negative exponents is beyond the scope of this book; however, we shall point out some elementary applications of it. It should be noted that the expansion of $(x + y)^n$ when n is a fraction or is negative has no last term since the coefficient never becomes zero; hence, it is impossible to complete the series, and we must be content with any desired or indicated number of terms. The following fact can be established although the proof will not be given.

The binomial expansion of x + y for fractional and negative exponents is valid only if the value of y is between those of x and −x.

Example 1

What are the first four terms in the expansion of $(2 + x)^{\frac{1}{2}}$? In what interval is the expansion valid?

Solution

The expansion is valid only if $2 > x > -2$ and is

$$(2 + x)^{\frac{1}{2}} = 2^{\frac{1}{2}} + (\tfrac{1}{2})2^{-\frac{1}{2}}x + \frac{\tfrac{1}{2}(-\tfrac{1}{2})2^{-\frac{3}{2}}x^2}{2!} + \frac{\tfrac{1}{2}(-\tfrac{1}{2})(-\tfrac{3}{2})2^{-\frac{5}{2}}x^3}{3!} + \cdots$$

$$= \sqrt{2} + \frac{x}{2\sqrt{2}} - \frac{x^2}{16\sqrt{2}} + \frac{x^3}{64\sqrt{2}} - \cdots$$

$$= \sqrt{2}\left(1 + \frac{x}{4} - \frac{x^2}{32} + \frac{x^3}{128} - \cdots\right)$$

Example 2

Determine an approximation to the square root of 10.

Solution

$$\sqrt{10} = 10^{\frac{1}{2}} = (9 + 1)^{\frac{1}{2}} = (3^2 + 1)^{\frac{1}{2}}$$

$$= (3^2)^{\frac{1}{2}} + \frac{1}{2}(3^2)^{-\frac{1}{2}}(1) + \frac{(\frac{1}{2})(-\frac{1}{2})(3^2)^{-\frac{3}{2}}(1)^2}{2}$$

$$+ \frac{(\frac{1}{2})(-\frac{1}{2})(-\frac{3}{2})(3^2)^{-\frac{5}{2}}(1)^3}{(2)(3)} + \cdots$$

$$= 3 + \left(\frac{1}{2}\right)\left(\frac{1}{3^2}\right)^{\frac{1}{2}}(1) + \frac{\left(-\frac{1}{4}\right)\left(\frac{1}{3^2}\right)^{\frac{3}{2}}(1)}{2} + \frac{\left(\frac{3}{8}\right)\left(\frac{1}{3^2}\right)^{\frac{5}{2}}(1)}{6} + \cdots$$

$$= 3 + \frac{1}{6} - \frac{1}{216} + \frac{1}{3888}$$

$$= 3 + .16667 - .00463 + .00026$$

$$= 3.16230$$

By comparing the four terms in the above expansion, we see that their values decrease very rapidly. The rate of this decrease increases as the expansion is carried further. In fact, the fifth term is $-.0000178$, and when this is combined with the other four terms, we obtain $\sqrt{10} = 3.1622822$, or, rounded to four decimal places, 3.1623. Hence, we conclude that this is the correct value of $\sqrt{10}$ to five figures. Obviously, the expansion can be extended until we obtain any degree of accuracy desired.

EXERCISE 73

Find the first four terms of the expansion in each of Problems 1 to 20.

1. $(x + y)^{-1}$.
2. $(a + b)^{-2}$.
3. $(a - x)^{-1}$.
4. $(x - a)^{-2}$.
5. $(a + 2x)^{-3}$.
6. $(2b - y)^{-4}$.
7. $(2b - 3z)^{-3}$.
8. $(3a + 2y)^{-5}$.
9. $(1 + r)^{\frac{1}{3}}$.
10. $(1 - d)^{\frac{2}{3}}$.
11. $(2 + x)^{\frac{3}{5}}$.
12. $(3 - y)^{\frac{3}{4}}$.
13. $(1 + r)^{-\frac{1}{2}}$.
14. $(2 - y)^{-\frac{9}{7}}$.
15. $(1 - d)^{-\frac{1}{3}}$.
16. $(2 + 3y)^{-\frac{3}{4}}$.

17. $\left(x + \frac{1}{x}\right)^{-2}$.
18. $\left(y - \frac{2}{y}\right)^{-3}$.
19. $\left(a - \frac{1}{a^2}\right)^{-\frac{1}{4}}$.
20. $\left(y^2 + \frac{2}{y}\right)^{-\frac{2}{3}}$.

By carrying the binomial expansion of the expression in each of Problems 21 to 24 to two terms, find the approximate value of the expression. Then calculate the value by means of logarithms and compare the results.

21. $\sqrt{146} = (144 + 2)^{\frac{1}{2}}$.
22. $\sqrt[3]{219}$.
23. $\sqrt[3]{750}$.
24. $\sqrt[5]{245}$.

Find the approximate value of the expression in each of Problems 25 to 28 by obtaining the binomial expansion to four terms. Then compute the value by means of logarithms and compare the results.

25. $(1.02)^{-6}$.
26. $(1.04)^{-5}$.
27. $(1.06)^{-8}$.
28. $(1.08)^{-4}$.

CHAPTER 18

COMPOUND INTEREST AND ANNUITIES

145. *Introduction.* One of the most practical applications of geometric progressions is their use in connection with investments. However, before studying this application, we need a few definitions.

If the interest due on an investment is added to the principal, we say that *interest is compounded* or converted. The sum obtained by adding the interest and the principal is called the *compound amount*, and it is used as the new principal. The length of time between consecutive interest payments is known as the *conversion period*. If the conversion period is different from one year, the stated annual rate is called the *nominal rate*.

Illustrative Example

If $100 is invested at 5 per cent per year and the interest is compounded semi-annually, the nominal rate is 5 per cent, the conversion period is 6 months, the interest rate per conversion period is $\frac{1}{2}(5$ per cent$) = 2\frac{1}{2}$ per cent, the interest for 6 months is $2.50, and the compound amount at the end of 6 months is $102.50. Hence, the interest for the second 6-month period is

$$\$102.50(.025) = \$2.56$$

146. *The amount and the present value.* We shall now assume that P dollars is invested at a rate of r per period and shall determine the compound amount due at the end of n conversion periods. The amount at the end of any period is obtained by multiplying the principal for the period by r and adding this result to the principal. This value is readily obtained by multiplying the principal for the period by $1 + r$. Since this must be done for each conversion period, the amount S due at the end of n periods is given by

(1) $$S = P(1 + r)^n$$

This formula is an equation in four unknowns, and it can be solved for any one of them if the other three are given. The amount of labor involved is materially decreased if we use the value of $(1 + r)^n$ and $(1 + r)^{-n}$ given in Tables IV and V.

Example 1

How much will $150 amount to in 7 years at 4 per cent compounded annually?

Solution

Substituting $P = \$150$, $r = .04$, and $n = 7$ in (1), we get

$$S = \$150(1.04)^7$$

If, in Table IV, which gives the values of $(1 + r)^n$, we look across from $n = 7$ and in the column headed by 4 per cent, we find that $1.04^7 = 1.3159$. Hence,

$$S = \$150(1.3159)$$
$$= \$197.38$$

Example 2

How long will it take $250 to accumulate to $820 if compounded semiannually at a nominal rate of 5 per cent?

Solution

The interest rate per conversion period is $\frac{1}{2}(5$ per cent$) = 2\frac{1}{2}$ per cent. Hence, using the formula for compound amount, we have

$$820 = 250(1.025)^n$$

or

$$1.025^n = \tfrac{820}{250} = 3.2800$$

Since 3.2800 is not given in the column headed by $2\frac{1}{2}$ per cent, we must interpolate. The numbers to use in the interpolation are 3.2715 and 3.3533. Hence, since the first of these corresponds to $n = 48$, the time is

$$48 + \left(\frac{.0085}{.0818}\right) \text{ conversion periods}$$

as seen from

n	$(1 + r)^n$		
48	3.2715		
	3.2800	.0085	.0818
49	3.3533		

Simplifying this and dividing by 2 since each interest period is 6 months, we find that the required time is 24.052 years.

The sum that must be invested now in order to produce the desired compound amount in a specified time at a specified rate is called the *present value*. Formula (1) is a relation between the compound amount S, the present value P, the rate r per period, and the number of periods n. If we solve the formula for P, we obtain

(2) $$P = S(1 + r)^{-n}$$

Example 3

What is the present value of $1000 due in 9 years at 6 per cent compounded annually?

Solution

Substituting in formula (2) for the accumulated value, we obtain

$$P = 1000(1.06)^{-9}$$

Hence, using Table V, we find

$$(1.06)^{-9} = .59190$$

Therefore,

$$P = (\$1000)(.59190)$$
$$= \$591.90$$

147. The effective rate of interest. DEFINITION. *The annual rate at which the principal increases if the nominal rate is j compounded m times per year is called the effective rate.*

Thus, the relation between nominal and effective rates is given by

$$1 + i = \left(1 + \frac{j}{m}\right)^{m}$$

since $1 will amount to $$(1 + i)$ in 1 year at the effective rate i and will accumulate to $\left(1 + \dfrac{j}{m}\right)^{m}$ in 1 year at the nominal rate j compounded m times per year.

We can find the value of $\left(1 + \dfrac{j}{m}\right)^{m}$ from the table of compound amounts and then obtain the value of the effective rate i by subtracting 1.

Example

What is the effective rate if the nominal rate is 8 per cent compounded quarterly?

Solution

If we substitute in the relation between nominal and effective rates, we get

$$1 + i = \left(1 + \frac{.08}{4}\right)^4$$
$$= (1.02)^4$$
$$= 1.0824$$

Hence, the effective rate is

$$i = 8.24 \text{ per cent}$$

EXERCISE 74

One of the letters S, m, n, P and j is missing in each of Problems 1 to 24.   Find its value.

1. $P = \$400$, $j = 3$ per cent, $m = 1$, $n = 5$ years.
2. $P = \$600$, $j = 4$ per cent, $m = 1$, $n = 13$ years.
3. $P = \$1250$, $j = 2\frac{1}{2}$ per cent, $m = 1$, $n = 20$ years.
4. $P = \$2500$, $j = 5$ per cent, $m = 1$, $n = 30$ years.
5. $P = \$700$, $j = 6$ per cent, $m = 4$, $n = 3$ years.
6. $P = \$1100$, $j = 5$ per cent, $m = 2$, $n = 7$ years.
7. $P = \$1500$, $j = 3$ per cent, $m = 2$, $n = 25$ years.
8. $P = \$3000$, $j = 4$ per cent, $m = 4$, $n = 12$ years.
9. $S = \$900$, $j = 2$ per cent, $m = 1$, $n = 42$ years.
10. $S = \$1750$, $j = 5$ per cent, $m = 1$, $n = 10$ years.
11. $S = \$1200$, $j = 2\frac{1}{2}$ per cent, $m = 1$, $n = 40$ years.
12. $S = \$5000$, $j = 1\frac{1}{2}$ per cent, $m = 1$, $n = 50$ years.
13. $S = \$750$, $j = 4$ per cent, $m = 2$, $n = 17$ years.
14. $S = \$1000$, $j = 6$ per cent, $m = 4$, $n = 11$ years.
15. $S = \$1200$, $j = 3$ per cent, $m = 2$, $n = 9$ years.
16. $S = \$10,000$, $j = 3$ per cent, $m = 2$, $n = 25$ years.
17. $S = \$500$, $P = \$276.44$, $m = 2$, $n = 12$ years.
18. $S = \$600$, $P = \$311.63$, $m = 4$, $n = 11$ years.
19. $S = \$789.44$, $P = \$400$, $m = 1$, $n = 23$ years.
20. $S = \$810.36$, $P = \$350$, $m = 2$, $n = 17$ years.
21. $P = \$520.49$, $S = \$700$, $j = 5$ per cent, $m = 2$.
22. $P = \$445.48$, $S = \$600$, $j = 6$ per cent, $m = 4$.
23. $P = \$900$, $S = \$1142.10$, $j = 3$ per cent, $m = 2$.
24. $P = \$800$, $S = \$1212.56$, $j = 6$ per cent, $m = 3$.

Find the effective rate that is equivalent to the nominal rate indicated in each of Problems 25 to 32.

25. $j = 6$ per cent, $m = 4$.
26. $j = 5$ per cent, $m = 2$.
27. $j = 4$ per cent, $m = 2$.
28. $j = 6$ per cent, $m = 3$.
29. $j = 3$ per cent, $m = 2$.
30. $j = 6$ per cent, $m = 2$.
31. $j = 8$ per cent, $m = 4$.
32. $j = 9$ per cent, $m = 3$.

33. Find the difference between the accumulated values of $1000 at 4 per cent converted annually for 20 years and $1000 at 3 per cent converted semiannually for 20 years.

34. What sum invested at 3 per cent converted semiannually for 20 years will have the same accumulated value as $1500 invested at 5 per cent converted annually for 5 years?

35. How long will it take a sum of money to double itself at 5 per cent converted semiannually?

36. How long will it take a sum of money to triple itself at $2\frac{1}{2}$ per cent converted annually?

37. What is the difference between the amount of $1000 at 6 per cent simple interest for 10 years and the amount of $1000 at 6 per cent converted semiannually for 10 years?

38. A man pays $8000 in cash for a farm and agrees to pay an additional $5000 at the end of 5 years and a payment of $3000 at the end of 10 years. If money is worth 5 per cent converted semiannually, what is the equivalent cash value of the farm?

39. Mr. Smith bought a house from Mr. Brown and agreed to pay $5000 in cash and $1000 at the end of each year for 10 years. When the seventh payment was made, Mr. Brown offered to accept $2700 in cash and cancel the remaining notes. If Smith can borrow money at 4 per cent converted semiannually, how much will he save by accepting the offer?

40. A man has the opportunity of selling a piece of property for $5900 in cash or for $7000 to be paid in semiannual installments of $1000 each, the first being due 3 years from the date of the sale. If money can be invested at 4 per cent converted semiannually, which proposition is better for the seller and by how much?

41. When his son was born, Mr. Jones deposited $500 in a savings bank that paid 3 per cent converted semiannually. On his son's eighth birthday, Mr. Jones invested $600 in bonds that earned 6 per cent converted quarterly. If the boy entered college when he was 18 years of age, how much was available from these two sources?

42. A man sold a piece of property for $5000 and agreed to accept as partial payment the present value of a note for $2500 due in 10 years, and he further agreed to accept a 5-year note for the remainder with interest at 6 per cent converted semiannually. If the present value of the first note was figured at 5 per cent converted annually, what was the final payment?

43. As the payment for a piece of property, a man accepts $2000 in cash and four notes for $2000 each due in 1, 2, 3, and 4 years. At 6 per cent converted quarterly, what was the equivalent cash price of the property?

44. Two investments of $4000 each are made. The first earns 4 per cent converted semiannually. The second earns no interest the first 2 years but earns 5 per cent annually thereafter. Find the difference in the amounts of the two investments at the end of a 7-year period.

45. A United States Savings Bond with a maturity value of $100 in 10 years can be purchased for $75. What rate converted annually is earned by such bonds?

46. On Jan. 1, 1940, a man signed a note for $5000 due in 10 years at 5 per cent converted semiannually. He made the following partial payments: Jan. 1, 1943, $1500; July 1, 1945, $1000; Jan. 1, 1947, $2000. Find the amount due at maturity.

47. Find the effective rate if $280 amounts to $370 in 9 years.

48. Find the nominal rate converted semiannually if $500 accumulates to $650 in 8 years.

148. *Annuities.* In this age of installment buying and the systematic investment of money, almost everyone who is earning an income is making equal periodic payments on some purchase or on some investment plan. In the latter case, many plans call for regular payments from the investor for a period of time and then guarantee to make regular payments to him after he reaches a certain age. Hence it is important that everyone understand the fundamental principles associated with such practices.

DEFINITION. *A sequence of equal payments made at equal intervals is called an* **annuity.**

DEFINITION. *If a payment is made at the beginning of each interval, the annuity is called an* **annuity due.**

DEFINITION. *If a payment is made at the end of each interval, the annuity is called an* **ordinary annuity.**

The length of time between payments is known as the *payment period.* The amount invested at the end or beginning of each payment period is called the *periodic payment.* The length of time between successive additions of the interest to the principal is called the *conversion period* or *interest period.* The *term* of an annuity is obtained by multiplying the number of payments by the length of time between consecutive payments. The accumulated value of an annuity is the sum of the compound amounts of the separate payments accumulated at the end of the term.

We shall consider only annuities whose interest period and payment period coincide.

149. *The accumulated value of an annuity.* We shall determine the accumulated value if $1 is invested at the end of each payment period for a term of n periods and if money is worth i per payment period. The first periodic payment is invested for

$(n - 1)$ periods, the second for $(n - 2)$ periods, the third for $(n - 3)$ periods, . . . , the last for 0 periods. Hence, using the formula for the accumulated value at compound interest, it is evident that these payments accumulate to $(1 + i)^{n-1}$, $(1 + i)^{n-2}$, $(1 + i)^{n-3}$, . . . , and 1, respectively, by the end of the term. These powers of $1 + i$ form a geometric series of n terms. Reversing their order, we have $a = 1$, $r = 1 + i$, and $n = n$. Therefore, the accumulated value of an ordinary annuity can be obtained by determining the sum of this geometric progression. Consequently, if we designate the accumulated value of the annuity by $s_{\overline{n}|i}$* we have,

$$s_{\overline{n}|i} = \frac{1 - 1(1 + i)^n}{1 - (1 + i)} = \frac{1 - (1 + i)^n}{-i} \qquad \text{since} \qquad s = \frac{a - ar^n}{1 - r}$$

Hence, multiplying the numerator and the denominator by -1, we see that

(1)
$$s_{\overline{n}|i} = \frac{(1 + i)^n - 1}{i}$$

is the accumulated value of an **ordinary annuity** *of $1 per period for a term of* **n** *periods, provided money is worth i per period and provided further that the interest period and payment period coincide.*

If the payment is R dollars per period and if the accumulated value is represented by S_n, we have

(2)
$$S_n = Rs_{\overline{n}|i}$$

Tables exist from which the values of $s_{\overline{n}|i}$ can be obtained for any values of n and i that usually occur in business transactions. Table VI is an abridged table of this kind, and it can be used for solving the problems in this book.

We can now obtain the formula for the accumulated value of an **annuity due** *by multiplying each member of* (2) *by* $(1 + i)$, *since each payment is made one period earlier than in the case of an ordinary annuity.*

Example

What is the accumulated value of an ordinary annuity if the semiannual payment is $100 for a term of 6 years and money is worth 5 per cent compounded semiannually?

* This symbol is read "*s* angle *n* at *i*."

Solution

Since money is worth 5 per cent compounded semiannually, the rate per period is $2\frac{1}{2}$ per cent; furthermore, there are 12 six-month periods in 6 years. Hence, substituting in the formula for the accumulated value of an ordinary annuity, we have

$$S_{12} = Rs_{\overline{12}|.025}$$

If, in Table VI, we look in the column headed by $2\frac{1}{2}$ per cent and in the row corresponding to $n = 12$, we find 13.7956. This is the amount of an ordinary annuity of \$1 per period for 12 periods at $2\frac{1}{2}$ per cent. Hence,

$$S_{12} = \$1379.56$$

NOTE: If this had been an annuity due instead of an ordinary annuity, we would have found the accumulated value by performing exactly the same calculations as above and then multiplying by 1.025, since each payment of an annuity due is made one period earlier than for an ordinary annuity. Thus,

$$S_{12} \text{ (due)} = (\$1379.56)(1.025)$$
$$= \$1414.05$$

150. The present value of an annuity. DEFINITION. *The present value of an annuity is the cash equivalent of the sequence of payments.*

Hence, if the present value is accumulated at the given rate for the term of the annuity, we must obtain a sum that is equal to the accumulated value. Consequently, if A_n and S_n represent the present and accumulated values of an annuity, we have

$$S_n = A_n(1 + i)^n$$

by use of the formula for compound amount. If we solve this equation for A_n, we get

$$A_n = S_n(1 + i)^{-n}$$

Replacing S_n by its value given in (2) of the preceding article, we obtain

$$A_n = R\left[\frac{(1 + i)^n - 1}{i}(1 + i)^{-n}\right]$$

Therefore,

(1) $$A_n = R\left[\frac{1 - (1 + i)^{-n}}{i}\right] = Ra_{\overline{n}|i}$$

*is the present value of an **ordinary annuity** of R dollars per period for a term of n periods provided money is worth i per period and provided further that the interest period and payment period coincide.*

The values of $a_{\overline{n}|i}$ for $n = 1$ to $n = 50$ and for i equal to $1\frac{1}{2}$, 2, $2\frac{1}{2}$, 3, 4, 5, and 6 per cent can be obtained from Table VII.

*The formula for the **present value of an annuity due*** *can be derived from* (1) *by multiplying by* $1 + i$ since each payment is made one period earlier than the corresponding payment of an ordinary annuity.

Example 1

What is the present value of an ordinary annuity of $50 per quarter for 10 years if money is worth 8 per cent compounded quarterly?

Solution

Since the number of periods is (10)4 = 40 and the rate is 2 per cent per period, we have

$$A_{40} = \$50 a_{\overline{40}|.02}$$

If we look, in Table VII, in the column headed by 2 per cent and across from $n = 40$, we find 27.3555. Hence,

$$A_{40} = \$50(27.3555)$$
$$= \$1367.78$$

NOTE: If this had been an annuity due, we would have obtained the present value by performing the same calculations as above and then multiplying by $1 + i$ since each payment of an annuity due is made one period earlier than the corresponding payment of an ordinary annuity. Thus, we would obtain

$$A_{40} \text{ (due)} = (\$1367.78)(1.02)$$
$$= \$1395.14$$

Example 2

Find the payment made at the end of each 6 months for 9 years that will accumulate to $5000 if money is worth 4 per cent converted semiannually.

Solution

Since each payment is made at the end of the interval, this is an ordinary annuity. Furthermore, the interest rate per period is $\frac{1}{2}$(4 per cent) = 2 per cent and there are 9(2) = 18 payments. The accumulated value S_{18} is $5000. If we substitute these values in formula (2) of Art. 149, we get

$$\$5000 = R s_{\overline{18}|.02}$$
$$= 21.4123R$$

Therefore,

$$R = \frac{\$5000}{21.4123}$$
$$= \$233.51$$

NOTE: If this had been an annuity due, the formula to solve for R would have been

$$\$5000 = Rs_{\overline{18}|.02}(1.02)$$

$$R = \frac{\$5000}{s_{\overline{18}|.02}(1.02)}$$

$$= \$228.93$$

EXERCISE 75

In Problems 1 to 32, j represents the annual interest rate; t, the term of the annuity in years; m, the number of conversion periods per year; and R, the periodic payment.

Find the present and the accumulated value of each annuity described in Problems 1 to 12 under the assumption that it is an ordinary annuity and then under the assumption that it is an annuity due.

1. $R = \$300, t = 6, j = 4$ per cent, $m = 1$.
2. $R = \$400, t = 8, j = 3$ per cent, $m = 1$.
3. $R = \$450, t = 9, j = 2\frac{1}{2}$ per cent, $m = 1$.
4. $R = \$600, t = 7, j = 5$ per cent, $m = 1$.
5. $R = \$350, t = 11, j = 5$ per cent, $m = 2$.
6. $R = \$900, t = 9, j = 4$ per cent, $m = 2$.
7. $R = \$750, t = 23, j = 3$ per cent, $m = 2$.
8. $R = \$800, t = 17, j = 6$ per cent, $m = 2$.
9. $R = \$500, t = 12, j = 6$ per cent, $m = 4$.
10. $R = \$150, t = 11, j = 8$ per cent, $m = 4$.
11. $R = \$70.67, t = 12, j = 6$ per cent, $m = 4$.
12. $R = \$44.29, t = 20, j = 4$ per cent, $m = 2$.

Find the periodic payment for each annuity described in Problems 13 to 20 under the assumption that it is an ordinary annuity and under the assumption that it is an annuity due.

13. $A_n = \$7850, t = 32, j = 4$ per cent, $m = 1$.
14. $S_n = \$7850, t = 32, j = 4$ per cent, $m = 1$.
15. $A_n = \$5700, t = 23, j = 5$ per cent, $m = 2$.
16. $S_n = \$5700, t = 23, j = 5$ per cent, $m = 2$.
17. $A_n = \$15,750, t = 11, j = 6$ per cent, $m = 4$.
18. $S_n = \$15,750, t = 11, j = 6$ per cent, $m = 4$.
19. $A_n = \$20,000, t = 20, j = 3$ per cent, $m = 2$.
20. $S_n = \$20,000, t = 20, r = 3$ per cent, $m = 2$.

Find the term in years of the annuity described in each of Problems 21 to 28.
21. $S_n = \$6040.20, R = \$100, j = 4$ per cent, $m = 2$.
22. $S_n = \$11,052.42, R = \$150, j = 3$ per cent, $m = 2$.
23. $S_n = \$7688.29, R = \$175, j = 6$ per cent, $m = 4$.
24. $S_n = \$6734.18, R = \$200, j = 8$ per cent, $m = 4$.
25. $A_n = \$2000, R = \$128.29, j = 2\frac{1}{2}$ per cent, $m = 1$.

26. $A_n = \$7500$, $R = \$382.65$, $j = 3$ per cent, $m = 1$.
27. $A_n = \$10,000$, $R = \$285.72$, $j = 6$ per cent, $m = 4$.
28. $A_n = \$6000$, $R = \$484.60$, $j = 5$ per cent, $m = 2$.

Find the annual rate of the annuity described in each of Problems 29 to 32.
29. $S_n = \$5000$, $R = \$268.83$, $t = 15$, $m = 1$.
30. $A_n = \$4000$, $R = \$159.34$, $t = 20$, $m = 2$.
31. $A_n = \$3500$, $R = \$235.25$, $t = 10$, $m = 2$.
32. $S_n = \$8000$, $R = \$333.11$, $t = 7\frac{1}{2}$, $m = 4$.

33. The beneficiary of a life-insurance policy is to receive $1000 at the end of each year for 10 years. Find the present value of this annuity if money is worth 4 per cent.

34. Mr. Davis bought a house for $10,000. He paid $1300 in cash and agreed to pay the remainder with interest at 5 per cent converted semiannually in equal semiannual payments. If the first payment was made 6 months after the purchase and the debt was retired at the end of 7 years, find the amount of each payment.

35. If the seller of the house in Problem 34 invested each payment immediately in bonds that yield 5 per cent converted semiannually, find the accumulated value of the investment 7 years after the house was sold.

36. The machinery in a plant cost $30,000 and must be replaced every 12 years. In order to create a fund for this replacement, a sum of money was invested at the end of each 3 months at 8 per cent converted quarterly. Find the amount of each investment if they were all the same.

37. In order to create a fund of $5000 to be available at the end of 12 years for his son's education, a man deposits a sum of money at the end of each quarter in an investment company that pays 6 per cent converted quarterly. Find the amount of each deposit.

38. The boy referred to in Problem 37 earned his own way through his 4 years in college. As a reward, his father continued to make the quarterly deposits through the 4 years and gave the accumulation for the 16 years to the boy as a graduation present. How much did the boy get?

39. A man deposited $500 semiannually in an investment company for 20 years. Then he withdrew the funds in equal semiannual payments. If the fund was exhausted in 20 years and the company paid 4 per cent converted semiannually, what was the amount of each withdrawal?

40. A man has the choice of paying $10,000 in cash for a house, or of paying $3000 in cash and the remainder in 20 semiannual installments of $500 each, the first installment being due 6 months after the purchase. If money is worth 4 per cent converted semiannually, which is the best trade? By how much?

41. According to the provisions of an insurance policy, a man is to receive 40 quarterly payments of $100 each, the first payment to be made in 10 years. Find the present value of the annuity at 6 per cent converted quarterly.

42. Find the amount of the quarterly premium necessary to establish the annuity in Problem 41, if the first payment is made now, the last is made 3 months before the annuity payments start, and the rate is the same.

43. In order to create a retirement fund of $25,000 due in 25 years, a man decided to make equal semiannual deposits with an investment company that pays 6 per cent converted semiannually, the first deposit to be made 6 months after the date of his decision. He became ill after making his tenth payment and did not resume them until he had missed 10 payments. Find the amount of the semiannual deposit and the accumulated value of his investment at the end of 25 years.

44. Suppose the man in Problem 43, after resuming his deposits, increased them so that the accumulated value of his investments would be $25,000. Find the amount of the revised semiannual deposit.

CHAPTER 19

PERMUTATIONS AND COMBINATIONS

A. PERMUTATIONS

151. Introduction. In this chapter we shall study situations illustrated by the two problems that follow.

1. A bus company that serves 100 towns wishes to have tickets printed so that there will be a ticket from each town in the area to every other town. How many sets of tickets must be printed?

2. A state traffic commission in designing the license plates for automobiles decided to use two letters of the alphabet followed by a four-digit number as the inscription on each plate. How many different plates can be made using this design?

Problems of this nature are solved by means of the fundamental principle discussed in the next article.

152. The fundamental principle. We shall first state the fundamental principle and then illustrate its use by solving the two above problems.

If a first event can happen in h_1 ways and if, after it has taken place, a second event can happen in h_2 ways, then the two events can happen in h_1h_2 ways.

Example 1

A bus ticket usually indicates the origin and the terminus of the trip covered by the ticket thus: From _____ to _____. In solving Problem 1 above, the first event mentioned in the fundamental principle is the choice of the town whose name is to appear in the first blank. Since there are 100 towns to choose from, this event can happen in 100 ways. Hence, $h_1 = 100$. After the first name is chosen, there are 99 choices for the second. Therefore, $h_2 = 99$. Hence the number of sets of tickets necessary is $h_1h_2 = 100 \times 99 = 9900$.

If more than two events are involved, we extend the fundamental principle in the following way: If, after the first two events have taken place, a third can happen in h_3 ways, a fourth in h_4 ways, and, finally, an nth in h_n ways; then the n events can happen in the order indicated in $h_1h_2h_3h_4 \ldots h_n$ ways.

Example 2

In the second problem of Art. 151, any letter or any digit can be used more than once on each plate. For example, AA1111 is a legitimate number. We shall assume that the digit following the second letter can be zero. The first event in this case is the choice of the letter for the first place on the plate. Since there are 26 letters to choose from, $h_1 = 26$. Similarly, $h_2 = 26$. Since any one of 0, 1, 2, 3, 4, 5, 6, 7, 8, and 9 can be used in each of the next four places on the plate, $h_3 = 10$, $h_4 = 10$, $h_5 = 10$, and $h_6 = 10$. Hence the total number of plates possible is

$$26 \times 26 \times 10 \times 10 \times 10 \times 10 = 6,760,000$$

Example 3

In this example we shall find the number of plates possible on which no letter and no digit appear more than once. In this case, $h_1 = 26$, $h_2 = 25$ (since only 25 letters are available for the second place), $h_3 = 10$, $h_4 = 9$, $h_5 = 8$, and $h_6 = 7$. Hence the total number of plates possible under the above restriction is

$$26 \times 25 \times 10 \times 9 \times 8 \times 7 = 3,276,000$$

EXERCISE 76

1. How many license plates can be formed if the inscription on each consists of a letter of the alphabet followed by a three-digit number?

2. How many of the plates described in Problem 1 have no two digits the same and have the first digit different from zero?

3. How many committees consisting of a junior, a senior, and a graduate student can be selected from 15 juniors, 18 seniors, and 6 graduate students?

4. How many signals composed of 3 flags each can be formed from 8 flags of different colors?

5. How many bouquets of 4 different species of flowers can be formed from 7 amaryllises, 10 hyacinths, 21 camellias, and 14 snapdragons if every flower is used at least once?

6. In how many ways can a nickel, a dime, a quarter, and a half dollar be distributed among 4 boys so that each boy gets 1 coin?

7. If, in Problem 6, the restriction that each boy receive 1 coin is removed, in how many ways can the 4 coins be distributed among the 4 boys?

8. How many sums of money of 25 cents each can be formed from 4 dimes and 4 nickels?

9. In how many ways can 6 people sit down on a bench that holds 4 people?

10. In how many ways can 4 men and 3 women be seated alternately in a row of 7 chairs?

11. In how many ways can the people in Problem 10 be seated if the men sit together?

12. In how many ways can the people in Problem 10 be seated if a man occupies the left end and there are no other restrictions?

13. How many four-digit numbers greater than 5000 can be formed with the digits 2, 3, 5, and 7 if no digit can be repeated?

14. Solve Problem 13 without the restriction that no digit can be repeated.

15. How many even four-digit numbers can be formed with the digits 2, 3, 5, and 7, if repetitions are allowed?

16. How many odd four-digit numbers can be formed with the digits 2, 3, 5, and 7 if no digit can be repeated?

17. A bill of fare lists 4 salads, 5 meats, 6 vegetables, and 7 desserts. In how many ways can a diner order a meal consisting of a salad, a meat, 2 vegetables, and a dessert?

18. How many basketball teams can be formed from 4 guards, 3 centers, and 5 forwards?

19. A football coach has 8 ends, 6 guards, 4 tackles, 2 centers, 2 quarterbacks, 3 fullbacks, and 7 halfbacks. How many teams can he select?

20. The mayor, 2 bankers, 2 doctors, and a speaker sit at one side of the head table at a banquet. If the speaker and the mayor sit at the center with the mayor at the right of the speaker, how many seating orders are possible?

153. Permutations of n different elements taken r at a time.

The problems dealing with the license plates in the previous article involve the arrangement of six characters or symbols on a horizontal line. If the characters are different, as in AB1234, any arrangement of them, provided the letters are placed first, constitutes a "number" for a plate. This situation illustrates the following definition.

DEFINITION. *Each arrangement of a set of n elements is called a permutation of the set.*

The arrangements *abc, acb, bac, bca, cab,* and *cba* constitute the six permutations of the letters *a, b,* and *c*. Furthermore, *ab, ba, ac, ca, bc,* and *cb* are the six permutations of the same three letters taken two at a time.

We shall let $_nP_r$ represent the number of permutations of n things taken r at a time and shall develop a formula for evaluating the symbol. We can fill the first place in the arrangement in n ways. After the first position has been filled, we have $n - 1$

choices for the second, then $n - 2$ for the third, and, finally, $n - (r - 1) = n - r + 1$ choices for the rth place. Hence,

$$_nP_r = n(n - 1)(n - 2) \cdots (n - r + 1)$$

If we multiply the right member of this equation by

$$\frac{(n - r)!}{(n - r)!}$$

we get

$$\frac{n(n - 1)(n - 2) \cdots (n - r + 1)(n - r)!}{(n - 1)!} = \frac{n!}{(n - r)!}$$

Therefore,

(1) $$_nP_r = \frac{n!}{(n - r)!}$$

In order to obtain the number of permutations of n things taken n at a time, we let $r = n$ in (1). Thus, we obtain

(2) $$_nP_n = n!$$

since, by definition $0! = 1$.

Example 1

The number of four-digit numbers that can be formed from the digits 1, 2, 3, and 4 is, by (2), $4! = 4 \times 3 \times 2 \times 1 = 24$.

Example 2

Six people enter a room that contains 10 chairs. In how many ways can they be seated?

Solution

Since only 6 of the chairs are to be occupied, the number of different seating arrangements is equal to the number of permutations of 10 things taken 6 at a time and is

$$_{10}P_6 = \frac{10!}{(10 - 6)!} = \frac{(10)(9)(8)(7)(6)(5)(4!)}{(4!)} = (10)(9)(8)(7)(6)(5) = 151{,}200$$

154. Permutations of n elements not all different. If the elements of a set of n things are not all different, the problem of determining the number of permutations of the set presents a new aspect. We shall suppose that s members of the set are alike and shall designate the $n - s$ different elements by t_1, t_2, $\ldots$, t_{n-s}. We can obtain all the permutations of the n elements by distributing t_1, t_2, . . . , t_{n-s} in the n positions in all possible ways and then by filling in the vacant places with the s identical elements.   This amounts to dividing the positions 1, 2, 3, . . . , n into $n - s$ groups in as many ways as possible, that is, to finding the number of permutations of n things taken $n - s$ at a time. By (1) of the preceding article, we have

$$_nP_{n-s} = \frac{n!}{[n - (n - s)]!} = \frac{n!}{s!}$$

Hence, if s members of a set of n elements are alike, the number of permutations of the n elements taken n at a time is equal to the number of permutations of n things taken n at a time divided by the number of permutations of s things taken s at a time.   By a repeated application of this principle, we can derive the following theorem:

THEOREM.   *If, in a set of **n** things, there are **g** groups, the first containing **n_1** members all of which are alike; the second containing **n_2** which are alike; the third, **n_3** which are alike; and so on to the gth group, which has **n_g** members alike; then, the number of permutations of the **n** things taken **n** at a time is given by*

$$\frac{n!}{n_1!n_2! \cdots n_g!}$$

Example 1

In how many ways can the letters of the word "Mississippi" be arranged?

Solution

The solution of this problem involves the number of permutations of 11 letters taken 11 at a time, the letters i and s each appearing four times and the letter p entering twice.   Hence, the number of arrangements is given by

$$\frac{11!}{4!4!2!} = \frac{(11)(10)(9)(8)(7)(6)(5)(4)(3)(2)(1)}{(4)(3)(2)(1)(4)(3)(2)(1)(2)(1)} = 34,650$$

EXERCISE 77

State the meaning of the symbol in each of Problems 1 to 4 then finds its value.

1. $_6P_4$.   **2.** $_7P_4$.   **3.** $_{11}P_2$.   **4.** $_{11}P_5$.

5. Show that $_nP_{n-1} = \,_nP_n$.   **6.** Show that $_nP_{n-2} = \frac{1}{2}(_nP_n)$.

7. Show that $_nP_{n-r} = \,_nP_n(1/r!)$.   **8.** Show that $(_nP_{n-r})(_rP_{r-1}) = \,_nP_n$.

9. How many permutations of 8 letters each can be formed from the letters in "Democrat"?   "Republican"?

10. How many permutations of 4 letters each can be formed from the letters in "formula"? In "number"?

11. How many batting orders are possible after a baseball coach selects his 9 players?

12. Work Problem 11 with the restriction that the catcher must bat first and the pitcher last.

13. In how many ways can 4 people seat themselves in a row of 10 chairs?

14. There are 10 buildings on a campus. In how many ways can a student visit all of them?

15. In how many ways can a group of 6 children including 2 sets of twins be seated in a row if the children in each pair of twins refuse to be separated?

16. In how many ways can a group of 6 children including 1 set of triplets be seated in a row if the triplets refuse to be separated?

17. In how many ways can the letters in the word "aardvark" be arranged?

18. In how many ways can the letters in the word "incantation" be arranged?

19. In how many ways can a primary Sunday-school class consisting of 4 boys and 4 girls be seated on a bench if one of the boys is timid and refuses to sit next to a girl?

20. In how many ways can the class in Problem 19 be seated with a boy on one end of the bench and a girl on the other?

21. In how many ways can a student council composed of 12 members including the officers be seated around a rectangular table if the president and secretary are seated at the head and the vice-president and treasurer at the foot, and there are 4 members on each side?

22. In how many ways can 12 persons be seated around a circular table if in deciding whether two arrangements are different we take into account (*a*) the order of seating only, (*b*) both the order and the background?

23. In how many essentially different ways can 12 beads be strung on a necklace?

24. Ten people enter a bus in which there are 5 double seats on one side that are vacant. In how many ways can they seat themselves?

25. Fifteen people enter a plane in which there are 5 double seats on one side and 5 single seats on the other. In how many ways can they take their seats?

26. At a reception given during an international congress of churches, the receiving line consisted of a representative from each of England, the United States, Canada, Australia, China, and Denmark and an interpreter for each of the last two. In how many ways can the line be formed with an English-speaking person first and with the Chinese and the Dane each standing next to his interpreter?

27. In how many ways can 6 mathematics books, 4 physics books, and 3 English books be arranged on a shelf so that all books on a subject are together?

28. In how many ways can 5 war orphans be distributed in 20 homes if no home takes more than one?

155. Combinations. The problem of finding the number of ways that a group of elements can be divided into subgroups in which the order is not considered involves the idea in the following definition.

DEFINITION. *A set of elements without regard to the order in which they are arranged is called a* **combination.**

According to the foregoing definition, the six permutations xyz, xzy, yxz, yzx, zxy, and zyx are the same combination.

Obviously, there is only one combination of n elements taken n at a time. However, the problem of determining the number of combinations of n things taken r at a time is both interesting and important. We shall designate this number by $_nC_r$. The number of permutations of any combination of r elements is, by (2) of Art. 153, $r!$. Hence

$$_nP_r = r!\,_nC_r$$

and

(1) $$_nC_r = \frac{_nP_r}{r!}$$

Replacing $_nP_r$ by its value obtained from (1) of Art. 153 we have

(2) $$_nC_r = \frac{n!}{r!(n-r)!}$$

If we multiply the expression (1) of Art. 142 by

$$\frac{(n-r+1)!}{(n-r+1)!}$$

we obtain

$$\frac{n(n-1)\cdots(n-r+2)[(n-r+1)]!\,x^{n-r+1}y^{r-1}}{(r-1)!(n-r+1)!}$$

$$= \frac{n!\,x^{n-r+1}y^{r-1}}{(r-1)![n-(r-1)]!} = {}_nC_{r-1}x^{n-r+1}y^{r-1}$$

Hence, we may express the expansion of $(x+y)^n$ in the form

(3) $$(x+y)^n = x^n + {}_nC_1x^{n-1}y + {}_nC_2x^{n-2}y^2 + \cdots$$
$$+ {}_nC_{n-1}xy^{n-1} + {}_nC_ny^n$$

The total number of combinations that can be obtained from a set of n things by taking them one at a time, two at a time, and so on to n at a time is

$$_nC_1 + {}_nC_2 + {}_nC_3 + \cdots + {}_nC_{n-1} + {}_nC_n$$

We shall now use (3) in order to obtain the value of this sum in terms of n.   If, in (3), we let $x = y = 1$, we obtain

$$(1 + 1)^n = 2^n = 1 + {}_nC_1 + {}_nC_2 + \cdots + {}_nC_{n-1} + {}_nC_n$$

Therefore,

$$2^n - 1 = {}_nC_1 + {}_nC_2 + \cdots + {}_nC_{n-1} + {}_nC_n$$

Hence, we have the following theorem:

THEOREM.   *The total number of combinations obtained by taking* **n** *elements 1 at a time, 2 at a time, 3 at a time, and so on to* **n** *at a time is equal to* **2^n − 1.**

Example 1

How many committees of 8 men can be formed from a group of 50 men?

Solution

The number of committees is equal to the number of combinations of 50 elements taken 8 at a time, that is, ${}_{50}C_8$. By (2),

$$
{}_{50}C_8 = \frac{50!}{8!\,42!} = \frac{\overset{10}{\cancel{(50)}}\,\overset{7}{\cancel{(49)}}\,(48)\,(47)\,\overset{23}{\cancel{(46)}}\,\overset{15}{\cancel{(45)}}\,\overset{11}{\cancel{(44)}}\,(43)\,(\cancel{42!})}{(8)\,(7)\,(\cancel{6})\,(\cancel{5})\,(4)\,(3)\,(2)\,(1)\,(\cancel{42!})}
$$

$$= 536{,}878{,}650$$

Example 2

A business firm wishes to employ 6 men and 4 boys.   In how many ways can the manager make the selection if 9 men and 6 boys apply?

Solution

The men can be selected in ${}_9C_6$ ways and the boys in ${}_6C_4$ ways.   Therefore, the total number of ways in which the selections can be made is

$$({}_9C_6)({}_6C_4) = \frac{9!}{6!(9-6)!}\,\frac{6!}{4!(6-4)!}$$

$$= \frac{\overset{3}{\cancel{(9)}}\,\overset{4}{\cancel{(8)}}\,(7)\,(\cancel{6!})\,(\cancel{6})\,(5)\,(\cancel{4!})}{(\cancel{6!})\,(\cancel{3})\,(\cancel{2})\,(1)\,(\cancel{4!})\,(\cancel{2})}$$

$$= 1260$$

EXERCISE 78

1. Find the value of ${}_7C_3$, ${}_9C_5$, ${}_{10}C_4$, ${}_{17}C_2$.
2. Show that ${}_nC_r = {}_nC_{n-r}$.   3. Show that ${}_9C_5 = ({}_9C_3)(\frac{3}{2})$.
4. Show that ${}_{10}C_6 = ({}_{10}C_5)(\frac{5}{6})$.

5. In how many ways can a group of 20 ladies be divided into subgroups of 4 each to play bridge?

6. In how many ways can 3 books be drawn from a circulating library containing 1000 volumes?

7. Ten buildings are arranged around a circular campus and a straight walk joins each building with every other one. How many walks are there?

8. If 6 coins are tossed in the air and allowed to fall, in how many ways can 4 tails and 2 heads appear?

9. In an athletic conference with 8 members, how many games are necessary if each football team plays every other one? If each team plays 10 games and plays no conference member more than once, how many of the 10 games were nonconference?

10. In how many ways can 100 bags of candy on a Christmas tree in an orphans' home be distributed among the 96 children living in the home?

11. A bag contains 4 red balls and 6 green balls. In how many ways can 6 balls be withdrawn in which 2 are red and 4 are green?

12. A father has $2 in nickels. In how many ways can he give his son 25 cents?

13. A father has $1 in nickels and $1 in dimes. In how many ways can he give his son 15 cents?

14. In how many ways can the father in Problem 13 give his son 20 cents?

15. A group of 9 people is to ride to a picnic ground in 2 cars. If one car can accommodate 6 passengers and the other 3, in how many ways can the group be divided for the ride?

16. In how many ways can 12 people ride in a 6-passenger car and two 3-passenger cars if the order of seating is not considered?

17. In how many ways can 4 books dealing with the same subject be selected from 6 mathematics books and 5 physics books?

18. In how many ways can a detail of 6 privates and 2 noncommissioned officers be selected from a squad of 20 privates and 5 noncommissioned officers?

19. In how many ways can a group of 8 men and 8 ladies be divided into groups with 2 men and 2 ladies in each group?

20. How many diagonals can be drawn in a convex polygon with 12 sides?

21. In how many ways can $1.50 be drawn from a cash drawer that contains 5 silver dollars, 10 half dollars, and 12 quarters?

22. In how many ways can a community-chest steering committee composed of three Rotarians, three Kiwanians, and three Lions be chosen from 20 Rotarians, 30 Kiwanians, and 40 Lions?

23. In how many ways can 7 people be seated in 3 rooms if there are 3 chairs in each room and if the order of seating in the separate rooms is not considered?

24. In how many ways can 9 war orphans be distributed to 3 homes, the first of which can take 4 children; the second, 3; and the third, 2?

25. How many sums of money can be formed from a penny, a nickel, a dime, a quarter, a half dollar, and a dollar?

26. How many sums of money more than 25 cents can be formed with the coins in Problem 25?

27. How many groups of 2 or more persons can be formed from 10 people?

28. How many groups of 4 or more persons can be formed from 10 people?

CHAPTER 20

PROBABILITY

156. *Mathematical probability.* If a set or a sequence of circumstances that causes an event to happen or fail to happen is subject to some known law, the outcome can be predicted with certainty. If, on the other hand, these circumstances are not subject to a law, the outcome is a matter of chance. For example, if three pennies are tossed simultaneously in the air, we know they will fall to the floor because they are subject to the law of gravitation. However, we cannot be sure that all three will fall heads up. In fact, since the three can fall heads up in only one way and can fail to fall heads up in $2^3 - 1 = 7$ ways, the chances or odds are against them falling in this way. In the parlance of betting, we say that the odds are 7 to 1 against their falling with three heads up.

The mathematical probability that an event will happen is a ratio that expresses a numerical evaluation of the chances in favor of the event's happening. This ratio is defined below.

DEFINITION. *If an event can happen in **h** ways and fail to happen in **f** ways, the probability **p** that it will occur is*

(1)
$$p = \frac{h}{h + f}$$

*and the probability **q** that it will fail to happen is*

(2)
$$q = \frac{f}{h + f}$$

By referring to (1) and (2), we see that

$$p + q = 1$$

Furthermore, if the event cannot fail to occur, $f = 0$, $p = 1$, and

366

$q = 0$. Conversely, if $p = 1$, we have by (1)

$$1 = \frac{h}{h + f}$$

Therefore, $f = 0$, and the event cannot fail. Hence, a probability of unity implies certainty, and conversely.

Example 1

In the above example involving the three pennies, the event of all three falling heads up can happen in only one way. Furthermore, since each can fall in two ways, the three can fall in 2^3 ways. Hence, they can fail to fall heads up in seven ways. Hence, the probability of the three falling heads up is

$$p = \frac{1}{1 + 7} = \frac{1}{8}$$

It should be emphasized that the mathematical probability that an event will happen in a certain manner is merely the ratio of the number of ways that it can happen in the desired manner to the total number of possibilities. It is obvious that there is no guarantee that $\frac{1}{8}$ of the total number of tosses of three pennies will result in three heads. In fact, in an experiment, three pennies were tossed in the air 100 times with three heads appearing 15 times, or in $\frac{3}{20}$ of the number of tosses.

Example 2

Each of the three-digit numbers that can be formed from the integers from 1 to 9, with no digit repeated, is written on a card. Then the cards are thoroughly shuffled and stacked. If one card is drawn from the stack, find the probability that the sum of the digits in the number on it will be 10.

Solution

The sets of three different integers chosen from 1 to 9 whose sum is 10 are 7, 2, 1; 6, 3, 1; and 5, 4, 1. From each of these sets, $_3P_3 = 3! = 6$ three-digit numbers can be formed. Hence, there are 18 cards in the stack on which the desired numbers exist. Hence, $h = 18$. Furthermore, there is a total of $_9P_3 = 504$ cards in the stack. Thus, $f = 504 - 18 = 486$. Consequently,

$$p = \frac{18}{18 + 486} = \frac{18}{504} = \frac{1}{28}$$

Example 3

What is the probability of drawing 3 white and 4 black balls from a bag that contains 5 white and 6 black balls if 7 balls are drawn simultaneously at random?

Solution

We must first determine the number $_5C_3$ of ways in which 3 white balls can be drawn from 5 white balls and the number $_6C_4$ of ways in which 4 black balls can be drawn from 6 black balls. We next determine the number $_{11}C_7$ of ways in which 7 balls can be drawn from 11. Then, we see that the desired combination of balls can be obtained in $(_5C_3)(_6C_4)$ ways; consequently, the probability of drawing this combination is

$$\frac{(_5C_3)(_6C_4)}{_{11}C_7} = \frac{\left(\dfrac{5!}{3!2!}\right)\left(\dfrac{6!}{4!2!}\right)}{\left(\dfrac{11!}{7!4!}\right)}$$

$$= \tfrac{5}{11}$$

157. Empirical probability. In interpreting results of certain experiments and in the analysis of statistical data, the ratio defined below is often used.

DEFINITION. *If out of **n** trials an event has occurred **h** times, the relative frequency of its occurrence is **h/n**.*

The experiment of tossing three pennies mentioned in the previous article was continued until 350 tosses had been made, and the relative frequency was calculated at the end of each 50 tosses. The results are shown in the table below, where n is the number of tosses, h is the number of times three heads appeared, and $R.F.$ is the relative frequency.

n	h	$R.F.$
50	8	.16
100	15	.150
150	19	.127
200	25	.125
250	31	.124
300	37	.123
350	45	.129

In this table it can be seen that as n increased, the relative frequency fluctuated about the mathematical probability, $\tfrac{1}{8} = .125$. It is assumed, and the assumption is justified by experience, that the larger n becomes, the more nearly the relative frequency approaches the mathematical probability. We make use of this assumption to define a ratio known as the *empirical probability* that is used extensively in the interpretation of statistics and in insurance.

DEFINITION. *If out of **n** trials, where **n** is a large number, an event has occurred **h** times, then the probability that it will happen in any one trial is defined to be **h/n**.*

Life-insurance companies make use of the above ratio applied to information tabulated in a *mortality table* in order to determine their rates. One of these tables is the American Experience Mortality Table (see Appendix, Table VIII), which was compiled from data gathered by several large life-insurance companies. Starting with 100,000 people ten years of age, it shows the number alive at the age of eleven years, twelve years, thirteen years, and so on to ninety-five years.

Example 1

A traffic census shows that out of 1000 vehicles passing a junction point on a highway 600 turned to the right. What is the probability of an automobile's turning to the right at this junction?

Solution

In this case, $n = 1000$, $h = 600$. Hence the desired probability is $\frac{600}{1000} = \frac{3}{5}$.

Example 2

According to the American Experience Mortality Table, what is the probability that a man 20 years of age will be alive at 30?

Solution

Table VIII shows that, out of 92,637 people alive at 20 years of age, 85,411 are living at the age of 30. Hence $h = 85,441$, $n = 92,637$, and the desired probability is $\frac{85,441}{92,637} = .9223$.

According to the definition, the empirical probability depends upon n and h, and in any situation it will probably change as n changes. If n is sufficiently large, the change in the probability due to a change in n should be small. Hence, in any case, the number of trials observed should be as large as the opportunity for observation permits.

158. *Mathematical expectation.* If the probability that an event will occur in one trial is p, then the *expected* number of occurrences in n trials is np. The latter product is called the *mathematical expectation* of the event.

If a person is to receive D dollars if an event occurs and the probability of its occurrence is p, then the *value of his expectation* is dP dollars.

Example

If the probability of a person's living to receive \$1000 at the age of 65 is $\frac{3}{5}$, the value of his expectation is \$600.

EXERCISE 79

1. A football team is composed of 3 sophomores, 4 juniors, and 4 seniors. If 1 player is hurt on the first play, find the probability that he is (*a*) a sophomore; (*b*) a junior.

2. If two coins are tossed simultaneously, find the probability that (*a*) both will fall tails; (*b*) one will fall heads and the other tails.

3. Find the probability of throwing (*a*) a four in one toss of a die; (*b*) an even number; (*c*) a number divisible by 3.

4. Find the probability of throwing a prime number in one toss of a die.

5. Find the probability of throwing (*a*) a two in one toss of a pair of dice; (*b*) a three; (*c*) a four; (*d*) a seven.

6. A bag contains 3 white, 5 black, and 4 red balls. If 1 ball is drawn from the bag at random, what is the probability that it is (*a*) white; (*b*) black; (*c*) red; (*d*) not black?

7. A box contains seven \$1 bills, six \$5 bills, and eight \$10 bills. If two bills are drawn simultaneously at random from the box, find the probability that (*a*) each will be a \$1; (*b*) \$6 will be drawn.

8. In Problem 7, find the probability that the two bills will amount to \$6 or more.

9. Three cards are drawn successively from a deck of 52 playing cards, and each is replaced before the next is drawn. Find the probability that all three are (*a*) hearts; (*b*) deuces; (*c*) in the same suit.

10. A man is to draw two tickets at random from a hat that contains 10 tickets numbered from 1 to 10. Find the probability that the sum of the two numbers drawn will be odd.

11. If 4 red and 4 black books are placed at random on a shelf, find the probability that the colors will alternate.

12. Find the probability that the books in Problem 11 will be so arranged that 4 books of the same color will be together.

13. Four married couples draw lots to decide who will be partners in a game. What is the probability that each man will be paired with his wife?

14. If the partners in Problem 13 are determined by each man's drawing a card from a set of 4 numbered 1, 2, 3, and 4, respectively, each woman's drawing a card from a similarly numbered set, and then those drawing the same numbers becoming partners, find the probability that each man will be paired with his wife.

15. A family of 4 take seats at random in a row of chairs. Find the probability that the father and mother are in adjacent chairs.

16. In Problem 15, what is the probability that the father and mother occupy the end chairs?

17. Three hundred small disks are numbered consecutively from 1 to 300 and placed in a box. After the box is well shaken, one disk is withdrawn. Find the probability that (a) the sum of the digits in the number on it is 3; (b) the number on it contains the digits 1, 2, and 3.

18. If two disks are drawn from the bag in Problem 17, what is the probability that the sum of the two numbers on them will be less than 20?

19. What is the probability that each of the two disks in Problem 18 will bear an even number?

20. What is the probability that one of the disks in Problem 18 will bear an even number and the other an odd?

21. In a city in which 15,000 automobiles are registered, 450 traffic accidents were reported in one year. Find the probability that a specified car will be involved in an accident during the next year.

22. If 40 cases of poliomyelitis were reported during one summer in a city where the population is 16,000, what is the probability that a specified person in this city will have polio?

23. In a college with an enrollment of 8000 students, an average of 7500 absences were reported per week during one semester. If each student was enrolled for 15 class meetings per week, what is the expected number of absences in one class of 32 members for one meeting?

24. In 10,000 miles of highway travel a motorist witnessed three serious accidents. What is the probability that he will witness an accident in the next mile of highway travel?

25. By use of Table VIII, find the probability that a man 21 years of age will die before he reaches the age of (a) 22 years; (b) 31 years.   Sub · & div.

26. By use of Table VIII find the probability that a youth 19 years of age will live to reach the age of 41 years.

27. By use of Table VIII find the probability that a man 60 years of age will live to reach the age of 75.

28. By use of Table VIII find the probability that a man 75 years of age will die before he is 85.

29. A man 60 years of age has a life-insurance policy that will pay him $2000 if he reaches the age of 80. Find the value of his expectation.

30. By the provisions of a will, a man 20 years of age is to receive $3000 when he reaches the age of 29. Find the value of his expectation.

31. A man 36 years of age is to receive $2000 if he is alive at the age of 41. Find the value of his expectation.

32. A man 40 years of age has the choice of two insurance policies. One will pay him $1600 if he reaches the age of 75, and the other will pay $3000 if he reaches the age of 80. Which policy offers him the best expectation, and by how much?

159. *Mutually exclusive events.* *Two or more events are said to be* **mutually exclusive** *if the occurrence of one of them excludes the possibility of the occurrence of any one of the others at the same trial.* For example, if a bag contains only red, white, and black balls, the events of drawing *either a red or a white ball* on one trial are mutually exclusive, since success in drawing one color excludes the possibility of drawing the other.

To make the above example more explicit, suppose the bag contains 3 red balls, 5 black balls, and 4 white balls, and we desire the probability of drawing either a red or a white ball in one trial. Since a red ball can be drawn in 3 ways and a white ball can be drawn in 4 ways, success in drawing one or the other can occur in $3 + 4 = 7$ ways. Hence, $h = 7$. Furthermore, failure to draw one of the desired colors can occur in 5 ways. Therefore, $f = 5$. Hence the desired probability is

$$\frac{3 + 4}{3 + 4 + 5} = \frac{3 + 4}{12} = \frac{3}{12} + \frac{4}{12} = \frac{7}{12}$$

Note that the probabilities of drawing a red ball and a black ball in one trial are $\frac{3}{12}$ and $\frac{4}{12}$, respectively, and the probability of drawing one or the other is the sum of these two. This illustrates the following theorem.

THEOREM. *The probability that some one of a set of mutually exclusive events will occur in a single trial is the sum of the probabilities of the separate events.*

Proof. Suppose that the events are $E_1, E_2, \ldots, E_r$; that E_1 can occur in h_1 ways, E_2 can occur in h_2 ways, $\ldots$, and E_r can occur in h_r ways in a single trial; and that one trial can happen in n different ways. Then, if $p_1, p_2, \ldots, p_r$ are the probabilities that $E_1, E_2, \ldots, E_r$ will occur, $p_1 = \dfrac{h_1}{n}$, $p_2 = \dfrac{h_2}{n}$, $\ldots$, and

$p_r = \dfrac{h_r}{n}$. The sum of the ways the separate events can happen is $h_1 + h_2 + \cdots + h_r$ and if p is the probability that some one of the r events will occur, we have

$$p = \frac{h_1 + h_2 + \cdots + h_r}{n}$$

$$= p_1 + p_2 + \cdots + p_r$$

since the trial can happen in n ways.

Example

If the probability of a horse A winning a race is $\frac{1}{5}$ and the probability of horse B winning the race is $\frac{1}{4}$, what is the probability that one or the other of the horses will win?

Solution

Since these events are mutually exclusive, the desired probability is the sum of the separate probabilities. Consequently, it is

$$\tfrac{1}{5} + \tfrac{1}{4} = \tfrac{9}{20}$$

160. Independent events. DEFINITION. *Two or more events are said to be **independent** if the occurrence of one of them does not affect the probability of the occurrence of any other.*

If 3 withdrawals of 1 ball each are made from the bag in the previous article and the ball is replaced after each drawing, the result of any one of the withdrawals does not affect the outcome of the other two. Hence the events are independent. The probability that all 3 colors will be drawn in 3 trials can be calculated as follows. The 3 colors can be drawn in $3 \times 5 \times 4$ ways. Furthermore, the 3 balls, regardless of color, can be drawn in 12^3 ways. Hence the desired probability is

$$\frac{3 \times 4 \times 5}{12^3} = \frac{3}{12} \times \frac{4}{12} \times \frac{5}{12} = \frac{5}{144}$$

Note that the required probability is the product of the probabilities that each color will be drawn in one trial. The theorem dealing with such situations and its proof is given below.

THEOREM. *The probability that all of a set of independent events will occur is the product of their separate probabilities.*

Proof. If there are two events E_1 and E_2 and if E_1 can occur in h_1 and fail in f_1 ways, E_2 can occur in h_2 ways and fail in f_2 ways;

then, the two events can occur and fail in $(h_1 + f_1)(h_2 + f_2)$ ways in a single trial and both can occur in h_1h_2 ways. Therefore, the probability p_{12} that both will occur is

$$p_{12} = \frac{h_1h_2}{(h_1 + f_1)(h_2 + f_2)}$$

Now this may be considered as a single event, another event added, and the probability of all three occurring calculated. If the third can occur in h_3 ways and fail in f_3, the probability p_{123} that all three will occur is

$$p_{123} = \frac{h_1h_2}{(h_1 + f_1)(h_2 + f_2)} \frac{h_3}{h_3 + f_3}$$

In fact, this process can be continued until we have r independent events and the probability $p_{123\ldots r}$ that all r will occur is

$$p_{123\ldots r} = \frac{h_1h_2h_3 \cdots h_r}{(h_1 + f_1)(h_2 + f_2) \cdots (h_r + f_r)}$$
$$= p_1 p_2 \cdots p_r$$

Example

If the probabilities that each of two brothers will live to be 60 years of age are .61 and .67, respectively, then the probability that both will reach the age of 60 is .61 $\times$ .67 = .41.

161. Dependent events. DEFINITION. *If the occurrence of one of a set of events affects the probability of another's occurring, the events are said to be dependent.*

We shall again refer to the bag of balls discussed in the two previous articles. If a ball is drawn from the bag and not replaced, the result of this drawing certainly affects the outcome of the second. For example, the probability of drawing a black ball first is $\frac{5}{12}$, but if a red ball is drawn first, the probability of drawing a black ball second is $\frac{5}{11}$. The probability of drawing a red ball first and a black ball second can be calculated thus. The balls can be drawn in the order red, black in 3 $\times$ 5 ways. Furthermore, the two balls, without regard to color, can be drawn in 12 $\times$ 11 ways. Hence, the desired probability is

$$\frac{3 \times 5}{12 \times 11} = \frac{3}{12} \times \frac{5}{11}$$

and we see that the required probability is the product of the probabilities of the two separate dependent events. This illustrates the theorem that follows.

THEOREM. *If the probability of event E_1 occurring is p_1 and if after it has happened the probability of a second event E_2 happening is p_2; then, the probability that both will occur in the order E_1E_2 is p_1p_2.*

Proof. If E_1 can occur in h_1 ways and fail in f_1 ways and if after this trial E_2 can occur in h_2 ways and fail in f_2 ways, then the events can happen in the order E_1E_2 in h_1h_2 ways, and they can occur or fail in $(h_1 + f_1)(h_2 + f_2)$ ways. Therefore, the probability that they will occur in the order E_1E_2 is

$$p_{12} = \frac{h_1h_2}{(h_1 + f_1)(h_2 + f_2)} = p_1p_2$$

We shall next let p_i be the probability that E_i will occur after $E_1E_2E_3 \ldots E_{i-1}$, $i = 1, 2, 3, \ldots, r$, have happened, and $p_{123\ldots r}$ be the probability that $E_1E_2E_3 \ldots E_r$ will take place in the indicated order. By repeated applications of the above theorem we obtain $p_{123} = p_{12}p_3 = p_1p_2p_3$,

$$p_{1234} = p_{123}p_4 = p_1p_2p_3p_4,$$

and so on, until we get

$$p_{123\ldots r} = p_1p_2p_3 \ldots p_r$$

Example

If the probability that a man 35 years of age will live to the age of 65 is .6; and *if he lives* to be 65 years of age, the probability that he will retire at that time is .5; then the probability that he will retire at 65 is .6 $\times$ .5 = .3.

EXERCISE 80

1. If the probabilities that A and B will win a race are $\frac{1}{2}$ and $\frac{1}{3}$, respectively, what is the probability that A or B will win?

2. If the probabilities that teams A, B, and C will win the conference championship are $\frac{1}{5}$, $\frac{1}{6}$, and $\frac{1}{10}$, respectively, find the probability that either A, or B, or C will win the title.

3. A civic club has a membership of 40 of whom 5 are named Smith and 3 are named Jones. If one delegate is chosen for a national convention, what is the probability that he will be a Smith or a Jones?

4. The probabilities that each of two candidates for the presidency of the student body will be elected are $\frac{2}{5}$ and $\frac{5}{11}$, respectively. Find the probability that one or the other will win the election.

5. A committee of 3 is to be selected by lot from a group of 5 girls and 4 boys. Find the probability that it will consist of more boys than girls.

6. One hundred tickets numbered from 1 to 100 are sold. Duplicate tickets are placed in a box and thoroughly mixed. Three tickets are drawn successively from the box and not replaced. The holders of the tickets that match those drawn from the box win the first, second, and third prizes, respectively. Find the probability that the holder of the ticket numbered 20 will win a prize.

7. A farmer estimates that if it rains as much as $\frac{1}{2}$ in. during the month of August, he will make 150 bales of cotton, and if it rains as much as 1 in., he will make 200 bales. If statistics show that the probabilities of receiving $\frac{1}{2}$ in. and 1 in. of rain are $\frac{1}{2}$ and $\frac{1}{3}$, respectively, find the probability that he will make at least 150 bales.

8. Three men and three ladies enter a room containing three chairs and a divan that seats three. If they take seats at random, what is the probability that there will be at least one lady on the divan?

9. In the Democratic primaries, a man has 3 opponents in a race for the nomination for an office. The nominee for this office will have 2 opponents in the general election. Find the probability that he will be elected.

10. Two balls are drawn successively from a box containing four white and six red balls. If the first ball is replaced before the second is drawn, find the probability that both balls will be red.

11. If, in Problem 10, the first ball is not replaced before the second is drawn, find the probability that both will be red.

12. The probability that a certain candidate will be elected to the presidency of the student body is $\frac{2}{5}$, and the probability that another candidate will be elected to the vice-presidency is $\frac{5}{11}$. Find the probability that both will be elected.

13. The probability that Mr. Brown will be elected county clerk is $\frac{2}{5}$. If he is elected, the probability that he will appoint Mr. Smith as his assistant is $\frac{5}{11}$. What is the probability that Mr. Smith will become assistant county clerk?

14. If a coin and a die are tossed, find the probability of obtaining a head and a four.

15. In Problem 14, find the probability of obtaining a head and at least a four.

16. What is the probability of throwing a head each time in 4 tosses of a coin?

17. Tom, Dick, and Harry shoot in the order named at a target and the probabilities of their hitting the bull's-eye are $\frac{2}{3}$, $\frac{3}{4}$, and $\frac{1}{2}$, respectively. Find the probability that each will be the first to hit the bull's-eye.

18. In Problem 5, find the probability that the 3 members of the committee will be of the same sex.

162

19. In Problem 5, find the probability that 2 members of the committee will be of the same sex and the third member will be of the opposite sex.

20. Find the probability that at least one girl will be selected for the committee in Problem 5.

21. Find the probability that either a six or a seven will be obtained in one toss of a pair of dice.

22. Find the probability that neither a five nor a six will be thrown in one toss of a pair of dice.

23. Find the probability of obtaining a two in each of two successive tosses of a pair of dice.

24. In 2 tosses of a pair of dice, find the probability that neither a two nor a seven will be thrown first and that a two will be thrown second.

25. One box contains 5 black and 3 white balls, and another contains 7 black and 5 white balls. If 1 ball is drawn from each box, find the probability that both will be (a) black; (b) white; (c) the same color.

26. If 1 of the boxes in Problem 25 is selected by lot and 1 ball is drawn from it, find the probability that it will be white.

27. If 2 balls are drawn simultaneously from the box in Problem 26, find the probability that both will be white.

28. If 1 ball is drawn from each of the boxes in Problem 25, find the probability that 1 will be white and the other black.

29. Three soldiers agree that if as many as two of them are alive in 25 years, they will meet for a reunion. If the probabilities that each will live 25 years are $\frac{4}{5}$, $\frac{5}{7}$, and $\frac{7}{10}$, respectively, find the probability that the reunion will take place.

30. A son is to become the executor of the family estate upon the death of his father. If the son is 27 and his father is 51, what is the probability that the former will be in control of the estate when he is 33 years of age?

31. A man who has a son, a grandson, and a great-grandson creates a trust fund of \$15,000 payable in n years to the oldest living one of the above descendants. Find the expectation of each if the probabilities of their living n years are $\frac{2}{3}$, $\frac{3}{4}$, and $\frac{9}{10}$ respectively.

32. A father 40 years of age agrees to take his son to Europe in 5 years. If the son is 13 years of age, what is the probability that they will both be alive to take the trip?

162. Repeated trials of an event. If we know the probability of an event's occurring in one trial, then the probability of its happening a given number of times in n trials is given by the following theorem:

THEOREM. *If p is the probability that an event will occur in one trial, then the probability that it will occur exactly r times in n trials* *is equal to*

$$_nC_r p^r (1 - p)^{n-r}$$

Proof. The r trials can be selected from the n trials in $_nC_r$ ways by Art. 155. The probability that it will occur r times and fail the remaining $n - r$ is $p^r(1 - p)^{n-r}$, by Art. 160, since the trials are independent and $1 - p$ is the probability of the event failing in any trial. By the theorem of Art. 159 the desired probability is therefore $_nC_r p^r (1 - p)^{n-r}$.

COROLLARY. *If p is the probability that an event will occur in one trial, then the probability that it will occur at least r times in n trials is equal to*

$$p^n + {}_nC_{n-1}p^{n-1}(1 - p) + {}_nC_{n-2}p^{n-2}(1 - p)^2 + \cdots$$
$$+ {}_nC_{r+1}p^{r+1}(1 - p)^{n-r-1} + {}_nC_r p^r(1 - p)^{n-r}.$$

Proof. The terms of this sum are the probabilities that the event will occur exactly n times, exactly $n - 1$ times, . . . , exactly $r + 1$ times, and exactly r times in n trials and the events are mutually exclusive.

The reader should notice that the expression in this corollary is the first $n - r + 1$ terms of the expansion of binomial $(p + q)^n$, where $q = 1 - p$.

Example

A bag contains 3 white and 4 red balls. The balls are drawn from the bag one at a time and are replaced after each drawing. (*a*) What is the probability of drawing exactly 3 red balls in 5 trials? (*b*) What is the probability of drawing at least 3 red balls in 5 trials?

Solution

(*a*) The probability of drawing a red ball in 1 trial is $\frac{4}{7}$. Therefore, the desired probability is

$$_nC_r p^r(1 - p)^{n-r} = {}_5C_3(\tfrac{4}{7})^3(1 - \tfrac{4}{7})^{5-3}$$
$$= \left(\frac{5!}{3!2!}\right)\left(\frac{4^3}{7^3}\right)\left(\frac{3^2}{7^2}\right)$$
$$= \frac{5,760}{16,807}$$

EXERCISE 81

1. Find the probability of throwing in 5 tosses of a coin (*a*) exactly 3 heads; (*b*) at least 3 heads.

2. Find the probability of throwing in 3 tosses of a die (*a*) exactly 2 fives; (*b*) at least 2 fives.

3. If 7 cards are drawn successively from a deck of 52 cards and each is replaced before the next is drawn, find the probability of drawing (*a*) exactly 5 hearts; (*b*) at least 5 hearts.

4. A box contains 3 white and 5 red balls. Four drawings of one ball each are made, and the ball is replaced after each. Find the probability of drawing (*a*) exactly 2 red balls; (*b*) at least 2 red balls.

5. A bag contains 3 white, 4 red, and 5 black balls. Five withdrawals of 1 ball each are made, and the ball is replaced after each. Find the probability that all five will be red.

6. In Problem 5, find the probability that exactly 3 balls will be red.

7. In Problem 5, find the probability that at least 3 balls will be red.

8. In Problem 5, find the probability that 2 balls will be red and 3 will be black.

9. In Problem 5, find the probability that 2 balls will be red, 1 will be black, and 2 will be white.

10. In Problem 5, find the probability that exactly 2 balls will be red and exactly 2 will be black.

11. In Problem 5, find the probability that the most probable number of white balls will be drawn.

12. In Problem 5, find the probability that the least probable number of white balls will be drawn.

13. If the probability that a certain basketball team will win the conference championship is $\frac{2}{3}$, find the probability that it will win exactly 3 championships in 5 years.

14. If the probability of a man of age x years living to the age of $x + n$ years is $\frac{3}{4}$, find the probability that exactly 4 out of 10 men of age x years will live n more years.

15. If the probability that a candidate will be elected to an office is $\frac{2}{3}$, find the probability that he will be elected for four successive terms and then be defeated for the fifth term.

16. If the probability that an accident will occur on a trip is .01, show that the probability of making the trip 501 times without accident is approximately $\frac{5}{800}$.

17. The probability that a senior will hear of and apply for a certain position is $\frac{1}{3}$. The probability that he will tell his roommate about it is $\frac{3}{5}$. The probability that he will be offered the position if he applies is $\frac{7}{12}$ provided he does not tell his roommate and $\frac{3}{8}$ if he does. Find the probability that he will be offered the position.

18. If q is the probability of failure in one trial, show that the probability of at least one success in n trials is $1 - q^n$.

CHAPTER 21

DETERMINANTS

163. *Introduction.* In this chapter, we shall generalize the discussion of determinants introduced in Arts. 43 and 44. For this purpose, we shall need the following definition:

DEFINITION. *An **inversion** occurs in any permutation of integers whenever a greater integer precedes a lesser.*

In the permutation 4312, 4 precedes 3, 1, and 2; furthermore, 3 precedes 1 and 2. Hence, there are five inversions in the sequence.

THEOREM 1. *The interchange of two adjacent elements in a permutation of integers either increases or decreases the number of inversions by unity.*

In order to prove this theorem, we let the two adjacent terms in a given permutation be r and s. If these two terms are interchanged, an inversion is added if $r < s$, and an inversion is removed if $r > s$.

164. *Determinants of order n.* DEFINITION. *The symbol*

$$D = \begin{vmatrix} a_{11}a_{12}a_{13} & \cdot \cdot \cdot & a_{1n} \\ a_{21}a_{22}a_{23} & \cdot \cdot \cdot & a_{2n} \\ a_{31}a_{32}a_{33} & \cdot \cdot \cdot & a_{3n} \\ \cdot \quad \cdot \quad \cdot & & \cdot \\ \cdot \quad \cdot \quad \cdot & & \cdot \\ a_{n1}a_{n2}a_{n3} & \cdot \cdot \cdot & a_{nn} \end{vmatrix}$$

*is called a **determinant** of order n. It is an abbreviation for the homogeneous polynomial obtained by*

1. Forming every possible product by taking as factors one and only one element from each row and each column of D.

2. Arranging the factors in each product so that the second (or

380

column) subscripts are in numerical[1] order and then preceding each factor with a positive or negative sign according as the number of inversions in the first (or row) subscripts is even or odd.

3. *Taking the algebraic sum of all products obtained by performing (1) and (2).*

The sum in the preceding definition is called the *expansion* or the value of D.

We should notice that in D the first subscript in each element designates the row in which the element appears and the second subscript represents the column.

Since each product in the expansion of D contains as factors exactly one element from each row and exactly one from each column, each of the integers from 1 to n appears once as a first subscript in each product and once as a second subscript. Furthermore, by the second provision of the definition, the second subscripts must be arranged in numerical order. Consequently, the first subscripts will appear as some permutation of 1, 2, 3, . . . , n. Thus we may obtain the expansion of D by

(1) *Writing the $n!$ permutations of 1, 2, 3, . . . , n.*

(2) *Writing $n!$ products each containing n elements of D with one of the permutations obtained in step 1 as first subscripts and the integers 1, 2, 3, . . . , n in their natural order as second subscripts.*

(3) *Attaching a plus or minus sign to each product according as the number of inversions in the first subscripts is even or odd.*

As one consequence of this discussion, we have the following theorem:

THEOREM 2. *The expansion of a determinant of order n contains $n!$ terms.*

Example

Using the foregoing procedure to obtain the expansion of

$$D' = \begin{vmatrix} a_{11} & a_{12} & a_{13} \\ a_{21} & a_{22} & a_{23} \\ a_{31} & a_{32} & a_{33} \end{vmatrix}$$

we have

1. The permutations of the integers 1, 2, 3 are 1, 2, 3 (no inversions); 1, 3,

---

[1] It is assumed in the definition that the columns are so arranged that the second subscripts are in numerical order. If this is not the case, then the factors in each product should be arranged so that the second subscripts are in the order in which they appear in the first row.

2 (one inversion); 2, 1, 3 (one inversion); 2, 3, 1 (two inversions); 3, 1, 2 (two inversions); and 3, 2, 1 (three inversions).

2 and 3. The expansion of D' may now be written as

$$a_{11}a_{22}a_{33} - a_{11}a_{32}a_{23} - a_{21}a_{12}a_{33} + a_{21}a_{32}a_{13} + a_{31}a_{12}a_{23} - a_{31}a_{22}a_{13}$$

We may use a modified form of the foregoing procedure to obtain the terms in the expansion of D' which contain any particular element. For example, to obtain those terms which contain a_{32}, we remember that this factor must occupy the second position in each product, since the second subscript is 2. Hence, we can use only those permutations in step 1 in which 3 occupies the second position; namely, 1, 3, 2 and 2, 3, 1. Thus, using 1, 2, 3 as second subscripts, we have $-a_{11}a_{32}a_{23} + a_{21}a_{32}a_{13}$. If we place this expression in the form $a_{32}(-a_{11}a_{23} + a_{21}a_{13})$, we may observe this interesting fact. The expression in parentheses is, by Art. 43, the negative of the expansion of

$$\begin{vmatrix} a_{11} & a_{13} \\ a_{21} & a_{23} \end{vmatrix}$$

which is a determinant made up of the elements of D' that are not in the same row or column with a_{32}.

THEOREM 3. *If the rows and columns of a determinant are interchanged, the value of the determinant is not altered.*

Because of this theorem, many of the later theorems dealing with determinants need only be proved for columns. We shall prove the theorem for a determinant of the fourth order. However, our method is general and can be applied with little change to a determinant of any order.

We shall consider the two determinants D_1 and D_2 in which the columns and rows of D_1 appear as rows and columns, respectively, of D_2.

$$D_1 = \begin{vmatrix} a_{11} & a_{12} & a_{13} & a_{14} \\ a_{21} & a_{22} & a_{23} & a_{24} \\ a_{31} & a_{32} & a_{33} & a_{34} \\ a_{41} & a_{42} & a_{43} & a_{44} \end{vmatrix} \qquad D_2 = \begin{vmatrix} a_{11} & a_{21} & a_{31} & a_{41} \\ a_{12} & a_{22} & a_{32} & a_{42} \\ a_{13} & a_{23} & a_{33} & a_{43} \\ a_{14} & a_{24} & a_{34} & a_{44} \end{vmatrix}$$

We first notice that in D_1 the column in which an element appears is denoted by the second subscript, while in D_2 this fact is designated by the first subscript. Hence, by the second provision of the definition, the terms in the expansion of D_2 must be arranged so that the *first subscripts* are in numerical order and the sign is determined by the number of inversions in the *second* subscript.

Referring to the second provision of the definition, we see that each term in D_1 is in the form

$$(1) \qquad\qquad a_{t_1 1} a_{t_2 2} a_{t_3 3} a_{t_4 4}$$

in which t_1, t_2, t_3, t_4 is a permutation of the integers 1, 2, 3, 4. The term is plus or minus according as the number of inversions in t_1, t_2, t_3, t_4 is even or odd.

If we rearrange the terms of (1) so that t_1, t_2, t_3, t_4, takes the order 1, 2, 3, 4, it then becomes, except possibly for sign, a term in the expansion of D_2. Hence, by rearranging each term in the expansion of D_1, we obtain, except possibly for sign, the expansion of D_2.

We shall now show that such a rearrangement of factors does not affect the sign of the term. For this purpose we shall need the idea of the total number of inversions in the subscripts in a term such as $a_{31} a_{44} a_{13} a_{22}$. The total number of inversions in this arrangement is the number in the first subscripts plus the number in the second, which, in this case, is $4 + 3 = 7$. By Theorem 1, an interchange of two adjacent terms in such an arrangement increases or decreases the number of inversions in each set of subscripts by unity. Hence, it increases or decreases the total number of inversions in the double subscripts by zero or two.

If the term (1) is converted into a term

$$(2) \qquad\qquad a_{1 s_1} a_{2 s_2} a_{3 s_3} a_{4 s_4}$$

by a succession of interchanges of adjacent factors, then, by the above discussion, the total number of inversions in (2) differs from that in (1) by an even number. However, there are no inversions in either the second subscripts of (1) or in the first subscripts in (2). Hence, the inversions in (1) are those in $t_1 t_2 t_3 t_4$, and those in (2) are the inversions in $s_1 s_2 s_3 s_4$. Thus, the number of inversions in (2) is even or odd according as the number in (1) is even or odd. Consequently, the signs of the terms in (1) and (2) are the same and $D_1 = D_2$.

165. *Minors of a determinant.* DEFINITION. *The $n - 1$ rowed determinant obtained from a determinant of order n by deleting the row and the column that contain a given element is called the **minor** of that element.*

Example

The minor of a_{23} in the determinant D is the determinant obtained by omitting the second row and the third column of D. Furthermore, the minor of the element 3 in

$$\begin{vmatrix} 1 & 2 & 4 \\ 2 & 5 & 3 \\ 4 & 6 & 5 \end{vmatrix} \quad \text{is} \quad \begin{vmatrix} 1 & 2 \\ 4 & 6 \end{vmatrix}$$

We shall now show that the algebraic sum of all terms in the expansion of the determinant D of Art. 164 which contain the element a_{ij} is equal, except possibly for sign, to the product of a_{ij} and its minor. We may obtain these terms by using the procedure of Art. 164. However, in writing the permutations of the first subscripts, we must have i in the jth position.[1] The subscripts permuted, then, are the integers from 1 to n except i. Each term in the expansion will have the form

$$(1) \qquad \pm a_{e_1 1} a_{e_2 2} a_{e_3 3} \cdots a_{ij} \cdots a_{e_n n}$$

where $e_1 e_2 e_3 \cdots i \cdots e_n$ is a permutation of the integers 1 to n with i in the jth position.

The minor A_{ij} of a_{ij} in D is the determinant made up of all elements of D except the ith row and the jth column. Hence, each term in A_{ij} is in the form $a_{e_1 1} a_{e_2 2} a_{e_3 3} \cdots a_{e_n n}$, where $e_1 e_2 e_3 \cdots e_n$ is a permutation of all integers from 1 to n except i and where j is missing from the second subscripts. The sign is determined by the number of inversions in $e_1 e_2 e_3 \cdots e_n$. If we multiply A_{ij} by a_{ij}, each term in the product is in the form

$$(2) \qquad \pm a_{ij} a_{e_1 1} a_{e_2 2} a_{e_3 3} \cdots a_{e_n n}$$

The expressions (1) and (2) are the same except for the position of a_{ij} and the fact that the sign of the former is determined by the inversions in $e_1 e_2 e_3 \cdots i \cdots e_n$ and that of the latter only by the inversions in $e_1 e_2 e_3 \cdots e_n$. In other words, we could

---

[1] As an example, see the discussion in the paragraph preceding Theorem 3, Art. 164.

determine the sign that must be given to (2) by neglecting i in (1) and then counting the inversions in the remaining subscripts. This brings up the question "How does neglecting one integer in a permutation affect the number of inversions in that permutation?" If the integer i, neglected, occupies the first position in the permutation, one inversion is removed for each of the $i - 1$ integers less than i. We may place a_{ij} in the first position in (1) by $j - 1$ interchanges of a_{ij} with the terms to the left of it. By Theorem 1, each interchange increases or decreases the number of inversions in the second subscript by unity. Now, neglecting i in the new arrangement decreases the number of inversions by $i - 1$. Hence, we have, by this procedure, introduced

$$j - 1 + i - 1 = j + i - 2$$

changes in the number of inversions. This number is even or odd according as $j + i$ is even or odd. Hence, the signs of (1) and (2) are the same if $j + i$ is even, and opposite if $j + i$ is odd. Furthermore, $(-1)^{i+j}$ is plus or minus according as $i + j$ is even or odd. *Hence, the terms in the expansion of D containing a_{ij} are equal to $(-1)^{i+j}a_{ij}A_{ij}$.*

By definition, each term in the expansion of D contains one element and only one from the jth column. Hence,

$$(3) \quad D = (-1)^{1+j}a_{1j}A_{1j} + (-1)^{2+j}a_{2j}A_{2j} + (-1)^{3+j}a_{3j}A_{3j}$$
$$+ \cdots + (-1)^{i+j}a_{ij}A_{ij} + \cdots + (-1)^{n+j}a_{nj}A_{nj}$$

This conclusion gives us a method that is used almost exclusively for the expansion of determinants, especially for those of order greater than three. The method is outlined in Theorem 4 below.

THEOREM 4. *The expansion of a determinant may be obtained by*

1. *Multiplying each element of a row or column by its minor and prefixing a plus or minus sign according as the sum of the number of the row and the column in which the element lies is even or odd.*

2. *Taking the algebraic sum of these products.*

3. *Repeating this process on each determinant thus obtained until we have the indicated sum of third-order determinants.*

4. *Expanding these third-order determinants and taking the algebraic sum of the numbers thus obtained. This method is called* **expanding the determinant by minors.**

Example

Expand

$$\begin{vmatrix} 1 & 2 & 4 & 3 \\ 2 & -1 & 2 & 1 \\ -3 & 3 & -3 & 2 \\ 2 & 5 & -2 & 4 \end{vmatrix}$$

Solution

If we expand in terms of the elements of the first column and follow the procedure set forth in Theorem 4, we obtain

$$1\begin{vmatrix} -1 & 2 & 1 \\ 3 & -3 & 2 \\ 5 & -2 & 4 \end{vmatrix} - 2\begin{vmatrix} 2 & 4 & 3 \\ 3 & -3 & 2 \\ 5 & -2 & 4 \end{vmatrix}$$

$$+ (-3)\begin{vmatrix} 2 & 4 & 3 \\ -1 & 2 & 1 \\ 5 & -2 & 4 \end{vmatrix} - 2\begin{vmatrix} 2 & 4 & 3 \\ -1 & 2 & 1 \\ 3 & -3 & 2 \end{vmatrix}$$

$$= 1(12 + 20 - 6 + 15 - 4 - 24)$$
$$- 2(-24 + 40 - 18 + 45 + 8 - 48)$$
$$- 3(16 + 20 + 6 - 30 + 4 + 16)$$
$$- 2(8 + 12 + 9 - 18 + 6 + 8)$$
$$= 1(13) - 2(3) - 3(32) - 2(25) = -139$$

EXERCISE 82

Determine the number of inversions in the permutation of integers in each of Problems 1 to 8.

1. 3 4 1 5 6 2.
2. 6 5 4 3 1 2.
3. 6 4 2 5 3 1.
4. 4 7 5 2 3 6 1.
5. 7 5 4 6 3 2 1.
6. 3 5 7 2 1 6 4.
7. 1 2 5 3 6 7 8.
8. 3 1 6 2 5 4 7.

In Problems 9 to 16, arrange the factors in each of the products according to the directions in the second division of the definition of a determinant, and then determine the sign of the product.

9. $a_{43}a_{31}a_{12}a_{24}$.
10. $a_{34}a_{22}a_{13}a_{41}$.
11. $a_{44}a_{31}a_{12}a_{23}$.
12. $a_{14}a_{21}a_{33}a_{42}$.
13. $a_{24}a_{33}a_{15}a_{52}a_{41}$.
14. $a_{54}a_{35}a_{21}a_{43}a_{12}$.
15. $a_{44}a_{32}a_{53}a_{25}a_{11}$.
16. $a_{15}a_{31}a_{23}a_{42}a_{54}$.

Use the methods of Arts. 43 and 44 to obtain the expansions of the determinants in Problems 17 to 24.

17. $\begin{vmatrix} 2 & 5 \\ 1 & 4 \end{vmatrix}$.

18. $\begin{vmatrix} 3 & 2 \\ -1 & 5 \end{vmatrix}$.

19. $\begin{vmatrix} -4 & -2 \\ 6 & 3 \end{vmatrix}$.

20. $\begin{vmatrix} 8 & -3 \\ -2 & 7 \end{vmatrix}$.

21. $\begin{vmatrix} 1 & 4 & 2 \\ 2 & 1 & 3 \\ 5 & 3 & 1 \end{vmatrix}$.

22. $\begin{vmatrix} 2 & -3 & 4 \\ -1 & 5 & 2 \\ 3 & 1 & -3 \end{vmatrix}$.

23. $\begin{vmatrix} 1 & 0 & 2 \\ 3 & -1 & 1 \\ 0 & 2 & -3 \end{vmatrix}.$

24. $\begin{vmatrix} -3 & 5 & 0 \\ 0 & 2 & -1 \\ 6 & 0 & -4 \end{vmatrix}.$

By expanding the determinants in Problems 25 to 28, show that the statement in each problem is true.

25. $\begin{vmatrix} 2 & 4 & 5 \\ 3 & 1 & 2 \\ 1 & 3 & 3 \end{vmatrix} = \begin{vmatrix} 2 & 3 & 1 \\ 4 & 1 & 3 \\ 5 & 2 & 3 \end{vmatrix}.$

26. $\begin{vmatrix} a & 1 & b \\ 2 & b & a \\ c & b & 2 \end{vmatrix} = \begin{vmatrix} a & 2 & c \\ 1 & b & b \\ b & a & 2 \end{vmatrix}.$

27. $\begin{vmatrix} a & c \\ b & d \end{vmatrix} = \begin{vmatrix} a+c & c \\ b+d & d \end{vmatrix}.$

28. $\begin{vmatrix} 1 & 2 & 1 \\ 2 & -1 & 2 \\ -3 & 4 & 3 \end{vmatrix} = \begin{vmatrix} 1+2x & 2 & 1 \\ 2-x & -1 & 2 \\ -3+4x & 4 & 3 \end{vmatrix}.$

By expanding the determinants in each of Problems 29 to 32, show that the statement in each problem is true.

29. The sum of the terms containing a in

$$\begin{vmatrix} 3 & 1 & a \\ 2 & 3 & 4 \\ 1 & 2 & 1 \end{vmatrix} \text{ is equal to } a\begin{vmatrix} 2 & 3 \\ 1 & 2 \end{vmatrix}.$$

30. The sum of the terms containing a in

$$\begin{vmatrix} 1 & 3 & 2 \\ 3 & 1 & a \\ 4 & 2 & 1 \end{vmatrix} \text{ is equal to } -a\begin{vmatrix} 1 & 3 \\ 4 & 2 \end{vmatrix}.$$

31. The sum of the terms containing a in

$$\begin{vmatrix} 2 & 1 & 1 \\ 3 & 2 & 1 \\ 2 & 1 & a \end{vmatrix} \text{ is equal to } a\begin{vmatrix} 2 & 1 \\ 3 & 2 \end{vmatrix}.$$

32. The sum of the terms containing a in

$$\begin{vmatrix} 3 & 4 & 1 \\ 1 & a & 1 \\ 2 & 0 & 3 \end{vmatrix} \text{ is equal to } a\begin{vmatrix} 3 & 1 \\ 2 & 3 \end{vmatrix}.$$

Expand the following determinants by minors.

33. $\begin{vmatrix} 3 & 4 & -1 \\ 2 & -3 & 2 \\ -1 & 2 & 1 \end{vmatrix}.$

34. $\begin{vmatrix} 3 & -2 & 4 \\ 5 & 1 & 0 \\ -2 & 3 & 2 \end{vmatrix}.$

35. $\begin{vmatrix} 1 & -2 & -3 \\ 2 & -1 & 1 \\ -3 & 2 & -1 \end{vmatrix}.$

36. $\begin{vmatrix} 3 & 0 & -1 \\ 2 & 1 & 0 \\ 0 & -2 & 1 \end{vmatrix}.$

37. $\begin{vmatrix} 1 & 3 & 4 & 4 \\ 2 & -1 & 2 & 0 \\ 0 & 2 & -3 & 2 \\ 3 & 0 & 0 & 1 \end{vmatrix}.$

38. $\begin{vmatrix} 2 & 3 & 1 & 0 \\ 0 & 0 & 4 & 2 \\ -1 & 2 & -2 & 1 \\ 0 & 1 & 3 & -2 \end{vmatrix}.$

39.
$$\begin{vmatrix} 2 & 1 & 1 & 0 \\ 0 & 1 & 1 & 1 \\ 1 & 1 & 0 & 0 \\ 1 & 1 & 2 & 1 \end{vmatrix}.$$

40.
$$\begin{vmatrix} 2 & 4 & 1 & 1 \\ 1 & 2 & 0 & 1 \\ 1 & 1 & 4 & 2 \\ 0 & 1 & 2 & 1 \end{vmatrix}.$$

41.
$$\begin{vmatrix} a & b & 0 & 0 \\ 0 & 0 & a & b \\ a & 0 & 0 & b \\ 0 & a & b & 0 \end{vmatrix}.$$

42.
$$\begin{vmatrix} a & b & a & 0 \\ 0 & a & b & a \\ a & 0 & a & b \\ b & a & 0 & a \end{vmatrix}.$$

43.
$$\begin{vmatrix} 1 & 1 & 0 & 0 & 0 \\ 1 & 0 & 1 & 0 & 0 \\ 0 & 0 & 1 & 0 & 0 \\ 0 & 0 & 0 & a & b \\ 0 & 0 & 0 & c & d \end{vmatrix}.$$

44.
$$\begin{vmatrix} a & 0 & 0 & 0 & a \\ a & 0 & 0 & a & 0 \\ 0 & a & a & 0 & a \\ 0 & 0 & a & a & 0 \\ 0 & a & 0 & 0 & a \end{vmatrix}.$$

166. Properties of determinants. For the convenience of the reader, we shall rewrite the expansion of the determinant D of Art. 165 in terms of the minors of the jth column.

$$(1) \quad D = (-1)^{1+j}a_{1j}A_{1j} + (-1)^{2+j}a_{2j}A_{2j} + (-1)^{3+j}a_{3j}A_{3j} \\ + \cdots + (-1)^{n+j}a_{nj}A_{nj}$$

THEOREM 5. *If each element of a row or column of a determinant is zero, the value of the determinant is zero.*

Proof. Suppose that all the elements of the jth column of D are zero, then expression (1) becomes

$$D = (-1)^{1+j}0A_{1j} + (-1)^{2+j}0A_{2j} + (-1)^{3+j}0A_{3j} + \cdots \\ + (-1)^{n+j}0A_{nj}$$
$$= 0$$

THEOREM 6. *If two rows or two columns of a determinant are interchanged, the algebraic sign of the determinant is changed.*

Proof. We shall first consider the case in which two adjacent columns, that is the jth and the $(j + 1)$st, of D are interchanged and shall designate the determinant thus obtained by D'. The minors of the elements in the jth column will not be altered by this change since the only column entering into them that has been shifted is the $(j + 1)$st and its position with respect to the $(j - 1)$st and the $(j + 2)$d has not been disturbed. Hence,

$$(2) \quad D' = (-1)^{1+j}a_{1j}A_{1j} + (-1)^{2+j}a_{2j}A_{2j} + \cdots \\ + (-1)^{n+j}a_{nj}A_{nj}$$

However, the value of j in (2) is now one greater than that in

(1) since the jth column has been moved one position to the right. Therefore, each exponent of -1 in (2) is one greater than that in the corresponding term of (1); hence, these terms are opposite in sign. Consequently, $D = -D'$.

We shall next interchange the positions of the jth and the $(j + k)$th columns of D, thereby obtaining D''. In order to accomplish this, we first move the jth column successively over the $k - 1$ columns between it and the $(j + k)$th, thus placing it immediately to the left of the $(j + k)$th. We now shift the $(j + k)$th column k positions to the left into the place vacated by the jth. Hence, we have made $k - 1 + k = 2k - 1$ interchanges. Therefore,

$$D'' = (-1)^{2k-1}D = -D$$

since $2k - 1$ is an odd number.

THEOREM 7. *If the elements of two rows or of two columns are identical, the value of the determinant is zero.*

Proof. Let the jth and kth columns of D be identical. If these are interchanged, the sign of the determinant is changed, by Theorem 6, and hence becomes $-D$. On the other hand, since the two columns that were moved are identical, D is not altered by the shift. Therefore, $D = -D$, and consequently, $D = 0$.

THEOREM 8. *If each element of a row or a column of a determinant is multiplied by k, the value of the determinant is multiplied by k.*

Proof. Suppose that each element in the jth column of D is multiplied by k, and let the determinant thus obtained be denoted by $\bar{D}$. By steps 1 and 2 of Theorem 4, the expansion of $\bar{D}$ in terms of the minors of the jth column is

$$\bar{D} = (-1)^{1+j}ka_{1j}A_{1j} + (-1)^{2+j}ka_{2j}A_{2j} + (-1)^{3+j}ka_{3j}A_{3j}$$
$$+ \cdots + (-1)^{n+j}ka_{nj}A_{nj}$$
$$= k[(-1)^{1+j}a_{1j}A_{1j} + (-1)^{2+j}a_{2j}A_{2j} + (-1)^{3+j}a_{3j}A_{3j}$$
$$+ \cdots + (-1)^{n+j}a_{nj}A_{nj}]$$
$$= kD$$

THEOREM 9. *If each element of a row or column of a determinant is expressed as the sum of two numbers, then the determinant can be expressed as the sum of two determinants.*

Proof. Let

$$D''' = \begin{vmatrix} a_{11}a_{12}a_{13} & \cdots & a_{1j} + b_{1j} & \cdots & a_{1n} \\ a_{21}a_{22}a_{23} & \cdots & a_{2j} + b_{2j} & \cdots & a_{2n} \\ a_{31}a_{32}a_{33} & \cdots & a_{3j} + b_{3j} & \cdots & a_{3n} \\ \cdot & \cdot & \cdot & \cdot & \cdot \\ \cdot & \cdot & \cdot & \cdot & \cdot \\ a_{n1}a_{n2}a_{n3} & \cdots & a_{nj} + b_{nj} & \cdots & a_{nn} \end{vmatrix}$$

By steps 1 and 2 of Theorem 4, the expansion of D''' in terms of minors of the jth column is

$$D''' = (-1)^{1+j}(a_{1j} + b_{1j})A_{1j} + (-1)^{2+j}(a_{2j} + b_{2j})A_{2j} +$$
$$(-1)^{3+j}(a_{3j} + b_{3j})A_{3j} + \cdots + (-1)^{n+j}(a_{nj} + b_{nj})A_{nj}$$
$$= [(-1)^{1+j}a_{1j}A_{1j} + (-1)^{2+j}a_{2j}A_{2j} + (-1)^{3+j}a_{3j}A_{3j} +$$
$$\cdots + (-1)^{n+j}a_{nj}A_{nj}] + [(-1)^{1+j}b_{1j}A_{1j} +$$
$$(-1)^{2+j}b_{2j}A_{2j} + (-1)^{3+j}b_{3j}A_{3j} + \cdots + (-1)^{n+j}b_{nj}A_{nj}]$$

$$= \begin{vmatrix} a_{11}a_{12}a_{13} & \cdots & a_{1j} & \cdots & a_{1n} \\ a_{21}a_{22}a_{23} & \cdots & a_{2j} & \cdots & a_{2n} \\ a_{31}a_{32}a_{33} & \cdots & a_{3j} & \cdots & a_{3n} \\ \cdot & \cdot & \cdot & \cdot & \cdot \\ \cdot & \cdot & \cdot & \cdot & \cdot \\ a_{n1}a_{n2}a_{n3} & \cdots & a_{nj} & \cdots & a_{nn} \end{vmatrix} + \begin{vmatrix} a_{11}a_{12}a_{13} & \cdots & b_{1j} & \cdots & a_{1n} \\ a_{21}a_{22}a_{23} & \cdots & b_{2j} & \cdots & a_{2n} \\ a_{31}a_{32}a_{33} & \cdots & b_{3j} & \cdots & a_{3n} \\ \cdot & \cdot & \cdot & \cdot & \cdot \\ \cdot & \cdot & \cdot & \cdot & \cdot \\ a_{n1}a_{n2}a_{n3} & \cdots & b_{nj} & \cdots & a_{nn} \end{vmatrix}$$

THEOREM 10. *If each element of a row or column of a determinant is multiplied by a constant* k *and added to the corresponding element of another row or column, the value of the determinant is not changed.*

Proof. We wish to prove that

$$D = \begin{vmatrix} a_{11}a_{12}a_{13} & \cdots & a_{1p} & \cdots & a_{1j} & \cdots & a_{1n} \\ a_{21}a_{22}a_{23} & \cdots & a_{2p} & \cdots & a_{2j} & \cdots & a_{2n} \\ a_{31}a_{32}a_{33} & \cdots & a_{3p} & \cdots & a_{3j} & \cdots & a_{3n} \\ \cdot & \cdot & \cdot & \cdot & \cdot & \cdot & \cdot \\ \cdot & \cdot & \cdot & \cdot & \cdot & \cdot & \cdot \\ a_{n1}a_{n2}a_{n3} & \cdots & a_{np} & \cdots & a_{nj} & \cdots & a_{nn} \end{vmatrix}$$

$$= \begin{vmatrix} a_{11}a_{12}a_{13} & \cdots & a_{1p} + ka_{1j} & \cdots & a_{1j} & \cdots & a_{1n} \\ a_{21}a_{22}a_{23} & \cdots & a_{2p} + ka_{2j} & \cdots & a_{2j} & \cdots & a_{2n} \\ a_{31}a_{32}a_{33} & \cdots & a_{3p} + ka_{3j} & \cdots & a_{3j} & \cdots & a_{3n} \\ \cdot & \cdot & \cdot & \cdot & \cdot & \cdot & \cdot \\ \cdot & \cdot & \cdot & \cdot & \cdot & \cdot & \cdot \\ a_{n1}a_{n2}a_{n3} & \cdots & a_{np} + ka_{nj} & \cdots & a_{nj} & \cdots & a_{nn} \end{vmatrix}$$

By Theorem 9, the determinant on the right is equal to the sum of the two determinants D and

$$\begin{vmatrix} a_{11}a_{12}a_{13} & \cdots & ka_{1j} & \cdots & a_{1j} & \cdots & a_{1n} \\ a_{21}a_{22}a_{23} & \cdots & ka_{2j} & \cdots & a_{2j} & \cdots & a_{2n} \\ a_{31}a_{32}a_{33} & \cdots & ka_{3j} & \cdots & a_{3j} & \cdots & a_{3n} \\ \cdot \quad \cdot \quad \cdot & \cdots & \cdot & \cdots & \cdot & \cdots & \cdot \\ \cdot \quad \cdot \quad \cdot & \cdots & \cdot & \cdots & \cdot & \cdots & \cdot \\ a_{n1}a_{n2}a_{n3} & \cdots & ka_{nj} & \cdots & a_{nj} & \cdots & a_{nn} \end{vmatrix}$$

By Theorem 8, this determinant is equal to the product of k and a determinant that contains two identical columns. Consequently, by Theorem 7, it is equal to zero.

167. Simplification of a determinant. We can materially decrease the amount of labor involved in expanding a determinant if we make use of the properties that are given in the preceding article. By repeated applications of Theorem 10 to any given determinant it is possible to replace all except one of the elements in any row or column by zeros, and these operations will not change the value of the determinant. We shall illustrate the procedure to be followed by evaluating a determinant and shall use the notation $r_j + kr_i$ to indicate that each element of the ith row has been multiplied by k and added to the corresponding element of the jth row and this sum used as the jth row of the new determinant. A similar notation will be used when referring to columns.

Example

Expand

$$\begin{vmatrix} 3 & 5 & 3 & 4 & -2 \\ 2 & 3 & 1 & -1 & 3 \\ 4 & 2 & -3 & 2 & 5 \\ 2 & 1 & 2 & 0 & -1 \\ 0 & -2 & 1 & 3 & 4 \end{vmatrix}$$

Solution

If we perform the operations indicated by $r_2 - r_4$ and $r_3 - 2r_4$, we get

$$\begin{vmatrix} 3 & 5 & 3 & 4 & -2 \\ 0 & 2 & -1 & -1 & 4 \\ 0 & 0 & -7 & 2 & 7 \\ 2 & 1 & 2 & 0 & -1 \\ 0 & -2 & 1 & 3 & 4 \end{vmatrix}$$

Next, performing $r_1 - 1\frac{1}{2}r_4$, we obtain

$$
\begin{vmatrix}
0 & 3\frac{1}{2} & 0 & 4 & -\frac{1}{2} \\
0 & 2 & -1 & -1 & 4 \\
0 & 0 & -7 & 2 & 7 \\
2 & 1 & 2 & 0 & -1 \\
0 & -2 & 1 & 3 & 4
\end{vmatrix}
= -2
\begin{vmatrix}
3\frac{1}{2} & 0 & 4 & -\frac{1}{2} \\
2 & -1 & -1 & 4 \\
0 & -7 & 2 & 7 \\
-2 & 1 & 3 & 4
\end{vmatrix}
$$

Performing the operations $r_2 + r_4$ and $r_3 + 7r_4$, we have

$$
-2
\begin{vmatrix}
3\frac{1}{2} & 0 & 4 & -\frac{1}{2} \\
0 & 0 & 2 & 8 \\
-14 & 0 & 23 & 35 \\
-2 & 1 & 3 & 4
\end{vmatrix}
= (-2)(1)
\begin{vmatrix}
3\frac{1}{2} & 4 & -\frac{1}{2} \\
0 & 2 & 8 \\
-14 & 23 & 35
\end{vmatrix}
$$

$$
= -2(3\frac{1}{2})
\begin{vmatrix}
2 & 8 \\
23 & 35
\end{vmatrix}
- 2(-14)
\begin{vmatrix}
4 & -\frac{1}{2} \\
2 & 8
\end{vmatrix}
$$

$$
= -7(70 - 184) + 28(32 + 1) = 1722
$$

EXERCISE 83

By use of the properties of determinants, prove, without expanding, that the statements in Problems 1 to 8 are true.

1. $\begin{vmatrix} a & b & c \\ d & e & f \\ 2a & 2b & 2c \end{vmatrix} = 0.$

2. $\begin{vmatrix} a & b & c \\ d & e & f \\ g & h & i \end{vmatrix} = - \begin{vmatrix} a & c & b \\ d & f & e \\ g & i & h \end{vmatrix}.$

3. $\begin{vmatrix} 1 & 2 & 1 \\ 2 & 5 & 2 \\ 3 & 7 & 3 \end{vmatrix} = 0.$

4. $\begin{vmatrix} a & c+d & c \\ b & e+f & e \\ c & g+a & g \end{vmatrix} = \begin{vmatrix} a & d & c \\ b & f & e \\ c & a & g \end{vmatrix}.$

5. $\begin{vmatrix} -3 & 2 & 6 \\ 4 & 0 & 4 \\ 5 & 1 & 10 \end{vmatrix} = 2 \begin{vmatrix} -3 & 2 & 3 \\ 4 & 0 & 2 \\ 5 & 1 & 5 \end{vmatrix}.$

6. $\begin{vmatrix} 1 & 0 & 3 \\ -2 & 1 & 2 \\ 3 & -2 & 4 \end{vmatrix} = \begin{vmatrix} 1 & 0 & 3 \\ -1 & 1 & 2 \\ 1 & -2 & 4 \end{vmatrix}.$

7. $\begin{vmatrix} a_1 & b_1 & c_1x + d_1 \\ a_2 & b_2 & c_2x + d_2 \\ a_3 & b_3 & c_3x + d_3 \end{vmatrix} = x \begin{vmatrix} a_1 & b_1 & c_1 \\ a_2 & b_2 & c_2 \\ a_3 & b_3 & c_3 \end{vmatrix} + \begin{vmatrix} a_1 & b_1 & d_1 \\ a_2 & b_2 & d_2 \\ a_3 & b_3 & d_3 \end{vmatrix}.$

8. $\begin{vmatrix} a_1 & b_1 + k_1a_1 & c_1 - 3k_2a_1 \\ a_2 & b_2 + k_1a_2 & c_2 - 3k_2a_2 \\ a_3 & b_3 + k_1a_3 & c_3 - 3k_2a_3 \end{vmatrix} = \begin{vmatrix} a_1 & b_1 & c_1 \\ a_2 & b_2 & c_2 \\ a_3 & b_3 & c_3 \end{vmatrix}.$

Expand the determinants in Problems 9 to 28 by the method of Art. 167.

9. $\begin{vmatrix} 2 & 1 & 5 & 2 \\ 3 & 0 & -1 & 4 \\ 2 & 1 & 5 & 3 \\ 1 & 2 & 2 & 1 \end{vmatrix}.$

10. $\begin{vmatrix} 3 & 2 & 1 & 2 \\ 1 & 3 & 1 & -3 \\ 1 & 2 & 2 & -2 \\ 2 & 1 & 1 & -1 \end{vmatrix}.$

11.
$$\begin{vmatrix} 1 & -3 & 4 & 2 \\ 2 & 1 & 3 & 2 \\ 1 & 1 & 2 & -1 \\ -2 & 1 & 3 & 2 \end{vmatrix}.$$

12.
$$\begin{vmatrix} 4 & 2 & 3 & 4 \\ 1 & 2 & 4 & 3 \\ 2 & 1 & 5 & 2 \\ 6 & 1 & 2 & 6 \end{vmatrix}.$$

13.
$$\begin{vmatrix} 3 & 2 & 1 & 1 \\ 2 & 4 & 1 & 6 \\ 1 & 3 & 4 & 1 \\ 1 & 2 & 1 & 3 \end{vmatrix}.$$

14.
$$\begin{vmatrix} 2 & 1 & 3 & 4 \\ -3 & 2 & 1 & -6 \\ 4 & 1 & -2 & 1 \\ 1 & -3 & 1 & 2 \end{vmatrix}.$$

15.
$$\begin{vmatrix} 1 & 2 & 5 & 3 \\ 3 & -1 & -2 & 4 \\ 3 & 6 & 1 & 9 \\ 5 & 1 & 2 & 1 \end{vmatrix}.$$

16.
$$\begin{vmatrix} 3 & 6 & 9 & 1 \\ -6 & 9 & -1 & -1 \\ 1 & 2 & 3 & 1 \\ 2 & 1 & 4 & 2 \end{vmatrix}.$$

17.
$$\begin{vmatrix} 3 & 2 & -1 & 4 \\ 7 & 1 & 3 & 2 \\ 2 & 0 & 2 & -3 \\ 5 & 3 & 1 & 5 \end{vmatrix}.$$

18.
$$\begin{vmatrix} 4 & 3 & 2 & 1 \\ 2 & -1 & 0 & 3 \\ -2 & -2 & -1 & 1 \\ 1 & 0 & 1 & -3 \end{vmatrix}.$$

19.
$$\begin{vmatrix} 1 & 6 & 2 & 2 \\ 2 & -1 & -7 & 3 \\ 3 & -5 & -9 & 3 \\ 4 & 3 & -1 & 2 \end{vmatrix}.$$

20.
$$\begin{vmatrix} 3 & 1 & 4 & 1 \\ 1 & 5 & 2 & 6 \\ 2 & 1 & -1 & 2 \\ -1 & 2 & 1 & 2 \end{vmatrix}.$$

21.
$$\begin{vmatrix} 1 & 2 & 2 & 4 & 2 \\ 3 & 3 & 6 & 6 & 3 \\ 2 & 1 & 4 & 2 & 1 \\ 1 & 4 & 2 & 8 & 2 \\ 4 & 1 & 1 & 3 & 1 \end{vmatrix}.$$

22.
$$\begin{vmatrix} 2 & 4 & 5 & 3 & 2 \\ 1 & 3 & 2 & 4 & 1 \\ 1 & 1 & 1 & 3 & 1 \\ 2 & 6 & 4 & 8 & 1 \\ 2 & 2 & 2 & 1 & 1 \end{vmatrix}.$$

23.
$$\begin{vmatrix} 2 & 1 & 3 & -2 & -4 \\ 5 & 1 & 3 & 2 & 3 \\ 4 & 2 & 6 & -4 & 5 \\ 3 & 4 & 4 & 1 & 2 \\ 1 & -3 & -9 & -1 & -2 \end{vmatrix}.$$

24.
$$\begin{vmatrix} 2 & 1 & -3 & -2 & 3 \\ 1 & 0 & 3 & 4 & 2 \\ -1 & 2 & -4 & 2 & 1 \\ 4 & 2 & -6 & -4 & 3 \\ 1 & 1 & -2 & 1 & 5 \end{vmatrix}.$$

25.
$$\begin{vmatrix} 1 & 2 & 1 & 3 & 2 & 1 \\ 0 & 1 & 0 & 0 & 0 & 0 \\ 0 & 1 & 3 & 2 & 1 & 2 \\ 0 & 2 & 1 & 0 & 0 & 0 \\ 0 & 3 & 2 & 0 & 2 & 0 \\ 0 & 2 & 1 & 0 & 1 & 1 \end{vmatrix}.$$

26.
$$\begin{vmatrix} 3 & 0 & 1 & 4 & 1 & 3 \\ 1 & 2 & 0 & 0 & 0 & 1 \\ 1 & 1 & 0 & 0 & 0 & 0 \\ 0 & 2 & 3 & 0 & 0 & 2 \\ 0 & 4 & 2 & 0 & 0 & 0 \\ 1 & 0 & 0 & 2 & 1 & 0 \end{vmatrix}.$$

27.
$$\begin{vmatrix} 1 & 0 & 2 & 0 & 3 & 0 \\ 0 & 1 & 0 & 3 & 0 & 2 \\ 2 & 0 & 1 & 0 & 1 & 0 \\ 0 & 1 & 0 & 2 & 0 & 3 \\ 3 & 0 & 1 & 0 & 2 & 0 \\ 0 & 1 & 0 & 2 & 0 & 1 \end{vmatrix}.$$

28.
$$\begin{vmatrix} 1 & 2 & 3 & 1 & 2 & 3 \\ 1 & 2 & 3 & 1 & 2 & 2 \\ 3 & 1 & 2 & 3 & 3 & 4 \\ 3 & 1 & 2 & 2 & 2 & 3 \\ 0 & 1 & 0 & 3 & 3 & 1 \\ 2 & 1 & 0 & 1 & 1 & 4 \end{vmatrix}.$$

Without expanding the determinants, show that the statements in Problems 29 and 30 are true.

29. If $ax + by = 0$, then $\begin{vmatrix} a & b \\ -y & x \end{vmatrix} = 0$. HINT: First show that the determinant is equal to $\dfrac{1}{xy} \begin{vmatrix} ax & by \\ -xy & xy \end{vmatrix}$ and then use Theorem 10.

30. If $ax + by + cz = 0$, then $\begin{vmatrix} a & b & c \\ -y/x & 2 & -y/z \\ -z/x & z/y & 0 \end{vmatrix} = 0$.

Without expanding the determinant, show that the determinant in each of Problems 31 to 36 is equal to zero for the indicated values of x. HINT: Substitute each indicated value of x in the determinant, and then reduce it to an equal determinant in which two rows or two columns are identical or in which each element of a row or column is the same multiple of the corresponding element in another row or column.

31. $\begin{vmatrix} x & 1 & 3 \\ 2 & x & 2 \\ 1 & 2 & 1 \end{vmatrix} \; x = 3, \, x = 4.$
    32. $\begin{vmatrix} 4 & 2 & x \\ 2 & 1 & 1 \\ 2 & x & 1 \end{vmatrix} \; x = 2, \, x = 1.$

33. $\begin{vmatrix} x-2 & 1 & 1 \\ 2 & 2 & 2 \\ 3 & 3 & x+1 \end{vmatrix} \; x = 3, \, x = 2.$

34. $\begin{vmatrix} x & 1 & x-3 \\ x-2 & x-2 & 0 \\ 3-x & 3-x & x-3 \end{vmatrix} \; x = 1, \, x = 2, \, x = 3.$

35. $\begin{vmatrix} x-1 & 2 & 0 \\ -1 & x-2 & 2 \\ 1 & 1 & x-3 \end{vmatrix} \; x = 1, \, x = 2, \, x = 3.$

36. $\begin{vmatrix} -1 & 2x & x \\ 1 & x & -1 \\ -x-2 & x+2 & x+2 \end{vmatrix} \; x = 1, \, x = -1, \, x = -2.$

168. Systems of linear equations. In this article we shall show how to solve a system of four linear equations in four unknowns by means of determinants. However, our method is general and can be applied with little change to a system of n linear equations in n unknowns. Any system of four linear equations in four unknowns can be written in the form

$$(1) \quad \begin{aligned} a_1x + b_1y + c_1z + d_1w &= e_1 \\ a_2x + b_2y + c_2z + d_2w &= e_2 \\ a_3x + b_3y + c_3z + d_3w &= e_3 \\ a_4x + b_4y + c_4z + d_4w &= e_4 \end{aligned}$$

in which a_i, b_i, c_i, d_i, and e_i are constants.

THEOREM. *If the determinant **D** of the coefficients is different from zero in any system of four linear equations in four unknowns, the system has a unique solution. Furthermore, the value of each unknown can be expressed as a quotient in which the divisor is **D** and the dividend is the determinant obtained from **D** by replacing the coefficients of the desired unknown by the constant terms of the equations.*

Proof. Since multiplying each element of a row or column of

$$D = \begin{vmatrix} a_1 & b_1 & c_1 & d_1 \\ a_2 & b_2 & c_2 & d_2 \\ a_3 & b_3 & c_3 & d_3 \\ a_4 & b_4 & c_4 & d_4 \end{vmatrix}$$

by a quantity multiplies the value of D by that quantity, we have

$$Dx = \begin{vmatrix} a_1x & b_1 & c_1 & d_1 \\ a_2x & b_2 & c_2 & d_2 \\ a_3x & b_3 & c_3 & d_3 \\ a_4x & b_4 & c_4 & d_4 \end{vmatrix}$$

Furthermore, multiplying the elements of column 2 by y, the elements of column 3 by z, and those of column 4 by w and adding the sums of these products to the corresponding elements of the first column, we obtain

$$Dx = \begin{vmatrix} a_1x + b_1y + c_1z + d_1w & b_1 & c_1 & d_1 \\ a_2x + b_2y + c_2z + d_2w & b_2 & c_2 & d_2 \\ a_3x + b_3y + c_3z + d_3w & b_3 & c_3 & d_3 \\ a_4x + b_4y + c_4z + d_4w & b_4 & c_4 & d_4 \end{vmatrix}$$

$$= \begin{vmatrix} e_1 & b_1 & c_1 & d_1 \\ e_2 & b_2 & c_2 & d_2 \\ e_3 & b_3 & c_3 & d_3 \\ e_4 & b_4 & c_4 & d_4 \end{vmatrix} = N_x$$

since the elements of the first column of the next to the last determinant are the left members of (1) and, therefore, are equal to the constant terms. Hence, if $D \neq 0$, we have

$$x = \frac{N_x}{D}$$

The value of y, of z, and of w can be obtained in a similar manner.

Therefore, we may obtain a unique set of values for the unknowns in (1).

We shall now show that this set of values satisfies the given system of equations. If we transpose the left member of the first equation of the system and replace x, y, z, and w by N_x/D, N_y/D, N_z/D, and N_w/D, respectively, and then multiply through by D, we get

$$e_1 D - a_1 N_x - b_1 N_y - c_1 N_z - d_1 N_w$$

We can readily see that this expression is equal to

$$\begin{vmatrix} e_1 & a_1 & b_1 & c_1 & d_1 \\ e_1 & a_1 & b_1 & c_1 & d_1 \\ e_2 & a_2 & b_2 & c_2 & d_2 \\ e_3 & a_3 & b_3 & c_3 & d_3 \\ e_4 & a_4 & b_4 & c_4 & d_4 \end{vmatrix} = D'$$

if we expand D' in terms of the elements of the first row. The reader should notice that the first and second columns of N_y are interchanged in the expansion by minors; hence, $-b_1 N_y$ appears above instead of $b_1 N_y$. The negative sign preceding $d_1 N_w$ can be accounted for in a similar manner. Furthermore, $D' = 0$ since it contains two identical rows. Therefore, the unique set of values for the unknowns satisfies the first equation of the system. We can show in a similar manner that they also satisfy the other three equations of the system.

Example

Solve the system

$$\begin{aligned} x + y + z + w &= 2 \\ 2x - y + 2z - w &= -5 \\ 3x + 2y + 3z + 4w &= 7 \\ x - 2y - 3z + 2w &= 5 \end{aligned}$$

by means of determinants.

Solution

The determinant of the coefficients is

$$D = \begin{vmatrix} 1 & 1 & 1 & 1 \\ 2 & -1 & 2 & -1 \\ 3 & 2 & 3 & 4 \\ 1 & -2 & -3 & 2 \end{vmatrix} = \begin{vmatrix} 1 & 1 & 1 & 1 \\ 3 & 0 & 3 & 0 \\ 3 & 2 & 3 & 4 \\ 1 & -2 & -3 & 2 \end{vmatrix}$$

if we perform $r_2 + r_1$.

Performing the operation $c_3 - c_1$, we get

$$D = \begin{vmatrix} 1 & 1 & 0 & 1 \\ 3 & 0 & 0 & 0 \\ 3 & 2 & 0 & 4 \\ 1 & -2 & -4 & 2 \end{vmatrix}$$

$$= -3 \begin{vmatrix} 1 & 0 & 1 \\ 2 & 0 & 4 \\ -2 & -4 & 2 \end{vmatrix}$$

if we expand in terms of the elements of the second row. Therefore, expanding in terms of the elements of the second column, we obtain

$$D = -(-4)(-3) \begin{vmatrix} 1 & 1 \\ 2 & 4 \end{vmatrix}$$

$$= -24$$

If we compute the value of

$$N_x = \begin{vmatrix} 2 & 1 & 1 & 1 \\ -5 & -1 & 2 & -1 \\ 7 & 2 & 3 & 4 \\ 5 & -2 & -3 & 2 \end{vmatrix}$$

we obtain $N_x = 0$. Hence,

$$x = \frac{N_x}{D} = \frac{0}{-24} = 0$$

If we substitute this value of x into any three of the given equations, we obtain a system of three linear equations in the three unknowns y, z, and w. If this system is solved by either of the methods given in Chap. 6, the solution $y = 1$, $z = -1$, and $w = 2$ will be obtained.

As we have stated previously, the method we have used in solving this system of equations is general and can be applied with little change to a system of n linear equations in n unknowns.

EXERCISE 84

Solve the systems of equations in Problems 1 to 24 by use of determinants.

1. $3x - y = 5$
   $2x + 3y = 7.$

2. $x - y = 2$
   $5x + y = 4.$

3. $x + y = 1$
   $2x + 3y = 0.$

4. $2x - y = 0$
   $5x - 2y = 1.$

5. $2x + y - z = 1$
   $3x - y + z = 4$
   $2x + 3y + z = 3.$

6. $x + y + z = 1$
   $-x - y + z = -5$
   $x - y - z = 3.$

7. $2x + y - 2z = 1$
   $x - y - 3z = -2$
   $4x + 2y + z = -3.$

8. $3x + y + 2z = 3$
   $6x - 3y + 4z = 1$
   $9x + 4y - 6z = 4.$

9. $\quad 2x + y \qquad = 2$
$\qquad\quad y + 3z = 2$
$\quad 2x \qquad + 6z = 3.$

11. $\quad x + 4y \qquad = -13$
$\qquad\quad 3y + 2z = -2$
$\quad 7x \qquad - 4z = 1.$

13. $x + y + z + w = 1$
$x - y + z - w = 1$
$x - y - z + w = -1$
$x - y + z + w = -1.$

15. $2x + y + z \qquad = 2$
$\qquad y + z + w = 2$
$x + y - z \qquad = 0$
$x \qquad + 2z - w = 1.$

17. $\quad x + y + z + 2w = -3$
$\quad x + 2y + z + 3w = -2$
$\quad x - 2y + z - 5w = 2$
$\quad 2x - y + 3z - 4w = -2.$

19. $5x - y + 2z - 3w = 3$
$\quad 2x - y + 2z - 3w = 0$
$\quad 5x - y - 4z - 3w = -9$
$\quad 5x + 3y - 4z - 3w = -21.$

21. $x + y + z = 2a$
$x - y \qquad = -a$
$x \qquad + z = 0.$

23. $x + y + z + w = 2c$
$x - y + z + w = 0$
$x \qquad - z + w = -c$
$x \qquad - w = 2a.$

25. Solve for x:
$\quad x + y + z + v + w = 0$
$\quad x + y \qquad + v \qquad = 1$
$\quad x \qquad + z \qquad + w = 0$
$\quad x - y - z \qquad = 0$
$\qquad y + z - v \qquad = 0.$

27. Solve for z:
$\quad 2x + y + 3z - 3v + w = -3$
$\quad 3x + y - z - 3v + w = 6$
$\quad x + 2y - 3z - 6v + 2w = 9$
$\quad 4x + 3y + 2z - 9v + 2w = 2$
$\quad x + y - z + 2v + w = 4.$

10. $3x + y \qquad = -2$
$\quad 2x \qquad + z = -1$
$\qquad y + 3z = 1.$

12. $2x - 4y \qquad = 1$
$\qquad 4y + 3z = 1$
$\qquad 40y - 24z = 1.$

14. $\quad x + y + z - w = -1$
$\quad 2x + y + z - w = 1$
$\quad x + 2y + z - w = 0$
$\quad 3x + y + z - 2w = 0.$

16. $2x + y + z \qquad = 1$
$\qquad 3y + z + w = 1$
$4x \qquad + z \qquad = 1$
$\qquad 6y \qquad + 3w = 2.$

18. $3x - 2y + z - 3w = 16$
$\quad 2x - 2y + z - 3w = 11$
$\quad 5x - 2y + z - 4w = 32$
$\quad 3x + y - z + 2w = 13.$

20. $2x + y - 3z + w = -3$
$\quad 4x + y - 6z + 2w = -7$
$\quad 6x + y + z + 3w = 9$
$\quad 6x + 2y - 6z + 2w = -5.$

22. $bx - ay + z = a$
$\quad x + by - z = b^2$
$\quad x + y - z = b.$

24. $x + y + z - w = 3a$
$\quad x - y \qquad = 2a$
$\quad x + y - 2z \qquad = -2c$
$\quad x + y - 2z + 2w = 0.$

26. Solve for y:
$\quad x \qquad + 2v + w = 3$
$\quad 2x + y \qquad + 4v + 2w = 8$
$\quad x \qquad + 2v + 3w = 3$
$\quad x + 2y \qquad + 3v + w = 8$
$\quad x + 2y + 2z + v + w = 6.$

28. Solve for z:
$\quad 2x \qquad + v \qquad = 1$
$\quad x + 2y \qquad = 2$
$\qquad y \qquad + 2v \qquad = 3$
$\qquad z \qquad + 2w = 6$
$\quad x - y - 2z + v - 2w = -6.$

169. *Linear systems containing more equations than unknowns.*
A system of linear equations in which the number of equations

exceeds the number of unknowns, in general, cannot be solved. However, under certain conditions, a solution exists. In this article we shall investigate the conditions under which a solution exists for a system of $n + 1$ equations in n unknowns. We shall discuss a system of four linear equations in three unknowns, but we shall use a general argument that can be applied to any linear system where the number of equations exceeds the number of unknowns by one.

We shall consider the system

(1)
$$\begin{aligned}
a_1x + b_1y + c_1z &= e_1 \\
a_2x + b_2y + c_2z &= e_2 \\
a_3x + b_3y + c_3z &= e_3 \\
a_4x + b_4y + c_4z &= e_4
\end{aligned}$$

and shall first define the *augmented determinant* of such a system.

DEFINITION. *The **augmented determinant** of a system of $n + 1$ linear equations in n unknowns is the determinant of order $n + 1$ in which the first n columns consist of the coefficients of the unknowns and the $(n + 1)$st column consists of the constant terms.*

In the system (1), the augmented determinant is

$$\bar{D} = \begin{vmatrix}
a_1 & b_1 & c_1 & e_1 \\
a_2 & b_2 & c_2 & e_2 \\
a_3 & b_3 & c_3 & e_3 \\
a_4 & b_4 & c_4 & e_4
\end{vmatrix}$$

We shall assume that at least one system consisting of three equations of (1) has a solution and that the equations have been arranged so that this system is the first three equations. This assumption implies that the determinant of the coefficients of this system is not zero.

If a solution of (1) exists, then obviously the solution of the first three equations must satisfy the fourth. If we solve the first three equations by the methods of Art. 168, we obtain

(2)
$$x = \frac{N_x}{D} \qquad y = \frac{N_y}{D} \qquad z = \frac{N_z}{D}$$

where

$$D = \begin{vmatrix} a_1 & b_1 & c_1 \\ a_2 & b_2 & c_2 \\ a_3 & b_3 & c_3 \end{vmatrix} \qquad N_x = \begin{vmatrix} e_1 & b_1 & c_1 \\ e_2 & b_2 & c_2 \\ e_3 & b_3 & c_3 \end{vmatrix}$$

$$N_y = \begin{vmatrix} a_1 & e_1 & c_1 \\ a_2 & e_2 & c_2 \\ a_3 & e_3 & c_3 \end{vmatrix} \qquad N_z = \begin{vmatrix} a_1 & b_1 & e_1 \\ a_2 & b_2 & e_2 \\ a_3 & b_3 & e_3 \end{vmatrix}$$

If the solution (2) satisfies the fourth equation in (1), then we have

$$a_4 \frac{N_x}{D} + b_4 \frac{N_y}{D} + c_4 \frac{N_z}{D} = e_4$$

If we clear the above equation of fractions and transpose $e_4 D$, we get

(3) $$a_4 N_x + b_4 N_y + c_4 N_z - e_4 D = 0$$

Now, if we interchange the first and second columns of N_x and then interchange the second and third columns of the determinant thus obtained, we get the minor A_4 of a_4 in $\bar{D}$. Since the above interchange involves two successive interchanges of adjacent columns, the sign of the determinant is not changed. Similarly, $N_y = -B_4$ in $\bar{D}$, $N_z = C_4$, and $D = E_4$. Hence, if we substitute these values in (3), we have

(4) $$a_4 A_4 - b_4 B_4 + c_4 C_4 - e_4 E_4 = 0$$

Next we notice that the left member of (4) is the expansion of $\bar{D}$ in terms of the elements and minors of the fourth row. Hence, we have the following theorem.

THEOREM.[1] *A system of $n + 1$ linear equations in n unknowns has a unique solution if and only if the augmented determinant is equal to zero and at least one of the minors of the elements in the last column is not zero.*

Example

In the system

$$2x + 3y = 1$$
$$x + 2y = 3$$
$$x + y = -2$$

---

[1] The case in which all first minors of the augmented determinant are zero is beyond the scope of this book. For a more complete discussion, see any text on the theory of equations.

$$\bar{D} = \begin{vmatrix} 2 & 3 & 1 \\ 1 & 2 & 3 \\ 1 & 1 & -2 \end{vmatrix} = -8 + 9 + 1 - 2 - 6 + 6 = 0,$$ and the second ordered

minor in the upper left corner $\begin{vmatrix} 2 & 3 \\ 1 & 2 \end{vmatrix} = 4 - 3 = 1.$ Hence the system has a

unique solution. Furthermore, this solution is

$$x = \frac{\begin{vmatrix} 1 & 3 \\ 3 & 2 \end{vmatrix}}{\begin{vmatrix} 2 & 3 \\ 1 & 2 \end{vmatrix}} = \frac{2 - 9}{4 - 3} = -7 \qquad y = \frac{\begin{vmatrix} 2 & 1 \\ 1 & 3 \end{vmatrix}}{\begin{vmatrix} 2 & 3 \\ 1 & 2 \end{vmatrix}} = \frac{6 - 1}{1} = 5$$

170. Systems of homogeneous linear equations. An equation is homogeneous if all of its terms are of the same degree in the unknown. Hence, a linear homogeneous equation involves no constant term.

The system of four linear equations in four unknowns

$$(1) \qquad \begin{aligned} a_1x + b_1y + c_1z + d_1w &= 0 \\ a_2x + b_2y + c_2z + d_2w &= 0 \\ a_3x + b_3y + c_3z + d_3w &= 0 \\ a_4x + b_4y + c_4z + d_4w &= 0 \end{aligned}$$

is obviously satisfied by the trivial solution $x = 0$, $y = 0$, $z = 0$, $w = 0$. However, under certain conditions, the system may have solutions other than the trivial one.

If we divide each of the above equations by w we have

$$(2) \qquad \begin{aligned} a_1 \frac{x}{w} + b_1 \frac{y}{w} + c_1 \frac{z}{w} + d_1 &= 0 \\[4pt] a_2 \frac{x}{w} + b_2 \frac{y}{w} + c_2 \frac{z}{w} + d_2 &= 0 \\[4pt] a_3 \frac{x}{w} + b_3 \frac{y}{w} + c_3 \frac{z}{w} + d_3 &= 0 \\[4pt] a_4 \frac{x}{w} + b_4 \frac{y}{w} + c_4 \frac{z}{w} + d_4 &= 0 \end{aligned}$$

We now have a system of four linear equations in the three ratios x/w, y/w, and z/w. By the theorem in the previous article, a solution exists if the determinant

$$(3) \qquad \begin{vmatrix} a_1 & b_1 & c_1 & d_1 \\ a_2 & b_2 & c_2 & d_2 \\ a_3 & b_3 & c_3 & d_3 \\ a_4 & b_4 & c_4 & d_4 \end{vmatrix} = 0$$

and the minor

$$D_4 = \begin{vmatrix} a_1 & b_1 & c_1 \\ a_2 & b_2 & c_2 \\ a_3 & b_3 & c_3 \end{vmatrix} \neq 0$$

The above argument is general and can be extended to apply to any system of equations where the number of equations is equal to the number of unknowns. We have assumed that there is one first minor of the determinant of the coefficients different from zero and that the equations have been arranged so that this minor is in the upper left corner of the determinant. Hence we have the following theorem.

THEOREM.[1] *A system of n linear homogeneous equations in n unknowns has a solution in which the values of the unknowns are not all zero if the determinant of the coefficients is zero and there is a first minor of this determinant that is not zero.*

We shall present a method for obtaining a solution of a system of homogeneous equations that satisfy the conditions of the theorem, and we shall assume that the equations have been so arranged that a first minor that is not zero is in the upper left corner of the determinant. If we solve the first three equations in (1) for x/w, y/w, and z/w, we obtain

$$\frac{x}{w} = \frac{\begin{vmatrix} -d_1 & b_1 & c_1 \\ -d_2 & b_2 & c_2 \\ -d_3 & b_3 & c_3 \end{vmatrix}}{\begin{vmatrix} a_1 & b_1 & c_1 \\ a_2 & b_2 & c_2 \\ a_3 & b_3 & c_3 \end{vmatrix}} = - \frac{\begin{vmatrix} b_1 & c_1 & d_1 \\ b_2 & c_2 & d_2 \\ b_3 & c_3 & d_3 \end{vmatrix}}{\begin{vmatrix} a_1 & b_1 & c_1 \\ a_2 & b_2 & c_2 \\ a_3 & b_3 & c_3 \end{vmatrix}} = - \frac{A_4}{D_4}$$

where A_4 is the minor of a_4 in (3). Similarly, $y/w = B_4/D_4$ and $z/w = -C_4/D_4$. Hence

$$x = -\frac{A_4}{D_4} w \qquad y = \frac{B_4}{D_4} w \qquad \text{and} \qquad z = -\frac{C_4}{D_4} w$$

where w can have any value other than zero. Hence, the number of solutions is unlimited. The trivial solution is obtained when $w = 0$. If we let $w = -D_4$ we obtain

(4) $x = A_4 \qquad y = -B_4 \qquad z = C_4 \qquad w = -D_4$

[1] The case in which all the first minors of the determinant of the coefficients are zero is beyond the scope of this book. A complete discussion of this case can be found in any text in the theory of equations.

Example

In the system of equations

$$x + y + z + 6w = 0$$
$$2x - 3y - z + w = 0$$
$$x + 2y + z + 7w = 0$$
$$x - y + z + 4w = 0$$

the determinant of the coefficients is

$$\begin{vmatrix} 1 & 1 & 1 & 6 \\ 2 & -3 & -1 & 1 \\ 1 & 2 & 1 & 7 \\ 1 & -1 & 1 & 4 \end{vmatrix} = \begin{vmatrix} 0 & 1 & 1 & 6 \\ 3 & -3 & -1 & 1 \\ 0 & 2 & 1 & 7 \\ 0 & -1 & 1 & 4 \end{vmatrix} \quad \text{(performing } C_1 - C_3)$$

$$= -3 \begin{vmatrix} 1 & 1 & 6 \\ 2 & 1 & 7 \\ -1 & 1 & 4 \end{vmatrix} = -3(4 - 7 + 12 + 6 - 7 - 8) = 0$$

and

$$D_4 = \begin{vmatrix} 1 & 1 & 1 \\ 2 & -3 & -1 \\ 1 & 2 & 1 \end{vmatrix} = -3 - 1 + 4 + 3 + 2 - 2 = 3$$

Hence the system of equations has nontrivial solutions, and, by (4), one of these solutions is

$$x = A_4 = \begin{vmatrix} 1 & 1 & 6 \\ -3 & -1 & 1 \\ 2 & 1 & 7 \end{vmatrix} = -7 + 2 - 18 + 12 - 1 + 21 = 9$$

$$y = -B_4 = - \begin{vmatrix} 1 & 1 & 6 \\ 2 & -1 & 1 \\ 1 & 1 & 7 \end{vmatrix} = -(-7 + 1 + 12 + 6 - 1 - 14) = 3$$

$$z = C_4 = \begin{vmatrix} 1 & 1 & 6 \\ 2 & -3 & 1 \\ 1 & 2 & 7 \end{vmatrix} = -21 + 1 + 24 + 18 - 2 - 14 = 6$$

$$w = -D_4 = -3$$

EXERCISE 85

Test the system of equations in each of Problems 1 to 8 for the existence of a solution. If a solution exists, find it.

1. $2x - y = 3$
$x + 2y = 1$
$5x - 5y = 8.$

2. $x - 2y = 5$
$3x + y = 1$
$2x + 3y = -4$

3. $2x + 5y = 4$
$3x + 4y = -1$
$x - 3y = -9.$

4. $2x + 6y = 8$
$x + y = 1$
$5x + y = -1.$

5.
$$x + y + 3z = 2$$
$$2x + 4y + 5z = 0$$
$$x - y - 2z = 0$$
$$x + y - z = -2.$$

6.
$$2x + y + z = 5$$
$$5x - y + 2z = 0$$
$$3x + y + z = 4$$
$$x + y + z = 6.$$

7.
$$x + y + z = 1$$
$$3x + 2y + z = 3$$
$$x - 2y - 5z = 2$$
$$2x + y - z = 1.$$

8.
$$2x + y - z = -4$$
$$x + 2y + z = 1$$
$$3x + 4y - 2z = -4$$
$$x - 2y + z = -3.$$

Test the system of equations in each of the following problems for the existence of nontrivial solutions. If nontrivial solutions exist, find one of them.

9.
$$3x + y - 3z = 0$$
$$x + y + z = 0$$
$$2x + y - z = 0.$$

10.
$$2x - y + z = 0$$
$$4x - y + 4z = 0$$
$$2x + y + 5z = 0.$$

11.
$$x + 2y + z = 0$$
$$3x - y - z = 0$$
$$2x + 3y - 4z = 0.$$

12.
$$2x + y + z = 0$$
$$3x + 4y + z = 0$$
$$x - 7y + 2z = 0.$$

13.
$$2x + y + z - w = 0$$
$$x + y + 3z - w = 0$$
$$x + 2y + 4z - w = 0$$
$$3x + y - z - w = 0.$$

14.
$$x + y + z - 2w = 0$$
$$2x + y + z - 3w = 0$$
$$x - y + z + 4w = 0$$
$$2x - y - z - w = 0.$$

15.
$$x + y + z - 3w = 0$$
$$3x + y - z + 5w = 0$$
$$2x + y - z + 4w = 0$$
$$x + y - z + 3w = 0.$$

16.
$$x + y + 3z - w = 0$$
$$x + 2y + 4z - w = 0$$
$$x + 3y + 4z - 2w = 0$$
$$x - 3y - z - w = 0.$$

CHAPTER 22

PARTIAL FRACTIONS

171. *Introduction.* Heretofore, in our work with fractions, we have been concerned with the matter of combining two or more by means of the four fundamental operations of algebra. At times, especially in calculus, it is necessary to express a fraction as the sum of two or more others that are simpler in form than the original. The fractions thus obtained are called *partial fractions*. In this chapter, we shall consider the problem of expressing a given fraction as the sum of partial fractions.

A rational fraction is the quotient of two polynomials. We shall deal exclusively with rational fractions in this chapter and shall develop methods that apply only to *proper fractions*, that is, those in which the numerator is of lower degree than the denominator.

By the corollary of Art. 106, we may express any polynomial as the product of integral powers of linear and irreducible quadratic factors. Consequently, every rational fraction belongs to one of the following four cases:

Case I. All factors of the denominator are linear and none of them are repeated.

Case II. All factors of the denominator are linear, but some are repeated.

Case III. The denominator contains irreducible quadratic factors none of which are repeated.

Case IV. The denominator contains irreducible quadratic factors some of which are repeated.

We shall employ the following theorem in the next four articles. The proof is omitted since it is beyond the scope of this book:

THEOREM 1. *If a proper rational fraction in lowest terms is expressed as the sum of partial fractions, then*

I. *To every factor $ax + b$ of the denominator that appears without repetition, there corresponds a partial fraction $A/(ax + b)$ where A is a constant.*

II. *To every factor $(ax + b)^k$ of the denominator, there correspond the fractions*

$$\frac{A_1}{ax + b} + \frac{A_2}{(ax + b)^2} + \cdots + \frac{A_k}{(ax + b)^k}$$

where $A_1, A_2, \ldots, A_k$ are constants.

III. *To every irreducible quadratic factor $ax^2 + bx + c$ of the denominator that appears without repetition, there corresponds the partial fraction $(Ax + B)/(ax^2 + bx + c)$, where A and B are constants.*

IV. *If $ax^2 + bx + c$ is irreducible, then to every factor $(ax^2 + bx + c)^k$ of the denominator, there correspond the partial fractions*

$$\frac{A_1x + B_1}{ax^2 + bx + c} + \frac{A_2x + B_2}{(ax^2 + bx + c)^2} + \cdots + \frac{A_kx + B_k}{(ax^2 + bx + c)^k}$$

where $A_1, A_2, \ldots, A_k, B_1, B_2, \ldots, B_k$ are constants.

172. Case I. Distinct linear factors. We shall illustrate the method to be applied in this case by the example that follows.

Example

Separate

(1)
$$\frac{2x^2 + x + 1}{(x + 2)(3x + 1)(x + 3)}$$

into partial fractions

Solution, Method 1

Each factor of the denominator of (1) is linear and appears only once. Hence, by (I) of Theorem 1, the partial fractions are

$$\frac{A}{x + 2} \qquad \frac{B}{3x + 1} \quad \text{and} \quad \frac{C}{x + 3}$$

Thus, we have

(2)
$$\frac{2x^2 + x + 1}{(x + 2)(3x + 1)(x + 3)} = \frac{A}{x + 2} + \frac{B}{3x + 1} + \frac{C}{x + 3}$$

in which A, B, and C are to be determined so that (2) holds for every value of x except possibly for those values that cause one of the denominators to vanish. After (2) is cleared of fractions, we have

(3) $\quad 2x^2 + x + 1 = A(3x + 1)(x + 3) + B(x + 2)(x + 3) + C(x + 2)(3x + 1)$

Performing the indicated multiplication and collecting the terms in (3), we have

(4) $\quad 2x^2 + x + 1 = x^2(3A + B + 3C) + x(10A + 5B + 7C) + (3A + 6B + 2C)$

If A, B, and C are determined so that

(5)
$$3A + B + 3C = 2$$
$$10A + 5B + 7C = 1$$
$$3A + 6B + 2C = 1$$

then the two members of (3) are identical, and, therefore, the equation is satisfied for every value of x. Consequently, for the values of A, B, and C thus determined, (2) is true for every value of x with the possible exception of those for which a denominator vanishes.

We can solve this system of three linear equations in A, B, and C by either of the methods of Chap. 6 and obtain $A = -\frac{7}{5}$, $B = \frac{1}{5}$, $C = 2$. Therefore,

(6)
$$\frac{2x^2 + x + 1}{(x + 2)(3x + 1)(x + 3)} = \frac{-7}{5(x + 2)} + \frac{1}{5(3x + 1)} + \frac{2}{x + 3}$$

Method 2

We shall present a second method for determining A, B, and C so that the two members of (2) are equal for all values of x except possibly for $x = -2$, $x = -3$, $x = -\frac{1}{3}$ for which one of the denominators vanishes.

If the members of (2) are equal for all values of x with the possible exception of the three mentioned above, then by the theorem of Art. 110 the members of (4) are equal for all values of x including these three. Since the right members of (3) and (4) are two forms of the same polynomial, the two members of (3) are equal for all values of x.

If we let $x = -2$, the coefficients of B and C in (3) vanish, and we have

$$8 - 2 + 1 = A(-5)(1)$$

Thus,

$$-5A = 7$$

and

$$A = -\frac{7}{5}$$

Similarly, when $x = -\frac{1}{3}$, (3) becomes

$$\tfrac{2}{9} - \tfrac{1}{3} + 1 = B(\tfrac{5}{3})(\tfrac{8}{3})$$

Clearing of fractions, we get

$$2 - 3 + 9 = 40B$$

Thus,

$$40B = 8$$
$$B = \tfrac{1}{5}$$

Finally, if we let $x = -3$, we have

$$18 - 3 + 1 = C(-1)(-8)$$

Thus,

$$8C = 16$$
$$C = 2$$

Hence, we have (6).

The use of Method 2 in Case I enables us to avoid solving the system of equations (5) and thus usually saves time and labor. It can frequently be employed to an advantage in other cases; in particular, if a linear factor appears in the denominator.

EXERCISE 86

Resolve into partial fractions.

1. $\dfrac{2}{(x-1)(3x-1)}$.   **2.** $\dfrac{5}{(x-2)(2x+1)}$.   **3.** $\dfrac{11}{(3x-1)(2x+3)}$.

4. $\dfrac{17}{(3x-2)(4x+3)}$.   **5.** $\dfrac{7x}{(x+2)(2x-3)}$.   **6.** $\dfrac{14x}{(2x-1)(3x+2)}$.

7. $\dfrac{5x}{(x-3)(2x-1)}$.   **8.** $\dfrac{11x}{(2x-5)(3x-2)}$.   **9.** $\dfrac{3x-1}{(x-2)(x+3)}$.

10. $\dfrac{3x+9}{(x-1)(x+2)}$.   **11.** $\dfrac{7x+4}{(x+2)(2x-1)}$.   **12.** $\dfrac{19x-8}{(2x+1)(3x-2)}$.

13. $\dfrac{-19x+7}{(x-1)(x+2)(x-3)}$.   **14.** $\dfrac{24x-33}{(x-2)(2x-1)(x+3)}$.

15. $\dfrac{13x-9}{(x-1)(2x-1)(3x+1)}$.   **16.** $\dfrac{-35x+28}{(x+2)(3x-1)(2x-3)}$.

17. $\dfrac{12x^2-x+1}{(3x+2)(2x-1)(3x-1)}$.   **18.** $\dfrac{5x^2+18x+22}{(x-1)(x+2)(2x+3)}$.

19. $\dfrac{2x^2+2x+6}{(x+3)(2x-1)(4x+3)}$.   **20.** $\dfrac{-16x^2+7x-46}{(5x-1)(4x+5)(2x-5)}$.

21.[1] $\dfrac{2x^2-4x-1}{x^2-3x-4}$.   **22.** $\dfrac{6x^2+23x-20}{2x^2+5x-3}$.

23. $\dfrac{6x^3+x^2-7x-8}{6x^2+x-2}$.   **24.** $\dfrac{4x^3-19x^2+17x-4}{4x^2-7x+3}$.

173. *Case II. Repeated linear factors.* If the denominator of a fraction in factored form contains only linear factors, but

---

[1] If the degree of the numerator is equal to or greater than the degree of the denominator, divide the numerator by the denominator and continue the division until a remainder R of lower degree than the denominator is obtained. Then express the fraction in the form

$$\frac{\text{Numerator}}{\text{Denominator}} = \text{quotient} + \frac{R}{\text{denominator}}$$

Then resolve the final fraction into partial fractions.

one or more are repeated, we use the method illustrated in the example below for expressing it as the sum of partial fractions.

Example

Separate

$$\frac{3x^2 + 5x + 1}{(x - 1)(x + 2)^2}$$

into partial fractions.

Solution, Method 1

By (I) of Theorem 1, we must have the partial fraction $A/(x - 1)$ corresponding to the factor $x - 1$ of the denominator, and by (II) of the same theorem, we must also have the partial fractions $B/(x + 2)$ and $C/(x + 2)^2$ corresponding to the factor $(x + 2)^2$. Hence, we have

(1) $$\frac{3x^2 + 5x + 1}{(x - 1)(x + 2)^2} = \frac{A}{x - 1} + \frac{B}{x + 2} + \frac{C}{(x + 2)^2}$$

and we must find the values of A, B, and C so that the members of (1) are equal for all values of x with the possible exception of $x = 1$ and $x = -2$. The first step in this process is to clear (1) of fractions, thus obtaining

(2) $$3x^2 + 5x + 1 = A(x + 2)^2 + B(x - 1)(x + 2) + C(x - 1)$$
(3) $$= (A + B)x^2 + (4A + B + C)x + (4A - 2B - C)$$

The members of (3) will be equal for all values of x if A, B, and C are determined so that the coefficients of the like powers of x in the right and left members are equal. Equating the coefficients of x^2, x, and the two constant terms, we obtain the following system of three linear equations in A, B, and C:

$$A + B = 3$$
$$4A + B + C = 5$$
$$4A - 2B - C = 1$$

The solution of this system of equations is $A = 1$, $B = 2$, and $C = -1$. Therefore,

$$\frac{3x^2 + 5x + 1}{(x - 1)(x + 2)^2} = \frac{1}{x - 1} + \frac{2}{x + 2} - \frac{1}{(x + 2)^2}$$

Method 2

This method of evaluating A, B, and C is similar to the second method in Case I. If the members of (2) are equal for all values of x with the possible exception of $x = 1$ and $x = -2$, then by the theorem of Art. 110 they are equal for all values of x.

If we let $x = 1$ in Eq. (2), the coefficients of B and C vanish and we have

$$3 + 5 + 1 = A(3)^2$$

Thus,

$$9A = 9$$

and

$$A = 1$$

If $x = -2$, the coefficients of A and B vanish in (2), and we have

$$12 - 10 + 1 = C(-2 - 1)$$
$$-3C = 3$$
$$C = -1$$

Since there is no value of x for which the coefficients of A and C vanish simultaneously in (2), we must resort to another method to evaluate B. Since the members of (2) hold for all values of x, we may substitute any convenient value for this variable together with the values of A and C above in (2) and obtain an equation containing only B. If $x = 0$, $A = 1$, and $C = -1$, Eq. (2) becomes

$$1 = (1)(4) + B(-1)(2) + (-1)(-1)$$

Thus,

$$1 = 5 - 2B$$
$$2B = 4$$

and

$$B = 2$$

EXERCISE 87

Resolve into partial fractions.

1. $\dfrac{2x - 1}{(x - 1)^2}$.

2. $\dfrac{3x + 10}{(x + 2)^2}$.

3. $\dfrac{4x - 5}{(2x - 1)^2}$.

4. $\dfrac{3x + 1}{(3x + 4)^2}$.

5. $\dfrac{2x^2 - x - 2}{(x - 1)^2}$.

6. $\dfrac{12x^2 - 8x - 1}{(2x - 1)^3}$.

7. $\dfrac{45x^2 + 9x + 17}{(3x + 1)^3}$.

8. $\dfrac{25x^2 - 35x + 13}{(5x - 4)^3}$.

9. $\dfrac{x^2 + 13x + 15}{(2x + 3)(x + 3)^2}$.

10. $\dfrac{-10x^2 - 12x + 88}{(3x + 5)(2x - 3)^2}$.

11. $\dfrac{-6x^2 + 16x + 41}{(5x + 2)(2x - 5)^2}$.

12. $\dfrac{5x + 29}{(4x - 1)(3x + 2)^2}$.

13. $\dfrac{-3x^3 - 9x^2 + 49x - 25}{(2x - 1)(x + 2)(x - 1)^2}$.

14. $\dfrac{3x^3 - 11x^2 - 18x + 46}{(x + 3)(x - 2)(x - 1)^2}$.

15. $\dfrac{-7x^3 + 32x^2 + 15x - 32}{(2x + 1)(3x - 1)(x - 3)^2}$.

16. $\dfrac{14x^3 + 34x^2 + 24x + 8}{(3x + 2)(2x + 3)(x + 2)^2}$.

17.[1] $\dfrac{2x^2 - 7x + 2}{(x - 1)^2}$.

18. $\dfrac{3x^2 + 22x + 27}{(x + 3)^2}$.

19. $\dfrac{3x^3 - 12x^2 - 3x + 10}{(3x - 2)(x - 2)^2}$.

20. $\dfrac{54x^3 + 27x^2 - 26x - 25}{(2x - 1)(3x + 2)^2}$.

[1] See footnote in Exercise 86.

174. Case III. Distinct quadratic factors. If the first power of an irreducible quadratic function appears among the factors of the denominator of a fraction that is to be resolved into partial fractions, it must appear as the denominator of one of the partial fractions. The numerator of the partial fraction that has the quadratic denominator must be a linear function. The linear factors of the denominator enter exactly as in the previous cases.

Example 1

Resolve

$$\frac{14x^3 + 14x^2 - 4x + 3}{(3x^2 - x + 1)(x - 1)(x + 2)}$$

into partial fractions.

Solution

The quadratic factor $3x^2 - x + 1$ is irreducible; hence, it must be used as the denominator of a partial fraction that has a linear function $Ax + B$ for its numerator. Each of the linear factors will enter as a denominator of a partial fraction with a constant numerator. Thus,

$$\frac{14x^3 + 14x^2 - 4x + 3}{(3x^2 - x + 1)(x - 1)(x + 2)} = \frac{Ax + B}{3x^2 - x + 1} + \frac{C}{x - 1} + \frac{D}{x + 2}$$

In order to find the values of A, B, C, and D so that the members of (1) are equal, we first clear (1) of fractions and obtain

$$(2) \quad 14x^3 + 14x^2 - 4x + 3 = (Ax + B)(x - 1)(x + 2)$$
$$+ C(3x^2 - x + 1)(x + 2)$$
$$+ D(3x^2 - x + 1)(x - 1)$$
$$(3) \qquad\qquad = (A + 3C + 3D)x^3$$
$$+ (A + B + 5C - 4D)x^2$$
$$+ (-2A + B - C + 2D)x + (-2B + 2C - D)$$

We may now obtain, by equating the coefficients of equal powers of x, the four linear equations in A, B, C, and D which follow:

$$A + 3C + 3D = 14$$
$$A + B + 5C - 4D = 14$$
$$-2A + B - C + 2D = -4$$
$$-2B + 2C - D = 3$$

The solution of this system can be obtained by the method of Art. 168 or by solving the last equation for D in terms of B and C, replacing each D in the other three equations by this value, solving the resulting system of three linear equations in three unknowns, and, finally, obtaining the value of D from the last equation. The solution thus obtained is $A = 2$, $B = 1$, $C = 3$, $D = 1$. Hence,

$$\frac{14x^3 + 14x^2 - 4x + 3}{(3x^2 - x + 1)(x - 1)(x + 2)} = \frac{2x + 1}{3x^2 - x + 1} + \frac{3}{x - 1} + \frac{1}{x + 2}$$

Example 2

Resolve

$$\frac{4x^4 + 4x^3 - x^2 + x + 1}{(x^2 + x + 1)(x^2 - x - 3)(x + 1)}$$

into partial fractions.

Solution

(1) $\dfrac{4x^4 + 4x^3 - x^2 + x + 1}{(x^2 + x + 1)(x^2 - x - 3)(x + 1)} = \dfrac{Ax + B}{x^2 + x + 1} + \dfrac{Cx + D}{x^2 - x - 3} + \dfrac{E}{x + 1}$

Clearing of fractions, we have

(2) $4x^4 + 4x^3 - x^2 + x + 1 = (Ax + B)(x^2 - x - 3)(x + 1)$
$$+ (Cx + D)(x^2 + x + 1)(x + 1)$$
$$+ E(x^2 + x + 1)(x^2 - x - 3)$$

(3) $$= (A + C + E)x^4 + (B + 2C + D)x^3$$
$$+ (-4A + 2C + 2D - 3E)x^2$$
$$+ (-3A - 4B + C + 2D - 4E)x$$
$$+ (-3B + D - 3E)$$

We may obtain the following system of equations by equating the coefficients of the equal powers of x:

$$A + C + E = 4$$
$$B + 2C + D = 4$$
$$-4A + 2C + 2D - 3E = -1$$
$$-3A - 4B + C + 2D - 4E = 1$$
$$-3B + D - 3E = 1$$

This system can be solved by the method of Art. 168 or by obtaining an expression for D in terms of B and E from the last equation, substituting this for D in the other four equations, thus getting a system of four linear equations in four unknowns, and solving the system by any of the available methods. The method suggested in Example 1 can be used. The solution is $A = 1$, $B = -1$, $C = 2$, $D = 1$, $E = 1$.

Therefore,

$$\frac{4x^4 + 4x^3 - x^2 + x + 1}{(x^2 + x + 1)(x^2 - x - 3)(x + 1)} = \frac{x - 1}{x^2 + x + 1} + \frac{2x + 1}{x^2 - x - 3} + \frac{1}{x + 1}$$

EXERCISE 88

Resolve into partial fractions.

1. $\dfrac{2}{(x + 1)(x^2 + 1)}$.

2. $\dfrac{-x^2 + x + 8}{(x - 1)(x^2 + 3)}$.

3. $\dfrac{-x^2 - x + 6}{(2x + 3)(x^2 + x + 1)}$.

4. $\dfrac{5x^2 + 8x - 2}{(3x - 2)(x^2 - x + 3)}$.

5. $\dfrac{6x^3 - 7x^2 + 13x + 8}{(x + 1)(x - 2)(x^2 + 5)}$.

6. $\dfrac{-9x^3 + 19x^2 + 2x + 3}{(2x - 3)(x + 2)(x^2 + 3)}$.

7. $\dfrac{5x^3 - 31x^2 - 3x - 23}{(3x - 1)(x - 3)(x^2 + 3x + 4)}.$

8. $\dfrac{7x^3 - 62x^2 - 57x - 8}{(4x + 1)(3x + 2)(x^2 + 5x + 3)}.$

9. $\dfrac{x^3 + 3x^2 + 14x + 12}{(x + 2)^2(x^2 + 2)}.$

10. $\dfrac{6x^3 - 27x^2 + 44x - 12}{(x - 3)^2(x^2 + 4)}.$

11. $\dfrac{10x^3 + 3x^2 - 19x + 12}{(2x - 1)^2(x^2 + x - 3)}.$

12. $\dfrac{4x^3 + 2x^2 + x}{(x + 1)^2(x^2 - x + 1)}.$

13. $\dfrac{2x^3 - 2x^2 + 4x - 2}{(x^2 + 1)(x^2 + 3)}.$

14. $\dfrac{-x^3 - x^2 + 11x + 11}{(x^2 + 3x + 1)(x^2 + 4)}.$

15. $\dfrac{-x^3 - 15x^2 + 18x + 10}{(x^2 - 3)(x^2 - 5x + 2)}.$

16. $\dfrac{x^3 - 8x^2 - 26x - 35}{(x^2 + 7)(x^2 - x - 4)}.$

17. $\dfrac{x^3 + 4x^2 - 7x + 6}{(x - 1)(x^2 + 1)}.$

18. $\dfrac{2x^3 + 4x^2 - 11x - 19}{(x + 4)(x^2 - 3)}.$

19. $\dfrac{8x^3 + 26x^2 + 21x - 12}{(2x + 7)(2x^2 + x + 1)}.$

20. $\dfrac{18x^3 - 41x^2 - 16x + 11}{(3x - 5)(2x^2 - x - 2)}.$

175. Case IV. Repeated quadratic factors. The final case to be considered is that in which the factors of the denominator of the given fraction contain powers of one or more irreducible quadratic functions. By IV of Theorem 1, to every factor of the type $(ax^2 + bx + c)^k$ appearing in the denominator of a rational fraction, there correspond the partial fractions

$$\frac{A_1x + B_1}{ax^2 + bx + c} + \frac{A_2x + B_2}{(ax^2 + bx + c)^2} + \cdots + \frac{A_kx + B_k}{(ax^2 + bx + c)^k}$$

The linear and nonrepeated quadratic factors of the given denominator enter in the same manner as in the previous cases. The numerator of each partial fraction whose denominator contains a quadratic function should be a linear function.

Example

Resolve

$$\frac{6x^4 + 11x^3 + 18x^2 + 14x + 6}{(x + 1)(x^2 + x + 1)^2}$$

into partial fractions.

Solution

The denominator contains a linear function and the square of an irreducible quadratic function as factors; hence, we let

$$\frac{6x^4 + 11x^3 + 18x^2 + 14x + 6}{(x + 1)(x^2 + x + 1)^2} = \frac{A}{x + 1} + \frac{Bx + C}{x^2 + x + 1} + \frac{Dx + E}{(x^2 + x + 1)^2}$$

and evaluate the undetermined constants after clearing of fractions. Thus,

$$6x^4 + 11x^3 + 18x^2 + 14x + 6 = A(x^2 + x + 1)^2$$
$$+ (Bx + C)(x^2 + x + 1)(x + 1) + (Dx + E)(x + 1)$$
$$= (A + B)x^4 + (2A + 2B + C)x^3$$
$$+ (3A + 2B + 2C + D)x^2 + (2A + B + 2C + D + E)x$$
$$+ (A + C + E)$$

Therefore, by equating the coefficients of equal powers of x, we obtain

$$A + B = 6$$
$$2A + 2B + C = 11$$
$$3A + 2B + 2C + D = 18$$
$$2A + B + 2C + D + E = 14$$
$$A + C + E = 6$$

We can solve this system by means of the method suggested in the solution of Example 2 of Art. 174. The solution is $A = 5$, $B = 1$, $C = -1$, $D = 3$, and $E = 2$. Therefore,

$$\frac{6x^4 + 11x^3 + 18x^2 + 14x + 6}{(x + 1)(x^2 + x + 1)^2} = \frac{5}{x + 1} + \frac{x - 1}{x^2 + x + 1} + \frac{3x + 2}{(x^2 + x + 1)^2}$$

EXERCISE 89

Resolve into partial fractions.

1. $\dfrac{3x^3 + 4x - 5}{(x^2 + 2)^2}.$

2. $\dfrac{2x^2 - 3x + 7}{(x^2 + 1)^2}.$

3. $\dfrac{2x^3 + x^2 + 4x + 1}{(x^2 + x + 1)^2}.$

4. $\dfrac{2x^3 + x^2 + 3x - 4}{(x^2 + x + 3)^2}.$

5. $\dfrac{x^5 + 2x^3 + 2x - 1}{(x^2 + 1)^3}.$

6. $\dfrac{x^3 + 4x - 1}{(x^2 + 3)^3}.$

7. $\dfrac{x^5 - 2x^4 + 4x^3 - 2x^2}{(x^2 - x + 1)^3}.$

8. $\dfrac{x^5 + 1}{(x^2 + 2)^3}.$

9. $\dfrac{x^4 - x^3 + 1}{x^2(x^2 + 1)^2}.$

10. $\dfrac{x^4 - x^3 + 4}{x(x^2 - 2)^2}.$

11. $\dfrac{x^5 + x^4 - 4x + 4}{x^2(x^2 - x + 2)^2}.$

12. $\dfrac{x^4 - x^3 - x^2 - 1}{x^3(x^2 + 1)^2}.$

13. $\dfrac{-4x^4 + 2x^3 - 3x^2 + 5x - 2}{(x^2 + 1)^2(x + 1)}.$

14. $\dfrac{2x^4 + 5x^3 + 19x^2 + 11x + 52}{(x + 2)(x^2 + 3)^2}.$

15. $\dfrac{x^4 - 3x^3 - 8x^2 + 47x - 58}{(2x - 3)(x^2 + x - 7)}.$

16. $\dfrac{2x^4 - 3x^3 - 2x^2 + 4x + 2}{(x + 1)(x^2 - x - 1)}.$

APPENDIX

TABLE I.—COMMON LOGARITHMS

N	0	1	2	3	4	5	6	7	8	9
10	0000	0043	0086	0128	0170	0212	0253	0294	0334	0374
11	0414	0453	0492	0531	0569	0607	0645	0682	0719	0755
12	0792	0828	0864	0899	0934	0969	1004	1038	1072	1106
13	1139	1173	1206	1239	1271	1303	1335	1367	1399	1430
14	1461	1492	1523	1553	1584	1614	1644	1673	1703	1732
15	1761	1790	1818	1847	1875	1903	1931	1959	1987	2014
16	2041	2068	2095	2122	2148	2175	2201	2227	2253	2279
17	2304	2330	2355	2380	2405	2430	2455	2480	2504	2529
18	2553	2577	2601	2625	2648	2672	2695	2718	2742	2765
19	2788	2810	2833	2856	2878	2900	2923	2945	2967	2989
20	3010	3032	3054	3075	3096	3118	3139	3160	3181	3201
21	3222	3243	3263	3284	3304	3324	3345	3365	3385	3404
22	3424	3444	3464	3483	3502	3522	3541	3560	3579	3598
23	3617	3636	3655	3674	3692	3711	3729	3747	3766	3784
24	3802	3820	3838	3856	3874	3892	3909	3927	3945	3962
25	3979	3997	4014	4031	4048	4065	4082	4099	4116	4133
26	4150	4166	4183	4200	4216	4232	4249	4265	4281	4298
27	4314	4330	4346	4362	4378	4393	4409	4425	4440	4456
28	4472	4487	4502	4518	4533	4548	4564	4579	4594	4609
29	4624	4639	4654	4669	4683	4698	4713	4728	4742	4757
30	4771	4786	4800	4814	4829	4843	4857	4871	4886	4900
31	4914	4928	4942	4955	4969	4983	4997	5011	5024	5038
32	5051	5065	5079	5092	5105	5119	5132	5145	5159	5172
33	5185	5198	5211	5224	5237	5250	5263	5276	5289	5302
34	5315	5328	5340	5353	5366	5378	5391	5403	5416	5428
35	5441	5453	5465	5478	5490	5502	5514	5527	5539	5551
36	5563	5575	5587	5599	5611	5623	5635	5647	5658	5670
37	5682	5694	5705	5717	5729	5740	5752	5763	5775	5786
38	5798	5809	5821	5832	5843	5855	5866	5877	5888	5899
39	5911	5922	5933	5944	5955	5966	5977	5988	5999	6010
40	6021	6031	6042	6053	6064	6075	6085	6096	6107	6117
41	6128	6138	6149	6160	6170	6180	6191	6201	6212	6222
42	6232	6243	6253	6263	6274	6284	6294	6304	6314	6325
43	6335	6345	6355	6365	6375	6385	6395	6405	6415	6425
44	6435	6444	6454	6464	6474	6484	6493	6503	6513	6522
45	6532	6542	6551	6561	6571	6580	6590	6599	6609	6618
46	6628	6637	6646	6656	6665	6675	6684	6693	6702	6712
47	6721	6730	6739	6749	6758	6767	6776	6785	6794	6803
48	6812	6821	6830	6839	6848	6857	6866	6875	6884	6893
49	6902	6911	6920	6928	6937	6946	6955	6964	6972	6981
50	6990	6998	7007	7016	7024	7033	7042	7050	7059	7067
51	7076	7084	7093	7101	7110	7118	7126	7135	7143	7152
52	7160	7168	7177	7185	7193	7202	7210	7218	7226	7235
53	7243	7251	7259	7267	7275	7284	7292	7300	7308	7316
54	7324	7332	7340	7348	7356	7364	7372	7380	7388	7396
N	0	1	2	3	4	5	6	7	8	9

TABLE I.—COMMON LOGARITHMS.—(*Continued*)

N	0	1	2	3	4	5	6	7	8	9
55	7404	7412	7419	7427	7435	7443	7451	7459	7466	7474
56	7482	7490	7497	7505	7513	7520	7528	7536	7543	7551
57	7559	7566	7574	7582	7589	7597	7604	7612	7619	7627
58	7634	7642	7649	7657	7664	7672	7679	7686	7694	7701
59	7709	7716	7723	7731	7738	7745	7752	7760	7767	7774
60	7782	7789	7796	7803	7810	7818	7825	7832	7839	7846
61	7853	7860	7868	7875	7882	7889	7896	7903	7910	7917
62	7924	7931	7938	7945	7952	7959	7966	7973	7980	7987
63	7993	8000	8007	8014	8021	8028	8035	8041	8048	8055
64	8062	8069	8075	8082	8089	8096	8102	8109	8116	8122
65	8129	8136	8142	8149	8156	8162	8169	8176	8182	8189
66	8195	8202	8209	8215	8222	8228	8235	8241	8248	8254
67	8261	8267	8274	8280	8287	8293	8299	8306	8312	8319
68	8325	8331	8338	8344	8351	8357	8363	8370	8376	8382
69	8388	8395	8401	8407	8414	8420	8426	8432	8439	8445
70	8451	8457	8463	8470	8476	8482	8488	8494	8500	8506
71	8513	8519	8525	8531	8537	8543	8549	8555	8561	8567
72	8573	8579	8585	8591	8597	8603	8609	8615	8621	8627
73	8633	8639	8645	8651	8657	8663	8669	8675	8681	8686
74	8692	8698	8704	8710	8716	8722	8727	8733	8739	8745
75	8751	8756	8762	8768	8774	8779	8785	8791	8797	8802
76	8808	8814	8820	8825	8831	8837	8842	8848	8854	8859
77	8865	8871	8876	8882	8887	8893	8899	8904	8910	8915
78	8921	8927	8932	8938	8943	8949	8954	8960	8965	8971
79	8976	8982	8987	8993	8998	9004	9009	9015	9020	9025
80	9031	9036	9042	9047	9053	9058	9063	9069	9074	9079
81	9085	9090	9096	9101	9106	9112	9117	9122	9128	9133
82	9138	9143	9149	9154	9159	9165	9170	9175	9180	9186
83	9191	9196	9201	9206	9212	9217	9222	9227	9232	9238
84	9243	9248	9253	9258	9263	9269	9274	9279	9284	9289
85	9294	9299	9304	9309	9315	9320	9325	9330	9335	9340
86	9345	9350	9355	9360	9365	9370	9375	9380	9385	9390
87	9395	9400	9405	9410	9415	9420	9425	9430	9435	9440
88	9445	9450	9455	9460	9465	9469	9474	9479	9484	9489
89	9494	9499	9504	9509	9513	9518	9523	9528	9533	9538
90	9542	9547	9552	9557	9562	9566	9571	9576	9581	9586
91	9590	9595	9600	9605	9609	9614	9619	9624	9628	9633
92	9638	9643	9647	9652	9657	9661	9666	9671	9675	9680
93	9685	9689	9694	9699	9703	9708	9713	9717	9722	9727
94	9731	9736	9741	9745	9750	9754	9759	9763	9768	9773
95	9777	9782	9786	9791	9795	9800	9805	9809	9814	9818
96	9823	9827	9832	9836	9841	9845	9850	9854	9859	9863
97	9868	9872	9877	9881	9886	9890	9894	9899	9903	9908
98	9912	9917	9921	9926	9930	9934	9939	9943	9948	9952
99	9956	9961	9965	9969	9974	9978	9983	9987	9991	9996
N	0	1	2	3	4	5	6	7	8	9

TABLE II.—TRIGONOMETRIC FUNCTIONS

Angles	Sines		Cosines		Tangents		Cotangents		Angles
	Nat.	Log.	Nat.	Log.	Nat.	Log.	Nat.	Log.	
0° 00′	.0000	∞	1.0000	0.0000	.0000	∞	∞	∞	90° 00′
10	.0029	7.4637	1.0000	0000	.0029	7.4637	343.77	2.5363	50
20	.0058	7648	1.0000	0000	.0058	7648	171.89	2352	40
30	.0087	9408	1.0000	0000	.0087	9409	114.59	0591	30
40	.0116	8.0658	.9999	0000	.0116	8.0658	85.940	1.9342	20
50	.0145	1627	.9999	0000	.0145	1627	68.750	8373	10
1° 00′	.0175	8.2419	.9998	9.9999	.0175	8.2419	57.290	1.7581	89° 00′
10	.0204	3088	.9998	9999	.0204	3089	49.104	6911	50
20	.0233	3668	.9997	9999	.0233	3669	42.964	6331	40
30	.0262	4179	.9997	9999	.0262	4181	38.188	5819	30
40	.0291	4637	.9996	9998	.0291	4638	34.368	5362	20
50	.0320	5050	.9995	9998	.0320	5053	31.242	4947	10
2° 00′	.0349	8.5428	.9994	9.9997	.0349	8.5431	28.636	1.4569	88° 00′
10	.0378	5776	.9993	9997	.0378	5779	26.432	4221	50
20	.0407	6097	.9992	9996	.0407	6101	24.542	3899	40
30	.0436	6397	.9990	9996	.0437	6401	22.904	3599	30
40	.0465	6677	.9989	9995	.0466	6682	21.470	3318	20
50	.0494	6940	.9988	9995	.0495	6945	20.206	3055	10
3° 00′	.0523	8.7188	.9986	9.9994	.0524	8.7194	19.081	1.2806	87° 00′
10	.0552	7423	.9985	9993	.0553	7429	18.075	2571	50
20	.0581	7645	.9983	9993	.6582	7652	17.169	2348	40
30	.0610	7857	.9981	9992	.0612	7865	16.350	2135	30
40	.0640	8059	.9980	9991	.0641	8067	15.605	1933	20
50	.0669	8251	.9978	9990	.0670	8261	14.924	1739	10
4° 00′	.0698	8.8436	.9976	9.9989	.0669	8.8446	14.301	1.1554	86° 00′
10	.0727	8613	.9974	9989	.0729	8624	13.727	1376	50
20	.0756	8783	.9971	9988	.0758	8795	13.197	1205	40
30	.0785	8946	.9969	9987	.0787	8960	12.706	1040	30
40	.0814	9104	.9967	9986	.0816	9118	12.251	0882	20
50	.0843	9256	.9964	9985	.0846	9272	11.826	0728	10
5° 00′	.0872	8.9403	.9962	9.9983	.0875	8.9420	11.430	1.0580	85° 00′
10	.0901	9545	.9959	9982	.0904	9563	11.059	0437	50
20	.0929	9682	.9957	9981	.0934	9701	10.712	0299	40
30	.0958	9816	.9954	9980	.0963	9836	10.385	0164	30
40	.0987	9945	.9951	9979	.0992	9966	10.078	0034	20
50	.1016	9.0070	.9948	9977	.1022	9.0093	9.7882	0.9907	10
6° 00′	.1045	9.0192	.9945	9.9976	.1051	9.0216	9.5144	0.9784	84° 00′
10	.1074	0311	.9942	9975	.1080	0336	9.2553	9664	50
20	.1103	0426	.9939	9973	.1110	0453	9.0098	9547	40
30	.1132	0539	.9936	9972	.1139	0567	8.7769	9433	30
40	.1161	0648	.9932	9971	.1169	0678	8.5555	9322	20
50	.1190	0755	.9929	9969	.1198	0786	8.3450	9214	10
7° 00′	.1219	9.0859	.9925	9.9968	.1228	9.0891	8.1443	0.9109	83° 00′
10	.1248	0961	.9922	9966	.1257	0995	7.9530	9005	50
20	.1276	1060	.9918	9964	.1287	1096	7.7704	8904	40
30	.1305	1157	.9914	9963	.1317	1194	7.5958	8806	30
40	.1334	1252	.9911	9961	.1346	1291	7.4287	8709	20
50	.1363	1345	.9907	9959	.1376	1385	7.2687	8615	10
8° 00′	.1392	9.1436	.9903	9.9958	.1405	9.1478	7.1154	0.8522	82° 00′
10	.1421	1525	.9899	9956	.1435	1569	6.9682	8431	50
20	.1449	1612	.9894	9954	.1465	1658	6.8269	8342	40
30	.1478	1697	.9890	9952	.1495	1745	6.6912	8255	30
40	.1507	1781	.9886	9950	.1524	1831	6.5606	8169	20
50	.1536	1863	.9881	9948	.1554	1915	6.4348	8085	10
9° 00′	.1564	9.1943	.9877	9.9946	.1584	9.1997	6.3138	0.8003	81° 00′
	Nat.	Log.	Nat.	Log.	Nat.	Log.	Nat.	Log.	
Angles	Cosines		Sines		Cotangents		Tangents		Angles

TABLE II.—TRIGONOMETRIC FUNCTIONS.—(*Continued*)

Angles	Sines		Cosines		Tangents		Cotangents		Angles
	Nat.	Log.	Nat.	Log.	Nat.	Log.	Nat.	Log.	
9° 00′	.1564	9.1943	.9877	9.9946	.1584	9.1997	6.3138	0.8003	81° 00′
10	.1593	2022	.9872	9944	.1614	2078	6.1970	7922	50
20	.1622	2100	.9868	9942	.1644	2158	6.0844	7842	40
30	.1650	2176	.9863	9940	.1673	2236	5.9758	7764	30
40	.1679	2251	.9858	9938	.1703	2313	5.8708	7687	20
50	.1708	2324	.9853	9936	.1733	2389	5.7694	7611	10
10° 00′	.1736	9.2397	.9848	9.9934	.1763	9.2463	5.6713	0.7537	80° 00′
10	.1765	2468	.9843	9931	.1793	2536	5.5764	7464	50
20	.1794	2538	.9838	9929	.1823	2609	5.4845	7391	40
30	.1822	2606	.9833	9927	.1853	2680	5.3955	7320	30
40	.1851	2674	.9827	9924	.1883	2750	5.3093	7250	20
50	.1880	2740	.9822	9922	.1914	2819	5.2257	7181	10
11° 00′	.1908	9.2806	.9816	9.9919	.1944	9.2887	5.1446	0.7113	79° 00′
10	.1937	2870	.9811	9917	.1974	2953	5.0658	7047	50
20	.1965	2934	.9805	9914	.2004	3020	4.9894	6980	40
30	.1994	2997	.9799	9912	.2035	3085	4.9152	6915	30
40	.2022	3058	.9793	9909	.2065	3149	4.8430	6851	20
50	.2051	3119	.9787	9907	.2095	3212	4.7729	6788	10
12° 00′	.2079	9.3179	.9781	9.9904	.2126	9.3275	4.7046	0.6725	78° 00′
10	.2108	3238	.9775	9901	.2156	3336	4.6382	6664	50
20	.2136	3296	.9769	9899	.2186	3397	4.5736	6603	40
30	.2164	3353	.9763	9896	.2217	3458	4.5107	6542	30
40	.2193	3410	.9757	9893	.2247	3517	4.4494	6483	20
50	.2221	3466	.9750	9890	.2278	3576	4.3897	6424	10
13° 00′	.2250	9.3521	.9744	9.9887	.2309	9.3634	4.3315	0.6366	77° 00′
10	.2278	3575	.9737	9884	.2339	3691	4.2747	6309	50
20	.2306	3629	.9730	9881	.2370	3748	4.2193	6252	40
30	.2334	3682	.9724	9878	.2401	3804	4.1653	6196	30
40	.2363	3734	.9717	9875	.2432	3859	4.1126	6141	20
50	.2391	3786	.9710	9872	.2462	3914	4.0611	6086	10
14° 00′	.2419	9.3837	.9703	9.9869	.2493	9.3968	4.0108	0.6032	76° 00′
10	.2447	3887	.9696	9866	.2524	4021	3.9617	5979	50
20	.2476	3937	.9689	9863	.2555	4074	3.9136	5926	40
30	.2504	3986	.9681	9859	.2586	4127	3.8667	5873	30
40	.2532	4035	.9674	9856	.2617	4178	3.8208	5822	20
50	.2560	4083	.9667	9853	.2648	4230	3.7760	5770	10
15° 00′	.2588	9.4130	.9659	9.9849	.2679	9.4281	3.7321	0.5719	75° 00′
10	.2616	4177	.9652	9846	.2711	4331	3.6891	5669	50
20	.2644	4223	.9644	9843	.2742	4381	3.6470	5619	40
30	.2672	4269	.9636	9839	.2773	4430	3.6059	5570	30
40	.2700	4314	.9628	9836	.2805	4479	3.5656	5521	20
50	.2728	4359	.9621	9832	.2836	4527	3.5261	5473	10
16° 00′	.2756	9.4403	.9613	9.9828	.2867	9.4575	3.4874	0.5425	74° 00′
10	.2784	4447	.9605	9825	.2899	4622	3.4495	5378	50
20	.2812	4491	.9596	9821	.2931	4669	3.4124	5331	40
30	.2840	4533	.9588	9817	.2962	4716	3.3759	5284	30
40	.2868	4576	.9580	9814	.2994	4762	3.3402	5238	20
50	.2896	4618	.9572	9810	.3026	4808	3.3052	5192	10
17° 00′	.2924	9.4659	.9563	9.9806	.3057	9.4853	3.2709	0.5147	73° 00′
10	.2952	4700	.9555	9802	.3089	4898	3.2371	5102	50
20	.2979	4741	.9546	9798	.3121	4943	3.2041	5057	40
30	.3007	4781	.9537	9794	.3153	4987	3.1716	5013	30
40	.3035	4821	.9528	9790	.3185	5031	3.1397	4969	20
50	.3062	4861	.9520	9786	.3217	5075	3.1084	4925	10
18° 00′	.3090	9.4900	.9511	9.9782	.3249	9.5118	3.0777	0.4882	72° 00′
	Nat.	Log.	Nat.	Log.	Nat.	Log.	Nat.	Log.	
Angles	Cosines		Sines		Cotangents		Tangents		Angles

TABLE II.—TRIGONOMETRIC FUNCTIONS.—(Continued)

Angles	Sines		Cosines		Tangents		Cotagents		Angles
	Nat.	Log.	Nat.	Log.	Nat.	Log.	Nat.	Log.	
18° 00′	.3090	9.4900	.9511	9.9782	.3249	9.5118	3.0777	0.4882	72° 00′
10	.3118	4939	.9502	9778	.3281	5161	3.0475	4839	50
20	.3145	4977	.9492	9774	.3314	5203	3.0178	4797	40
30	.3173	5015	.9483	9770	.3346	5245	2.9887	4755	30
40	.3201	5052	.9474	9765	.3378	5287	2.9600	4713	20
50	.3228	5090	.9465	9761	.3411	5329	2.9319	4671	10
19° 00′	.3256	9.5126	.9455	9.9757	.3443	9.5370	2.9042	0.4630	71° 00′
10	.3283	5163	.9446	9752	.3476	5411	2.8770	4589	50
20	.3311	5199	.9436	9748	.3508	5451	2.8502	4549	40
30	.3338	5235	.9426	9743	.3541	5491	2.8239	4509	30
40	.3365	5270	.9417	9739	.3574	5531	2.7980	4469	20
50	.3393	5306	.9407	9734	.3607	5571	2.7725	4429	10
20° 00′	.3420	9.5341	.9397	9.9730	.3640	9.5611	2.7475	0.4389	70° 00′
10	.3448	5375	.9387	9725	.3673	5650	2.7228	4350	50
20	.3475	5409	.9377	9721	.3706	5689	2.6985	4311	40
30	.3502	5443	.9367	9716	.3739	5727	2.6746	4273	30
40	.3529	5477	.9356	9711	.3772	5766	2.6511	4234	20
50	.3557	5510	.9346	9706	.3805	5804	2.6279	4196	10
21° 00′	.3584	9.5543	.9336	9.9702	.3839	9.5842	2.6051	0.4158	69° 00′
10	.3611	5576	.9325	9697	.3872	5879	2.5826	4121	50
20	.3638	5609	.9315	9692	.3906	5917	2.5605	4083	40
30	.3665	5641	.9304	9687	.3939	5954	2.5386	4046	30
40	.3692	5673	.9293	9682	.3973	5991	2.5172	4009	20
50	.3719	5704	.9283	9677	.4006	6028	2.4960	3972	10
22° 00′	.3746	9.5736	.9272	9.9672	.4040	9.6064	2.4751	0.3936	68° 00′
10	.3773	5767	.9261	9667	.4074	6100	2.4545	3900	50
20	.3800	5798	.9250	9661	.4108	6136	2.4342	3864	40
30	.3827	5828	.9239	9656	.4142	6172	2.4142	3828	30
40	.3854	5859	.9228	9651	.4176	6208	2.3945	3792	20
50	.3881	5889	.9216	9646	.4210	6243	2.3750	3757	10
23° 00′	.3907	9.5919	.9205	9.9640	.4245	9.6279	2.3559	0.3721	67° 00′
10	.3934	5948	.9194	9635	.4279	6314	2.3369	3686	50
20	.3961	5978	.9182	9629	.4314	6348	2.3183	3652	40
30	.3987	6007	.9171	9624	.4348	6383	2.2998	3617	30
40	.4014	6036	.9159	9618	.4383	6417	2.2817	3583	20
50	.4041	6065	.9147	9613	.4417	6452	2.2637	3548	10
24° 00′	.4067	9.6093	.9135	9.9607	.4452	9.6486	2.2460	0.3514	66° 00′
10	.4094	6121	.9124	9602	.4487	6520	2.2286	3480	50
20	.4120	6149	.9112	9596	.4522	6553	2.2113	3447	40
30	.4147	6177	.9100	9590	.4557	6587	2.1943	3413	30
40	.4173	6205	.9088	9584	.4592	6620	2.1775	3380	20
50	.4200	6232	.9075	9579	.4628	6654	2.1609	3346	10
25° 00′	.4226	9.6259	.9063	9.9573	.4663	9.6687	2.1445	0.3313	65° 00′
10	.4253	6286	.9051	9567	.4699	6720	2.1283	3280	50
20	.4279	6313	.9038	9561	.4734	6752	2.1123	3248	40
30	.4305	6340	.9026	9555	.4770	6785	2.0965	3215	30
40	.4331	6366	.9013	9549	.4806	6817	2.0809	3183	20
50	.4358	6392	.9001	9543	.4841	6850	2.0655	3150	10
26° 00′	.4384	9.6418	.8988	9.9537	.4877	9.6882	2.0503	0.3118	64° 00′
10	.4410	6444	.8975	9530	.4913	6914	2.0353	3086	50
20	.4436	6470	.8962	9524	.4950	6946	2.0204	3054	40
30	.4462	6495	.8949	9518	.4986	6977	2.0057	3023	30
40	.4488	6521	.8936	9512	.5022	7009	1.9912	2991	20
50	.4514	6546	.8923	9505	.5095	7040	1.9768	2960	10
27° 00′	.4540	9.6570	.8910	9.9499	.5095	9.7072	1.9626	0.2928	63° 00′
	Nat.	Log.	Nat.	Log.	Nat.	Log.	Nat.	Log.	
Angles	Cosines		Sines		Cotangents		Tangents		Angles

TABLE II.—TRIGONOMETRIC FUNCTIONS.—*(Continued)*

Angles	Sines		Cosines		Tangents		Cotangents		Angles
	Nat.	Log.	Nat.	Log.	Nat.	Log.	Nat.	Log.	
27° 00′	.4540	9.6570	.8910	9.9499	.5095	9.7072	1.9626	0.2928	63° 00′
10	.4566	6595	.8897	9492	.5132	7103	1.9486	2897	50
20	.4592	6620	.8884	9486	.5169	7134	1.9347	2866	40
30	.4617	6644	.8870	9479	.5206	7165	1.9210	2835	30
40	.4643	6668	.8857	9473	.5243	7196	1.9074	2804	20
50	.4669	6692	.8843	9466	.5280	7226	1.8940	2774	10
28° 00′	.4695	9.6716	.8829	9.9459	.5317	9.7257	1.8807	0.2743	62° 00′
10	.4720	6740	.8816	9453	.5354	7287	1.8676	2713	50
20	.4746	6763	.8802	9446	.5392	7317	1.8546	2683	40
30	.4772	6787	.8788	9439	.5430	7348	1.8418	2652	30
40	.4797	6810	.8774	9432	.5467	7378	1.8291	2622	20
50	.4823	6833	.8760	9425	.5505	7408	1.8165	2592	10
29° 00′	.4848	9.6856	.8746	9.9418	.5543	9.7438	1.8040	0.2562	61° 00′
10	.4874	6878	.8732	9411	.5581	7467	1.7917	2533	50
20	.4899	6901	.8718	9404	.5619	7497	1.7796	2503	40
30	.4924	6923	.8704	9397	.5658	7526	1.7675	2474	30
40	.4950	6946	.8689	9390	.5696	7556	1.7556	2444	20
50	.4975	6968	.8675	9383	.5735	7585	1.7437	2415	10
30° 00′	.5000	9.6990	.8660	9.9375	.5774	9.7614	1.7321	0.2386	60° 00′
10	.5025	7012	.8646	9368	.5812	7644	1.7205	2356	50
20	.5050	7033	.8631	9361	.5851	7673	1.7090	2327	40
30	.5075	7055	.8616	9353	.5890	7701	1.6977	2299	30
40	.5100	7076	.8601	9346	.5930	7730	1.6864	2270	20
50	.5125	7097	.8587	9338	.5969	7759	1.6753	2241	10
31° 00′	.5150	9.7118	.8572	9.9331	.6009	9.7788	1.6643	0.2212	59° 00′
10	.5175	7139	.8557	9323	.6048	7816	1.6534	2184	50
20	.5200	7160	.8542	9315	.6088	7845	1.6426	2155	40
30	.5225	7181	.8526	9308	.6128	7873	1.6319	2127	30
40	.5250	7201	.8511	9300	.6168	7902	1.6212	2098	20
50	.5275	7222	.8496	9292	.6208	7930	1.6107	2070	10
32° 00′	.5299	9.7242	.8480	9.9284	.6249	9.7958	1.6003	0.2042	58° 00′
10	.5324	7262	.8465	9276	.6289	7986	1.5900	2014	50
20	.5348	7282	.8450	9268	.6330	8014	1.5798	1986	40
30	.5373	7302	.8434	9260	.6371	8042	1.5697	1958	30
40	.5398	7322	.8418	9252	.6412	8070	1.5597	1930	20
50	.5422	7342	.8403	9244	.6453	8097	1.5497	1903	10
33° 00′	.5446	9.7361	.8387	9.9236	.6494	9.8125	1.5399	0.1875	57° 00′
10	.5471	7380	.8371	9228	.6536	8153	1.5301	1847	50
20	.5495	7400	.8355	9219	.6577	8180	1.5204	1820	40
30	.5519	7419	.8339	9211	.6619	8208	1.5108	1792	30
40	.5544	7438	.8323	9203	.6661	8235	1.5013	1765	20
50	.5568	7457	.8307	9194	.6703	8263	1.4919	1737	10
34° 00′	.5592	9.7476	.8290	9.9186	.6745	9.8290	1.4826	0.1710	56° 00′
10	.5616	7494	.8274	9177	.6787	8317	1.4733	1683	50
20	.5640	7513	.8258	9169	.6830	8344	1.4641	1656	40
30	.5664	7531	.8241	9160	.6873	8371	1.4550	1629	30
40	.5688	7550	.8225	9151	.6916	8398	1.4460	1602	20
50	.5712	7568	.8208	9142	.6959	8425	1.4370	1575	10
35° 00′	.5736	9.7586	.8192	9.9134	.7002	9.8452	1.4281	0.1548	55° 00′
10	.5760	7604	.8175	9125	.7046	8479	1.4193	1521	50
20	.5783	7622	.8158	9116	.7089	8506	1.4106	1494	40
30	.5807	7640	.8141	9107	.7133	8533	1.4019	1467	30
40	.5831	7657	.8124	9098	.7177	8559	1.3934	1441	20
50	.5854	7675	.8107	9089	.7221	8586	1.3848	1414	10
36° 00′	.5878	9.7692	.8090	9.9080	.7265	9.8613	1.3764	0.1387	54° 00′
	Nat.	Log.	Nat.	Log.	Nat.	Log.	Nat.	Log.	
Angles	Cosines		Sines		Cotangents		Tangents		Angles

TABLE II.—TRIGONOMETRIC FUNCTIONS.—(*Continued*)

Angles	Sines		Cosines		Tangents		Cotangents		Angles
	Nat.	Log.	Nat.	Log.	Nat.	Log.	Nat.	Log.	
36° 00′	.5878	9.7692	.8090	9.9080	.7265	9.8613	1.3764	0.1387	54° 00′
10	.5901	7710	.8073	9070	.7310	8639	1.3680	1361	50
20	.5925	7727	.8056	9061	.7355	8666	1.3597	1334	40
30	.5948	7744	.8039	9052	.7400	8692	1.3514	1308	30
40	.5972	7761	.8021	9042	.7445	8718	1.3432	1282	20
50	.5995	7778	.8004	9033	.7490	8745	1.3351	1255	10
37° 00′	.6018	9.7795	.7986	9.9023	.7536	9.8771	1.3270	0.1229	53° 00′
10	.6041	7811	.7969	9014	.7581	8797	1.3190	1203	50
20	.6065	7828	.7951	9004	.7627	8824	1.3111	1176	40
30	.6088	7844	.7934	8995	.7673	8850	1.3032	1150	30
40	.6111	7861	.7916	8985	.7720	8876	1.2954	1124	20
50	.6134	7877	.7898	8975	.7766	8902	1.2876	1098	10
38° 00′	.6157	9.7893	.7880	9.8965	.7813	9.8928	1.2790	0.1072	52° 00′
10	.6180	7910	.7862	8955	.7860	8954	1.2723	1046	50
20	.6202	7926	.7844	8945	.7907	8980	1.2647	1020	40
30	.6225	7941	.7826	8935	.7954	9006	1.2572	0994	30
40	.6248	7957	.7808	8925	.8002	9032	1.2497	0968	20
50	.6271	7973	.7790	8915	.8050	9058	1.2423	0942	10
39° 00′	.6293	9.7989	.7771	9.8905	.8098	9.9084	1.2349	0.0916	51° 00′
10	.6316	8004	.7753	8895	.8146	9110	1.2276	0890	50
20	.6338	8020	.7735	8884	.8195	9135	1.2203	0865	40
30	.6361	8035	.7716	8874	.8243	9161	1.2131	0839	30
40	.6383	8050	.7698	8864	.8292	9187	1.2059	0813	20
50	.6406	8066	.7679	8853	.8342	9212	1.1988	0788	10
40° 00′	.6428	9.8081	.7660	9.8843	.8391	9.9238	1.1918	0.0762	50° 00′
10	.6450	8096	.7642	8832	.8441	9264	1.1847	0736	50
20	.6472	8111	.7623	8821	.8491	9289	1.1778	0711	40
30	.6494	8125	.7604	8810	.8541	9315	1.1708	0685	30
40	.6517	8140	.7585	8800	.8591	9341	1.1640	0659	20
50	.6539	8155	.7566	8789	.8642	9366	1.1571	0634	10
41° 00′	.6561	9.8169	.7547	9.8778	.8693	9.9392	1.1504	0.0608	49° 00′
10	.6583	8184	.7528	8767	.8744	9417	1.1436	0583	50
20	.6604	8198	.7509	8756	.8796	9443	1.1369	0557	40
30	.6626	8213	.7490	8745	.8847	9468	1.1303	0532	30
40	.6648	8227	.7470	8733	.8899	9494	1.1237	0506	20
50	.6670	8241	.7451	8722	.8952	9519	1.1171	0481	10
42° 00′	.6691	9.8255	.7431	9.8711	.9004	9.9544	1.1106	0.0456	48° 00′
10	.6713	8269	.7412	8699	.9057	9570	1.1041	0430	50
20	.6734	8283	.7392	8688	.9110	9595	1.0977	0405	40
30	.6756	8297	.7373	8676	.9163	9621	1.0913	0379	30
40	.6777	8311	.7353	8665	.9217	9646	1.0850	0354	20
50	.6799	8324	.7333	8653	.9271	9671	1.0786	0329	10
43° 00′	.6820	9.8338	.7314	9.8641	.9325	9.9697	1.0724	0.0303	47° 00′
10	.6841	8351	.7294	8629	.9380	9722	1.0661	0278	50
20	.6862	8365	.7274	8618	.9435	9747	1.0599	0253	40
30	.6884	8378	.7254	8606	.9490	9772	1.0538	0228	30
40	.6905	8391	.7234	8594	.9545	9798	1.0477	0202	20
50	.6926	8405	.7214	8582	.9601	9823	1.0416	0177	10
44° 00′	.6947	9.8418	.7193	9.8569	.9657	9.9848	1.0355	0.0152	46° 00′
10	.6967	8431	.7173	8557	.9713	9874	1.0295	0126	50
20	.6988	8444	.7153	8545	.9770	9899	1.0235	0101	40
30	.7009	8457	.7133	8532	.9827	9924	1.0176	0076	30
40	.7030	8469	.7112	8520	.9884	9949	1.0117	0051	20
50	.7050	8482	.7092	8507	.9942	9975	1.0058	0025	10
45° 00′	.7071	9.8495	.7071	9.8495	1.0000	0.0000	1.0000	0.0000	45° 00′
	Nat.	Log.	Nat.	Log.	Nat.	Log.	Nat.	Log.	
Angles	Cosines		Sines		Cotangents		Tangents		Angles

Table III.—Powers and Roots

No.	Sq.	Sq. Root	Cube	Cube Root	No.	Sq.	Sq. Root	Cube	Cube Root
1	1	1.000	1	1.000	51	2,601	7.141	132,651	3.708
2	4	1.414	8	1.260	52	2,704	7.211	140,608	3.733
3	9	1.732	27	1.442	53	2,809	7.280	148,877	3.756
4	16	2.000	64	1.587	54	2,916	7.348	157,464	3.780
5	25	2.236	125	1.710	55	3,025	7.416	166,375	3.803
6	36	2.449	216	1.817	56	3,136	7.483	175,616	3.826
7	49	2.646	343	1.913	57	3,249	7.550	185,193	3.849
8	64	2.828	512	2.000	58	3,364	7.616	195,112	3.871
9	81	3.000	729	2.080	59	3,481	7.681	205,379	3.893
10	100	3.162	1,000	2.154	60	3,600	7.746	216,000	3.915
11	121	3.317	1,331	2.224	61	3,721	7.810	226,981	3.936
12	144	3.464	1,728	2.289	62	3,844	7.874	238,328	3.958
13	169	3.606	2,197	2.351	63	3,969	7.937	250,047	3.979
14	196	3.742	2,744	2.410	64	4,096	8.000	262,144	4.000
15	225	3.873	3,375	2.466	65	4,225	8.062	274,625	4.021
16	256	4.000	4,096	2.520	66	4,356	8.124	287,496	4.041
17	289	4.123	4,913	2.571	67	4,489	8.185	300,763	4.062
18	324	4.243	5,832	2.621	68	4,624	8.246	314,432	4.082
19	361	4.359	6,859	2.668	69	4,761	8.307	328,509	4.102
20	400	4.472	8,000	2.714	70	4,900	8.367	343,000	4.121
21	441	4.583	9,261	2.759	71	5,041	8.426	357,911	4.141
22	484	4.690	10,648	2.802	72	5,184	8.485	373,248	4.160
23	529	4.796	12,167	2.844	73	5,329	8.544	389,017	4.179
24	576	4.899	13,824	2.884	74	5,476	8.602	405,224	4.198
25	625	5.000	15,625	2.924	75	5,625	8.660	421,875	4.217
26	676	5.099	17,576	2.962	76	5,776	8.718	438,976	4.236
27	729	5.196	19,683	3.000	77	5,929	8.775	456,533	4.254
28	784	5.291	21,952	3.037	78	6,084	8.832	474,552	4.273
29	841	5.385	24,389	3.072	79	6,241	8.888	493,039	4.291
30	900	5.477	27,000	3.107	80	6,400	8.944	512,000	4.309
31	961	5.568	29,791	3.141	81	6,561	9.000	531,441	4.327
32	1,024	5.657	32,768	3.175	82	6,724	9.055	551,368	4.344
33	1,089	5.745	35,937	3.208	83	6,889	9.110	571,787	4.362
34	1,156	5.831	39,304	3.240	84	7,056	9.165	592,704	4.380
35	1,225	5.916	42,875	3.271	85	7,225	9.220	614,125	4.397
36	1,296	6.000	46,656	3.302	86	7,396	9.274	636,056	4.414
37	1,369	6.083	50,653	3.332	87	7,569	9.327	658,503	4.431
38	1,444	6.164	54,872	3.362	88	7,744	9.381	681,472	4.448
39	1,521	6.245	59,319	3.391	89	7,921	9.434	704,969	4.465
40	1,600	6.325	64,000	3.420	90	8,100	9.487	729,000	4.481
41	1,681	6.403	68,921	3.448	91	8,281	9.539	753,571	4.498
42	1,764	6.481	74,088	3.476	92	8,464	9.592	778,688	4.514
43	1,849	6.557	79,507	3.503	93	8,649	9.644	804,357	4.531
44	1,936	6.633	85,184	3.530	94	8,836	9.695	830,584	4.547
45	2,025	6.708	91,125	3.557	95	9,025	9.747	857,375	4.563
46	2,116	6.782	97,336	3.583	96	9,216	9.798	884,736	4.579
47	2,209	6.856	103,823	3.609	97	9,409	9.849	912,673	4.595
48	2,304	6.928	110,592	3.634	98	9,604	9.899	941,192	4.610
49	2,401	7.000	117,649	3.659	99	9,801	9.950	970,299	4.626
50	2,500	7.071	125,000	3.684	100	10,000	10.000	1,000,000	4.642

Table IV.—Compound Amount: $(1 + r)^n$

n	$1\frac{1}{2}$ %	2 %	$2\frac{1}{2}$ %	3 %	4 %	5 %	6 %
1	1.0150	1.0200	1.0250	1.0300	1.0400	1.0500	1.0600
2	1.0302	1.0404	1.0506	1.0609	1.0816	1.1025	1.1236
3	1.0457	1.0612	1.0769	1.0927	1.1249	1.1576	1.1910
4	1.0614	1.0824	1.1038	1.1255	1.1699	1.2155	1.2625
5	1.0773	1.1041	1.1314	1.1593	1.2167	1.2763	1.3382
6	1.0934	1.1262	1.1597	1.1941	1.2653	1.3401	1.4185
7	1.1098	1.1487	1.1887	1.2299	1.3159	1.4071	1.5036
8	1.1265	1.1717	1.2184	1.2668	1.3686	1.4775	1.5938
9	1.1434	1.1951	1.2489	1.3048	1.4233	1.5513	1.6895
10	1.1605	1.2190	1.2801	1.3439	1.4802	1.6289	1.7908
11	1.1779	1.2434	1.3121	1.3842	1.5395	1.7103	1.8983
12	1.1956	1.2682	1.3449	1.4258	1.6010	1.7959	2.0122
13	1.2136	1.2936	1.3785	1.4685	1.6651	1.8856	2.1329
14	1.2318	1.3195	1.4130	1.5126	1.7317	1.9799	2.2609
15	1.2502	1.3459	1.4483	1.5580	1.8009	2.0789	2.3966
16	1.2690	1.3728	1.4845	1.6047	1.8730	2.1829	2.5404
17	1.2880	1.4002	1.5216	1.6528	1.9479	2.2920	2.6928
18	1.3073	1.4282	1.5597	1.7024	2.0258	2.4066	2.8543
19	1.3270	1.4568	1.5987	1.7535	2.1068	2.5270	3.0256
20	1.3469	1.4859	1.6386	1.8061	2.1911	2.6533	3.2071
21	1.3671	1.5157	1.6796	1.8603	2.2788	2.7860	3.3996
22	1.3876	1.5460	1.7216	1.9161	2.3699	2.9253	3.6035
23	1.4084	1.5769	1.7646	1.9736	2.4647	3.0715	3.8197
24	1.4295	1.6084	1.8087	2.0328	2.5633	3.2251	4.0489
25	1.4509	1.6406	1.8539	2.0938	2.6658	3.3864	4.2919
26	1.4727	1.6734	1.9003	2.1566	2.7725	3.5557	4.5494
27	1.4948	1.7069	1.9478	2.2213	2.8834	3.7335	4.8223
28	1.5172	1.7410	1.9965	2.2879	2.9987	3.9201	5.1117
29	1.5400	1.7758	2.0464	2.3566	3.1187	4.1161	5.4184
30	1.5631	1.8114	2.0976	2.4273	3.2434	4.3219	5.7435
31	1.5865	1.8476	2.1500	2.5001	3.3731	4.5380	6.0881
32	1.6103	1.8845	2.2038	2.5751	3.5081	4.7649	6.4534
33	1.6345	1.9222	2.2589	2.6523	3.6484	5.0032	6.8406
34	1.6590	1.9607	2.3153	2.7319	3.7943	5.2533	7.2510
35	1.6839	1.9999	2.3732	2.8139	3.9461	5.5160	7.6861
36	1.7091	2.0399	2.4325	2.8983	4.1039	5.7918	8.1473
37	1.7348	2.0807	2.4933	2.9852	4.2681	6.0814	8.6361
38	1.7608	2.1223	2.5557	3.0748	4.4388	6.3855	9.1543
39	1.7872	2.1647	2.6196	3.1670	4.6164	6.7048	9.7035
40	1.8140	2.2080	2.6851	3.2620	4.8010	7.0400	10.2857
41	1.8412	2.2522	2.7522	3.3599	4.9931	7.3920	10.9029
42	1.8688	2.2972	2.8210	3.4607	5.1928	7.7616	11.5570
43	1.8969	2.3432	2.8915	3.5645	5.4005	8.1497	12.2505
44	1.9253	2.3901	2.9638	3.6715	5.6165	8.5572	12.9855
45	1.9542	2.4379	3.0379	3.7816	5.8412	8.9850	13.7646
46	1.9835	2.4866	3.1139	3.8950	6.0748	9.4343	14.5905
47	2.0133	2.5363	3.1917	4.0119	6.3178	9.9060	15.4659
48	2.0435	2.5871	3.2715	4.1323	6.5705	10.4013	16.3939
49	2.0741	2.6388	3.3533	4.2562	6.8333	10.9213	17.3775
50	2.1052	2.6916	3.4371	4.3839	7.1067	11.4674	18.4202

TABLE V.—PRESENT VALUE: $(1 + r)^{-n}$

n	$1\frac{1}{2}\%$	2%	$2\frac{1}{2}\%$	3%	4%	5%	6%
1	.985 22	.980 39	.97561	.97087	.96154	.95238	.94340
2	.970 66	.961 17	.95181	.94260	.92456	.90703	.89000
3	.956 32	.942 32	.92860	.91514	.88900	.86384	.83962
4	.942 18	.923 85	.90595	.88849	.85480	.82270	.79209
5	.928 26	.905 73	.88385	.86261	.82193	.78353	.74726
6	.914 54	.887 97	.86230	.83748	.79031	.74622	.70496
7	.901 03	.870 56	.84127	.81309	.75992	.71068	.66506
8	.887 71	.853 49	.82075	.78941	.73069	.67684	.62741
9	.874 59	.836 76	.80073	.76642	.70259	.64461	.59190
10	.861 67	.820 35	.78120	.74409	.67556	.61391	.55839
11	.848 93	.804 26	.76214	.72242	.64958	.58468	.52679
12	.836 39	.788 49	.74356	.70138	.62460	.55684	.49697
13	.824 03	.773 03	.72542	.68095	.60057	.53032	.46884
14	.811 85	.757 88	.70773	.66112	.57748	.50507	.44230
15	.799 85	.743 01	.69047	.64186	.55526	.48102	.41727
16	.788 03	.728 45	.67362	.62317	.53391	.45811	.39365
17	.776 39	.714 16	.65720	.60502	.51337	.43630	.37136
18	.764 91	.700 16	.64117	.58739	.49363	.41552	.35034
19	.753 61	.686 43	.62553	.57029	.47464	.39573	.33051
20	.742 47	.672 97	.61027	.55368	.45639	.37689	.31180
21	.731 50	.659 78	.59539	.53755	.43883	.35894	.29416
22	.720 69	.646 84	.58086	.52189	.42196	.34185	.27751
23	.710 04	.634 16	.56670	.50669	.40573	.32557	.26180
24	.699 54	.621 72	.55288	.49193	.39012	.31007	.24698
25	.689 21	.609 53	.53939	.47761	.37512	.29530	.23300
26	.679 02	.597 58	.52623	.46369	.36065	.28124	.21981
27	.668 99	.585 86	.51340	.45019	.34682	.26785	.20737
28	.659 10	.574 37	.50088	.43708	.33348	.25509	.19563
29	.649 36	.563 11	.48866	.42435	.32069	.24295	.18456
30	.639 76	.552 07	.47674	.41199	.30832	.23138	.17411
31	.630 31	.541 25	.46511	.39999	.29646	.22036	.16425
32	.620 99	.530 63	.45377	.38834	.28506	.20987	.15496
33	.611 82	.520 23	.44270	.37703	.27409	.19987	.14619
34	.602 77	.510 03	.43191	.36604	.26355	.19035	.13791
35	.593 87	.500 03	.42137	.35538	.25342	.18129	.13011
36	.585 09	.490 22	.41109	.34503	.24367	.17266	.12274
37	.576 44	.480 61	.40107	.33498	.23430	.16444	.11579
38	.567 92	.471 19	.39128	.32523	.22529	.15661	.10924
39	.559 53	.461 95	.38174	.31575	.21662	.14915	.10306
40	.551 26	.452 89	.37243	.30656	.20829	.14205	.09722
41	.543 12	.444 01	.36335	.29763	.20028	.13528	.09172
42	.535 09	.435 30	.35448	.28896	.19257	.12884	.08653
43	.527 18	.426 77	.34584	.28054	.18517	.12270	.08163
44	.519 39	.418 40	.33740	.27237	.17805	.11686	.07701
45	.511 71	.410 20	.32917	.26444	.17120	.11130	.07265
46	.504 15	.402 15	.32115	.25674	.16461	.10600	.06854
47	.496 70	.394 27	.31331	.24926	.15828	.10095	.06466
48	.489 36	.386 54	.30567	.24200	.15219	.09614	.06100
49	.482 13	.378 96	.29822	.23495	.14634	.09156	.05755
50	.475 00	.371 53	.29094	.22811	.14071	.08720	.05429

TABLE VI.—AMOUNT OF AN ANNUITY: $s_{\overline{n}|i}$

n	$2\frac{1}{2}\%$	2%	$2\frac{1}{2}\%$	3%	4%	5%	6%
1	1.0000	1.0000	1.0000	1.0000	1.0000	1.0000	1.0000
2	2.0150	2.0200	2.0250	2.0300	2.0400	2.0500	2.0600
3	3.0452	3.0604	3.0756	3.0909	3.1216	3.1525	3.1836
4	4.0909	4.1216	4.1525	4.1836	4.2465	4.3101	4.3746
5	5.1523	5.2040	5.2563	5.3091	5.4163	5.5256	5.6371
6	6.2296	6.3081	6.3877	6.4684	6.6330	6.8019	6.9753
7	7.3230	7.4343	7.5474	7.6625	7.8983	8.1420	8.3938
8	8.4328	8.5830	8.7361	8.8923	9.2142	9.5491	9.8975
9	9.5593	9.7546	9.9545	10.1591	10.5828	11.0266	11.4913
10	10.7027	10.9497	11.2034	11.4639	12.0061	12.5779	13.1808
11	11.8633	12.1687	12.4835	12.8078	13.4864	14.2068	14.9716
12	13.0412	13.4121	13.7956	14.1920	15.0258	15.9171	16.8699
13	14.2368	14.6803	15.1404	15.6178	16.6268	17.7130	18.8821
14	15.4504	15.9739	16.5190	17.0863	18.2919	19.5986	21.0151
15	16.6821	17.2934	17.9319	18.5989	20.0236	21.5786	23.2760
16	17.9324	18.6393	19.3802	20.1569	21.8245	23.6575	25.6725
17	19.2014	20.0121	20.8647	21.7616	23.6975	25.8404	28.2129
18	20.4894	21.4123	22.3863	23.4144	25.6454	28.1324	30.9057
19	21.7967	22.8406	23.9460	25.1169	27.6712	30.5390	33.7600
20	23.1237	24.2974	25.5447	26.8704	29.7781	33.0660	36.7856
21	24.4705	25.7833	27.1833	28.6765	31.9692	35.7193	39.9927
22	25.8376	27.2990	28.8629	30.5368	34.2480	38.5052	43.3923
23	27.2251	28.8450	30.5844	32.4529	36.6179	41.4305	46.9958
24	28.6335	30.4219	32.3490	34.4265	39.0826	44.5020	50.8156
25	30.0630	32.0303	34.1578	36.4593	41.6459	47.7271	54.8645
26	31.5140	33.6709	36.0117	38.5530	44.3117	51.1135	59.1564
27	32.9867	35.3443	37.9120	40.7096	47.0842	54.6691	63.7058
28	34.4815	37.0512	39.8598	42.9309	49.9676	58.4026	68.5281
29	35.9987	38.7922	41.8563	45.2189	52.9663	62.3227	73.6398
30	37.5387	40.5681	43.9027	47.5754	56.0849	66.4388	79.0582
31	39.1018	42.3794	46.0003	50.0027	59.3283	70.7608	84.8017
32	40.6883	44.2270	48.1503	52.5028	62.7015	75.2988	90.8898
33	42.2986	46.1116	50.3540	55.0778	66.2095	80.0638	97.3432
34	43.9331	48.0338	52.6129	57.7302	69.8579	85.0670	104.1838
35	45.5921	49.9945	54.9282	60.4621	73.6522	90.3203	111.4348
36	47.2760	51.9944	57.3014	63.2759	77.5983	95.8363	119.1209
37	48.9851	54.0343	59.7339	66.1742	81.7022	101.6281	127.2681
38	50.7199	56.1149	62.2273	69.1594	85.9703	107.7095	135.9042
39	52.4807	58.2372	64.7830	72.2342	90.4091	114.0950	145.0585
40	54.2679	60.4020	67.4026	75.4013	95.0255	120.7998	154.7620
41	56.0819	62.6100	70.0876	78.6633	99.8265	127.8398	165.0477
42	57.9231	64.8622	72.8398	82.0232	104.8196	135.2318	175.9505
43	59.7920	67.1595	75.6608	85.4839	110.0124	142.9933	187.5076
44	61.6889	69.5027	78.5523	89.0484	115.4129	151.1430	199.7580
45	63.6142	71.8927	81.5161	92.7199	121.0294	159.7002	212.7435
46	65.5684	74.3306	84.5540	96.5015	126.8706	168.6852	226.5081
47	67.5519	76.8172	87.6679	100.3965	132.9454	178.1194	241.0986
48	69.5652	79.3535	90.8596	104.4084	139.2632	188.0254	256.5645
49	71.6087	81.9406	94.1311	108.5406	145.8337	198.4267	272.9584
50	73.6828	84.5794	97.4843	112.7969	152.6671	209.3480	290.3359

TABLE VII.—PRESENT VALUE OF AN ANNUITY: $a_{\overline{n}|i}$

n	1½%	2%	2½%	3%	4%	5%	6%
1	.9852	.9804	.9756	.9709	.9615	.9524	.9434
2	1.9559	1.9416	1.9274	1.9135	1.8861	1.8594	1.8334
3	2.9122	2.8839	2.8560	2.8286	2.7751	2.7232	2.6730
4	3.8544	3.8077	3.7620	3.7171	3.6299	3.5460	3.4651
5	4.7826	4.7135	4.6458	4.5797	4.4518	4.3295	4.2124
6	5.6972	5.6014	5.5081	5.4172	5.2421	5.0757	4.9173
7	6.5982	6.4720	6.3494	6.2303	6.0021	5.7864	5.5824
8	7.4859	7.3255	7.1701	7.0197	6.7327	6.4632	6.2098
9	8.3605	8.1622	7.9709	7.7861	7.4353	7.1078	6.8017
10	9.2222	8.9826	8.7521	8.5302	8.1109	7.7217	7.3601
11	10.0711	9.7868	9.5142	9.2526	8.7605	8.3064	7.8869
12	10.9075	10.5753	10.2578	9.9540	9.3851	8.8633	8.3838
13	11.7315	11.3484	10.9832	10.6350	9.9856	9.3936	8.8527
14	12.5434	12.1062	11.6909	11.2961	10.5631	9.8986	9.2950
15	13.3432	12.8493	12.3814	11.9379	11.1184	10.3797	9.7122
16	14.1313	13.5777	13.0550	12.5611	11.6523	10.8378	10.1059
17	14.9076	14.2919	13.7122	13.1661	12.1657	11.2741	10.4773
18	15.6726	14.9920	14.3534	13.7535	12.6593	11.6896	10.8276
19	16.4262	15.6785	14.9789	14.3238	13.1339	12.0853	11.1581
20	17.1686	16.3514	15.5892	14.8775	13.5903	12.4622	11.4699
21	17.9001	17.0112	16.1845	15.4150	14.0292	12.8212	11.7641
22	18.6208	17.6580	16.7654	15.9369	14.4511	13.1630	12.0416
23	19.3309	18.2922	17.3321	16.4436	14.8568	13.4886	12.3034
24	20.0304	18.9139	17.8850	16.9355	15.2470	13.7986	12.5504
25	20.7196	19.5235	18.4244	17.4131	15.6221	14.0939	12.7834
26	21.3986	20.1210	18.9506	17.8768	15.9828	14.3752	13.0032
27	22.0676	20.7069	19.4640	18.3270	16.3296	14.6430	13.2105
28	22.7267	21.2813	19.9649	18.7641	16.6631	14.8981	13.4062
29	23.3761	21.8444	20.4535	19.1885	16.9837	15.1411	13.5907
30	24.0158	22.3965	20.9303	19.6004	17.2920	15.3725	13.7648
31	24.6461	22.9377	21.3954	20.0004	17.5885	15.5928	13.9291
32	25.2671	23.4683	21.8492	20.3888	17.8736	15.8027	14.0840
33	25.8790	23.9886	22.2919	20.7658	18.1476	16.0025	14.2302
34	26.4817	24.4986	22.7238	21.1318	18.4112	16.1929	14.3681
35	27.0756	24.9986	23.1452	21.4872	18.6646	16.3742	14.4982
36	27.6607	25.4888	23.5563	21.8323	18.9083	16.5469	14.6210
37	28.2371	25.9695	23.9573	22.1672	19.1426	16.7113	14.7368
38	28.8051	26.4406	24.3486	22.4925	19.3679	16.8679	14.8460
39	29.3646	26.9026	24.7303	22.8082	19.5845	17.0170	14.9491
40	29.9158	27.3555	25.1028	23.1148	19.7928	17.1591	15.0463
41	30.4590	27.7995	25.4661	23.4124	19.9931	17.2944	15.1380
42	30.9941	28.2348	25.8206	23.7014	20.1856	17.4232	15.2245
43	31.5212	28.6616	26.1664	23.9819	20.3708	17.5459	15.3062
44	32.0406	29.0800	26.5038	24.2543	20.5488	17.6628	15.3832
45	32.5523	29.4902	26.8330	24.5187	20.7200	17.7741	15.4558
46	33.0565	29.8923	27.1542	24.7754	20.8847	17.8801	15.5244
47	33.5532	30.2866	27.4675	25.0247	21.0429	17.9810	15.5890
48	34.0426	30.6731	27.7732	25.2667	21.1951	18.0772	15.6500
49	34.5247	31.0521	28.0714	25.5017	21.3415	18.1687	15.7076
50	34.9997	31.4236	28.3623	25.7298	21.4822	18.2559	15.7619

TABLE VIII.—AMERICAN EXPERIENCE TABLE OF MORTALITY

Age	Number living	Number dying	Yearly probability of dying	Yearly probability of living	Age	Number living	Number dying	Yearly probability of dying	Yearly probability of living
10	100 000	749	0.007 490	0.992 510	53	66 797	1 091	0.016 333	0.983 667
11	99 251	746	0.007 516	0.992 484	54	65 706	1 143	0.017 396	0.982 604
12	98 505	743	0.007 543	0.992 457	55	64 563	1 199	0.018 571	0.981 429
13	97 762	740	0.007 569	0.992 431	56	63 364	1 260	0.019 885	0.980 115
14	97 022	737	0.007 596	0.992 404	57	62 104	1 325	0.021 335	0.978 665
15	96 285	735	0.007 634	0.992 366	58	60.779	1 394	0.022 936	0.977 064
16	95 550	732	0.007 661	0.992 339	59	59 385	1 468	0.024 720	0.975 280
17	94 818	729	0.007 688	0.992 312	60	57 917	1 546	0.026 693	0.973 307
18	94 089	727	0.007 727	0.992 273	61	56 371	1 628	0.028 880	0.971 120
19	93 362	725	0.007 765	0.992 235	62	54 743	1 713	0.031 292	0.968 708
20	92 637	723	0.007 805	0.992 195	63	53 030	1 800	0.033 943	0.966 057
21	91 914	722	0.007 855	0.992 145	64	51 230	1 889	0.036 873	0.963 127
22	91 192	721	0.007 906	0.992 094	65	49 341	1 980	0.040 129	0.959 871
23	90 471	720	0.007 958	0.992 042	66	47 361	2 070	0.043 707	0.956 293
24	89 751	719	0.008 011	0.991 989	67	45 291	2 158	0.047 647	0.952 353
25	89 032	718	0.008 065	0.991 935	68	43 133	2 243	0.052 002	0.947 998
26	88 314	718	0.008 130	0.991 870	69	40 890	2 321	0.056 762	0.943 238
27	87 596	718	0.008 197	0.991 803	70	38 569	2 391	0.061 993	0.938 007
28	86 878	718	0.008 264	0.991 736	71	36 178	2 448	0.067 665	0.932 335
29	86 160	719	0.008 345	0.991 655	72	33 730	2 487	0.073 733	0.926 267
30	85 441	720	0.008 427	0.991 573	73	31 243	2 505	0.080 178	0.919 822
31	84 721	721	0.008 510	0.991 490	74	28 738	2 501	0.087 028	0.912 972
32	84 000	723	0.008 607	0.991 393	75	26 237	2 476	0.094 371	0.905 629
33	83 277	726	0.008 718	0.991 282	76	23 761	2 431	0.102 311	0.897 689
34	82 551	729	0.008 831	0.991 169	77	21 330	2 369	0.111 064	0.888 936
35	81 822	732	0.008 946	0.991 054	78	18 961	2 291	0.120 827	0.879 173
36	81 090	737	0.009 089	0.990 911	79	16 670	2 196	0.131 734	0.868 266
37	80 353	742	0.009 234	0.990 766	80	14 474	2 091	0.144 466	0.855 534
38	79 611	749	0.009 408	0.990 592	81	12 383	1 964	0.158 605	0.841 395
39	78 862	756	0.009 586	0.990 414	82	10 419	1 816	0.174 297	0.825 703
40	78 106	765	0.009 794	0.990 206	83	8 603	1 648	0.191 561	0.808 439
41	77 341	774	0.010 008	0.989 992	84	6 955	1 470	0.211 359	0.788 641
42	76 567	785	0.010 252	0.989 748	85	5 485	1 292	0.235 552	0.764 448
43	75 782	797	0.010 517	0.989 483	86	4 193	1 114	0.265 681	0.734 319
44	74 985	812	0.010 829	0.989 171	87	3 079	933	0.303 020	0.696 980
45	74 173	828	0.011 163	0.988 837	88	2 146	744	0.346 692	0.653 308
46	73 345	848	0.011 562	0.988 438	89	1 402	555	0.395 863	0.604 137
47	72 497	870	0.012 000	0.988 000	90	847	385	0.454 545	0.545 455
48	71 627	896	0.012 509	0.987 491	91	462	246	0.532 468	0.467 532
49	70 731	927	0.013 106	0.986 894	92	216	137	0.634 259	0.365 741
50	69 804	962	0.013 781	0.986 219	93	79	58	0.734 177	0.265 823
51	68 842	1 001	0.014 541	0.985 459	94	21	18	0.857 143	0.142 857
52	67 841	1 044	0.015 389	0.984 611	95	3	3	1.000 000	0.000 000

ANSWERS

Note: Answers to three problems out of each four are provided.

Exercise 1

1. 2. **2.** 0. **3.** 4. **5.** 4. **6.** −14. **7.** −1. **9.** −1. **10.** 13. **11.** 0. **13.** 8.
14. −6. **15.** −4. **17.** $6x$. **18.** $-3a$. **19.** $7b$. **21.** $-a + 3b$. **22.** $2x + 2y$.
23. $4b − 8c$. **25.** $7x + 3y + z$. **26.** $2a − 8b − c$. **27.** $-2r − 2s − 2t$.
29. $9a − 11b + c$. **30.** $-5y + 4z$. **31.** $-6r − 6s + 10t$. **33.** $a − 8b + 3c$.
34. $-10x − 11y + 12z$. **35.** $3r − 3s − t$. **37.** 4. **38.** −10. **39.** 12. **41.** $-b$.
42. $x − 4y$. **43.** $-7b − 6c$. **45.** $7a − 8b − 2c$. **46.** $-2x − 10y − 2z$.
47. $-5r − 11s + 17t$. **49.** 5. **50.** 7. **51.** 15. **53.** 2. **54.** 18. **55.** −3.
57. $2a − b − 2c$. **58.** $3x + y − 2z$. **59.** $3h + i + 2k$. **61.** $a − 7b + 7c$.
62. $-3x − 7y$. **63.** $-2x − 3y − z$. **65.** $-a + 3b$. **66.** $2x − 5y$. **67.** $-5s + 13t$.

Exercise 2

1. $6a^3$. **2.** $12b^6$. **3.** $15y^8$. **5.** $18a^3b^4$. **6.** $10x^5y^4$. **7.** $24r^5s^7$. **9.** $6a^3b^4$. **10.** $8c^5d^6$.
11. $18r^6s^3$. **13.** $24a^4b^3c^5$. **14.** $24r^5s^7t^7$. **15.** $6x^7y^7z^3$. **17.** $24a^3b^3c^3$. **18.** $6x^3y^5z^4$.
19. $48r^3s^5t^3$. **21.** a^6. **22.** b^6. **23.** x^{12}. **25.** $8a^6b^3$. **26.** $9c^6d^4$. **27.** $64x^6y^9z^3$.
29. $2x^2 + 3xy − 2y^2$. **30.** $6a^2 − ab − 2b^2$. **31.** $6r^2 + rs − 12s^2$.
33. $x^2 + 2xy + y^2 − z^2$. **34.** $a^2 − b^2 − 2bc − c^2$. **35.** $6r^2 − 7rs − rt − 3s^2 + 7st − 2t^2$.
37. $x^3 − x^2y − 3xy^2 − y^3$. **38.** $2a^3 − 9a^2b + 13ab^2 − 6b^3$.
39. $-6b^3 − 16b^2c + bc^2 + 6c^3$. **41.** $2x^4 − 5x^3y − 5x^2y^2 + 13xy^3 − 4y^4$.
42. $6a^4 − 16a^3b + 15a^2b^2 + 6ab^3 − 20b^4$. **43.** $12u^4 − u^3v − 32u^2v^2 + 11uv^3 + 10v^4$.
45. $x^5 + x^4 − 3x^3 + 3x − 2$. **46.** $a^5 − 2a^4 + 3a^3 − 3a^2 + 2a − 1$.
47. $2y^5 + y^4 − 3y^3 + 3y^2 − 5y + 2$. **49.** $2a^2 + 2ab + 4b^2$. **50.** $6x^2 − 6xy − 4y^2$.
51. $3s^2$. **53.** $-2a^3 − 15ab$. **54.** $4b^2 + 4c^2 − 12c^3$. **55.** $-6x^2 − 3xy − 2x$.

Exercise 3

1. a^2. **2.** b. **3.** c^4. **5.** $4a^2$. **6.** $3x^3$. **7.** $3b^3$. **9.** ab^2. **10.** c^2d^2. **11.** y^2. **13.** $4ac^2$.
14. $5x^2y^4c^2$. **15.** $5s$. **17.** $\dfrac{a^4}{b^6}$. **18.** $\dfrac{8x^6}{y^3}$. **19.** $\dfrac{4c^6}{9d^4}$. **21.** $2a − 3$. **22.** $3c − 2$. **23.** $x − 3y$.

25. $2x^2 − x + 3$. **26.** $3b^2 − 2b + 1$. **27.** $5y^2 − 3y − 2$. **29.** $x^2 + xy + y^2$.
30. $2a^2 − ab + 2b^2$. **31.** $2u^2 + 2uv + 2v^2$. **33.** $y^2 + y + 1$. **34.** $x^3 − x^2 + 1$.
35. $2a^3 − a^2 + 1$. **37.** Quotient, $x − 1$; remainder, x.
38. Quotient, $2a^2 − 3a + 6$; remainder, $-6a$. **39.** Quotient, $2x − y$; remainder, $-2xy^2$.

Supplementary Problems for Chap. 1

1. 6. **2.** 1. **3.** 2. **5.** 1. **6.** 31. **7.** 23. **9.** 1. **10.** 5. **11.** 7. **13.** $3a$. **14.** $6x$.
15. $-3y$. **17.** $2y − 2x$. **18.** $3a − b$. **19.** $10a − 6b + 2c$. **21.** 14. **22.** −26.
23. −26. **25.** 1. **26.** 84. **27.** −4. **29.** 3. **30.** 47. **31.** 73. **33.** 17. **34.** 210.

35. 66. **37.** $-7b - 13c.$ **38.** $-4x - 4y.$ **39.** $12r - 11s.$ **41.** $10x + 2y - 7z.$
42. $-11a + 4b + 2c.$ **43.** $4r - s - 5t.$ **45.** $3a - 7b.$ **46.** $-6x + 8y.$ **47.** $-3c.$
49. $8a - 5b + 7c.$ **50.** $x + 5y - 2z.$ **51.** $8r + 5s + 3t.$ **53.** $-9a^2 - a + 4.$
54. $6x^2 - 3x + 6.$ **55.** $6a^2 + 4ab - 3b^2.$ **57.** $8a^2b - 4ab^2.$ **58.** $3x^2y + xy^2.$
59. $-7a^3b^2.$ **61.** $3a^2.$ **62.** $-5x^3.$ **63.** $-5ab^2.$ **65.** $2a^3b^3 - 2a^4b^2.$ **66.** $x^5y^3 + x^5y^2.$
67. $12a^3b^3c^2 - 5a^3b^2c^3.$ **69.** $a^2 - 4ab + 4b^2.$ **70.** $6a^2 - 11ab - 10b^2.$
71. $12x^2 - 17xy + 6y^2.$ **73.** $6a^2 + 5ab + 5ac - 4b^2 + 14bc - 6c^2.$
74. $6x^2 - 2xy - 9xz - 20y^2 - 59yz - 42z^2.$ **75.** $20r^4 - 39r^3 + 16r^2 - 3r - 6.$
77. $a^8 + a^4b^2 + b^4.$ **78.** $-x^{12} - 2x^6y^4 - 9y^8.$ **79.** $-a^6 + a^4 + a^2b^4 - b^4.$
81. $2x - 3y.$ **82.** $4a - b.$ **83.** $3h - 4k.$ **85.** $x^2 - xy + y^2.$ **86.** $x^2 + xy + y^2.$
87. $a^2 - 2ab + 2b^2.$ **89.** $3x + 2y - 4z.$ **90.** $2b + 3c - 2d.$ **91.** $2a + 3b - c.$
93. Quotient, $3x + y - 2$; remainder, $3y.$ **94.** Quotient, $4x^2 - 3x + 1$; remainder $5x - 1.$
95. Quotient, $a^2 - 2a + b$, remainder, $2ab.$ **97.** $-a - 11c.$ **98.** $2a^3 - 3b^2 + 12c^2.$
99. $6x^3 + 12y^3.$ **101.** $8b^2 - 3a^2.$ **102.** $-6y^2.$ **103.** $2d^2 + 24cd^2 - 6c^2d.$
105. $5x^2 - x^2y - xy^2.$ **106.** $2x^2 - xy - 6y^2.$ **107.** $-8a^2 - 27ab - b^2.$

Exercise 4

1. $x^2 + 3x + 2.$ **2.** $2x^2 + 3x + 1.$ **3.** $4a^2 + 9a + 2.$ **5.** $2x^2 + 5x - 3.$
6. $3b^2 + 5b - 2.$ **7.** $5a^2 + 9a - 2.$ **9.** $6x^2 + 5x - 6.$ **10.** $10h^2 - 19h - 15.$
11. $21i^2 + 13i - 20.$ **13.** $6r^2 + 13rs + 6s^2.$ **14.** $42a^2 + 47ab + 10b^2.$
15. $8x^2 + 22xy + 15y^2.$ **17.** $8a^2 - 26ab + 15b^2.$ **18.** $20x^2 - 56xy + 15y^2.$
19. $16c^2 - 62cd + 21d^2.$ **21.** $15h^2 - 19hk - 56k^2.$ **22.** $110i^2 - 13ij - 6j^2.$
23. $36x^2 + 9xy - 10y^2.$ **25.** $a^2 + 4ab + 4b^2.$ **26.** $x^2 + 6xy + 9y^2.$ **27.** $4x^2 + 12x + 9.$
29. $4x^2 - 4x + 1.$ **30.** $9i^2 - 6ij + j^2.$ **31.** $9a^2 - 24ab + 16b^2.$ **33.** $25a^2 - 20ab + 4b^2.$
34. $16x^2 + 40xy + 25y^2.$ **35.** $49r^2 - 42rs + 9s^2.$ **37.** $64u^2 - 48uv + 9v^2.$
38. $9i^2 + 66ij + 121j^2.$ **39.** $144z^2 - 120zw + 25w^2.$ **41.** 221. **42.** 891. **43.** 2484.
45. $x^2 - 25.$ **46.** $x^2 - 49.$ **47.** $a^2 - b^2.$ **49.** $a^2 - 4x^2.$ **50.** $x^2 - 9y^2.$ **51.** $9x^2 - b^2.$
53. $4a^2 - 9b^2.$ **54.** $9x^2 - 16z^2.$ **55.** $16y^2 - 25c^2.$ **57.** $4x^6 - y^2.$ **58.** $9a^4 - 4b^2.$
59. $25b^4 - 36c^6.$ **61.** $\dfrac{h^2}{9} - \dfrac{k^2}{4}.$ **62.** $\dfrac{4x^2}{25} - \dfrac{y^2}{16}.$ **63.** $\dfrac{a^4}{4} - \dfrac{4b^6}{9}.$ **65.** $\dfrac{x^2}{9} - \dfrac{4}{x^2}.$

66. $\dfrac{x^4}{25} - \dfrac{4}{9x^2}.$ **67.** $\dfrac{4a^2}{x^2} - \dfrac{y^2}{9b^2}.$ **69.** $a^2 + b^2 + d^2 + 2ab + 2ad + 2bd.$

70. $w^2 + x^2 + y^2 + 2wx - 2wy - 2xy.$ **71.** $m^2 + n^2 + t^2 + 2mn - 2mt - 2nt.$
73. $p^2 + q^2 + 4r^2 - 2pq + 4pr - 4qr.$ **74.** $p^2 + 4d^2 + q^2 - 4pd - 2pq + 4qd.$
75. $a^4 - 4a^3 + 10a^2 - 12a + 9.$
77. $a^2 + 4b^2 + c^2 + 9d^2 - 4ab + 2ac - 6ad - 4bc + 12bd - 6cd.$
78. $4x^2 + y^2 + 9z^2 + 4 - 4xy + 12xz - 8x - 6yz + 4y - 12z.$
79. $a^6 + 4a^5 + 2a^4 - 2a^3 + 5a^2 - 2a + 1.$ **81.** $15a^2 + 30ab + 15b^2 - a - b - 6.$
82. $90x^2 - 60xy + 10y^2 + 3x - y - 21.$ **83.** $48a^2 - 48ac + 12c^2 - 2a + c - 20.$
85. $a^4 - 3a^2 + 1.$ **86.** $x^4 + 3x^2 + 4.$ **87.** $4b^4 + c^4.$ **89.** $a^6 + a^4 - a^2 - 1.$
90. $x^6 - 3x^4 + 3x^2 - 1.$ **91.** $4b^8 - b^6 - 4b^4 + b^2.$

Exercise 5

1. $a(c - d - a).$ **2.** $3x(x - 2y + 3y^2).$ **3.** $2ab(a - 2b + 4a^2b).$ **5.** $2(a - b)(c + 2b).$
6. $x(x - y).$ **7.** $2(3r - 2s)(2u - t).$ **9.** $(x + a)(x - a).$ **10.** $(w + b)(w - b).$
11. $(y + 2x)(y - 2x).$ **13.** $(4w + x)(4w - x).$ **14.** $(5b + y)(5b - y).$
15. $(c + 6d)(c - 6d).$ **17.** $(2a + 3b)(2a - 3b).$ **18.** $(3h + 4k)(3h - 4k).$
19. $(6r + 5s)(6r - 5s).$ **21.** $(3x^2 + 4y^3)(3x^2 - 4y^3).$ **22.** $(7a^4 + 5b)(7a^4 - 5b).$

23. $(5x^3 - 3y^2)(5x^3 + 3y^2)$. **25.** $(\frac{2}{3}r^2 + \frac{5}{4}s)(\frac{2}{3}r^2 - \frac{5}{4}s)$. **26.** $(\frac{3}{4}i^3 + \frac{7}{5}j^2)(\frac{3}{4}i^3 - \frac{7}{5}j^2)$.

27. $(\frac{9}{10}a^6 - \frac{8}{3}b)(\frac{9}{10}a^6 + \frac{8}{3}b)$. **29.** $(a^2 + b)(a^2 - b)(a^4 + b^2)$.

30. $(2x + d^2)(2x - d^2)(4x^2 + d^4)$. **31.** $(3c^3 + 2c)(3c^3 - 2c)(9c^6 + 4c^2)$. **33.** $(a + 2)^2$.

34. $(x + 3)^2$. **35.** $(y + 5)^2$. **37.** $(2h - 1)^2$. **38.** $(3k - 1)^2$. **39.** $(4s - 1)^2$.

41. $(2a + 3b)^2$. **42.** $(3x + 5y)^2$. **43.** $(6c + 7d)^2$. **45.** $\left(\dfrac{a}{2} - \dfrac{2}{b}\right)^2$. **46.** $\left(\dfrac{c}{3} + \dfrac{3}{d}\right)^2$.

47. $\left(\dfrac{2x}{3} - \dfrac{9y}{4}\right)^2$. **49.** $(2r^3 - 3s^2)^2$. **50.** $(4a^4 - 3b^5)^2$. **51.** $(5h^2 + 6k^5)^2$.

53. $(x + 3)(x + 2)$. **54.** $(3y + 1)(y + 1)$. **55.** $(4a + 1)(a + 1)$. **57.** $(5c - 2)(c - 3)$.

58. $(7z - 5)(z - 3)$. **59.** $(8c - 5)(c - 1)$. **61.** $(2y - 1)(y + 2)$. **62.** $(3x + 1)(x - 2)$.

63. $(5h - 3)(h + 1)$. **65.** $(3r - 1)(2r + 5)$. **66.** $(8y - 5)(y + 1)$.

67. $(3y - 7)(3y + 1)$. **69.** $(3a + 6b)(a + 2b)$. **70.** $(5x + 8y)(x + 2y)$.

71. $(9u - 7v)(2u - v)$. **73.** $(8h - 3k)(h + k)$. **74.** $(2c + 9d)(c - d)$.

75. $(3a - 2b)(a + 5b)$. **77.** $(3p - 2q)(2p - 3q)$. **78.** $(4y + 3z)(3y + 2z)$.

79. $(5b - 4c)(3b - c)$. **81.** $(8a - 5b)(2a + 3b)$. **82.** $(8x - 3y)(2x + 5y)$.

83. $(8h - 3k)(3h + 4k)$. **85.** $a^2(6a - 5)(4a + 9)$. **86.** $2x^3(2x - 3)(2x + 9)$.

87. $(2a^3 - 3b^2)(3a^3 + 2b^2)$. **89.** $(6x^4y^3 - 7)(4x^4y^3 + 5)$. **90.** $(12c^5b^4 - 17)(c^5b^4 + 2)$.

91. $(4h^3 - 3k^5)(3h^3 + 5k^5)$. **93.** $(a + b + c)(a + b - c)$.

94. $(x - 2y + 2z)(x - 2y - 2z)$. **95.** $(3z + w - 3x)(3z + w + 3x)$.

97. $(5a + b + 2)(5a - b - 2)$. **98.** $(6 + 2x - y)(6 - 2x + y)$.

99. $(7x + 2y - 3z)(7x - 2y + 3z)$. **101.** $(a + 2b + c - 3d)(a + 2b - c + 3d)$.

102. $(3x - 4y + 2z - 5w)(3x - 4y - 2z + 5w)$.

103. $(5r - 4s + 4t + 3u)(5r - 4s - 4t - 3u)$.

Exercise 6

1. $(a - b)(a^2 + ab + b^2)$. **2.** $(c - d)(c^2 + cd + d^2)$. **3.** $(r + s)(r^2 - rs + s^2)$.

5. $(x - 2y)(x^2 + 2xy + 4y^2)$. **6.** $(a - 3b)(a^2 + 3ab + 9b^2)$.

7. $(j + 4k)(j^2 - 4jk + 16k^2)$. **9.** $(2u - 3v)(4u^2 + 6uv + 9v^2)$.

10. $(3p - 4q)(9p^2 + 12pq + 16q^2)$. **11.** $(5x + 2y)(25x^2 - 10xy + 4y^2)$.

13. $(a^2b - 2)(a^4b^2 + 2a^2b + 4)$. **14.** $(2h^3k^2 - 3)(4h^6k^4 + 6h^3k^2 + 9)$.

15. $(4u^4v^3 + 5)(16u^8v^6 - 20u^4v^3 + 25)$. **17.** $(a - b)(a + b)(a^2 + b^2)$.

18. $(h - k)(h + k)(h^2 + k^2)$. **19.** $(x + 2)(x - 2)(x^2 + 4)$.

21. $(x - y)(x + y)(x^2 + xy + y^2)(x^2 - xy + y^2)$. **22.** $(a^2 + 4)(a^4 - 4a^2 + 16)$.

23. $(3c - 1)(3c + 1)(9c^2 + 3c + 1)(9c^2 - 3c + 1)$. **25.** $(x^4 + y^4)(x^8 - x^4y^4 + y^8)$.

26. $(r^2 - s)(r^2 + s)(r^4 + s^2)$. **27.** $(p^3 + q^2)(p^6 - p^3q^2 + q^4)$.

29. $(a - b)(a^2 + ab + b^2)(a^6 + a^3b^3 + b^6)$.

30. $(2a - 1)(2a + 1)(4a^2 - 2a + 1)(4a^2 + 2a + 1)$.

31. $(x + y)(x^4 - x^3y + x^2y^2 - xy^3 + y^4)$.

33. $(x - y)(x + y)(x^6 + x^5y + x^4y^2 + x^3y^3 + x^2y^4 + xy^5 + y^6)$
$$(x^6 - x^5y + x^4y^2 - x^3y^3 + x^2y^4 - xy^5 + y^6).$$

34. $(x - y)(x + y)(x^2 + xy + y^2)(x^2 - xy + y^2)(x^6 + x^3y^3 + y^6)(x^6 - x^3y^3 + y^6)$.

35. $(x - y)(x^4 + x^3y + x^2y^2 + xy^3 + y^4)(x^{10} + x^5y^5 + y^{10})$.

37. $(m - n - 1)(m^2 - 2mn + n^2 + m - n + 1)$.

38. $(s + t + 1)(s^2 + 2st + t^2 - s - t + 1)$.

39. $(2a - b + 2)(4a^2 - 4ab + b^2 - 4a + 2b + 4)$.

41. $(1 - 2c + 3d)(1 + 2c - 3d + 4c^2 - 12cd + 9d^2)$.

42. $(4 + u - v)(16 - 4u + 4v + u^2 - 2uv + v^2)$.

43. $(a^3 - a^2 + 1)(a^6 + a^5 + a^4 - a^3 - 2a^2 + 1)$.

Exercise 7

1. $(a+1)(b+1)$.   **2.** $(x+1)(y+2)$.   **3.** $(u+2)(v+3)$.   **5.** $(a-b)(a+1)$.

6. $(x-2y)(y+1)$.   **7.** $(c+2d)(2c-3)$.   **9.** $(a+b)(c+d)$.   **10.** $(x-y)(y+z)$.

11. $(2r-5s)(3t+u)$.   **13.** $(2a-5b)(3a-2c)$.   **14.** $(4x-3y)(x-6z)$.

15. $(5h-3k)(3h+7j)$.   **17.** $(a-b+c)(a-1)$.   **18.** $(x-y-z)(x+1)$.

19. $(r-2s-t)(r-3u)$.   **21.** $(x+y)(x-y-1)$.   **22.** $(a-b)(a+b-1)$.

23. $(a-b)(a-b-c)$.   **25.** $(x-y)(x^2+xy+y^2-x+y)$.

26. $(a+b)(a+b-a^2+ab-b^2)$.   **27.** $(x-y)(x+2y-x^2-xy-y^2)$.

29. $(h-2k+4)(h-2k-4)$.   **30.** $(r+3s+2t)(r+3s-2t)$.

31. $(5a+b-2d)(5a-b+2d)$.   **33.** $(x-2y+2z+3w)(x-2y-2z-3w)$.

34. $(2a-b+c-3d)(2a-b-c+3d)$.   **35.** $(2r+3s+t+4u)(2r+3s-t-4u)$.

37. $(a-b)(a-2b+3c)$.   **38.** $(x-y)(x-2y-z)$.   **39.** $(2s-3t)(2r-3s+4t)$.

41. $(a^2+a+2)(a^2-a+2)$.   **42.** $(x^2+x+1)(x^2-x+1)$.

43. $(c^2-2c+3)(c^2+2c+3)$.   **45.** $(x^2+2x+2)(x^2-2x+2)$.

46. $(a^2+ab+2b^2)(a^2-ab+2b^2)$.   **47.** $(y^2+yz+3z^2)(y^2-yz+3z^2)$.

49. $(3a^2+2ab-2b^2)(3a^2-2ab-2b^2)$.   **50.** $(4x^2-3xy+3y^2)(4x^2+3xy+3y^2)$.

51. $(5r^2+4rs-2s^2)(5r^2-4rs-2s^2)$.

Supplementary Problems for Chap. 2

1. $3x^2+7x+2$.   **2.** $5a^2+11a+2$.   **3.** $3c^2+13cd+4d^2$.   **5.** $20s^2-23st+6t^2$.

6. $10a^2-41ab+21b^2$.   **7.** $6h^2-17hk+12k^2$.   **9.** $20s^2-7st-6t^2$.

10. $10a^2+29ab-21b^2$.   **11.** $28t^2-13tu-6u^2$.   **13.** $24x^2-5xy-14y^2$.

14. $45c^2-cd-28d^2$.   **15.** $30a^2-3ab-72b^2$.   **17.** $32h^2-4hk-55k^2$.

18. $84x^2+xy-28y^2$.   **19.** $45c^2+cd-66d^2$.   **21.** a^2-9.   **22.** b^2-16.   **23.** $4c^2-1$.

25. $4x^2-y^2$.   **26.** $9t^2-s^2$.   **27.** $16a^2-9b^2$.   **29.** $36c^2-25d^2$.   **30.** $49h^2-9k^2$.

31. $64h^2-25k^2$.   **33.** $a^2+4ab+4b^2$.   **34.** $4x^2-4xy+y^2$.   **35.** $4r^2+12rs+9s^2$.

37. $\frac{1}{4}x^2+2xy+4y^2$.   **38.** $\frac{4}{9}a^2-2ab+\frac{9}{4}b^2$.   **39.** $\frac{9}{16}r^2+4rs+\frac{64}{9}s^2$.

41. $25a^4+20a^2b^3+4b^6$.   **42.** $9x^6-30x^3y^4+25y^8$.   **43.** $36p^{10}+84p^5q^2+49q^4$.

45. $a^2+2ab+b^2-c^2$.   **46.** $x^2+2xy+y^2-z^2$.   **47.** $u^2+2uv+v^2-4w^2$.

49. $r^2+6rt+9t^2-4s^2$.   **50.** $4a^2+16ac+16c^2-9b^2$.   **51.** $x^2-4y^2-4yz-z^2$.

53. $a^2+b^2+c^2+2ab+2ac+2bc$.   **54.** $a^2+b^2+c^2-2ab+2ac-2bc$.

55. $x^2+y^2+4z^2+2xy-4xz-4yz$.

57. $a^2+4b^2+c^2+9d^2+4ab+2ac+6ad+4bc+12bd+6cd$.

58. $x^6+4x^5+2x^4-10x^3-11x^2+6x+9$.

59. $a^9-6a^5+5a^4+20a^3-20a^2-16a+16$.

61. $2x(x-3y-5z)$.   **62.** $3uv(u+2v-3w)$.   **63.** $4st(3r-2s+5t)$.

65. $3xy(3xy^2+2x^2y+1)$.   **66.** $4pq(4p^2q^2-5p+7q)$.   **67.** $5uv(2uv-4uw-5vw)$.

69. $(x-3)(x+3)$.   **70.** $(a-4)(a+4)$.   **71.** $(2u-7b)(2u+7b)$.

73. $5(3b^2+4c)(3b^2-4c)$.   **74.** $2b^3(2b^3+3)(2b^3-3)$.   **75.** $3cd(3c+2d)(3c-2d)$.

77. $(3a+b)^2$.   **78.** $(4x-y)^2$.   **79.** $(3u+2v)^2$.   **81.** $(5h^3-2t^2)^2$.   **82.** $(7a^2-2b^4)^2$.

83. $(3x+2y^5)^2$.   **85.** $(x-3)(x-2)$.   **86.** $(y+3)(y+4)$.   **87.** $(a+3)(a-2)$.

89. $(3x+2y)(2x-y)$.   **90.** $(3r-t)(2r+3t)$.   **91.** $(4a-b)(3a+4b)$.

93. $(c+d)(c^2-cd+d^2)$.   **94.** $(u-v)(u^2+uv+v^2)$.   **95.** $(2x+y)(4x^2-2xy+y^2)$.

97. $(3a+4b)(9a^2-12ab+16b^2)$.   **98.** $(2a^2+1)(4a^4-2a^2+1)$.

99. $(3+x^3)(9-3x^3+x^6)$.   **101.** $k(b+3)(d-4)$.   **102.** $c(y-2)(a+4)$.

103. $(a+b+c)(x-y)$.   **105.** $(a-b)(a+b+1)$.   **106.** $(x+y)(x^2-xy+y^2+1)$.

107. $(u-v)(u+v+u^2+uv+v^2)$.   **109.** $(x+y)(x-y)(x^2+y^2)$.

110. $(a+2)(a-2)(a^2+4)$.   **111.** $(z+3w)(z-3w)(z^2+9w^2)$.

113. $(a - b)(a + b)(a^2 + ab + b^2)(a^2 - ab + b^2)$.

114. $(x + y)(x^2 - xy + y^2)(x^6 - x^3y^3 + y^6)$.

115. $(r - s^2)(r + s^2)(r^2 + rs^2 + s^4)(r^2 - rs^2 + s^4)$.

117. $(a - b)(a^4 + a^3b + a^2b^2 + ab^3 + b^4)$.

118. $(x + y)(x^6 - x^5y + x^4y^2 - x^3y^3 + x^2y^4 - xy^5 + y^6)$.

119. $(u + v)(u - v)(u^4 + u^3v + u^2v^2 + uv^3 + v^4)(u^4 - u^3v + u^2v^2 - uv^3 + v^4)$.

121. $(x^2 + x + 1)(x^2 - x + 1)$.　**122.** $(a^2 + a + 3)(a^2 - a + 3)$.

123. $(2b^2 + b + 1)(2b^2 - b + 1)$.　**125.** $(2x^2 - 3xy - 2y^2)(2x^2 + 3xy - 2y^2)$.

126. $(a^2 - 2ab + 2b^2)(a^2 + 2ab + 2b^2)$.　**127.** $(3b^2 + 2bc - 2c^2)(3b^2 - 2bc - 2c^2)$.

129. $(x - y)(x - y - 1)$.　**130.** $(a - b)(a^2 + ab + b^2 - a + b)$.

131. $(x^2 + 2)(x^4 - x^2 + 4)$.　**133.** $(2 + a - 2b)(2 - a + 2b)$.

134. $(3x^2 + x + 3y)(3x^2 - x - 3y)$.　**135.** $(a + b + x + y)(a + b - x - y)$.

Exercise 8

1. $\dfrac{2}{x - y}$.　**2.** $\dfrac{-a - b}{a - b}$ or $-\dfrac{a + b}{a - b}$.　**3.** $\dfrac{3y - 2x - z}{z + y - x}$.　**5.** $\dfrac{a^2}{2ab}$.　**6.** $\dfrac{6x^2}{9xy}$.

7. $\dfrac{a^2 + 2ab + b^2}{a^2 - b^2}$.　**9.** $\dfrac{y}{3x}$.　**10.** $\dfrac{3a}{4b}$.　**11.** $\dfrac{a - b}{a + b}$.　**13.** $\dfrac{3a^2 - 6ab}{6a^2}$.　**14.** $\dfrac{8xy - 12y^2}{12xy}$.

15. $\dfrac{4v^2 - 16uv}{20v^2}$.　**17.** $\dfrac{x^2 - xy - 2y^2}{x^2 - y^2}$.　**18.** $\dfrac{-2a^2 - ab + b^2}{a^2 - b^2}$.　**19.** $\dfrac{3h^2 + 10hk + 8k^2}{2h^2 + 3hk - 2k^2}$.

21. $\dfrac{5x^2 - 3xy - 2y^2}{x^3 - y^3}$.　**22.** $\dfrac{a^4 + a^2b^2 + b^4}{a^3 - b^3}$.　**23.** $\dfrac{b^3 - 2bc^2 - c^3}{b^3 + c^3}$.　**25.** $\dfrac{x - 2}{x + 2}$.　**26.** $\dfrac{a + 3}{a - 2}$.

27. $\dfrac{2h - 1}{3h + 1}$.　**29.** $\dfrac{2x - 3y}{3x + 2y}$.　**30.** $\dfrac{a - 3b}{a + 2b}$.　**31.** $\dfrac{w + 2z}{w - 2z}$.　**33.** $\dfrac{s - 2t}{2s - t}$.　**34.** $\dfrac{x - y}{x + y}$.

35. $\dfrac{3h - 2k}{2h + k}$.　**37.** $\dfrac{a^2 - ab + b^2}{a - b}$.　**38.** $\dfrac{x^2 + xy + y^2}{x + y}$.　**39.** $\dfrac{1}{u^2 + v^2}$.　**41.** $\dfrac{b^4 + b^2c^2 + c^4}{b^2 + c^2}$.

42. $\dfrac{a^2 - ab + b^2}{a - b}$.　**43.** $\dfrac{1}{x^2 - y^2}$.　**45.** $\dfrac{1}{2x + 1}$.　**46.** $\dfrac{1}{3a + 1}$.　**47.** $\dfrac{1}{5y + 1}$.　**49.** $\dfrac{1}{2x + 1}$.

50. $\dfrac{1}{2(3b + 2)}$.　**51.** 1.

Exercise 9

1. $\dfrac{c}{2}$.　**2.** $\dfrac{7y^2z}{3}$.　**3.** $\dfrac{3w}{2v}$.　**5.** $7c^2$.　**6.** $90q^2r$.　**7.** $\dfrac{8c}{7d^3}$.　**9.** $\dfrac{3x^2y}{4abz}$.　**10.** $\dfrac{4mnp^2t^5}{5s^2u}$.　**11.** $\dfrac{2b^4}{ac^4d}$.

13. $\dfrac{5}{3}$.　**14.** $\dfrac{2x}{5y}$.　**15.** $\dfrac{2k}{3h}$.　**17.** $\dfrac{2a + b}{2a^2 + 4ab}$.　**18.** $\dfrac{x - 3y}{6xy}$.　**19.** $\dfrac{2c(b + c)}{3b + 2c}$.　**21.** b.

22. $\dfrac{2x - y}{2}$.　**23.** $\dfrac{c(3c + 5d)}{8d}$.　**25.** $\dfrac{1}{x^2y}$.　**26.** $\dfrac{(a - b)b}{a}$.　**27.** q.　**29.** 1.　**30.** $\dfrac{y}{x}$.　**31.** 1.

33. $\dfrac{2x^2 + x - 1}{x^2 - 4x + 3}$.　**34.** $\dfrac{(y + 2)^2}{4y^2 - 1}$.　**35.** $\dfrac{a^2 - b^2}{4a^2 - b^2}$.　**37.** $\dfrac{a - b}{a - 2b}$.　**38.** $\dfrac{2u - v}{u - v}$.　**39.** $\dfrac{r + s}{2r - s}$.

41. $x^2 + y^2$.　**42.** $\dfrac{1}{a^2 - b^2}$.　**43.** $\dfrac{u^2 + 3uv + 2v^2}{2u - v}$.　**45.** $\dfrac{a + 1}{a - 1}$.　**46.** $\dfrac{x^2 - 6x + 8}{x^2 - 4x + 3}$.

47. $\left(\dfrac{y - 1}{y + 1}\right)^2$.　**49.** 1.　**50.** 1.　**51.** $\dfrac{2c - 1}{2c + 1}$.

Exercise 10

1. $\dfrac{9x^3y}{12x^2y^2}$. 2. $\dfrac{25a^3bc}{15ab^2c^2}$. 3. $\dfrac{28u^3v^4w^2}{20u^2v^3w^4}$. 5. $\dfrac{3x+9}{(x-2)(x+3)}$. 6. $\dfrac{4a^2+6a}{(3a-1)(2a+3)}$.

7. $\dfrac{6x^2+13xy+6y^2}{4x^2-9y^2}$. 9. $\dfrac{2a^3c^2}{36a^2c^3},\dfrac{16a^2b^2c}{36a^2c^3},\dfrac{15c^3}{36a^2c^3}$. 10. $\dfrac{80x^3z}{180x^2y^2z^2},\dfrac{75xy^3}{180x^2y^2z^2},\dfrac{96yz^3}{180x^2y^2z^2}$.

11. $\dfrac{27rs^2t}{72r^2s^3t^2},\dfrac{30s^2t^5}{72r^2s^3t^2},\dfrac{28r^4}{72r^2s^3t^2}$. 13. $\dfrac{3x+6}{x^2-4},\dfrac{2x^2-4x}{x^2-4},\dfrac{4x^2}{x^2-4}$.

14. $\dfrac{a(a^2-b^2)}{(a^2-b^2)^2},\dfrac{(a-b)^3}{(a^2-b^2)^2},\dfrac{(a+b)^3}{(a^2-b^2)^2}$.

15. $\dfrac{(x-y)^2}{(x+y)(x-y)(x-2y)},\dfrac{(x-2y)^2}{(x+y)(x-y)(x-2y)},\dfrac{(x+y)^2}{(x+y)(x-y)(x-2y)}$.

17. $\frac{11}{12}$. 18. $\frac{37}{42}$. 19. $-\frac{1}{9}$. 21. $\dfrac{60a^2+64b^2-27c^2}{144abc}$. 22. $\dfrac{54y^2z^3-45xz-14x^3}{72x^2yz^2}$.

23. $\dfrac{8u^3v-10v^4+3u^4}{36u^2v^3}$. 25. $\dfrac{5}{3b}$. 26. $\dfrac{1}{12x}$. 27. $-\dfrac{u}{9}$. 29. $\dfrac{1}{a+b}$. 30. 1. 31. $\dfrac{u}{v}$. 33. $\dfrac{1}{a}$.

34. $\dfrac{y}{2x-y}$. 35. $\dfrac{2}{u}$. 37. $\dfrac{u-v}{u+v}$. 38. $\dfrac{a+b}{2a-b}$. 39. $\dfrac{2x+y}{x-2y}$. 41. $\dfrac{x}{x+y}$. 42. $\dfrac{3a}{a+b}$.

43. $\dfrac{2u}{2u-3v}$. 45. $\dfrac{2y}{(x-y)(y-z)}$. 46. $\dfrac{-x^4}{x^3-1}$. 47. $\dfrac{4(x+1)}{x^2+x+1}$. 49. $\dfrac{x^2-1}{x^2+1}$.

50. $\dfrac{1}{a+b}$. 51. $\dfrac{-2y^3(x^2+y^2)}{x^6-y^6}$.

Exercise 11

1. 1. 2. 1. 3. 3. 5. $x-1$. 6. $\dfrac{x-1}{x}$. 7. $\dfrac{x}{2x-1}$. 9. $\dfrac{2c}{b}$. 10. $\dfrac{4}{3z}$. 11. $\dfrac{2s(3r-2s)}{3r}$.

13. $\dfrac{a+b}{a-b}$. 14. $\dfrac{a}{a-2}$. 15. $\dfrac{x-y}{x+y}$. 17. $-x-1$. 18. $\dfrac{2(x+1)}{x+3}$. 19. $a+1$.

21. $\dfrac{a-6b}{a^2-4b^2}$. 22. $\dfrac{x^2-y^2}{x}$. 23. $\dfrac{u-v}{u+v}$. 25. $-a$. 26. $\dfrac{y-x}{xy}$. 27. $\dfrac{1}{b^2(a+b)}$.

Supplementary Problems for Chap. 3

1. $\dfrac{3b}{2a}$. 2. $\dfrac{9x^2z^2}{5y^3}$. 3. $\dfrac{6t^4}{rs^2}$. 5. $\dfrac{x}{y}$. 6. $\dfrac{ab}{c}$. 7. $\dfrac{s}{t}$. 9. $\dfrac{y}{x+y}$. 10. $\dfrac{a-b}{ab}$. 11. $\dfrac{r(p+q)}{p}$.

13. $\dfrac{x+5y}{x+4y}$. 14. $\dfrac{a-b}{a-2b}$. 15. $\dfrac{c+d}{c-d}$. 17. $\dfrac{a-3b}{2a-b}$. 18. $\dfrac{s-y}{s+2y}$. 19. $\dfrac{x^2y^2}{x^2+xy+y^2}$.

21. $\dfrac{a+b}{a^2+ab+b^2}$. 22. $\dfrac{c-2d}{c^2-2cd+4d^2}$. 23. $\dfrac{r^2+s^2}{r^4+r^2s^2+s^4}$. 25. $\dfrac{2b}{3}$. 26. $\dfrac{9y}{4x}$. 27. $\dfrac{5bc}{4a}$.

29. $\dfrac{9ce^3}{d}$. 30. $\dfrac{2xz^3}{9y}$. 31. $\dfrac{8k^2}{5}$. 33. $\dfrac{x-y}{x}$. 34. $\dfrac{ab(a+2b)}{c(a+b)}$. 35. $\dfrac{c^4}{d^2(c+2d)}$. 37. hk.

38. $\dfrac{x(x+3y)}{y}$. 39. $\dfrac{a(a-2b)}{b(a-b)}$. 41. $\dfrac{2x-1}{2x-5}$. 42. $\dfrac{a-b}{a+b}$. 43. $\dfrac{b-c}{2b+c}$. 45. $\dfrac{u+v}{u+2v}$.

46. $\dfrac{g+h}{g-h}$. **47.** $\dfrac{(x-y)(x^2-xy+y^2)}{x^4-x^2y^2+y^4}$. **49.** $\dfrac{-a}{a-b}$. **50.** $\dfrac{2y-x}{x-y}$. **51.** $\dfrac{x^2-y^2}{x^2+y^2-xy}$.

53. $\dfrac{5x+10}{x^2-5x-14}$. **54.** $\dfrac{-4(x+5)}{(2-3x)(x+5)}$. **55.** $\dfrac{(a-2)^2}{a^3-8}$ **57.** 1. **58.** $\frac{13}{24}$. **59.** $\frac{25}{72}$.

61. $\dfrac{7}{3x}$. **62.** $\dfrac{2(x-5)}{5}$. **63.** $\dfrac{1}{a}$. **65.** $\dfrac{10y^2+11xy}{6x(2x+y)}$. **66.** $\dfrac{3b^2+8ab}{4a(2a+b)}$. **67.** $\dfrac{u^2+2v^2}{3u(u+v)}$.

69. $\dfrac{5xy}{(x-2y)(2x+y)}$. **70.** $\dfrac{13a^2+9ab}{2(a-2b)(3a+b)}$. **71.** $-\dfrac{16u^2+23uv}{6(2u+3v)(u+2v)}$.

73. $\dfrac{1}{x+3y}$ **74.** $\dfrac{2}{2a-3b}$. **75.** $\dfrac{1}{r-4s}$. **77.** $\frac{4}{21}$. **78.** $\frac{39}{20}$. **79.** 5. **81.** $\dfrac{x}{2x+1}$.

82. $\dfrac{x^2}{x^2+x+1}$. **83.** $\dfrac{a}{a-b}$. **85.** $\dfrac{x+2}{2x+3}$. **86.** $\dfrac{a+2b}{a-4b}$. **87.** $\dfrac{2c+d}{c-2d}$. **89.** $x-1$.

90. $2a-1$. **91.** $2x+y$. **93.** $\dfrac{a-a^2}{a+1}$. **94.** $-\dfrac{1}{x+1}$ **95.** $d+1$.

Exercise 12

13. 3. **14.** -2. **15.** $\frac{1}{2}$. **17.** -5. **18.** 3. **19.** $\frac{1}{2}$. **21.** -5. **22.** $\frac{2}{3}$. **23.** 4. **25.** -2.

26. 2. **27.** -2. **29.** 4. **30.** 0. **31.** $\frac{2}{3}$. **33.** 6. **34.** 8. **35.** 12. **37.** $\dfrac{1}{ab}$ **38.** -1.

39. $\dfrac{1}{a-b}$. **41.** -7. **42.** 2. **43.** 3. **45.** 5. **46.** 5. **47.** $\frac{5}{6}$. **49.** $-\frac{7}{2}$. **50.** $-\frac{1}{2}$.

51. $\frac{2}{9}$. **53.** $\dfrac{a}{2b}$. **54.** $\dfrac{c+d}{c-d}$. **55.** $\dfrac{a-b}{a+b}$. **57.** 5. **58.** 2. **59.** -2. **61.** 3. **62.** 4.

63. 6. **65.** -2. **66.** -4. **67.** -3. **69.** 1. **70.** 3. **71.** 3. **81.** $\dfrac{s-c}{s}$.

82. $\dfrac{c-m+md}{c}$. **83.** $\dfrac{l-a+d}{d}$. **85.** $34-2h$. **86.** $\dfrac{2s-na}{n}$. **87.** $\dfrac{S-Sr}{1-r^n}$.

89. $\dfrac{A}{1+rt}$. **90.** $\dfrac{N\varphi_2+et}{N}$. **91.** $\dfrac{v-r+rB_2t}{rt}$.

Exercise 13

1. 18, 19, 20. **2.** 11, 26. **3.** 6, 13. **5.** 14 by 28 ft. **6.** Dick, \$8; Tom, \$21.
7. John, \$12; Tom, \$6. **9.** \$600. **10.** \$.90, \$1.10. **11.** 60 by 150 ft.
13. \$4000 at 3 per cent, \$3000 at 4 per cent. **14.** \$5000. **15.** \$60, \$85. **17.** 124.
18. 18 years. **19.** 18 years, 6 years. **21.** 53 miles per hr., 43 miles per hr.
22. 18 knots, 22 knots. **23.** 60 miles per hr., 50 miles per hr. **25.** 900 miles.
26. 180 miles. **27.** $2\frac{2}{3}$ days. **29.** $1\frac{1}{3}$ hr. **30.** 40 min. **31.** $4\frac{4}{5}$ hr. **33.** $7\frac{1}{2}$ hr.
34. 12 hr. **35.** 20 lb. **37.** $7\frac{1}{3}$ gal. **38.** 50 lb. **39.** 2 gal. **41.** 150 miles per hr.
42. 60 miles per hr., 45 miles per hr. **43.** 4 miles per hr. **45.** 60 miles. **46.** 4 miles.
47. 12 ft. from the man.

Exercise 14

1. 8, 11, 2, 0. **2.** 1, 3, 0, -7. **3.** 13, 0, -2, -12. **5.** 3, 1, 3. **6.** -3, 51, 126.
7. 13, 0, 85. **9.** $\frac{3}{5}$, 0, $-\frac{7}{15}$. **10.** $\frac{1}{12}$, 0, $-\frac{3}{4}$. **11.** 0, -3, 1. **13.** $\frac{4}{3}$, $\frac{15}{7}$. **14.** $-\frac{3}{2}$, $\frac{40}{27}$.

15. $-\frac{1}{2}, -\frac{9}{5}$. **17.** $y^2 - 1, y^2 - 2y, 4y^2 - 1$. **18.** $t^2 - 3t + 5, t^2 + t + 3, 9y^2 - 9y + 3$.

19. $2t^2 + 1, \dfrac{3t^2 + 4t + 2}{t^2}, \frac{1}{2}t^2 + 2t + 3$. **21.** $\frac{5}{2}$. **22.** $-\dfrac{1}{x^2}$. **23.** $(x - 2)^2$. **25.** $5, -1$.

26. $-1, 29$. **27.** $18\pi, 20\pi$. **29.** $15, 1$. **30.** $32, 410$. **31.** $-10, 42$.

Exercise 15

2. On the Y axis; on the X axis; on a line bisecting the first and third quadrants; on a line bisecting the second and fourth quadrants. **3.** On a line parallel to the Y axis and three units to the right of it; on a line parallel to the Y axis and 4 units to the left of it; on a line parallel to the X axis and 5 units above it; on a line parallel to the X axis and 6 units below it. **5.** Fourth; third; first; fourth; third; second; fourth; first; first. **18.** $1.3, -2.3$. **19.** $.8, -3.8$. **21.** $-1.3, -4.7$. **22.** $1.1, -2.6$. **23.** $-.6, 2.6$. **25.** $-.4, 2.7$.

Exercise 17

1. $x = 3, y = -2$. **2.** $x = -4, y = 2$. **3.** $x = 4, y = -1$. **5.** $x = 1, y = 1\frac{1}{2}$.
6. $x = -\frac{1}{2}, y = 1$. **7.** $x = -2\frac{1}{2}, y = 2$. **9.** $x = 2.3, y = 1.3$. **10.** Inconsistent.
11. Inconsistent. **13.** Dependent. **14.** Dependent. **15.** $x = 1.1, y = -1.6$.
17. Inconsistent. **18.** Inconsistent. **19.** $x = 1, y = -.2$. **21.** $x = .4, y = 0$.
22. $x = -.5, y = 1.4$. **23.** Dependent.

Exercise 18

1. $x = 1, y = 2$. **2.** $x = -2, y = -1$. **3.** $x = 2, y = -3$. **5.** $x = 3, y = -1$.
6. $x = -3, y = -4$. **7.** $x = -5, y = 2$. **9.** $x = 1\frac{1}{2}, y = 2$. **10.** $x = 1\frac{1}{3}, y = 1\frac{1}{2}$.
11. $x = 2\frac{2}{3}, y = -1\frac{1}{4}$. **13.** $x = 3, y = 4$. **14.** $x = 0, y = -5$.
15. $x = -3, y = -\frac{5}{4}$. **17.** $x = -2, y = 1$. **18.** $x = 2, y = -1$. **19.** $x = 3, y = 2$.
21. $x = 2, y = 5$. **22.** $x = 4, y = -6$. **23.** $x = -5, y = 7$. **25.** $x = \frac{4}{3}, y = \frac{5}{6}$.
26. $x = \frac{1}{2}, y = \frac{3}{2}$. **27.** $x = \frac{2}{3}, y = \frac{3}{4}$. **29.** $x = 1, y = 3$. **30.** $x = 2, y = -3$.
31. $x = \frac{1}{2}, y = \frac{2}{3}$. **33.** $x = 2, y = -1$. **34.** $x = 1, y = -2$. **35.** $x = 3, y = 1$.
37. $x = -3, y = 2$. **38.** $x = 10, y = 2$. **39.** $x = -5, y = -4$. **41.** $x = 2, y = -2$.
42. $x = 1, y = 3$. **43.** $x = -2, y = 1$. **45.** $x = m/a, y = 0$. **46.** $x = 1, y = -1$.
47. $x = 1, y = 0$. **49.** $x = 7, y = -\frac{7}{5}$. **50.** $x = \frac{1}{5}, y = -\frac{1}{6}$. **51.** $x = \frac{1}{2}, y = -1$.
53. $x = 3, y = \frac{3}{2}$. **54.** $x = \frac{1}{2}, y = \frac{1}{2}$. **55.** $x = \frac{1}{3}, y = -1$.

Exercise 19

1. $x = 1, y = -2, z = 3$. **2.** $x = 2, y = 1, z = -3$. **3.** $x = 3, y = -4, z = 2$.
5. $x = 4, y = 5, z = -3$. **6.** $x = -3, y = -2, z = 5$. **7.** $x = 7, y = -5, z = 3$.
9. $x = 5, y = -6, z = 4$. **10.** $x = 8, y = 5, z = 6$. **11.** $x = 2, y = 4, z = 1$.
13. $x = \frac{1}{2}, y = \frac{2}{3}, z = \frac{3}{4}$. **14.** $x = \frac{3}{2}, y = \frac{2}{5}, z = \frac{4}{3}$. **15.** $x = \frac{7}{8}, y = \frac{5}{6}, z = \frac{3}{4}$.
17. $x = -\frac{3}{4}, y = \frac{4}{3}, z = \frac{5}{2}$. **18.** $x = \frac{2}{5}, y = \frac{3}{5}, z = \frac{1}{4}$. **19.** $x = \frac{5}{6}, y = \frac{2}{3}, z = \frac{7}{4}$.
21. $x = -3, y = 2, z = 4$. **22.** $x = 5, y = -6, z = 7$. **23.** $x = 2, y = \frac{1}{2}, z = \frac{3}{4}$.
25. $x = 7, y = 4, z = -5$. **26.** $x = -5, y = -2, z = 8$. **27.** $x = 2, y = 3, z = -5$.

Exercise 20

1. \$144, \$156. **2.** 125 miles, 140 miles. **3.** James, 12; Frank, 9. **5.** 40 nickels, 25 dimes.
6. 38. **7.** 35. **9.** \$80, \$85. **10.** 25 at \$8, 15 at \$10. **11.** \$6500, \$60. **12.** 30 on bus, 10 in cars. **13.** 72 lb., 84 lb. **14.** \$4000 at 4 per cent, \$3750 at 3 per cent. **15.** Plane,

120 miles per hr.; wind, 20 miles per hr. **17.** 50 miles per hr., 40 miles per hr. **18.** Car, 60 miles per hr.; truck, 48 miles per hr. **19.** 20 lb. of 10 per cent, 40 lb. of 25 per cent. **21.** 6 gal. of 90 per cent, 15 gal. of 97 per cent. **22.** Painter, 6 days; helper, 9 days. **23.** Eastward plane, 180 miles per hr.; westward plane, 170 miles per hr. **25.** Bat, \$1.50; ball, \$2; glove, \$4.50. **26.** 10 seniors, 15 juniors, 20 sophomores. **27.** 70 dimes, 60 quarters, 20 half dollars. **29.** Father, 40 years; son, 15 years; daughter, 10 years. **30.** 12 miles on horseback, 20 miles in car, 350 miles on train. **31.** Tom, 4 hr.; Dick, 3 hr.; Harry, 6 hr.

Exercise 21

1. 5. **2.** 2. **3.** 17. **5.** 0. **6.** 18. **7.** 0. **9.** -5. **10.** 33. **11.** -6. **13.** -34. **14.** 0. **15.** 0. **17.** $x = 2, y = 1$. **18.** $x = 3, y = -2$. **19.** $x = -2, y = 3$. **21.** $x = 2, y = \frac{1}{2}$. **22.** $x = \frac{1}{3}, y = 1$. **23.** $x = 0, y = \frac{2}{3}$. **25.** $x = a, y = a - b$. **26.** $x = b, y = a$. **27.** $x = a, y = b$. **29.** $x = 1, y = 2, z = 3$. **30.** $x = 3, y = 1, z = 1$. **31.** $x = 2, y = -1, z = -2$. **33.** $x = \frac{1}{2}, y = \frac{1}{4}, z = 0$. **34.** $x = \frac{1}{3}, y = \frac{2}{3}, z = -\frac{1}{6}$. **35.** $x = 2, y = 1, z = 2$. **37.** $x = 4, y = 0, z = -3$. **38.** $x = 2, y = 3, z = 0$. **39.** $x = a - b, y = b, z = a$. **41.** $x = a, y = b, z = -a + b$. **42.** $x = a - b, y = a + b, z = a$.

Exercise 22

1. 32. **2.** 729. **3.** 625. **5.** 9. **6.** 4. **7.** 64. **9.** 100. **10.** 1728. **11.** 4. **13.** $\frac{16}{25}$. **14.** $\frac{9}{16}$. **15.** $\frac{8}{27}$. **17.** 4096. **18.** 5184. **19.** 2304. **21.** $6a^{10}$. **22.** $12x^7$. **23.** $6a^{11}$. **25.** a^4. **26.** b^4. **27.** $4c^2d$. **29.** $9x^6$. **30.** $25a^8$. **31.** $-64b^6$. **33.** $8x^2y^2$. **34.** $9cd^2e^2$.

35. $7a^5b^4$. **37.** $8x^6y^3$. **38.** $27a^3b^6c^9$. **39.** $81a^4$. **41.** $\dfrac{3k^2}{2h^2}$. **42.** $\dfrac{9r^2}{4t^3}$. **43.** $\dfrac{3a^2c^4}{2b}$. **45.** $\dfrac{2a^5b}{3c^2}$.

46. $\dfrac{4x^6w^3}{3y^2z^2}$. **47.** $\dfrac{9h^7}{2j^2k^2}$. **49.** $\dfrac{4s^4}{9r^4}$. **50.** $\dfrac{8h^3}{27k^6}$. **51.** $\dfrac{16a^8}{81b^{12}c^{16}}$. **53.** $144a^{14}$. **54.** $216c^{21}$.

55. $64a^{10}b^6c^8$. **57.** $\dfrac{4}{r^2}$. **58.** $\dfrac{c^3}{8b^3}$. **59.** $\dfrac{16y^4z^4}{x^4}$. **61.** $\dfrac{a^2}{b^6}$. **62.** $\dfrac{8}{d^{12}}$. **63.** $\dfrac{256x^4}{y^8}$. **65.** b^7.

66. a^2x^2. **67.** h^6k^4. **69.** $\dfrac{64c^6}{27e^3}$. **70.** $\dfrac{x^4}{y^2}$. **71.** $\dfrac{16b^4}{a^4}$. **73.** a^{5n}. **74.** b^{4x}. **75.** 1. **77.** a^4x^{4n}.

78. $a^{2n-6}b^{n-3}$. **79.** a^2x^{4n}. **81.** a^2b^{2n}. **82.** $a^{5n}b^{3n}$. **83.** a^6b^{5x}.

Exercise 23

1. $\frac{1}{4}$. **2.** $\frac{1}{25}$. **3.** 1. **5.** 1. **6.** 1. **7.** $\frac{1}{8}$. **9.** $\frac{1}{27}$. **10.** $\frac{1}{64}$. **11.** $\frac{1}{64}$. **13.** 9. **14.** $\frac{2}{25}$. **15.** $\frac{1}{256}$. **17.** $\frac{1}{36}$. **18.** $\frac{9}{4}$. **19.** $\frac{4}{9}$. **21.** $\frac{27}{64}$. **22.** $\frac{729}{256}$. **23.** $\frac{625}{729}$. **25.** $4x^2y^{-3}$. **26.** $2a^2b^{-1}$. **27.** $3h^2k^{-1}j^{-3}$. **29.** $3^{-1}x^{-2}z^{-2}$. **30.** $4(3^{-1})x^2y^{-2}z^{-2}$. **31.** $3a^{-1}b^{-1}$.

33. $6a^3b^{-1}c^3$. **34.** $18h^{-1}jk^6$. **35.** $8r^{-1}st^3$. **37.** $\dfrac{1}{y^2}$. **38.** $\dfrac{b}{y^4}$. **39.** $\dfrac{1}{z^3}$. **41.** $\dfrac{1}{x^2}$. **42.** $\dfrac{1}{x^5}$.

43. $\dfrac{1}{ax}$. **45.** $\dfrac{a^3}{c^2}$. **46.** $\dfrac{x^3}{w^2y^3}$. **47.** $\dfrac{8}{r^5s}$. **49.** a^4b^6. **50.** $\dfrac{1}{x^9y^6}$. **51.** $\dfrac{a^4}{b^6}$. **53.** $\dfrac{8q^2}{5pr}$. **54.** $\dfrac{3x^4z^2}{2y^3}$.

55. $\dfrac{b^5}{2a^3c}$. **57.** $\dfrac{4h^2j}{k^3}$. **58.** $\dfrac{3x^4z^2}{2y^3}$. **59.** $\dfrac{3e^2}{4bc^3d^2}$. **61.** $\dfrac{b^{15}}{a^3c^6}$. **62.** $\dfrac{y^{15}}{x^5z^5}$. **63.** $\dfrac{b^6}{a^4x^2y^8}$. **65.** $\dfrac{y^8}{x^3}$.

66. $\dfrac{c^{21}}{125d^9}$. **67.** $\dfrac{b^{15}}{a^6}$. **69.** $3x^a$. **70.** $\dfrac{5}{x^a}$. **71.** $\dfrac{2a}{b}$. **73.** $\dfrac{a+b}{ab}$. **74.** $\dfrac{2b+3x}{bx}$.

75. $\dfrac{3y^2 + 2x^2}{xy}$. **77.** $\dfrac{a^3 + b^2}{a^2b^2}$. **78.** $\dfrac{x + y^2}{xy}$. **79.** $\dfrac{xy - x^3}{y}$. **81.** $\dfrac{xy}{y - x}$. **82.** $\dfrac{xy}{x + y}$.

83. $\dfrac{x + y}{x - y}$. **85.** $x + y$. **86.** $x^2 + xy + y^2$. **87.** $x + 2y$. **89.** $\dfrac{-2x - 4}{(x - 1)^4}$.

90. $\dfrac{-6(2x + 5)}{(x + 1)^3}$. **91.** $\dfrac{-10(2x - 1)}{(x - 3)^3}$.

Exercise 24

1. 3. **2.** 3. **3.** .1. **5.** 2. **6.** 8. **7.** 16. **9.** .01. **10.** 1000. **11.** 27. **13.** $\frac{4}{9}$.
14. $\frac{32}{243}$. **15.** $\frac{243}{32}$. **17.** $\frac{1}{2}$. **18.** $\frac{1}{5}$. **19.** $\frac{1}{4}$. **21.** $\frac{5}{3}$. **22.** $\frac{125}{8}$. **23.** 10. **25.** 5.
26. 4. **27.** 5. **29.** 8. **30.** 4. **31.** $2^{\frac{1}{2}}$. **33.** $8x^2y^3$. **34.** $3a^2b^3$. **35.** $2h^2k$. **37.** $5^{\frac{2}{3}}ab^{\frac{2}{3}}$.
38. $2^{\frac{2}{3}}x^{\frac{2}{3}}y^2$. **39.** $2^{\frac{1}{3}}a^{\frac{5}{3}}c$. **41.** $\dfrac{2^{\frac{2}{3}}x^{\frac{1}{3}}y^{\frac{2}{3}}}{3^{\frac{1}{3}}z^{\frac{1}{3}}}$. **42.** $\dfrac{3^{\frac{1}{4}}a^{\frac{1}{4}}x^{\frac{3}{4}}}{4^{\frac{1}{4}}b^{\frac{1}{4}}y^{\frac{3}{4}}}$. **43.** $\dfrac{3^{\frac{1}{4}}p^{\frac{3}{4}}q^{\frac{1}{2}}}{4^{\frac{1}{4}}r^{\frac{3}{4}}}$. **45.** $x\sqrt{x}$. **46.** $\sqrt[3]{b^2}$.

47. $\sqrt[4]{c^3}$. **49.** $\sqrt[4]{x^3y^3}$. **50.** $2ab^2\sqrt{ab}$. **51.** $2y^2\sqrt[3]{x^2}$. **53.** $4\sqrt[3]{\dfrac{x}{y^2}}$. **54.** $27\sqrt[3]{\dfrac{x^2}{y}}$.

55. $\sqrt[5]{\dfrac{a^2}{x^3y}}$. **57.** $\sqrt[8]{\dfrac{c^7}{a^3b^5}}$. **58.** $\dfrac{3}{b}\sqrt[4]{\dfrac{a^2}{b}}$. **59.** $\sqrt[3]{\dfrac{1}{x^2y}}$. **61.** $a^{\frac{5}{6}}$. **62.** $b^{\frac{7}{12}}$. **63.** $c^{\frac{1}{2}}$. **65.** $y^{\frac{1}{4}}$.

66. $h^{\frac{1}{3}}$. **67.** $r^{\frac{5}{6}}$. **69.** $3xy^2$. **70.** $\dfrac{4y}{a^2}$. **71.** $\dfrac{2h^{\frac{1}{3}}}{k^{\frac{1}{2}}}$. **73.** $\dfrac{b^3}{5a^5}$. **74.** $\dfrac{3q^{\frac{2}{3}}}{c^2}$. **75.** $\dfrac{x^9}{64y^4}$. **77.** $\dfrac{k^3}{8h^{\frac{3}{2}}}$.

78. $\dfrac{a^{\frac{1}{2}}}{3^{\frac{1}{3}}b^{\frac{1}{3}}}$. **79.** $\dfrac{r^{\frac{1}{2}}y^3}{5}$. **81.** $\dfrac{8d^2q^{\frac{1}{4}}}{pr^2}$. **82.** $\dfrac{81ac^{\frac{1}{3}}}{b^{\frac{1}{3}}}$. **83.** $\dfrac{c^2de^{\frac{1}{4}}}{27}$. **85.** $3v^2$. **86.** $\dfrac{10k}{h}$. **87.** $4rs^{\frac{1}{2}}$.

89. $\dfrac{xy^2z^{\frac{1}{2}}}{2}$. **90.** $\dfrac{4ac}{b^2}$. **91.** $rs^{\frac{3}{8}}$. **93.** $6u^4v^4$. **94.** $12k^{\frac{1}{2}}$. **95.** $\dfrac{5^{\frac{1}{2}}z^{\frac{2}{3}}}{x^5}$. **97.** $\dfrac{4x^2y^{\frac{2}{3}}}{5}$. **98.** $\dfrac{3b^{\frac{1}{4}}}{4a^{\frac{1}{2}}}$.

99. $\dfrac{2k}{h^{\frac{1}{4}}}$. **101.** $x - y$. **102.** $a^{\frac{2}{3}} - a^{\frac{1}{2}}$. **103.** $x + y$. **105.** $\dfrac{r^6 - 1}{r^3}$. **106.** $4w^3 - 4w^2 + w$.

107. $3u^{\frac{2}{3}} + u - 2u^{\frac{1}{3}}$. **109.** $\dfrac{4x + 4}{(3x + 1)^{\frac{2}{3}}}$. **110.** $\dfrac{8x + 5}{(2x + 3)^{\frac{1}{3}}}$. **111.** $\dfrac{3x - 2}{(2x - 3)^{\frac{1}{2}}}$.

113. $\dfrac{5x}{(3x - 1)^{\frac{2}{3}}(2x + 1)^{\frac{1}{3}}}$. **114.** $\dfrac{7x - 3}{(5x - 2)^{\frac{1}{2}}(2x - 1)^{\frac{1}{2}}}$. **115.** $\dfrac{7x + 1}{(x + 1)^{\frac{1}{4}}(x - 1)^{\frac{2}{3}}}$.

117. $w^{a^2 - b^2}$. **118.** z^a. **119.** $x^{a^2 - 1}$.

Exercise 25

1. $4\sqrt{2}$. **2.** $4\sqrt{6}$. **3.** $8\sqrt{2}$. **5.** $5\sqrt{6}$. **6.** $8\sqrt{5}$. **7.** $15\sqrt{2}$. **9.** $2\sqrt[3]{2}$.
10. $3\sqrt[3]{3}$. **11.** $5\sqrt[3]{2}$. **13.** $2\sqrt[4]{2}$. **14.** $3\sqrt[4]{2}$. **15.** $2\sqrt[4]{24}$. **17.** $x\sqrt{2}$.
18. $xy^2\sqrt{5}$. **19.** $a^3b\sqrt{7}$. **21.** $rs^2\sqrt[3]{4}$. **22.** $u^3v^2\sqrt[3]{6}$. **23.** $p^3q^4\sqrt[4]{2}$. **25.** $2x\sqrt{2x}$.
26. $2y^2\sqrt{3y}$. **27.** $3ab^2\sqrt{3b}$. **29.** $3ab^2\sqrt[3]{2ab}$. **30.** $4xy^2\sqrt[3]{3x^2y^2}$. **31.** $2u^2v^3\sqrt[3]{6uv}$.
33. $2ab^2c\sqrt[4]{5ac^2}$. **34.** $2xy^3z^2\sqrt[5]{2x^2z}$. **35.** $3p^4qr^2\sqrt[5]{q^2r^2}$. **37.** $7a^4b^5c^6\sqrt{6ac}$.
38. $6x^4y^6z^7\sqrt{11z}$. **39.** $16h^8j^4k^2\sqrt{3hk}$. **41.** $\dfrac{3\sqrt{x}}{2y}$. **42.** $\dfrac{2a^2\sqrt{5a}}{b^3}$. **43.** $\dfrac{2b\sqrt[3]{2}}{c^2}$.

45. $\dfrac{4x}{y^2}\sqrt{\dfrac{x}{y}}$. 46. $\dfrac{3a}{b^2}\sqrt[3]{\dfrac{a}{b}}$. 47. $\dfrac{3b^2\sqrt[4]{b}}{c^3}$. 49. $\dfrac{3ab\sqrt{2b}}{5c^2}$. 50. $\dfrac{5e^2f^2\sqrt{2e}}{8g^4}$.

51. $\dfrac{6x^3y^3\sqrt{2y}}{7z^5}$. 53. $\dfrac{2ab^2}{3c^2}\sqrt[3]{\dfrac{5a^2}{2c}}$. 54. $\dfrac{2xy^3}{3z^2}\sqrt[4]{4x^3}$. 55. $\dfrac{2uv}{3w^4}\sqrt[5]{2u^4v}$.

57. $(a-b)\sqrt{a+b}$. 58. $(2a+b)\sqrt{2a-b}$. 59. $(x-2)\sqrt{(x-1)(x+3)}$.

61. $3x^{\frac{1}{3}}y^{\frac{3}{8}}$. 62. $2x^{\frac{1}{4}}$. 63. $2x^{\frac{1}{2}}\sqrt{2x^{\frac{1}{2}}}$. 65. $a^nb^n\sqrt{b^n}$. 66. $b^n\sqrt[3]{a^{2n}}$. 67. a^2b^3.

69. $\sqrt{2}$. 70. $\sqrt{5}$. 71. $\sqrt[3]{3}$. 73. $\sqrt{x}$. 74. $\sqrt[5]{x}$. 75. $\sqrt{2x}$. 77. $2a\sqrt{ab}$.

78. $y\sqrt{3x}$. 79. $3u^2v^2\sqrt{v}$. 81. $\sqrt[4]{4rs^2}$. 82. $\sqrt[4]{3h^2k^3}$. 83. $\sqrt[3]{x+1}$. 85. $\sqrt{a}$.

86. $\sqrt[6]{x}$. 87. $\sqrt[8]{8a^3}$. 89. $\sqrt[3]{2}$. 90. $\sqrt[12]{5ab^6}$. 91. $\sqrt[6]{3a^2b^3}$.

Exercise 26

1. 4. 2. 9. 3. 15. 5. 4. 6. 3. 7. 6. 9. $\frac{8}{3}$. 10. $\frac{3}{4}$. 11. $\frac{2}{3}$. 13. 9. 14. 2. 15. 5.

17. $\dfrac{\sqrt{6}}{3}$. 18. $\dfrac{\sqrt{10}}{4}$. 19. $\dfrac{\sqrt{21}}{6}$. 21. $2a^2b\sqrt{3b}$. 22. $2a^2y^3\sqrt{15y}$.

23. $4u^2v^4w^2\sqrt{6w}$. 25. $4h^4k\sqrt{3}$. 26. $6c^3d^5\sqrt{2}$. 27. $5a^3b^2\sqrt{3a}$. 29. $4uv^2\sqrt[3]{v^2}$.

30. $3c^2d^3\sqrt[3]{2d^2}$. 31. $2p^3q^2\sqrt[3]{p^2q}$. 33. $\dfrac{\sqrt{2}}{2y}$. 34. $\dfrac{b^2\sqrt{3}}{2a}$. 35. $\dfrac{2\sqrt{15}}{5cd^3}$. 37. $\dfrac{r^2\sqrt{2s}}{2s^3}$.

38. $\dfrac{2\sqrt{5}}{5xy}$. 39. $\dfrac{a\sqrt{15b}}{3b^2}$. 41. $\dfrac{\sqrt[3]{18c^2d}}{3d^2}$. 42. $\dfrac{v\sqrt[4]{12u^3}}{2u^2}$. 43. $\dfrac{2t\sqrt[3]{9tu}}{3u^2}$. 45. 6.

46. $2\sqrt{6}$. 47. $\dfrac{\sqrt{10}}{10}$. 49. $\dfrac{\sqrt[3]{18a}}{3ab}$. 50. $\dfrac{e^2\sqrt{2cde}}{2c^2d}$. 51. $\dfrac{v\sqrt{3}}{6uw^4}$. 53. $2xy^3\sqrt{2}$.

54. $\dfrac{3x^2\sqrt{xy}}{y}$. 55. $\dfrac{6a^2\sqrt{c}}{b^2}$. 57. $\dfrac{(a-b)\sqrt{a+b}}{a+b}$. 58. $(x+y)\sqrt{x^2-y^2}$.

59. $\dfrac{\sqrt{u-v}}{u-v}$. 61. $\dfrac{\sqrt[3]{a+b}}{a+b}$. 62. $\dfrac{\sqrt[3]{x^2-y^2}}{x-y}$. 63. $\dfrac{\sqrt[3]{(c+d)^2}}{c+d}$.

Exercise 27

1. $3\sqrt{3}$. 2. $4\sqrt{2}$. 3. $-\sqrt{5}$. 5. $4\sqrt[3]{2}$. 6. $3\sqrt[3]{4}$. 7. $-2\sqrt[3]{3}$.

9. $3\sqrt{2}-2\sqrt[3]{3}$. 10. $7\sqrt[4]{2}-3\sqrt{2}$. 11. $10\sqrt{2}-5\sqrt{5}$. 13. $3x^2\sqrt{2y}$.

14. $a^2\sqrt{3b}$. 15. $u^3\sqrt{5v}$. 17. $\dfrac{\sqrt{a}}{a}$. 18. $\dfrac{\sqrt{2x}}{x}$. 19. $\dfrac{2a\sqrt{3a}}{b}$. 21. $b\sqrt{a}+a\sqrt{b}$.

22. $3s\sqrt{2r}-2r\sqrt{3s}$. 23. $v^2\sqrt[3]{u^2v}+u^3\sqrt[3]{uv^2}$. 25. $c\sqrt{3d}-d\sqrt{2c}$.

26. $\sqrt{2pq}\left(\dfrac{1}{q}+\dfrac{1}{p}\right)$. 27. $\sqrt{3hk}\left(\dfrac{h}{2k}+\dfrac{k^2}{h}\right)$. 29. $3\sqrt{2ab}$. 30. $x\sqrt[3]{xy}$.

31. $3\dfrac{\sqrt{6ab}}{2b}$. 33. $\dfrac{2a\sqrt{a^2-b^2}}{a^2-b^2}$. 34. $2\sqrt{x^2-y^2}$. 35. $(x-9)\left(\dfrac{\sqrt{x}}{x}+\dfrac{\sqrt{y}}{y}\right)$.

37. $\frac{3}{2}\sqrt{x+1}$. 38. $\dfrac{3(x+2)\sqrt{x+3}}{x+3}$. 39. $\dfrac{5(x+1)\sqrt{x+1}}{2}$.

Exercise 28

1. 1. **2.** $-2\sqrt{6}$. **3.** $2+10\sqrt{3}$. **5.** $-42-\sqrt{15}$. **6.** $-\frac{1}{2}$. **7.** $\frac{1}{4}$. **9.** $a-b$.

10. $x+2\sqrt{xy}+y$. **11.** $h\sqrt{h}-3h\sqrt{k}+3k\sqrt{h}-k\sqrt{k}$.

13. $r-s-rs+2s\sqrt{r}$. **14.** $a+2b-c-2\sqrt{2ab}$. **15.** $xy+xz-yz-2x\sqrt{yz}$.

17. $\sqrt{40},\ \sqrt{48},\ \sqrt{54}$. **18.** $\sqrt[3]{48},\ \sqrt[3]{108},\ \sqrt[3]{128}$. **19.** $\sqrt[4]{486},\ \sqrt[4]{512},\ \sqrt[4]{528}$.

21. $\sqrt{2a^5},\ \sqrt{2a^3},\ \sqrt{2a^2}$. **22.** $\sqrt{24a^2b^3},\ \sqrt{27a^2b^3},\ \sqrt{28a^2b^3}$.

23. $\sqrt{600},\ \sqrt{612},\ \sqrt{637}$. **25.** $\sqrt[3]{135},\ \sqrt[3]{147},\ \sqrt[3]{150}$. **26.** $\sqrt{a^5},\ \sqrt{a^3},\ \sqrt{a}$.

27. $\sqrt{288},\ \sqrt{294},\ \sqrt{320},\ \sqrt{325}$. **29.** $\sqrt[6]{27x^3},\ \sqrt[6]{16x^4}$. **30.** $\sqrt[12]{256a^4b^8},\ \sqrt[12]{8a^9b^3}$.

31. $\sqrt[12]{64x^6y^6},\ \sqrt[12]{81x^8y^4},\ \sqrt[12]{x^9y^6}$. **33.** $\sqrt[24]{64a^{12}b^{18}},\ \sqrt[24]{81a^{20}b^4},\ \sqrt[24]{64a^{15}b^{21}}$.

34. $\sqrt[12]{a},\ \sqrt[12]{81a^2},\ \sqrt[12]{8a^2}$. **35.** $\sqrt[12]{x^2y},\ \sqrt[12]{xy^2},\ \sqrt[12]{xy^2}$. **37.** $2\sqrt[6]{2}$. **38.** $2\sqrt[12]{32}$.

39. $4a^2\sqrt[6]{2a}$. **41.** $\sqrt[12]{16x^5}$. **42.** $b\sqrt[12]{128a^7b^5}$. **43.** $\sqrt[4]{3x^3y}$. **45.** $\sqrt{3}+1$.

46. $\sqrt{5}-2$. **47.** $\sqrt{6}-2$. **49.** $\sqrt{5}$. **50.** $\sqrt{3}$. **51.** $\sqrt{2}$. **53.** $\sqrt{2}+2\sqrt{3}$.

54. $\sqrt{5}-3\sqrt{3}$. **55.** $3\sqrt{2}-2\sqrt{7}$. **57.** $\sqrt{x}-\sqrt{y}$. **58.** $5-2\sqrt{6}$.

59. $\sqrt{a}+\sqrt{b}$. **61.** $1+\sqrt{2}-\sqrt{3}$. **62.** $\sqrt{3}+\sqrt{2}+\sqrt{5}$. **63.** $1+\sqrt{2}$.

65. .577. **66.** .447. **67.** -2.414. **69.** $-.268$. **70.** .127. **71.** .818.

Exercise 29

1. $\pm\frac{2}{3}$. **2.** $\pm\frac{1}{4}$. **3.** $\pm\frac{6}{5}$. **5.** ±2. **6.** ±2. **7.** ±3. **9.** $\pm\frac{2\sqrt{3}}{3}$. **10.** $\pm\frac{3\sqrt{2}}{2}$.

11. $\pm\sqrt{3}$. **13.** $\pm2i$. **14.** $\pm3i$. **15.** $\pm3i$. **17.** $\pm\frac{3}{2}i$. **18.** $\pm\frac{5}{2}i$. **19.** $\pm\sqrt{5}i$.

21. $2,\ -1$. **22.** $3,\ -2$. **23.** $-4,\ 3$. **25.** $-3,\ -1$. **26.** $2,\ 1$. **27.** $3,\ 4$. **29.** $\frac{1}{2},\ 1$.

30. $-\frac{1}{3},\ 1$. **31.** $\frac{1}{4},\ -1$. **33.** $-\frac{1}{2},\ -3$. **34.** $\frac{1}{3},\ 2$. **35.** $\frac{1}{4},\ -2$. **37.** $\frac{1}{3},\ -\frac{1}{2}$. **38.** $\frac{1}{3},\ -\frac{3}{2}$.

39. $\frac{3}{2},\ \frac{1}{4}$. **41.** $-\frac{3}{2},\ \frac{2}{3}$. **42.** $\frac{4}{3},\ -\frac{1}{2}$. **43.** $\frac{1}{5},\ -\frac{3}{2}$. **45.** $-\frac{2}{5},\ \frac{3}{2}$. **46.** $\frac{3}{4},\ \frac{2}{5}$. **47.** $\frac{5}{8},\ -\frac{1}{2}$.

49. $\frac{3}{8},\ \frac{2}{5}$. **50.** $-\frac{3}{7},\ \frac{2}{3}$. **51.** $\frac{6}{5},\ \frac{2}{7}$. **53.** $\frac{7}{6},\ -\frac{2}{9}$. **54.** $\frac{5}{9},\ -\frac{3}{4}$. **55.** $-\frac{12}{5},\ -\frac{2}{7}$.

57. $\frac{3}{16},\ -\frac{5}{4}$. **58.** $-\frac{2}{15},\ \frac{5}{3}$. **59.** $-\frac{7}{12},\ -\frac{4}{3}$. **61.** $a,\ -3a$. **62.** $\frac{b}{2},\ -\frac{2b}{3}$. **63.** $-\frac{b}{a},\ \frac{3b}{2a}$.

65. $a,\ b$. **66.** $-\frac{b}{a},\ -\frac{a}{b}$. **67.** $-b,\ \frac{a}{2}$.

Exercise 30

1. $-3,\ -1$. **2.** $2,\ -4$. **3.** $4,\ -6$. **5.** $1,\ -2$. **6.** $2,\ -3$. **7.** $3,\ 2$. **9.** $\frac{5}{2},\ \frac{3}{2}$.

10. $\frac{5}{2},\ -\frac{1}{2}$. **11.** $\frac{5}{3},\ \frac{1}{3}$. **13.** $-2,\ \frac{1}{2}$. **14.** $\frac{2}{3},\ -3$. **15.** $\frac{3}{2},\ -1$. **17.** $-4,\ \frac{2}{3}$. **18.** $\frac{5}{3},\ -\frac{3}{2}$.

19. $-\frac{1}{2},\ -\frac{2}{3}$. **21.** $\frac{7}{2},\ -\frac{3}{4}$. **22.** $-\frac{1}{4},\ -\frac{2}{3}$. **23.** $\frac{3}{2},\ -\frac{4}{5}$. **25.** $1\pm\sqrt{2}$. **26.** $2\pm\sqrt{3}$.

27. $3\pm\sqrt{2}$. **29.** $\frac{1\pm\sqrt{2}}{2}$. **30.** $\frac{2\pm\sqrt{3}}{3}$. **31.** $\frac{3\pm2\sqrt{2}}{2}$. **33.** $\frac{-3\pm\sqrt{3}}{3}$.

34. $\frac{-3\pm\sqrt{5}}{6}$. **35.** $\frac{4\pm\sqrt{7}}{2}$. **37.** $-1\pm i$. **38.** $2\pm i$. **39.** $-1\pm3i$. **41.** $\frac{1\pm i}{2}$.

42. $\frac{5\pm i}{2}$. **43.** $\frac{1\pm2i}{3}$. **45.** $\frac{2\pm\sqrt{3}i}{2}$. **46.** $\frac{-2\pm\sqrt{3}i}{2}$. **47.** $\frac{-5\pm\sqrt{3}i}{2}$.

49. a, $-2a$. **50.** $3b$, $-b$. **51.** a, $-b$. **53.** $a - b$, $a + b$. **54.** $\dfrac{a}{b}$, $\dfrac{b^2 - a}{b}$.

55. $\dfrac{a^2 - b}{a}$, $\dfrac{b}{a}$. **57.** $\dfrac{a}{2}$, $-\dfrac{b}{3}$. **58.** $\dfrac{a - b}{a + b}$, 1. **59.** $\dfrac{a + b}{a}$, $-\dfrac{b}{a}$. **61.** 2.618, $.382$.

62. 1.707, $.293$. **63.** 1.577, $.423$. **65.** 1.593, $.157$. **66.** $.631$, $.227$. **67.** 1.274, $.392$.
69. $-.360$, -1.390. **70.** 1.272, $-.472$.

Exercise 31

1. $3, 2$. **2.** $4, 1$. **3.** $-3, 2$. **5.** $3, \frac{1}{2}$. **6.** $\frac{2}{3}, -1$. **7.** $\frac{1}{4}, -2$. **9.** $\frac{2}{3}, -\frac{3}{2}$. **10.** $\frac{4}{3}, -\frac{2}{5}$.
11. $\frac{3}{4}, \frac{2}{3}$. **13.** $-\frac{1}{2}, -\frac{5}{8}$. **14.** $-\frac{3}{2}, -\frac{3}{4}$. **15.** $\frac{7}{9}, -\frac{1}{3}$. **17.** $1 \pm \sqrt{2}$. **18.** $-2 \pm \sqrt{3}$.

19. $3 \pm \sqrt{2}$. **21.** $\dfrac{1 \pm \sqrt{2}}{2}$. **22.** $\dfrac{-2 \pm \sqrt{3}}{3}$. **23.** $\dfrac{3 \pm \sqrt{2}}{2}$. **25.** $\dfrac{3 \pm \sqrt{3}}{3}$.

26. $\dfrac{3 \pm 3\sqrt{21}}{10}$. **27.** $\dfrac{1 \pm \sqrt{7}}{6}$. **29.** $\dfrac{-3 \pm 3\sqrt{3}}{2}$. **30.** $\dfrac{1 \pm \sqrt{13}}{4}$. **31.** $\dfrac{2 \pm \sqrt{2}}{3}$.

33. $-1 \pm i$. **34.** $2 \pm i$. **35.** $3 \pm 2i$. **37.** $\dfrac{1 \pm i}{2}$. **38.** $\dfrac{3 \pm i}{2}$. **39.** $\dfrac{1 \pm 2i}{3}$.

41. $\dfrac{-1 \pm \sqrt{5}\,i}{3}$. **42.** $\dfrac{3 \pm 3\sqrt{15}\,i}{8}$. **43.** $\dfrac{-3 \pm 3\sqrt{13}\,i}{7}$. **45.** $\dfrac{4 \pm \sqrt{2}\,i}{6}$.

46. $\dfrac{1 \pm \sqrt{35}\,i}{12}$. **47.** $\dfrac{-2 \pm \sqrt{46}\,i}{10}$. **49.** p, $-q$. **50.** s, $-r$. **51.** $a, \dfrac{1}{a}$. **53.** $\dfrac{c}{d}$, $-\dfrac{2c}{d}$.

54. $2m + n$, $2m - n$. **55.** $\dfrac{2p}{q}$, $\dfrac{q}{2p}$. **57.** $\dfrac{h}{h + 1}$, $\dfrac{h}{h - 1}$. **58.** $\dfrac{a + 1}{a}$, $\dfrac{a - 1}{a}$.

59. $\dfrac{a + b}{a}$, -1. **61.** $x + 1$, $-x - 2$. **62.** $x - 3$, $-x + 2$. **63.** $\dfrac{y + 1}{2}$, $\dfrac{-y + 3}{2}$.

65. $\dfrac{y + 2}{3}$, $\dfrac{-y + 2}{3}$. **66.** $\dfrac{x + 3}{4}$, $\dfrac{-x + 3}{4}$. **67.** $\dfrac{2x + 1}{3}$, $\dfrac{-2x + 2}{3}$. **69.** 1.215, $-.549$.

70. 3.842, -2.342. **71.** $.927$, -2.427. **73.** $.724$, $.276$. **74.** 3.345, -1.345.
75. $.547$, $-.261$. **77.** $.783$, $-.383$. **78.** 3.915, $.085$. **79.** $.694$, $-.360$.

Exercise 32

1. ± 3, ± 2. **2.** ± 4, ± 3. **3.** ± 1, $\pm \frac{1}{2}$. **5.** ± 3, $\pm \sqrt{3}$. **6.** ± 2, $\pm \sqrt{5}$.
7. ± 3, $\pm \sqrt{2}$. **9.** $\pm \sqrt{3}$, $\pm 2i$. **10.** $\pm \sqrt{5}$, $\pm 3i$. **11.** $\pm 2i$, $\pm i$.

13. $\pm \dfrac{\sqrt{2}}{2}$, $\pm \dfrac{1}{2}i$. **14.** $\pm \frac{1}{2}\sqrt{6}$, $\pm \frac{3}{2}i$. **15.** $\pm \dfrac{\sqrt{5}}{5}$, $\pm \dfrac{\sqrt{2}}{4}i$. **17.** $1, 2$. **18.** $-\frac{2}{3}, \frac{1}{2}$.

19. $\frac{1}{3}, -\frac{3}{2}$. **21.** $1, -2$. **22.** ± 2, ± 1, $\pm 2i$, $\pm i$. **23.** $\frac{1}{2}, -1$. **25.** ± 2, ± 1.
26. ± 2, ± 1. **27.** $\pm \frac{1}{2}$, ± 1. **29.** $-4, 1, -2, -1$. **30.** $5, 2, 1, -2$. **31.** $\frac{3}{2}, 1, -\frac{1}{2}, -1$.

33. $-2, 1, \dfrac{-1 \pm \sqrt{13}}{2}$. **34.** $1, -3, -1 \pm \sqrt{2}$. **35.** $\frac{1}{2}, -1, \dfrac{-1 \pm \sqrt{17}}{4}$.

37. $-\frac{6}{5}, -\frac{3}{4}$. **38.** $-3, 0$. **39.** $-1, 1$. **41.** $-4, \frac{11}{6}$. **42.** $5, \frac{1}{3}$. **43.** $\frac{1}{4}, -2$. **45.** $5, 1$.
46. $\frac{7}{3}, \frac{2}{3}$. **47.** $\frac{31}{36}, \frac{13}{16}$.

Exercise 33

1. 1. **2.** 4. **3.** $-\frac{1}{9}$. **5.** 2. **6.** 3. **7.** No solution. **9.** 0, 2. **10.** 0, -3. **11.** $-\frac{1}{2}$, 1.
13. 1, 2. **14.** $\frac{1}{2}$. **15.** $\frac{2}{3}$. **17.** 1, $\frac{1}{2}$. **18.** 2. **19.** 3. **21.** 2. **22.** 12, 4. **23.** 7. **25.** $\frac{3}{2}$, 1.
26. -2. **27.** 3. **29.** ± 2. **30.** 3, $\frac{19}{5}$. **31.** 4, $-\frac{16}{3}$. **33.** 1. **34.** 2. **35.** -3. **37.** 4.
38. 2. **39.** 3. **41.** $3b$. **42.** a. **43.** $a^2, 5a^2$.

Exercise 34

1. 6, 7. **2.** 7, 8; -5, -6. **3.** 7. **5.** 6, 24; -24, -6. **6.** 16, 18; -18, -16. **7.** 8, 32.
9. 2 units. **10.** $\frac{3}{2}$, $\frac{2}{3}$. **11.** 6, -2. **13.** 9 by 4 ft. **14.** 70 by 140 ft. **15.** 12 by 20 ft.
17. 8 by 12 ft. **18.** 10 by 20 ft. **19.** 5 ft., 12 ft. **21.** Square, 6 by 6 ft; rectangle, 9 by 2 ft.
22. 1 in. **23.** 4 miles per hr. **25.** 200 miles per hr. **26.** 35 miles per hr., 40 miles per hr.
27. 10 miles per hr, $7\frac{1}{2}$ miles per hr. **29.** 3 days, 6 days. **30.** \$100, \$150. **31.** 110 doz.,
100 doz.; or 40 doz., 30 doz.

Exercise 35

1. Rational and unequal. **2.** Imaginary. **3.** Rational and equal. **5.** Irrational and
unequal. **6.** Rational and equal. **7.** Imaginary. **9.** Rational and unequal.
10. Rational and equal. **11.** Imaginary. **13.** Real and unequal. **14.** Real and equal.
15. Imaginary. **17.** Real and equal. **18.** Real and unequal. **19.** Imaginary. **21.** Sum,
$-\frac{5}{2}$; product, $\frac{1}{2}$. **22.** Sum, $\frac{4}{3}$; product, $\frac{5}{3}$. **23.** Sum, $\frac{7}{5}$; product, $-\frac{8}{5}$. **25.** Sum, -3,
product, 4. **26.** Sum, $\frac{5}{3}$; product, $\frac{2}{3}$. **27.** Sum, $\frac{2}{3}$; product, $-\frac{5}{3}$. **29.** Sum, $\sqrt{2}$; product, $\sqrt{5}$. **30.** Sum, $-3\sqrt{3}$; product, $\sqrt{2}$. **31.** Sum, $2+\sqrt{3}$; product, $8+3\sqrt{3}$.
33. 0, 1. **34.** -1. **35.** -2, 1. **37.** 1. **38.** 3. **39.** 4. **41.** 2. **42.** $\frac{1}{4}$. **43.** 3, 1.
45. $x^2 - x - 6 = 0$. **46.** $x^2 - 4x + 3 = 0$. **47.** $x^2 + 8x + 15 = 0$.
49. $6x^2 - 5x - 6 = 0$. **50.** $12x^2 - 13x + 3 = 0$. **51.** $16x^2 - 30x - 25 = 0$.
53. $x^2 - 6x + 7 = 0$. **54.** $x^2 + x - 1 = 0$. **55.** $4x^2 - 2x + 1 = 0$.
57. $(24x - 25)(x + 2)$. **58.** $(16x - 27)(2x + 1)$. **59.** $(14x + 27)(2x - 3)$.
61. $(6x - 1)(2x + 15)$. **62.** $(8x + 27)(3x + 1)$. **63.** $(35x + 16)(x - 2)$.

Exercise 36

1. .4, -2.4. **2.** -1. **3.** No zeros. **5.** No zeros. **6.** 3.4, .6. **7.** $-.6$, 2.6. **9.** No zeros.
10. 1, -1.7. **11.** $y = -8\frac{1}{4}$ at $x = -\frac{5}{2}$; two points. **13.** $y = 0$ at $x = 3$; one point.
14. $y = 0$ at $x = -2$; one point. **15.** $y = -6\frac{1}{8}$ at $x = -\frac{5}{4}$; two points. **17.** $y = -\frac{5}{4}$ at
$x = -\frac{3}{4}$; two points. **18.** $y = 6\frac{1}{12}$ at $x = -\frac{7}{6}$; two points. **19.** $y = -\frac{11}{20}$ at $x = \frac{7}{10}$;
no points. **21.** 400 by 400 ft. **22.** $\frac{1}{2}$. **23.** 72 and 72.

Exercise 38

1. $x = 4, y = -13$; $x = 1, y = 2$. **2.** $x = 2, y = 1$; $x = -1, y = 2$.
3. $x = 38, y = 8$; $x = 2, y = -1$. **5.** $x = 3, y = 4$; $x = -4, y = -3$.
6. $x = 3, y = -2$; $x = -2, y = 3$. **7.** $x = 1, y = 4$; $x = -4, y = 1$.
9. $x = 3, y = 1$; $x = 2, y = -3$. **10.** $x = -3, y = 2$; $x = 5, y = 1$.
11. $x = 1, y = 4$; $x = -3, y = -2$. **13.** $x = 3, y = 1$; $x = -5, y = -2$.
14. $x = 2, y = 3$; $x = -4, y = 4$. **15.** $x = 4, y = 1$; $x = -6, y = -2$.
17. $x = 3, y = 4$; $x = -1, y = 1$. **18.** $x = 3, y = 2$; $x = -2, y = 1$.
19. $x = 2, y = 4$; $x = -1, y = 0$. **21.** $x = 3, y = -2$; $x = -2, y = 0$.
22. $x = 2, y = -1$; $x = -1, y = 1$. **23.** $x = 1, y = -2$; $x = -2, y = -1$.

25. $x = a, y = a;$ $x = \dfrac{13a}{5}, y = -\dfrac{11a}{5}.$ **26.** $x = ab, y = a^2;$ $x = b^2, y = ab.$

27. $x = a^2, y = a;$ $x = 2ab, y = 2b.$ **29.** $x = \dfrac{a+b}{a}, y = \dfrac{a-b}{b};$ $x = \dfrac{a-b}{a}, y = \dfrac{a+b}{b}.$

30. $x = \dfrac{a}{b}, y = \dfrac{a-b}{a};$ $x = 1, y = 0.$ **31.** $x = \dfrac{a^2-b^2}{a}, y = \dfrac{a^2}{b}, x = 0, y = b.$

Exercise 39

1. $x = 1, y = 3;$ $x = 1, y = -3;$ $x = -1, y = 3;$ $x = -1, y = -3.$ **2.** $x = 2, y = 3;$ $x = 2, y = -3;$ $x = -2, y = 3;$ $x = -2, y = -3.$ **3.** $x = 3, y = 4;$ $x = 3, y = -4;$ $x = -3, y = 4;$ $x = -3, y = -4.$ **5.** $x = 4, y = 1;$ $x = 4, y = -1;$ $x = -4, y = 1;$ $x = -4, y = -1.$ **6.** $x = 6, y = 5;$ $x = 6, y = -5;$ $x = -6, y = 5;$ $x = -6, y = -5.$ **7.** $x = 4, y = 7;$ $x = 4, y = -7;$ $x = -4, y = 7;$ $x = -4, y = -7.$ **9.** $x = \frac{1}{2}, y = \frac{3}{4};$ $x = \frac{1}{2}, y = -\frac{3}{4}; x = -\frac{1}{2}, y = \frac{3}{4}; x = -\frac{1}{2}, y = -\frac{3}{4}.$ **10.** $x = \frac{1}{3}, y = \frac{3}{2}; x = -\frac{1}{3}, y = \frac{3}{2}; x = \frac{1}{3}, y = -\frac{3}{2}; x = -\frac{1}{3}, y = -\frac{3}{2}.$ **11.** $x = \frac{2}{3}, y = \frac{1}{4}; x = \frac{2}{3}, y = -\frac{1}{4}; x = -\frac{2}{3}, y = \frac{1}{4}; x = -\frac{2}{3}, y = -\frac{1}{4}.$ **13.** $x = 2, y = 3;$ $x = -2, y = 3;$ $x = 1, y = 2;$ $x = -1, y = 2.$ **14.** $x = 3, y = 4;$ $x = 3, y = -4;$ $x = 2, y = 3;$ $x = 2, y = -3.$ **15.** $x = 1, y = 3;$ $x = -1, y = 3; x = 5, y = 2; x = -5, y = 2.$ **17.** $x = 1, y = \frac{1}{2}; x = 1, y = -\frac{1}{2}; x = \frac{1}{2}, y = 1; x = \frac{1}{2}, y = -1.$ **18.** $x = 2, y = \frac{1}{2}; x = -2, y = \frac{1}{2}; x = 1, y = -2; x = -1, y = -2.$ **19.** $x = \frac{1}{3}, y = \frac{2}{3}; x = -\frac{1}{3}, y = \frac{2}{3}; x = \frac{3}{2}, y = \frac{1}{2}; x = -\frac{3}{2}, y = \frac{1}{2}.$ **21.** $x = 1, y = 2; x = -3, y = 1.$ **22.** $x = 2, y = -4; x = 1, y = 3.$ **23.** $x = -2, y = 3; x = 3, y = -5.$ **25.** $x = \frac{3}{2}, y = \frac{1}{3}; x = \frac{1}{2}, y = 3.$ **26.** $x = \frac{11}{2}, y = -\frac{39}{22}; x = -2, y = 3.$ **27.** $x = \frac{2}{3}, y = 3; x = -\frac{47}{12}, y = -12.$ **29.** $x = \sqrt{2}, y = \sqrt{3}; x = \sqrt{2}, y = -\sqrt{3}; x = -\sqrt{2}, y = \sqrt{3}; x = -\sqrt{2}, y = -\sqrt{3}.$ **30.** $x = 2\sqrt{3}, y = 3\sqrt{2}; x = 2\sqrt{3}, y = -3\sqrt{2}; x = -2\sqrt{3}, y = 3\sqrt{2}; x = -2\sqrt{3}, y = -3\sqrt{2}.$ **31.** $x = \sqrt{5}, y = \frac{2}{3}; x = \sqrt{5}, y = -\frac{2}{3}; x = -\sqrt{5}, y = \frac{2}{3}; x = -\sqrt{5}, y = -\frac{2}{3}.$

Exercise 40

1. $x = 3, y = 3;$ $x = -3, y = -3;$ $x = 2, y = -1;$ $x = -2, y = 1.$ **2.** $x = \frac{3}{2}, y = 1;$ $x = -\frac{3}{2}, y = -1; x = 1, y = 2; x = -1, y = -2.$ **3.** $x = 4, y = 3; x = -4, y = -3;$ $x = \frac{1}{3}, y = -1; x = -\frac{1}{3}, y = 1.$ **5.** $x = 2, y = -1; x = -2, y = 1; x = 2, y = -2; x = -2, y = 2.$ **6.** $x = 3, y = 1; x = -3, y = -1; x = 2, y = -3; x = -2, y = 3.$ **7.** $x = 2, y = 1; x = -2, y = -1; x = 3, y = 2; x = -3, y = -2.$ **9.** $x = \frac{1}{2}, y = 1;$ $x = -\frac{1}{2}, y = -1; x = \frac{3}{4}, y = \frac{1}{4}; x = -\frac{3}{4}, y = -\frac{1}{4}.$ **10.** $x = \frac{1}{4}, y = \frac{1}{2}; x = -\frac{1}{4}, y = -\frac{1}{2}; x = \frac{1}{2}, y = 2; x = -\frac{1}{2}, y = -2.$ **11.** $x = 2, y = 3; x = -2, y = -3; x = \frac{3}{4}, y = \frac{1}{2}; x = -\frac{3}{4}, y = -\frac{1}{2}.$ **13.** $x = 1, y = -3; x = -1, y = 3; x = 2, y = -1; x = -2, y = 1.$ **14.** $x = 2, y = -4; x = -2, y = 4; x = 3, y = -2; x = -3, y = 2.$ **15.** $x = 5, y = -3; x = -5, y = 3; x = 2, y = -4; x = -2, y = 4.$ **17.** $x = \frac{1}{2}, y = -\frac{3}{2}; x = -\frac{1}{2}, y = \frac{2}{3}; x = \frac{1}{3}, y = -\frac{3}{2}; x = -\frac{1}{3}, y = \frac{3}{2}.$ **18.** $x = \frac{3}{4}, y = -\frac{1}{2}; x = -\frac{3}{4}, y = \frac{1}{2}; x = \frac{1}{4}, y = \frac{3}{2}; x = -\frac{1}{4}, y = -\frac{3}{2}.$ **19.** $x = \frac{4}{3}, y = -\frac{1}{6}; x = -\frac{4}{3}, y = \frac{1}{6}; x = \frac{1}{2}, y = \frac{2}{3}; x = -\frac{1}{2}, y = -\frac{2}{3}.$ **21.** $x = 1, y = \frac{1}{3}; x = -1, y = -\frac{1}{3}; x = \sqrt{2}, y = 2\sqrt{2}; x = -\sqrt{2}; y = -\sqrt{2}.$ **22.** $x = 2, y = \frac{3}{4}; x = -2, y = -\frac{3}{4}; x = 2\sqrt{3}, y = \sqrt{3}; x = -2\sqrt{3}, y = -\sqrt{3}.$ **23.** $x = 4, y = -\frac{3}{2}; x = -4, y = \frac{3}{2}; x = \sqrt{5}, y = 2\sqrt{5}; x = -\sqrt{5}, y = -2\sqrt{5}.$ **25.** $x = 3 + 4i, y = 3 + 2i; x = -3 - 4i, y = -3 - 2i; x = 3 - 4i, y = 3 - 2i; x = -3 + 4i, y = -3 + 2i.$ **26.** $x = 3 + i, y = 1 - 3i; x = -3 - i, y = -1 + 3i; x = 3 - i, y = 1 + 3i; x = -3 + i,$

$y = -1 - 3i$. **27.** $x = 1 + 2i$; $y = 3 - 2i$; $x = -1 - 2i$, $y = -3 + 2i$; $x = 1 - 2i$,
$y = 3 + 2i$; $x = -1 + 2i$, $y = -3 - 2i$. **29.** $x = 1 + \sqrt{2}$, $y = 2 - \sqrt{2}$;
$x = -1 - \sqrt{2}$, $y = -2 + \sqrt{2}$; $x = 1 - \sqrt{2}$, $y = 2 + \sqrt{2}$; $x = -1 + \sqrt{2}$,
$y = -2 - 2\sqrt{2}$. **30.** $x = 2 - \sqrt{2}$, $y = 1 + 2\sqrt{2}$; $x = -2 + \sqrt{2}$,
$y = -1 - 2\sqrt{2}$; $x = 2 + \sqrt{2}$, $y = 1 - 2\sqrt{2}$; $x = -2 - \sqrt{2}$, $y = -1 + 2\sqrt{2}$.
31. $x = \sqrt{2} + \sqrt{3}$, $y = 2\sqrt{2} - \sqrt{3}$; $x = -\sqrt{2} - \sqrt{3}$, $y = -2\sqrt{2} + \sqrt{3}$;
$x = \sqrt{2} - \sqrt{3}$, $y = 2\sqrt{2} + \sqrt{3}$; $x = -\sqrt{2} + \sqrt{3}$, $y = -2\sqrt{2} - \sqrt{3}$.

Exercise 41

1. $x = 3$, $y = -1$; $x = -2$, $y = 4$. **2.** $x = 5$, $y = -3$; $x = -2$, $y = 1$. **3.** $x = 2$,
$y = \frac{1}{2}$; $x = 3$, $y = 1$. **5.** $x = 3$, $y = \frac{1}{3}$; $x = -3$, $y = -\frac{1}{3}$; $x = \frac{1}{2}$, $y = 2$; $x = -\frac{1}{2}$,
$y = -2$. **6.** $x = 3$, $y = -2$; $x = -3$, $y = 2$; $x = 4$, $y = -\frac{3}{2}$; $x = -4$, $y = \frac{3}{2}$.
7. $x = 6$, $y = -\frac{1}{4}$; $x = -6$, $y = \frac{1}{4}$; $x = \frac{3}{2}$, $y = -1$; $x = -\frac{3}{2}$, $y = 1$. **9.** $x = 2$, $y = 6$;
$x = -2$, $y = 6$; $x = \frac{2}{3}$, $y = \frac{2}{3}$; $x = -\frac{2}{3}$, $y = \frac{2}{3}$. **10.** $x = 1$, $y = \frac{1}{2}$; $x = -1$, $y = \frac{1}{2}$;
$x = 2$, $y = 2$; $x = -2$, $y = 2$. **11.** $x = \frac{1}{3}$, $y = \frac{1}{3}$; $x = -\frac{1}{3}$, $y = \frac{1}{3}$; $x = 2$, $y = 12$;
$x = -2$, $y = 12$. **13.** $x = 4$, $y = 1$; $x = 3$, $y = 5$. **14.** $x = 6$, $y = -4$; $x = 4$, $y = 1$.
15. $x = \frac{3}{4}$, $y = -\frac{2}{3}$; $x = \frac{1}{4}$, $y = \frac{1}{3}$. **17.** $x = 3$, $y = 1$; $x = 2$, $y = 3$. **18.** $x = 4$, $y = 3$;
$x = \frac{1}{3}$, $y = \frac{1}{2}$. **19.** $x = 4$, $y = -2$; $x = 1$, $y = \frac{1}{2}$. **21.** $x = 3$, $y = 2$; $x = 4$, $y = 3$.
22. $x = 3$, $y = -2$; $x = 2$, $y = -1$. **23.** $x = 4$, $y = -5$; $x = 1$, $y = -2$. **25.** $x = 3$,
$y = -2$; $x = -2$, $y = 3$; $x = 2$, $y = -4$; $x = -4$, $y = 2$. **26.** $x = 2$, $y = 1$; $x = 1$,
$y = 2$; $x = 5$, $y = -3$; $x = -3$, $y = 5$. **27.** $x = 3$, $y = -4$, $x = -4$, $y = 3$; $x = 1$,
$y = -3$; $x = -3$, $y = 1$. **29.** $x = 4$, $y = -2$; $x = -2$, $y = 4$; $x = 1$, $y = -3$;
$x = -3$, $y = 1$. **30.** $x = \frac{2}{3}$, $y = -\frac{1}{3}$; $x = -\frac{1}{3}$, $y = \frac{2}{3}$; $x = \frac{3}{4}$, $y = -\frac{1}{4}$; $x = -\frac{1}{4}$, $y = \frac{3}{4}$.
31. $x = 2$, $y = -1$; $x = -1$, $y = 2$; $x = 2$, $y = -3$; $x = -3$, $y = 2$.

Exercise 42

1. 24, 32. **2.** 18, 15; $-18, -15$. **3.** 8, 9. **5.** 16 yd., 14 yd. **6.** 8 ft., 6 ft. **7.** 12 ft., 5 ft.
9. 80 by 40 yd. **10.** 50 by 32 ft. **11.** 20 by 16 in. **13.** 40 miles per hr., 120 miles.
14. 140 miles per hr., 100 miles per hr., 20 miles per hr. **15.** 8 ft. high, 8 ft. wide.
17. 6 in., 8 in. **18.** 4 by 3 cm. **19.** 12 ft., 6 ft., 3 ft. **21.** 8 ft., 15 ft. **22.** 100, \$150.
23. 125, \$60; 150, \$50. **25.** $\frac{1}{2}\sqrt{2} + \frac{1}{2}\sqrt{6}$. **26.** $\sqrt{3} + \frac{1}{2}\sqrt{5}$. **27.** $\sqrt{3} + \sqrt{2}$.
29. $\frac{1}{2}\sqrt{5} + \frac{1}{2}\sqrt{7}$. **30.** $\sqrt{2} + \frac{1}{2}\sqrt{6}$. **31.** $\frac{1}{2}\sqrt{22} + \frac{1}{2}\sqrt{10}$.

Exercise 43

1. $\frac{15}{2}$. **2.** $\frac{7}{2}$. **3.** $\frac{45}{2}$. **5.** $\frac{14}{5}$. **6.** $\frac{54}{1}$. **7.** $\frac{200}{1}$. **9.** 50 miles per hr. **10.** 75 cents per
dozen. **11.** 510 lb. per bale. **13.** $\frac{5}{12}$. **14.** $\frac{1}{20}$. **15.** 7.8. **17.** $\frac{9}{4}$. **18.** $2\frac{1}{4}$. **19.** 3.
21. $5\frac{1}{4}$. **22.** $-\frac{1}{5}$. **23.** 3, -4. **25.** $2\frac{1}{2}$. **26.** $\frac{1}{2}$. **27.** ± 6. **29.** ± 12. **30.** $\pm 10\sqrt{6}$.
31. 4. **33.** 12.5. **34.** $33\frac{1}{3}$. **35.** 9. **37.** 14. **38.** 9. **39.** $x = 6$, $y = 8$. **41.** $x = 14$,
$y = 6$. **42.** $x = 8$, $y = 3$. **43.** $6\frac{2}{3}$ ft., $5\frac{1}{3}$ ft. **45.** 700 miles.

Exercise 44

1. (a) $m = kn$, (b) $s = \dfrac{k}{t}$, (c) $r = ksm$, (d) $w = \dfrac{kx}{y^2}$. **2.** 14. **3.** 6. **5.** 1. **6.** 100. **7.** 40.

9. 2816 cu. in. **10.** $\dfrac{340°}{9}$. **11.** Intensity at 5 ft. is $\frac{49}{25}$ of the intensity at 7 ft. **13.** 24 cc.

14. 600 bbl. **15.** 900 bbl. **17.** 1280 lb. **18.** $10\sqrt{15}$ miles. **19.** $\frac{1}{100}$ sec. **21.** The attractions are the same. **22.** The energy at 50 miles per hr. is 25 times that at 10 miles per hr. **23.** 670 days. **25.** The first is $\frac{9}{4}$ as strong as the second. **26.** The resistance of the longer wire is $\frac{1}{2}$ that of the shorter.

Exercise 45

1. $6 + 8i$. **2.** $6 + i$. **3.** $7 + 4i$. **5.** $2 + 4i$. **6.** $-1 + i$. **7.** $3 + 4i$. **9.** $13 + 5i$.
10. $14 + 2i$. **11.** 4. **13.** $8 + i$. **14.** $-20i$. **15.** $4 + i$. **17.** $14 - 3i$. **18.** $23 + 14i$.
19. $21 + i$. **21.** $-7 - 24i$. **22.** $-21 + 10i$. **23.** $7 + 24i$. **25.** $4 + 6i$.
26. $13 + 13i$. **27.** $5 + 15i$. **29.** $\dfrac{12 + 5i}{13}$. **30.** $\dfrac{17 + i}{29}$. **31.** $\dfrac{19 - 9i}{26}$. **33.** $-i$.
34. $\dfrac{3 - 4i}{5}$. **35.** $\dfrac{8 + 6i}{5}$. **37.** $\dfrac{5 - 5i}{2}$. **38.** $\dfrac{5 - 5i}{2}$. **39.** $\dfrac{9 + 46i}{13}$. **41.** $2 - 3i$.
42. $7 - i$. **43.** $-6i$. **45.** $3 + 2i$. **46.** $7 + 4i$. **47.** $5 + 3i$. **49.** $-1 - i$. **50.** $-2i$.
51. 2. **57.** $-6 + 17i$. **58.** $17 - 11i$. **59.** $23 + 14i$. **61.** $x = 2, y = -2$. **62.** $x = 3$,
$y = 4$. **63.** $x = 3, y = 2$. **65.** $x = 3, y = 3$. **66.** $x = 3, y = 2$. **67.** $x = -2, y = -1$.
69. $x = 3, y = 5$. **70.** $x = 2, y = 3$. **71.** $x = 2, y = 1$. **73.** $x = 2, y = 3$. **74.** $x = 3$,
$y = 2$. **75.** $x = 7, y = 3$.

Exercise 46

17. $\sqrt{2}\,(\cos 45° + i \sin 45°)$. **18.** $\sqrt{2}\,(\cos 315° + i \sin 315°)$.
19. $\sqrt{2}\,(\cos 225° + i \sin 225°)$. **21.** $2(\cos 30° + i \sin 30°)$.
22. $2(\cos 300° + i \sin 300°)$. **23.** $2(\cos 210° + i \sin 210°)$.
25. $2(\cos 0° + i \sin 0°)$. **26.** $\cos 90° + i \sin 90°$. **27.** $3(\cos 270° + i \sin 270°)$.
29. $5[\cos (\arctan \frac{4}{3}) + i \sin (\arctan \frac{4}{3})]$. **30.** $13[\cos (\arctan \frac{12}{5}) + i \sin (\arctan \frac{12}{5})]$.

31. $13\left[\cos\left(\arctan\dfrac{-5}{12}\right) + i \sin\left(\arctan\dfrac{-5}{12}\right)\right]$.

33. $2\sqrt{5}\left[\cos\left(\arctan\dfrac{-2}{1}\right) + i \sin\left(\arctan\dfrac{-2}{1}\right)\right]$.

34. $\sqrt{5}\,[\cos (\arctan 2) + i \sin (\arctan 2)]$.

35. $\sqrt{34}\left[\cos\left(\arctan\dfrac{5}{-3}\right) + i \sin\left(\arctan\dfrac{5}{-3}\right)\right]$.

Exercise 47

NOTE: In the answers to this and the following exercise, the abbreviation cis θ will be used for $\cos \theta + i \sin \theta$.

1. $8 \text{ cis } 30° = 4\sqrt{3} + 4i$. **2.** $6 \text{ cis } 60° = 3 + 3\sqrt{3}\,i$. **3.** $2 \text{ cis } 45° = \sqrt{2} + \sqrt{2}\,i$.
5. $4 \text{ cis } 120° = -2 + 2\sqrt{3}\,i$. **6.** $18 \text{ cis } 135° = -9\sqrt{2} + 9\sqrt{2}\,i$.

7. $5 \text{ cis } 150° = -\dfrac{5\sqrt{3}}{2} + \dfrac{5}{2}i$. **9.** $35 \text{ cis } 90° = 35i$. **10.** $14 \text{ cis } 180° = -14$.

11. $10 \text{ cis } 270° = -10i$. **13.** $4 \text{ cis } 30° = 2\sqrt{3} + 2i$.
14. $3 \text{ cis } 45° = \frac{1}{2}(3\sqrt{2} + 3\sqrt{2}\,i)$. **15.** $4 \text{ cis } 60° = 2 + 2\sqrt{3}\,i$.
17. $3 \text{ cis } (-30°) = \frac{1}{2}(3\sqrt{3} - 3i)$. **18.** $2 \text{ cis } (-45°) = \sqrt{2} - \sqrt{2}\,i$.
19. $3 \text{ cis } (-120°) = \frac{1}{2}(-3 - 3\sqrt{3}\,i)$. **21.** $24 \text{ cis } 30° = 12\sqrt{3} + 12i$.

22. $4 \text{ cis } 45° = 2\sqrt{2} + 2\sqrt{2}\,i.$ **23.** $36 \text{ cis } 180° = -36.$
25. $\text{cis } 60° = \frac{1}{2}(1 + \sqrt{3}\,i).$ **26.** $3 \text{ cis } 30° = \frac{1}{2}(3\sqrt{3} + 3i).$ **27.** $3 \text{ cis } 0° = 3.$
29. $4\sqrt{2} \text{ cis } 345°.$ **30.** $4\sqrt{2} \text{ cis } 285°.$ **31.** $4\sqrt{2} \text{ cis } 195°.$ **33.** $4 \text{ cis } 300°.$
34. $4 \text{ cis } 240°.$ **35.** $2\sqrt{2} \text{ cis } 45°.$ **37.** $\sqrt{2} \text{ cis } 195°.$ **38.** $2 \text{ cis } 210°.$ **39.** $2 \text{ cis } 150°.$

Exercise 48

1. $2\sqrt{2} \text{ cis } 135°.$ **2.** $2 \text{ cis } 270°.$ **3.** $4 \text{ cis } 180°.$ **5.** $32 \text{ cis } 120°.$ **6.** $64 \text{ cis } 0°.$
7. $64 \text{ cis } 180°.$ **9.** $8 \text{ cis } 270°.$ **10.** $32 \text{ cis } 90°.$ **11.** $729 \text{ cis } 180°.$ **13.** $125 \text{ cis } 201°.$
14. $28,561 \text{ cis } 92°.$ **15.** $625 \text{ cis } 148°.$ **17.** $125\sqrt{5} \text{ cis } 81°.$ **18.** $676 \text{ cis } 316°.$
19. $169\sqrt{13} \text{ cis } 260°.$ **21.** $\sqrt[6]{2} \text{ cis } (15 + k120)°, \; k = 0, 1, 2.$ **22.** $\sqrt[10]{2} \text{ cis } (63 + k72)°,$
$k = 0, 1, 2, 3, 4.$ **23.** $\sqrt[18]{2} \text{ cis } (15 + k40)°, \; k = 0, 1, 2, 3, 4, 5, 6, 7, 8.$
25. $\sqrt[6]{2} \text{ cis } (40 + k60)°, \; k = 0, 1, 2, 3, 4, 5.$ **26.** $\sqrt[8]{2} \text{ cis } (15 + k45)°,$
$k = 0, 1, 2, 3, 4, 5, 6, 7.$ **27.** $\sqrt[3]{2} \text{ cis } (10 + k120)°, \; k = 0, 1, 2.$ **29.** $\sqrt[6]{2} \text{ cis } (55 + k60)°,$
$k = 0, 1, 2, 3, 4, 5.$ **30.** $\sqrt[10]{8} \text{ cis } (9 + k72)°, \; k = 0, 1, 2, 3, 4.$ **31.** $\sqrt[4]{12} \text{ cis } (60 + k90)°,$
$k = 0, 1, 2, 3.$ **33.** $\sqrt[3]{2} \text{ cis } (210 + k240°), \; k = 0, 1, 2.$ **34.** $\sqrt[4]{8} \text{ cis } (45 + k270)°,$
$k = 0, 1, 2, 3.$ **35.** $\sqrt[5]{4} \text{ cis } (60 + k144)°, \; k = 0, 1, 2, 3, 4.$ **37.** $2 \text{ cis } (0 + k90)°,$
$k = 0, 1, 2, 3.$ **38.** $2 \text{ cis } (18 + k72)°, \; k = 0, 1, 2, 3, 4.$ **39.** $2 \text{ cis } (60 + k120)°,$
$k = 0, 1, 2.$ **41.** $\sqrt{5} \text{ cis } (\frac{1}{2} \arctan \frac{4}{3} + k180)°, \; k = 0, 1.$ **42.** $\sqrt[16]{13} \text{ cis } (38° + k45°),$
$k = 0, 1, 2, 3, 4, 5, 6, 7.$ **43.** $\sqrt[12]{10} \text{ cis } (27° + k60°), \; k = 0, 1, 2, 3, 4, 5.$
45. $2 \text{ cis } (0 + k90)°, \; k = 0, 1, 2, 3.$ **46.** $3 \text{ cis } (0 + 120)°, \; k = 0, 1, 2, 3, 4, 5.$
47. $2 \text{ cis } (36 + k72)°, \; k = 0, 1, 2, 3, 4.$ **49.** $\text{cis } (22\frac{1}{2} + k90)°, \; k = 0, 1, 2, 3.$
50. $\text{cis } (18 + k72)°, \; k = 0, 1, 2, 3, 4.$ **51.** $3 \text{ cis } (90 + k120)°, \; k = 0, 1, 2.$

Exercise 49

1. $3.$ **2.** $-9.$ **3.** $52.$ **5.** $-2.$ **6.** $-108.$ **7.** $2.$ **9.** $-7.$ **10.** $0.$ **11.** $-15.$ **13.** $-6.$
14. $469.$ **15.** $-1.$ **37.** $1, 2, -3.$ **38.** $-2, 4, -5.$ **39.** $\frac{1}{2}, -\frac{2}{3}, \frac{3}{4}.$ **41.** $2, -1, -3.$
42. $4, -1, 1.$ **43.** $2, 3, -4.$

Exercise 50

1. $x^2 + x + 6, 13.$ **2.** $x^2 - x, 1.$ **3.** $2x^2 + 3x + 4, -1.$ **5.** $-3x^2 - x + 1, 0.$
6. $-5x^2 + 2x + 7, -15.$ **7.** $-x^2 - 5x + 3, -18.$ **9.** $x^3 + 4x^2 - x + 6, -3.$
10. $x^3 - 8x^2 + 2x - 12, 19.$ **11.** $-2x^3 + 9x^2 - 12x + 13, -24.$
13. $x^4 + 2x^3 - 5x^2 - 3x - 2, -3.$ **14.** $x^4 + 2x^2 + x, 1.$ **15.** $2x^4 - 3x^2 - x + 5, -12.$
17. $3x^2 + 15x + 74, 371.$ **18.** $2x^3 - 4x^2 + 7x - 13, 26.$ **19.** $x^4 + x^3 + x^2 + x, 1.$
21. $4x^3 + 2x^2 - 4x - 2, 0.$ **22.** $6x^2 - 6x + 3, -3.$ **23.** $12x^2 + 12x + 8, 9.$
25. $x^5 - 2x^4 + 4x^3 - 8x^2 + 16x - 5, 0.$ **26.** $2x^5 + 2x^4 + 2x^3 + x^2 + x + 2, 2.$
27. $3x^3 - 9x^2 + 27x + 1, -3.$ **29.** $x^2 + 1, 2a.$ **30.** $2x^2 + ax + 4a^2, 0.$
31. $2x^3 - 2a^2x + a^3, 4a^4.$ **33.** $-3.$ **34.** $-4.$ **35.** $6.$ **37.** $0.$ **38.** $0.$ **39.** $3, -1.$

Exercise 52

In the answers from 1 to 7, the degree is given first, then each root followed by its multiplicity.

1. $5; -2, 3; 3, 2.$ **2.** $5; 1, 1; -3, 1; 4, 3.$ **3.** $7; -5, 4; 2, 3.$ **5.** $7; \frac{5}{2}, 4; -\frac{7}{3}, 3.$ **6.** $20;$
$-\frac{9}{5}, 10; \frac{1}{2}, 3; -4, 7.$ **7.** $12; \frac{2}{3}, 6; -\frac{3}{2}, 3; 3, 2; -2, 1.$ **9.** $2, -2;$ between 1 and 2, 0 and
1, -2 and $-1.$ **10.** $2, -2;$ between 1 and 2, -1 and 0, -2 and $-1.$ **11.** $4, -3;$ between
2 and 3; 1 and 2, -3 and $-2.$ **13.** $5, -4;$ between 3 and 4, 1 and 2, -4 and $-3.$ **14.** $4,$

−4; between 3 and 4; −1 and 0, −4 and −3. **15.** 1, −6; between 0 and 1, −1 and 0, −6 and −5. **17.** 3, −6; between 2 and 3, 1 and 2, −1 and −2, −5 and −6. **18.** 7, −1; between 4 and 5, 2 and 3, 0 and 1, −1 and 0. **19.** 6, −5; between 5 and 6, 1 and 2, −2 and −1, −4 and −5. **21.** 2, −4; between 1 and 2, 0 and 1, −2 and −1, −3 and −2. **22.** 3, −3; between 2 and 3, 0 and 1, −1 and 0, −3 and −2. **23.** 4, −5; between 3 and 4, 0 and 1, −2 and −1, −4 and −3. **25.** 1, −1; between −1 and 0. **26.** 1, −3; between 0 and 1. **27.** 2, −5; between 1 and 2. **29.** 1, −4; between 0 and 1, −1 and 0. **30.** 1, −5; between 0 and 1, −2 and −1. **31.** 3, −5; between 2 and 3, −3 and −4. **33.** Between 0 and $\frac{1}{2}$, $\frac{1}{2}$ and 1, −2 and −1. **34.** Between 0 and $\frac{1}{2}$, $\frac{1}{2}$ and 1, −2 and −1. **35.** Between 1 and $1\frac{1}{2}$, $1\frac{1}{2}$ and 2, 3 and 4. **37.** Between −1 and $-\frac{1}{2}$, $-\frac{1}{2}$ and 0, 1 and 2. **38.** Between −3 and $-2\frac{1}{2}$, $-2\frac{1}{2}$ and −2, 0 and 1. **39.** Between 1 and $1\frac{1}{2}$, $1\frac{1}{2}$ and 2, −1 and 0.

Exercise 53

1. −2, 1, 2. **2.** −1, 2, 3. **3.** −5, −2, 1. **5.** −1, $-\frac{1}{2}$, $1\frac{1}{2}$. **6.** −2, $-\frac{1}{2}$, $\frac{1}{3}$.
7. −1, $1\frac{1}{2}$, 2. **9.** $-\frac{1}{2}$, $\frac{1}{3}$, $\frac{1}{2}$. **10.** $-1\frac{1}{2}$, $1\frac{1}{2}$, $1\frac{1}{2}$. **11.** $\frac{1}{2}$, $\frac{2}{3}$, $\frac{3}{4}$. **13.** −1, 1, 1, 2.
14. −5, 1, 1, 2. **15.** −3, −1, 1, 4. **17.** −2, −1, $\frac{1}{3}$, 3. **18.** $-\frac{1}{3}$, 1, 2, 3.
19. −3, $-\frac{1}{4}$, $\frac{1}{2}$, 2. **21.** −1, $\frac{1}{4}(-1 \pm \sqrt{41})$. **22.** −2, $\frac{1}{4}(1 \pm \sqrt{33})$.
23. $\frac{1}{2}$, $\frac{1}{2}(-1 \pm \sqrt{23}\,i)$. **25.** 1, $\frac{1}{2}(-1 \pm \sqrt{3}\,i)$. **26.** $\frac{1}{2}$, $\pm i$. **27.** $-\frac{1}{3}$, −1 ± i.
29. −1, 2, ±i. **30.** ±1, 1 ± i. **31.** $\pm\frac{1}{2}$, 1 ± 2i. **33.** ±1, $\frac{1}{2}(-1 \pm \sqrt{3i})$.
34. $-1\frac{1}{2}$, −1, $-\frac{2}{3}$, ± i. **35.** −1, 1, 1, ± i.

Exercise 54

1. 2, 1. **2.** 2, 1. **3.** 1, 2. **5.** 0, 1. **6.** 0, 1. **7.** 1, 0. **9.** 2, 2. **10.** 4, 0. **11.** 0, 0.
17. $x^3 - 4x^2 + 6x - 4 = 0$. **18.** $x^3 - 5x^2 + 17x - 13 = 0$.
19. $x^3 - 3x^2 + 7x + 75 = 0$. **21.** $x^4 - 1 = 0$. **22.** $x^4 + 5x^2 + 4 = 0$.
23. $x^4 - 6x^3 + 15x^2 - 18x + 10 = 0$. **25.** $x^5 + x^4 + 5x^3 + 5x^2 + 4x + 4 = 0$.
26. $x^5 - 3x^4 + 5x^3 - 5x^2 + 4x - 2 = 0$. **27.** $x^5 - 8x^4 + 21x^3 - 12x^2 - 22x + 20 = 0$

Exercise 55

1. .4+, 1.8+, −1.2−. **2.** .7+, −.4+, −1.9+. **3.** .3+, 2.4+, −.4−.
5. −.2−, .7−, 2.2+. **6.** −.7+, .8−, 3.9−. **7.** −.3−, .4−, 2.6+. **9.** .26. **10.** .47.
11. .59. **13.** .45. **14.** .71. **15.** .21. **17.** 1.16. **18.** 2.08. **19.** .75.

Exercise 56

1. $x^3 + 4x^2 - x - 6 = 0$. **2.** $x^3 + 14x^2 + 51x + 57 = 0$.
3. $2x^3 + 21x^2 + 76x + 93 = 0$. **5.** $x^4 + 13x^3 + 46x^2 + 57x + 20 = 0$.
6. $2x^4 + 7x^3 + 9x^2 + 5x + 4 = 0$. **7.** $3x^4 + 16x^3 + 24x^2 - 9x - 33 = 0$.
9. $x^3 - 1.7x^2 + .63x - .919 = 0$. **10.** $3x^3 + 1.7x^2 + 2.21x - 2.409 = 0$.
11. $2x^3 + 2.2x^2 - 2.36x + .456 = 0$. **13.** .12. **14.** .53. **15.** .66. **17.** 1.24. **18.** 1.18.
19. 1.42. **21.** 1.67. **22.** 1.45. **23.** .82. **25.** 1.351. **26.** 1.087. **27.** −2.940.
29. 2.414, −.414. **30.** 1.866, .134. **31.** 1.618, −.618. **33.** 1.442. **34.** 1.260.
35. 1.913. **37.** 1.189. **38.** 1.495. **39.** 1.246.

Exercise 57

1. 1, 1 + 3i, 1 − 3i. **2.** −2, −2 + 3i, −2 − 3i. **3.** 1, $1 + 2\sqrt{3}\,i$, $1 - 2\sqrt{3}\,i$.
5. 3, $3 + 2\sqrt{3}\,i$, $3 - 2\sqrt{3}\,i$. **6.** −1, $-1 + 3\sqrt{3}\,i$, $-1 - 3\sqrt{3}\,i$.

7. $1, 1 + 3\sqrt{3}\,i, 1 - 3\sqrt{3}\,i.$ **9.** $-1, -4 - \sqrt{3}, -4 + \sqrt{3}.$

10. $4, 1 - \sqrt{3}, 1 + \sqrt{3}.$ **11.** $5, 2 + \sqrt{3}, 2 - \sqrt{3}.$ **13.** $1 + 2\sqrt{3}, 1 - 2\sqrt{3}, 1.$

14. $2 + \sqrt{3}, 2 - \sqrt{3}, 2.$ **15.** $3 + 3\sqrt{3}, 3 - 3\sqrt{3}, 3.$ **17.** $\pm 1, 2, -3$

18. $\pm 2, 1, -3.$ **19.** $1, 2, 3, -\frac{1}{2}.$ **21.** $\pm\sqrt{3}, 1, 2.$ **22.** $\pm\sqrt{2}, 2, -1.$

23. $\pm\sqrt{2}, \frac{1}{2}(-1 \pm \sqrt{5}).$ **25.** $\frac{1}{2}(-1 \pm \sqrt{5}), \frac{1}{2}(-1 \pm \sqrt{13}).$

26. $-1 \pm \sqrt{5}, \frac{1}{2}(1 \pm \sqrt{11}\,i).$ **27.** $-1 \pm i, \frac{1}{2}(-1 \pm \sqrt{3}\,i).$

Exercise 59

17. $x < 2.$ **18.** $x < 3.$ **19.** $x > -1.$ **21.** $x > 2\frac{1}{2}.$ **22.** $x < \frac{4}{3}.$ **23.** $x > -3.$

25. $x < 1.$ **26.** $x > \frac{5}{3}.$ **27.** $x > 2.$ **29.** $x > -2.$ **30.** $x < 3.$ **31.** $x > \frac{5}{2}.$ **33.** $x < \frac{3}{2}.$

34. $x < -4.$ **35.** $x < \frac{5}{3}.$ **37.** $-3 < x < 1.$ **38.** $2 < x < 4.$ **39.** $x > -1, x < -3.$

41. $-1\frac{1}{2} < x < 4\frac{1}{2}.$ **42.** $-\frac{32}{3} < x < \frac{8}{3}.$ **43.** $x < -\frac{20}{3}, x > \frac{10}{3}.$ **45.** $-\frac{4}{3} < x < 3.$

46. $\frac{1}{2} < x < 1.$ **47.** $x > \frac{5}{2}, x < -\frac{2}{3}.$ **49.** $-\frac{3}{2} < x < \frac{1}{3}.$ **50.** $-\frac{1}{2} < x < 3.$

51. $x < -\frac{1}{3}, x > \frac{3}{2}.$ **53.** $x < -\frac{3}{2}, -\frac{2}{3} < x < 1.$ **54.** $x < -2, -\frac{1}{2} < x < \frac{2}{3}.$

55. $-\frac{4}{3} < x < \frac{3}{2}, x > 2.$ **57.** $x < -2, -\frac{1}{2} < x < 3.$ **58.** $x < -1\frac{1}{2}, 1 < x < 2.$

59. $-2 < x < \frac{1}{3}, x > \frac{3}{2}.$ **61.** $x < -a, x > a.$ **62.** All values of x. **63.** $-a < x < a.$

65. $x > -1.$ **66.** $x < 2, x > -3.$ **67.** $\frac{1}{2} < x < 1.$

Exercise 60

1. $5^2 = 25.$ **2.** $4^2 = 16.$ **3.** $3^3 = 27.$ **5.** $2^5 = 32.$ **6.** $4^3 = 64.$ **7.** $3^{-2} = \frac{1}{9}.$

9. $3^{-3} = \frac{1}{27}.$ **10.** $16^{\frac{1}{2}} = 4.$ **11.** $27^{\frac{5}{3}} = 243.$ **13.** $(1/4)^{\frac{3}{2}} = 1/8.$ **14.** $(1/8)^{\frac{2}{3}} = 1/4.$

15. $(9/16)^{\frac{1}{2}} = \frac{3}{4}.$ **17.** $(a^{\frac{1}{2}})^8 = a^4.$ **18.** $(a^2)^{1\frac{1}{2}} = a^3.$ **19.** $\log_2 8 = 3.$ **21.** $\log_5 25 = 2.$

22. $\log_{32} 4 = \frac{2}{5}.$ **23.** $\log_8 4 = \frac{2}{3}.$ **25.** $\log_3 \left(\frac{1}{3}\right) = -1.$ **26.** $\log_2 \left(\frac{1}{8}\right) = -3.$

27. $\log_{\frac{1}{2}} 16 = -4.$ **29.** $\log_{27} \left(\frac{1}{9}\right) = -\frac{2}{3}.$ **30.** $\log_{32} \left(\frac{1}{8}\right) = -\frac{3}{5}.$ **31.** $2.$ **33.** $2.$ **34.** $2.$

35. $3.$ **37.** $3.$ **38.** $5.$ **39.** $\frac{1}{2}.$ **41.** $\frac{1}{2}.$ **42.** $\frac{1}{2}.$ **43.** $\frac{1}{3}.$ **45.** $\frac{1}{3}.$ **46.** $\frac{1}{4}.$ **47.** $3.$ **49.** $8.$

50. $18.$ **51.** $9.$ **53.** $81.$ **54.** $125.$ **55.** $256.$ **57.** $2.$ **58.** $2.$ **59.** $3.$ **61.** $36.$ **62.** $27.$

63. $243.$ **65.** $32.$ **66.** $27.$

Exercise 61

1. $1.$ **2.** $0.$ **3.** $1.$ **5.** $2.$ **6.** $1.$ **7.** $0.$ **9.** $2.$ **10.** $-1.$ **11.** $-2.$ **13.** $-3.$ **14.** $-2.$

15. $-4.$ **17.** $1.7657.$ **18.** $0.9877.$ **19.** $0.9201.$ **21.** $0.7767.$ **22.** $9.5821 - 10.$

23. $8.3979 - 10.$ **25.** $7.3010 - 10.$ **26.** $8.5682 - 10.$ **27.** $7.5185 - 10.$

29. $8.0792 - 10.$ **30.** $0.7007.$ **31.** $1.3160.$ **33.** $3.3284.$ **34.** $4.5065.$ **35.** $5.9063.$

37. $4.0086.$ **38.** $7.8513.$ **39.** $5.9117.$ **41.** $1.7878.$ **42.** $2.9292.$ **43.** $9.2117 - 10.$

45. $1.5990.$ **46.** $8.5018 - 10.$ **47.** $7.7787 - 10.$ **49.** $9.8599 - 10.$ **50.** $2.3320.$

51. $6.7888 - 10.$ **53.** $1.0195.$ **54.** $4.8891.$ **55.** $9.7956 - 10.$ **57.** $1.0927.$ **58.** $1.6710.$

59. $0.9992.$

Exercise 62

1. $6420.$ **2.** $19.3.$ **3.** $0.0306.$ **5.** $37,800.$ **6.** $0.00805.$ **7.** $427.$ **9.** $4920.$ **10.** $740.$

11. $0.000602.$ **13.** $0.0000227.$ **14.** $12.6.$ **15.** $5530.$ **17.** $17.3.$ **18.** $222.$ **19.** $9.52.$

21. $386.$ **22.** $6.96.$ **23.** $0.243.$ **25.** $0.415.$ **26.** $0.00248.$ **27.** $0.0932.$ **29.** $3.72.$

30. $13.3.$ **31.** $0.158.$ **33.** $30.55.$ **34.** $7626.$ **35.** $402.5.$ **37.** $0.03565.$ **38.** $0.8013.$

39. $44.77.$ **41.** $522.4.$ **42.** $0.008324.$ **43.** $4.723.$ **45.** $0.2826.$ **46.** $3818.$

47. $127,400,000.$

Exercise 63

1. $16.7.$ **2.** $14.5.$ **3.** $7.81.$ **5.** $0.000707.$ **6.** $0.128.$ **7.** $0.363.$ **9.** $1.56.$ **10.** $10.1.$

11. $1.22.$ **13.** $0.0561.$ **14.** $0.824.$ **15.** $0.507.$ **17.** $7.84.$ **18.** $7.71.$ **19.** $0.907.$

21. 9.03. **22.** 0.000,000,118. **23.** 5.76. **25.** 24.0. **26.** 16.3. **27.** 14.4. **29.** 2.86.
30. 0.637. **31.** 0.291. **33.** 13,790. **34.** 19.05. **35.** .9362. **37.** 0.1685. **38.** 1.246.
39. 1.016. **41.** 4.571. **42.** 1.128. **43.** 0.002782. **45.** 2.329. **46.** 13,950. **47.** 0.01898.
49. $\log c + \log x - \log (x + 1)$. **50.** $\log c + 2 \log x - \log (x - 2)$.
51. $\log c + 2 \log x + \frac{1}{2} \log (x - 1)$. **53.** $\frac{1}{2} \log (x + y) - \log c - 2 \log (x - y)$.
54. $\log c + 2 \log x + \log y - \frac{1}{2} \log (x - 2y)$.
55. $\log c + \frac{1}{2} \log x - \log y - 2 \log (x + 3y)$.

57. $\log (c/x)$. **58.** $\log cx/(x - 1)$. **59.** $\log \dfrac{c(x + 1)^2}{x}$. **61.** $\log \dfrac{x + y}{\sqrt{x}}$.

62. $\log c \sqrt{2x + y}$. **63.** $\log \dfrac{c^2 x}{3x - 2y}$.

Exercise 64

1. 4.048. **2.** 1.852. **3.** .3921. **5.** 4.113. **6.** 1.791. **7.** 5.267. **9.** 2.023. **10.** 4.074.
11. 4.006. **13.** 3.103. **14.** 2.614. **15.** 1.993. **17.** 3.003. **18.** 4.540 **19.** 4.331.
21. 3.845. **22.** 3.878. **23.** 3.776.

Exercise 65

1. $x = \log_e y$. **2.** $x = \log_e y - \log_e 3$. **3.** $x = - \log_e y$. **5.** $n = \log_r y - \log_r a$.
6. $n = 1 + \log_r (L/a)$. **7.** $n = \log_{1+r} (S/A)$. **9.** $x = \frac{1}{2}(e^{-y} - e^y)$. **10.** $x = \frac{1}{2}(e^{-y} + e^y)$.
11. $x = \frac{1}{2}(-1 \pm \sqrt{9 + 4e^{2y}})$. **13.** 4. **14.** 4. **15.** 1.5. **17.** 1. **18.** 2, −3. **19.** 1, 2.
21. 7.838. **22.** 5.886. **23.** 1.017. **25.** 1. **26.** 2. **27.** 2. **29.** 2.
30. 1.5. **31.** 5, −1. **33.** $x = 1.2103, y = -.5794$. **34.** $x = .7, y = .3$.
35. $x = 6, y = -1$. **37.** $x = .2315, y = .0347$. **38.** $x = 4.82, y = 2.96$.
39. $x = 22.36, y = 4.472$.

Exercise 67

1. 2, 5, 8, 11, 14, 17. **2.** 3, 5, 7, 9, 11. **3.** 3, 1, −1, −3, −5, −7, −9. **5.** 2, 5, 8, 11.
6. 4, 1, −2, −5, −8, −11, −14, −17. **7.** 4, 7, 10, 13, 16. **9.** 5, 7, 9, 11, 13, 15, 17.
10. 12, 10, 8, 6, 4, 2. **11.** −1, 2, 5, 8, 11. **13.** 11. **14.** −1. **15.** 3. **17.** 12. **18.** $\frac{4}{3}$.
19. $-\frac{21}{2}$. **21.** 42. **22.** 30. **23.** −4. **25.** 55. **26.** 0. **27.** 48. **29.** $a = 1, s = -20$.
30. $a = -10, s = 10$. **31.** $a = -5, d = -2$. **33.** $d = 1\frac{1}{2}, l = 8$.
34. $d = -3, l = -7$. **35.** $n = 6, d = 4$. **37.** $n = 8, s = -16$. **38.** $n = 8, s = 20$.
39. $a = 2, l = 12$. **41.** $n = 12, l = 2; n = 7, l = -3$.
42. $n = 12, l = 1; n = 9, l = -2$. **43.** $n = 7, a = 5$. **45.** 5, 8, 11. **46.** 5, 7, 9, 11.
47. −1, 3, 7, 11. **49.** 204. **50.** 221. **51.** 315. **53.** \$4700, \$40,700. **54.** \$4849.
55. \$1700, \$1405, \$1215, \$1130. **57.** \$7000, \$7700, \$8500, \$9400, \$10,400, \$11,500,
\$12,700, \$14,000, \$15,400. **58.** \$1102. **59.** 852. **61.** \$11.25. **62.** 25 sec.
63. $2x - 5y = 0$.

Exercise 68

1. −3, 6, −12, 24, −48. **2.** 2, 1, $\frac{1}{2}$, $\frac{1}{4}$, $\frac{1}{8}$, $\frac{1}{16}$. **3.** 4, −2, 1, $-\frac{1}{2}$, $\frac{1}{4}$, $-\frac{1}{8}$, $\frac{1}{16}$.
5. 1, 3, 9, 27, 81. **6.** 32, −16, 8, −4, 2, −1. **7.** $\frac{8}{27}$, $\frac{4}{9}$, $\frac{2}{3}$, 1, $1\frac{1}{2}$, $\frac{9}{4}$, $\frac{27}{8}$. **9.** 81. **10.** $\frac{1}{16}$.
11. −24. **13.** −20. **14.** 2046. **15.** $15\frac{3}{4}$. **17.** 63. **18.** 121. **19.** $\frac{279}{8}$. **21.** 2, 4.
22. ± 1, $\frac{1}{2}$, $\pm \frac{1}{4}$. **23.** 2, 2. **25.** $\pm 3 \sqrt{3}$, 9, $\pm 9 \sqrt{3}$. **26.** −3, 1. **27.** $\frac{4}{9}$, $\frac{2}{3}$, 1, $\frac{3}{2}$, $\frac{9}{4}$.
29. $l = 48, s = 93$. **30.** $l = 162, s = 242$. **31.** $r = -2, s = -84$. **33.** $a = -2, s = 40$.
34. $a = 243, s = 363$. **35.** $n = 8, s = -510$. **37.** $a = 1, l = -243$. **38.** $a = 4\frac{1}{2}, l = \frac{8}{9}$.
39. $l = 729, n = 6$. **41.** $a = 1, r = -1$. **42.** $r = -2, a = 3$. **43.** $a = 8, n = 5$.
45. $r = 2, n = 6$. **46.** $r = \frac{1}{2}, n = 7$. **47.** $r = 3, l = 45; r = -4, l = 80$. **53.** 254.
54. $2048n$. **55.** $\frac{729}{4096}$. **57.** \$983.04. **58.** \$32.76. **59.** $\frac{3072}{3125}$ gal. **61.** \$20,480, \$3645.
62. Two.

Exercise 69

1. 6. **2.** 6. **3.** 18. **5.** 10. **6.** -8. **7.** 4. **9.** $\frac{16}{7}$. **10.** $8\frac{3}{4}$. **11.** 27, $-\frac{27}{5}$. **13.** $\frac{2}{9}$.
14. $\frac{5}{9}$. **15.** $\frac{2}{3}$. **17.** $\frac{5}{33}$. **18.** $\frac{14}{111}$. **19.** $\frac{20}{37}$. **21.** $3\frac{3}{11}$. **22.** $58\frac{2}{11}$. **23.** $3\frac{41}{333}$. **25.** 1.
26. 1. **27.** 3. **29.** 120 ft. **30.** 32 in. **31.** \$2000. **33.** 18 ft. **34.** 128 sq. in.
35. $32(2 + \sqrt{2})$. **37.** $1/(x-1)$. **38.** $x < 0$, $x > 1$, $1/(2x-2)$.
39. $x < 0$, $x > \frac{4}{3}$, $2/(3x-4)$.

Exercise 70

1. H.P. $\frac{1}{9}, \frac{1}{11}$. **2.** H.P. $-\frac{1}{8}, -\frac{1}{11}$. **3.** A.P. **5.** G.P. **6.** H.P. $-\frac{1}{5}, -\frac{1}{7}$.
7. H.P. $-\frac{1}{9}, -\frac{1}{13}$. **9.** A.P. **10.** G.P. **11.** H.P. 1, -2. **13.** $\frac{1}{2}$. **14.** $\frac{1}{29}$. **15.** $\frac{1}{4}$.
17. $\frac{1}{3}$. **18.** $-\frac{2}{3}$. **19.** $\frac{1}{5}$. **21.** $\frac{1}{5}, \frac{1}{8}$. **22.** $\frac{5}{11}, \frac{5}{14}, \frac{5}{17}$. **23.** $\frac{1}{7}, \frac{1}{9}, \frac{1}{11}, \frac{1}{13}$.

Exercise 72

1. $x^6 + 6x^5y + 15x^4y^2 + 20x^3y^3 + 15x^2y^4 + 6xy^5 + y^6$.
2. $a^7 + 7a^6b + 21a^5b^2 + 35a^4b^3 + 35a^3b^4 + 21a^2b^5 + 7ab^6 + b^7$.
3. $u^8 + 8u^7v + 28u^6v^2 + 56u^5v^3 + 70u^4v^4 + 56u^3v^5 + 28u^2v^6 + 8uv^7 + v^8$.
5. $x^5 - 5x^4y + 10x^3y^2 - 10x^2y^3 + 5xy^4 - y^5$.
6. $a^9 - 9a^8b + 36a^7b^2 - 84a^6b^3 + 126a^5b^4 - 126a^4b^5 + 84a^3b^6 - 36a^2b^7 + 9ab^8 - b^9$.
7. $c^8 - 8c^7d + 28c^6d^2 - 56c^5d^3 + 70c^4d^4 - 56c^3d^5 + 28c^2d^6 - 8cd^7 + d^8$.
9. $x^5 + 10x^4y + 40x^3y^2 + 80x^2y^3 + 80xy^4 + 32y^5$.
10. $81x^4 + 108x^3y + 54x^2y^2 + 12xy^3 + y^4$.
11. $x^5 + 20x^4y + 160x^3y^2 + 640x^2y^3 + 1280xy^4 + 1024y^5$.
13. $64x^6 - 576x^5y + 2160x^4y^2 - 4320x^3y^3 + 4860x^2y^4 - 2916xy^5 + 729y^6$.
14. $81x^4 - 432x^3y + 864x^2y^2 - 768xy^3 + 256y^4$. **15.** $2187x^7 - 10,206x^6y + 20,412x^5y^2$
$- 22,680x^4y^3 + 15,120x^3y^4 - 6048x^2y^5 + 1344xy^6 - 128y^7$.
17. $x^{18} + 9x^{16}a + 36x^{14}a^2 + 84x^{12}a^3 + 126x^{10}a^4 + 126x^8a^5 + 84x^6a^6 + 36x^4a^7 + 9x^2a^8 + a^9$.
18. $128x^7 - 448x^6a^2 + 672x^5a^4 - 560x^4a^6 + 280x^3a^8 - 84x^2a^{10} + 14xa^{12} - a^{14}$.
19. $x^{12} + 6x^{10}y^3 + 15x^8y^6 + 20x^6y^9 + 15x^4y^{12} + 6x^2y^{15} + y^{18}$.

21. $x^7 + 7x^5 + 21x^3 + 35x + \dfrac{35}{x} + \dfrac{21}{x^3} + \dfrac{7}{x^5} + \dfrac{1}{x^7}$.

22. $32x^5 - 240x^3 + 720x - \dfrac{1080}{x} + \dfrac{810}{x^3} - \dfrac{243}{x^5}$.

23. $\dfrac{4096}{a^{24}} + \dfrac{3072}{a^{18}} + \dfrac{960}{a^{12}} + \dfrac{160}{a^6} + 15 + \dfrac{3a^6}{4} + \dfrac{a^{12}}{64}$.

25. $x^{50} + 100x^{49}y + 4900x^{48}y^2 + 156,800x^{47}y^3$.
26. $a^{100} - 300a^{99}b + 44,550a^{98}b^2 - 4,365,900a^{97}b^3$.
27. $c^{40} + 120c^{39}d + 7020c^{38}d^2 + 266,760c^{37}d^3$. **29.** 104,060,401. **30.** 941,192.
31. 1.1592740743. **33.** $160a^3c^3$. **34.** $280x^3y^4$. **35.** $90,720a^4b^4$. **37.** $672x^6y^3$.
38. $30,618x^8y^5$. **39.** $462x^5y^6$. **41.** $512,512x^{10}y^6$. **42.** $72,930a^9b^8$. **43.** $70x^4$. **45.** 1120.
46. $28x^5/27$. **47.** $-5b^6/54a^3$. **49.** $-84x^2y^5$. **50.** $-80a^2b^6$. **51.** $3360x^4y^3$.

Exercise 73

1. $x^{-1} - x^{-2}y + x^{-3}y^2 - x^{-4}y^3$. **2.** $a^{-2} - 2a^{-3}b + 3a^{-4}b^2 - 4a^{-5}b^3$.
3. $a^{-1} + a^{-2}x + a^{-3}x^2 + a^{-4}x^3$. **5.** $a^{-3} - 6a^{-4}x + 24a^{-5}x^2 - 80a^{-6}x^3$.

6. $\dfrac{b^{-4}}{16} + \dfrac{b^{-5}y}{8} + \dfrac{5b^{-6}y^2}{32} + \dfrac{5b^{-7}y^3}{32}$. **7.** $\dfrac{b^{-3}}{8} + \dfrac{9b^{-4}z}{16} + \dfrac{27b^{-5}z^2}{16} + \dfrac{135b^{-6}z^3}{32}$.

9. $1 + \frac{1}{2}r - \frac{1}{8}r^2 + \frac{1}{16}r^3$. **10.** $1 - \frac{3}{4}d - \frac{3}{32}d^2 - \frac{5}{128}d^3$. **11.** $2^{\frac{2}{3}}(1 + \frac{1}{3}x - \frac{1}{36}x^2 + \frac{1}{162}x^3)$.
13. $1 - \frac{1}{2}r + \frac{3}{8}r^2 - \frac{5}{16}r^3$. **14.** $2^{-\frac{2}{7}}(1 + \frac{1}{7}y + \frac{9}{196}y^2 + \frac{6}{343}y^3)$.
15. $1 + \frac{1}{3}d + \frac{2}{9}d^2 + \frac{14}{81}d^3$. **17.** $x^{-2} - 2x^{-4} + 3x^{-6} - 4x^{-8}$.
18. $y^{-3} + 6y^{-5} + 24y^{-7} + 80y^{-9}$. **19.** $a^{-\frac{1}{4}}(1 + \frac{1}{4}a^{-3} + \frac{5}{32}a^{-6} + \frac{15}{128}a^{-9})$.

Exercise 74

1. \$463.72. **2.** \$999.06. **3.** \$2048.25. **5.** \$836.92. **6.** \$1554.30. **7.** \$3157.80.
9. \$391.77. **10.** \$1074.34. **11.** \$446.92. **13.** \$382.52. **14.** \$519.39. **15.** \$917.89.
17. 5 per cent. **18.** 6 per cent. **19.** 3 per cent. **21.** 6 years. **22.** 5 years. **23.** 8 years.
25. 6.14 per cent. **26.** 5.06 per cent. **27.** 4.04 per cent. **29.** 3.02 per cent.
30. 6.09 per cent. **31.** 8.24 per cent. **33.** \$377.10. **34.** \$1055.36. **35.** 14.04 years.
37. \$206.10. **38.** \$13,736.81. **39.** \$72.99. **41.** \$1942.95. **42.** \$4656.91. **43.** \$8908.62.
45. 2.92 per cent. **46.** \$2505.20. **47.** 3.14 per cent.

Exercise 75

1. \$1572.63, \$1989.90, \$1635.54, \$2069.50. **2.** \$2807.88, \$3556.92, \$2892.12, \$3663.63.
3. \$3586.90, \$4479.52, \$3676.57, \$4591.51. **5.** \$5867.89, \$10,102.02, \$6014.59, \$10,354.57.
6. \$13,492.80; \$19,271.07; \$13,762.66; \$19,656.49.
7. \$24,792.38; \$49,176.30; \$25,164.27; \$49,913.94.
9. \$17,021.30; \$34,782.60; \$17,276.62; \$35,304.34.
10. \$4362.00; \$10,425.40; \$4449.24; \$10,633.91.
11. \$2405.79, \$4916.17, \$2441.88, \$4989.91. **13.** \$439.20, \$422.30. **14.** \$125.20, \$120.38.
15. \$209.91, \$204.79. **17.** \$491.56, \$484.30. **18.** \$255.31, \$251.54. **19.** \$668.54, \$658.66.
21. 20 years. **22.** 25 years. **23.** $8\frac{1}{2}$ years. **25.** 20 years. **26.** 30 years. **27.** $12\frac{1}{2}$ years.
29. 3 per cent. **30.** 5 per cent. **31.** 6 per cent. **33.** \$8110.90. **34.** \$744.17.
35. \$12,292.94. **37.** \$71.88. **38.** \$7633.98. **39.** \$1104.02. **41.** \$1673.88. **42.** \$55.13.
43. \$221.64, \$18,832.90.

Exercise 76

1. 26,000. **2.** 16,848. **3.** 1620. **5.** 20,580. **6.** 24. **7.** 256. **9.** 360. **10.** 144.
11. 576. **13.** 12. **14.** 128. **15.** 64. **17.** 4200. **18.** 720. **19.** 10,160,640.

Exercise 77

1. 360. **2.** 840. **3.** 110. **9.** 40,320; 1,814,400. **10.** 840; 360. **11.** 362,880. **13.** 5040.
14. 3,628,800. **15.** 96. **17.** 3360. **18.** 831,600. **19.** 8640. **21.** 161,280.
22. 39,916,800; 479,001,600. **23.** 239,500,800. **25.** 15!. **26.** 1920. **27.** 622,080.

Exercise 78

1. 35; 126; 210; 136. **5.** 4845. **6.** 166,167,000. **7.** 45. **9.** 28; 3. **10.** 3,921,225.
11. 90. **13.** 1340. **14.** 6790. **15.** 84. **17.** 20. **18.** 387,600. **19.** 784. **21.** 9344.
22. 45,728,592,000. **23.** 1050. **25.** 63. **26.** 56. **27.** 1013.

Exercise 79

1. $\frac{3}{11}, \frac{4}{11}$. **2.** $\frac{1}{4}, \frac{1}{2}$. **3.** $\frac{1}{6}, \frac{1}{2}, \frac{1}{3}$. **5.** $\frac{1}{36}, \frac{1}{18}, \frac{1}{12}, \frac{1}{6}$. **6.** $\frac{1}{4}, \frac{5}{12}, \frac{1}{3}, \frac{7}{12}$. **7.** $\frac{1}{10}, \frac{1}{5}$.
9. $\frac{1}{64}, \frac{1}{2197}, \frac{1}{16}$. **10.** $\frac{5}{9}$. **11.** $\frac{1}{35}$. **13.** $\frac{1}{28}$. **14.** $\frac{1}{16}$. **15.** $\frac{1}{2}$. **17.** $\frac{1}{30}, \frac{1}{75}$.
18. $\frac{27}{14950}$. **19.** $\frac{149}{598}$. **21.** .3. **22.** .0025. **23.** 2. **25.** .007855, .07826. **26.** .8284.
27. .4530. **29.** \$499.82. **30.** \$2790.25. **31.** \$1907.54.

Exercise 80

1. $\frac{5}{6}$. 2. $\frac{7}{15}$. 3. $\frac{1}{5}$. 5. $\frac{17}{42}$. 6. $\frac{14701}{485100}$. 7. $\frac{5}{6}$. 9. $\frac{1}{12}$. 10. $\frac{9}{25}$. 11. $\frac{1}{3}$. 13. $\frac{2}{11}$.
14. $\frac{1}{12}$. 15. $\frac{1}{4}$. 17. $\frac{2}{3}, \frac{1}{4}, \frac{1}{24}$. 18. $\frac{1}{6}$. 19. $\frac{5}{6}$. 21. $\frac{11}{36}$. 22. $\frac{3}{4}$. 23. $\frac{1}{1296}$.

25. $\frac{35}{96}, \frac{5}{32}, \frac{25}{48}$. 26. $\frac{19}{48}$. 27. $\frac{239}{1848}$. 29. $\frac{291}{350}$. 30. $\left(\frac{83,277}{87,596}\right)\left(\frac{3369}{34,421}\right) = .093$.

31. \$10,000, \$3750, \$1125.

Exercise 81

1. $\frac{5}{16}, \frac{1}{2}$. 2. $\frac{5}{72}, \frac{2}{27}$. 3. $\frac{189}{16384}, \frac{211}{16384}$. 5. $\frac{1}{243}$. 6. $\frac{40}{243}$. 7. $\frac{17}{81}$. 9. $\frac{25}{288}$.
10. $\frac{125}{864}$. 11. $\frac{405}{1024}$. 13. $\frac{80}{243}$. 14. $\frac{8505}{524288}$. 15. $\frac{16}{243}$. 17. $\frac{11}{72}$.

Exercise 82

1. 6. 2. 14. 3. 12. 5. 19. 6. 11. 7. 1. 9. Minus. 10. Plus. 11. Plus.
13. Minus. 14. Minus. 15. Plus. 17. 3. 18. 17. 19. 0. 21. 46. 22. -107.
23. 13. 33. -38. 34. 94. 35. -2. 37. -15. 38. 112. 39. 0. 41. $ab(a^2 - b^2)$.
42. $4a^2b^2 - b^4$. 43. $bc - ad$.

Exercise 83

9. -27. 10. -24. 11. 124. 13. 16. 14. 245. 15. -742. 17. -64. 18. 16.
19. 114. 21. 0. 22. 20. 23. -5096. 25. -4. 26. 24. 27. -8.

Exercise 84

1. $x = 2, y = 1$. 2. $x = 1, y = -1$. 3. $x = 3, y = -2$. 5. $x = 1, y = 0, z = 1$.
6. $x = 2, y = 1, z = -2$. 7. $x = -2, y = 3, z = -1$. 9. $x = \frac{1}{2}, y = 1, z = \frac{1}{3}$.
10. $x = -\frac{2}{3}, y = 0, z = \frac{1}{3}$. 11. $x = 3, y = -4, z = 5$. 13. $x = 1, y = 1, z = 0, w = -1$.
14. $x = 2, y = 1, z = -1, w = 3$. 15. $x = \frac{1}{2}, y = \frac{1}{4}, z = \frac{3}{4}, w = 1$.
17. $x = 1, y = 3, z = -3, w = -2$. 18. $x = 5, y = 7, z = -3, w = -6$.
19. $x = 1, y = -3, z = 2, w = 3$. 21. $x = a, y = 2a, z = -a$. 22. $x = a, y = b, z = a$.
23. $x = a, y = c, z = c, w = -a$. 25. $x = 1$. 26. $y = 2$. 27. $z = -2$.

Exercise 85

1. $x = \frac{7}{5}, y = -\frac{1}{5}$. 2. $x = 1, y = -2$. 3. $x = -3, y = 2$. 5. $x = \frac{1}{2}, y = -\frac{3}{2}, z = 1$.
6. $x = -1, y = 3, z = 4$. 7. No solution. 9. $x = 4, y = -6, z = 2$.
10. $x = -3, y = -4, z = 2$. 11. No solution. 13. $x = 2, y = -1, z = 1, w = 4$.
14. $x = 2, y = 6, z = -4, w = 2$. 15. $x = 2, y = -2, z = -6, w = -2$.

Exercise 86

1. $\dfrac{1}{x-1} - \dfrac{3}{3x-1}$. 2. $\dfrac{1}{x-2} - \dfrac{2}{2x+1}$. 3. $\dfrac{3}{3x-1} - \dfrac{2}{2x+3}$. 5. $\dfrac{2}{x+2} + \dfrac{3}{2x-3}$.

6. $\dfrac{2}{2x-1} + \dfrac{4}{3x+2}$. 7. $\dfrac{3}{x-3} - \dfrac{1}{2x-1}$. 9. $\dfrac{1}{x-2} + \dfrac{2}{x+3}$. 10. $\dfrac{4}{x-1} - \dfrac{1}{x+2}$.

11. $\dfrac{2}{x+2} + \dfrac{3}{2x-1}$. 13. $\dfrac{2}{x-1} + \dfrac{3}{x+2} - \dfrac{5}{x-3}$. 14. $\dfrac{1}{x-2} + \dfrac{4}{2x-1} - \dfrac{3}{x+3}$.

15. $\dfrac{1}{x-1} + \dfrac{2}{2x-1} - \dfrac{6}{3x+1}$. 17. $\dfrac{1}{3x+2} + \dfrac{2}{2x-1} - \dfrac{2}{3x-1}$.

18. $\dfrac{3}{x-1} + \dfrac{2}{x+2} - \dfrac{5}{2x+3}$. **19.** $\dfrac{2}{7(x+3)} + \dfrac{3}{7(2x-1)} - \dfrac{1}{4x+3}$.

21. $2 + \dfrac{3}{x-4} - \dfrac{1}{x+1}$. **22.** $3 - \dfrac{2}{2x-1} + \dfrac{5}{x+3}$. **23.** $x + \dfrac{2}{3x+2} - \dfrac{3}{2x-1}$.

Exercise 87

1. $\dfrac{2}{x-1} + \dfrac{1}{(x-1)^2}$. **2.** $\dfrac{3}{x+2} + \dfrac{4}{(x+2)^2}$. **3.** $\dfrac{2}{2x-1} - \dfrac{3}{(2x-1)^2}$.

5. $\dfrac{2}{x-1} + \dfrac{3}{(x-1)^2} - \dfrac{1}{(x-1)^3}$. **6.** $\dfrac{3}{2x-1} + \dfrac{2}{(2x-1)^2} - \dfrac{2}{(2x-1)^3}$.

7. $\dfrac{5}{3x+1} - \dfrac{7}{(3x+1)^2} + \dfrac{19}{(3x+1)^3}$. **9.** $-\dfrac{1}{2x+3} + \dfrac{1}{x+3} + \dfrac{5}{(x+3)^2}$.

10. $\dfrac{2}{3x+5} - \dfrac{3}{2x-3} + \dfrac{5}{(2x-3)^2}$. **11.** $\dfrac{1}{5x+2} - \dfrac{1}{2x-5} + \dfrac{3}{(2x-5)^2}$.

13. $-\dfrac{5}{2x-1} + \dfrac{3}{x+2} - \dfrac{2}{x-1} + \dfrac{4}{(x-1)^2}$. **14.** $\dfrac{1}{x+3} - \dfrac{2}{x-2} + \dfrac{4}{x-1} - \dfrac{5}{(x-1)^2}$.

15. $\dfrac{1}{2x+1} - \dfrac{2}{3x-1} - \dfrac{1}{x-3} + \dfrac{2}{(x-3)^2}$. **17.** $2 - \dfrac{3}{x-1} - \dfrac{3}{(x-1)^2}$.

18. $3 + \dfrac{4}{x+3} - \dfrac{12}{(x+3)^2}$. **19.** $1 + \dfrac{2}{3x-2} - \dfrac{5}{(x-2)^2}$.

Exercise 88

1. $\dfrac{1}{x+1} - \dfrac{x-1}{x^2+1}$. **2.** $\dfrac{2}{x-1} - \dfrac{3x+2}{x^2+3}$. **3.** $\dfrac{3}{2x+3} - \dfrac{2x-1}{x^2+x+1}$.

5. $\dfrac{1}{x+1} + \dfrac{2}{x-2} + \dfrac{3x-4}{x^2+5}$. **6.** $\dfrac{1}{2x-3} - \dfrac{3}{x+2} - \dfrac{2x-5}{x^2+3}$.

7. $\dfrac{2}{3x-1} - \dfrac{1}{x-3} + \dfrac{2x-1}{x^2+3x+4}$. **9.** $\dfrac{1}{x+2} - \dfrac{2}{(x+2)^2} + \dfrac{3}{x^2+2}$.

10. $\dfrac{2}{x-3} + \dfrac{3}{(x-3)^2} + \dfrac{4x}{x^2+4}$. **11.** $\dfrac{1}{2x-1} - \dfrac{2}{(2x-1)^2} + \dfrac{2x+3}{x^2+x-3}$.

13. $\dfrac{x}{x^2+1} + \dfrac{x-2}{x^2+3}$. **14.** $\dfrac{x+2}{x^2+3x+1} - \dfrac{2x-3}{x^2+4}$. **15.** $\dfrac{2x-1}{x^2-3} - \dfrac{3x+4}{x^2-5x+2}$.

17. $1 + \dfrac{2}{x-1} + \dfrac{3x-5}{x^2+1}$. **18.** $2 - \dfrac{3}{x+4} - \dfrac{x+1}{x^2-3}$. **19.** $2 - \dfrac{5}{2x+7} + \dfrac{2x-3}{2x^2+x+1}$.

Exercise 89

1. $\dfrac{3x}{x^2+2} - \dfrac{2x+5}{(x^2+2)^2}$. **2.** $\dfrac{2}{x^2+1} - \dfrac{3x-5}{(x^2+1)^2}$. **3.** $\dfrac{2x-1}{x^2+x+1} + \dfrac{3x+2}{(x^2+x+1)^2}$.

5. $\dfrac{x}{x^2+1} + \dfrac{x-1}{(x^2+1)^3}$. **6.** $\dfrac{x}{(x^2+3)^2} + \dfrac{x-1}{(x^2+3)^3}$.

7. $\dfrac{x}{x^2-x+1} + \dfrac{x+1}{(x^2-x+1)^2} - \dfrac{x+1}{(x^2-x+1)^3}$. **9.** $\dfrac{1}{x^2} - \dfrac{x+2}{(x^2+1)^2}$.

10. $\dfrac{1}{x} - \dfrac{1}{x^2 - 2} + \dfrac{4x - 2}{(x^2 - 2)^2}$.   **11.** $\dfrac{1}{x^2} + \dfrac{x + 1}{x^2 - x + 2} + \dfrac{x - 7}{(x^2 - x + 2)^2}$.

13. $\dfrac{2}{x^2 + 1} + \dfrac{3x}{(x^2 + 1)^2} - \dfrac{4}{x + 1}$.   **14.** $\dfrac{2}{x + 2} + \dfrac{5}{x^2 + 3} - \dfrac{3x - 2}{(x^2 + 3)^2}$.

15. $\dfrac{-1}{2x - 3} + \dfrac{x}{x^2 + x - 7} - \dfrac{2x - 3}{(x^2 + x - 7)^2}$.

INDEX